M000036323

BASIC TELEVISION AND VIDEO SYSTEMS

Dedicated to Ruth and Harriet Deborah

Author of *Basic Electronics*
Electronic Circuits and Applications
Coauthor of *Applications of Electronics*

BASIC TELEVISION AND VIDEO SYSTEMS

FIFTH EDITION

Bernard Grob
Instructor, Technical Career Institutes, Inc.
(formerly RCA Institutes, Inc.)

GLENCOE
McGraw-Hill

New York, New York
Columbus, Ohio
Mission Hills, California
Peoria, Illinois

Sponsoring Editor: George Z. Kuredjian
Editing Supervisor: Larry Goldberg
Design and Art Supervisor: Caryl Valerie Spinka
Production Supervisor: Frank Bellantoni

Text Designer: Sharkey Design
Cover Type Designer: Renée Kilbride
Cover Illustrator: John Weiman
Technical Studio: Fine Line, Inc.

Library of Congress Cataloging in Publication Data

Grob, Bernard.
Basic television and video systems.

Rev. ed. of: Basic television, principles and servicing.—
4th ed.— . . . 1975.
Includes bibliographical references and index.
1. Television. I. Title.
TK6630.G75 1984 621.388 83-5476
ISBN 0-07-024933-4

Basic Television and Video Systems, Fifth Edition
Imprint 1995

5 6 7 8 9 10 11 12 13 14 15 RRDC 03 02 01 00 99 98 97 96 95

ISBN 0-07-024933-4

CONTENTS

PREFACE

This textbook is designed for a course in television and video systems in which the principles of operation and servicing are emphasized. The student using this book is expected to have a background in electronic circuits, especially those pertaining to communications. The only mathematics requirement is a basic understanding of algebra.

The state of the art in television has advanced so rapidly that relatively complex functions involving numerous components and circuits have been reduced to a single integrated circuit. The focus in this text is therefore on circuit functions rather than on the circuit elements themselves. For that reason the block diagram becomes the key to understanding the system. This is not to imply that the need for circuit diagrams does not exist; rather, circuit diagrams are shown only to emphasize specific features, such as scanning-voltage power supplies and color demodulators.

The term *video* is used in this text in its broadest sense. The television set itself has become an instrument beyond that of a broadcast receiver, and this fifth edition reflects the change. As in previous editions the servicing approach is used throughout the book. A final chapter on testing and troubleshooting ties together all of these techniques.

Organization The first ten chapters of this text are devoted to cameras, picture tubes, and video signals. Chapter 11 explains transmission in the television broadcast channels for the AM picture signal and the FM sound signal.

In Chaps. 12 to 14 circuits for television receivers are covered, beginning with the general requirements for the signal circuits, raster circuits, and sync circuits. These principles apply to monochrome as well as color receivers. The special features of color TV receivers are discussed in Chap. 14. The discussion uses the block diagram approach to emphasize functions since ICs are used for many of the circuits. Chapter 15, "Cable Television," explains how a TV receiver is used with the cable channels. Finally Chap. 16 describes test equipment, with emphasis on color-bar signal generators and oscilloscopes. Included are practical methods to localize troubles in video cassette recorders and the setup procedures for video cameras.

Learning Aids To help the student, each chapter starts with a short introduction and list of the main topics. This helps the reader visualize what material is covered in the chapter. Test point questions are found in the text after each section. For reinforcement, the answers are given at the end of each chapter.

At the end of each chapter is a summary of the main points and a group of self-examination questions. Answers for these questions are at the back of the book.

To help the teacher, a wide range of essay questions are given at the end of each chapter. These questions can be assigned to review definitions, to refer to the illustrations, and to make drawings. A group of numerical problems are included for almost all the chapters when quantitative work is applicable. The calculations include basic principles such as the *RC* time constant, decibel units, and resonance.

The special questions at the end of the chapters have two purposes. Some of the questions are subjective, to find out what the student thinks in terms of actual experiences with television. Other questions present more advanced ideas for more advanced students.

Credits The photographs have been made available by many companies in the video and television field, as noted in each illustration. This courtesy is gratefully acknowledged. I also want to thank my colleague Gerald McGinty for his invaluable assistance in preparation of the manuscript.

For the final credit, it is a pleasure to thank my wife Ruth for her help and encouragement.

Bernard Grob

BASIC TELEVISION AND VIDEO SYSTEMS

1

APPLICATIONS OF TELEVISION

The word *television* means "to see at a distance." In our practical TV broadcasting system, the visual information you see in the scene is converted to an electric signal which is transmitted to the receiver. The electrical variations that correspond to changes in light values form the *video signal.* At the receiver, the video signal is used to reassemble the image on the screen of the picture tube, as illustrated in Fig. 1-1. In monochrome television, the picture is reproduced in black and white and shades of gray. In color television, all the natural colors are added as combinations of red, green, and blue in the main parts of the picture.

Originally, television was conceived of as another method of broadcasting entertainment and news programs but with pictures, much as radio broadcasting does for sound. Commercial broadcasting is still the largest field in the application of television. However, the ability to reproduce pictures, text material, graphics, and visual information has become so useful that many more applications are common now. You can watch a program from a foreign country relayed by satellite TV or play back a video cassette recorder, or a video game can be connected to your TV receiver. The same idea applies to using the TV receiver as the display for a small, personal computer. Examples are shown in Figs. 1-2 and 1-3. The TV display can be either in monochrome or color. Some of the main applications for video signals and television systems are described in the following topics:

1-1 Video, Audio, Television, and Radio Signals
1-2 Television Broadcasting
1-3 Television Studio Operations
1-4 Video Tape Recorders
1-5 Cable Television (CATV)
1-6 Closed-Circuit Television (CCTV)
1-7 Video Home Entertainment Center
1-8 Videotext Data Terminal
1-9 Development of Television Broadcasting

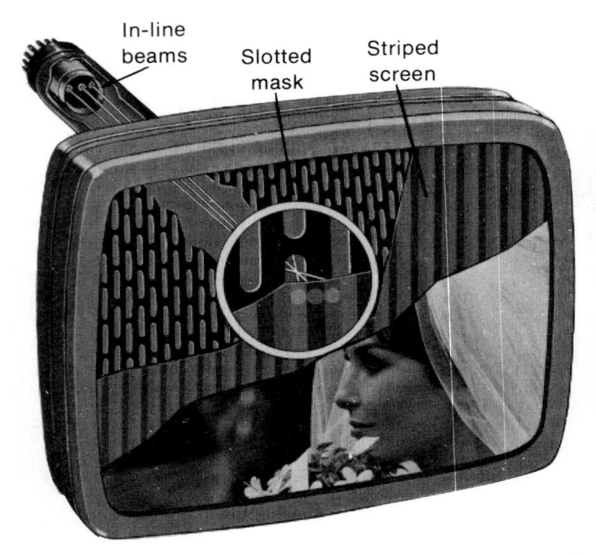

Fig. 1-1 Image reproduced on fluorescent screen of color picture tube in TV receiver. (*RCA*)

Fig. 1-3 Odyssey video game connected to TV receiver on channel 4 for visual display. (*N.A.P. Consumer Electronics Corp.*)

Fig. 1-2 Personal computer used with TV receiver for visual display. (*Texas Instruments Incorporated*)

1-1 VIDEO, AUDIO, TELEVISION, AND RADIO SIGNALS

There are so many uses for these signals that it is worthwhile to consider the specific purpose of each. *Video* is a Latin word meaning "I see." Similarly, *audio* means "I hear." The two terms correspond—video to light and audio to sound. The comparison is illustrated in Fig. 1-4. For the more familiar audio system in Fig. 1-4*a,* the microphone converts sound waves to corresponding electrical variations for the audio signal. The loudspeaker receives this audio signal at the input terminals, either by direct connection or as part of a wireless broadcasting system. Then the loudspeaker reproduces the original sound as we would hear it at the microphone.

In Fig. 1-4*b,* the camera tube converts its light input to corresponding electrical variations for the video signal. The camera tube is to video as the microphone is to audio. At the end of the video system, the picture tube converts the video signal voltage from the input to light at the output. The video information is reproduced

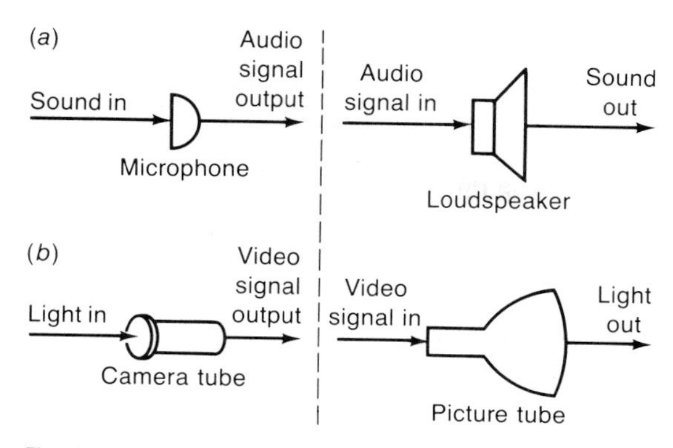

Fig. 1-4 How audio and video signals are used in electronics. (*a*) Audio signal for sound. (*b*) Video signal for pictures.

on the screen of the picture tube as we would see the scene at the camera tube.

HOW VIDEO DIFFERS FROM AUDIO The light image is converted to an electric signal for only one small area at a time. Then the video signal produced by the camera tube consists of sequential variations in time for the different areas. For this reason, a scanning procedure is necessary to cover the entire picture, dot by dot from left to right and line by line from top to bottom. The scanning is very fast—one horizontal line takes only 63.5 microseconds (μs). Because of the rapid variations, the video signal has high frequencies—up to approximately 4 megahertz (MHz).

Furthermore, the scanning procedure requires that synchronizing pulses be used with the video signal, in order to time the scanning at the camera tube and at the picture tube. At the picture tube, the small areas of light or shade and of color, when used, are reassembled in the correct position to create the whole image.

VIDEO AND AUDIO BASEBAND SIGNALS For either a video or an audio signal, the range of frequencies in the variations is called the *baseband*. These frequencies actually correspond to the desired visual or aural information, without any extra complications such as encoding or modulation for special functions. In audio systems, the baseband frequencies are 20 to 20,000 hertz (Hz), although 50 to 15,000 Hz is used commonly for high-fidelity audio. In video systems, the baseband frequencies range from 0 Hz for direct current up to 4 MHz. The audio baseband signal can be connected to a loudspeaker to reproduce the desired sound. Also the video baseband signal can be fed to a picture tube to reproduce the desired picture.

The reason for converting sound and visual information to baseband electric signals is that audio and video signals can be amplified—by almost any amount. Furthermore, signal processing by electronic circuits is easy and convenient for various uses.

RADIO BROADCASTING SIGNALS In wireless radio transmission, the audio baseband signal is used to modulate a radio-frequency (RF) carrier wave. Modulation is necessary because the audio frequencies are too low for efficient radiation. Furthermore, different carrier frequencies are used for different stations. The receiver can be tuned to each carrier frequency. At the receiver, the modulated RF signal is detected to recover the original audio information.

TELEVISION BROADCAST SIGNALS The same idea applies in radio as in television broadcasting. The video baseband signal modulates a high-frequency carrier wave to provide wireless transmission. At the receiver, the video detector recovers the original video signal. Television broadcasting is very similar to radio broadcasting, except that video modulation is used for the picture signal. The associated sound signal also is transmitted on a separate carrier wave. All these systems require electromagnetic radio waves for transmission. In television broadcasting, amplitude modulation (AM) is used for the picture signal and frequency modulation (FM) for the associated sound signal.

Test Point Questions 1-1

Answers at End of Chapter

- **a.** Is a picture tube similar to a microphone or to a loudspeaker?
- **b.** Name two baseband signals.
- **c.** Which has higher frequencies, audio or video signals?

1-2 TELEVISION BROADCASTING

The term *broadcast* means "to send out in all directions." As shown in Fig. 1-5, the transmitting antenna radiates electromagnetic radio waves which can be picked up by the receiving antenna. The television transmitter has two functions: visual and aural transmission. Both the AM picture signal and the FM sound signal are emitted from the common radiating antenna. The service area is about 75 mi [121 km] in all directions from the transmitter.

In visual transmission, the camera tube converts the light image to a video signal. The camera tube is a cathode-ray tube (CRT), with a photoelectric image plate and an electron gun enclosed in a vacuum glass envelope. A common type is the vidicon shown in Fig. 1-6. Basically, the camera tube takes an optical image of the scene on its photoelectric plate, which is scanned in horizontal lines by the electron beam. The scanning goes from left to right and top to bottom, as viewed by the camera. It takes $\frac{1}{30}$ s to scan the entire picture frame, comprising a total of 525 scanning lines. As a result, the output of the camera tube is a sequence of electrical variations—the video signal—that corresponds to the picture information. The video signal is

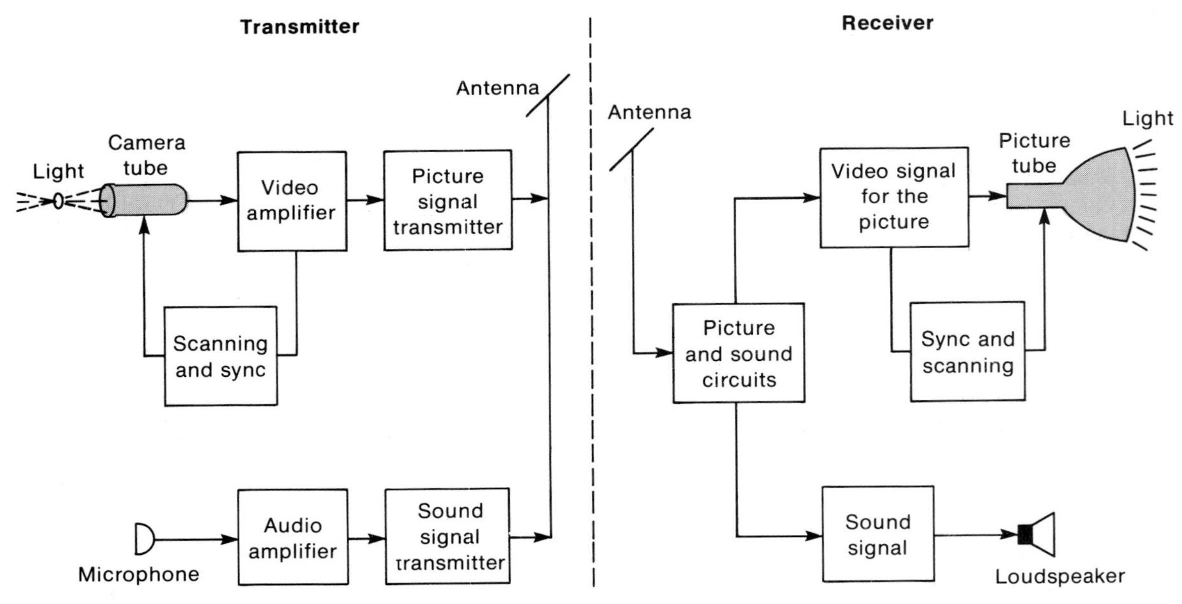

Fig. 1-5 Block diagram of television broadcasting system.

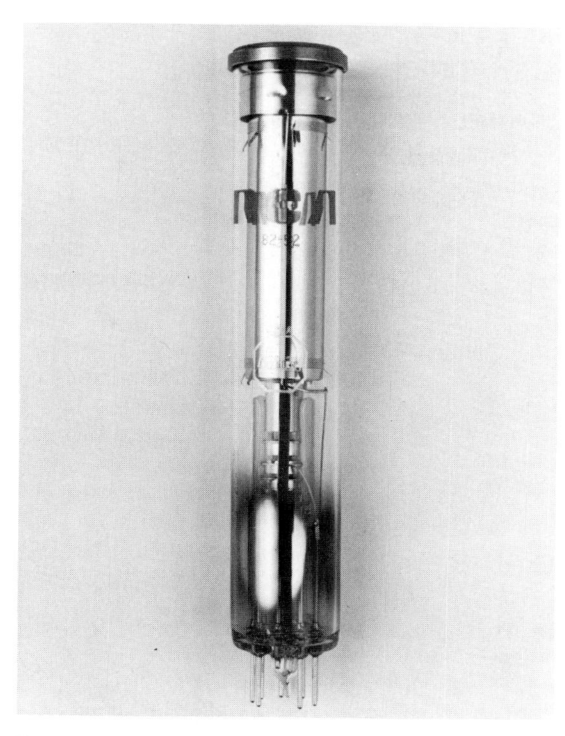

Fig. 1-6 Vidicon camera tube. Length is 6 in. [152.4 mm]. (*RCA*)

amplified, and synchronizing pulses are added. Amplitude modulation of the picture carrier results in the AM picture signal.

The receiving antenna intercepts both the picture and the sound carrier signals. The signals are amplified and then detected to recover the original modulation. The video detector output includes the video signal needed to reproduce the picture.

Then the detected video signal is amplified enough to drive the grid-cathode circuit of the picture tube. As shown in Fig. 1-7, the picture tube is very similar to the CRT used in an oscilloscope. The glass faceplate at the front has a fluorescent coating on its inside surface. The narrow neck contains the electron gun. When the electron beam strikes the phosphor screen, light is emitted.

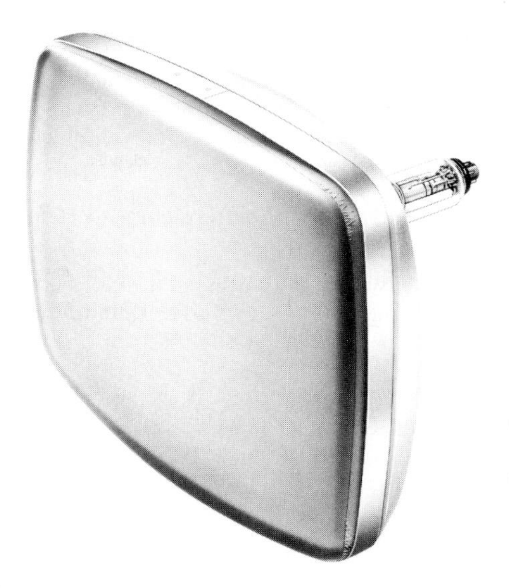

Fig. 1-7 Type 12BNP4 monochrome picture tube. Electron gun is in narrow neck. Screen diagonal is 12 in. [304.8 mm]. The P4 indicates white phosphor screen. (*RCA*)

Assume that video signal voltage makes the control grid less negative. Then the beam current increases, making the spot of light brighter. The maximum light output is peak white in the picture.

For the opposite case, more negative voltage decreases the beam current and brightness. When the grid voltage is negative enough to cut off the beam current, there is no light output. This value corresponds to black on the screen.

The block diagram in Fig. 1-5 illustrates the system for monochrome. In color television, a color camera and a color picture tube are used. The color camera provides video signals for the red, green, and blue picture information. Similarly, the color picture tube reproduces the image in red, green, and blue with all their color mixtures including white.

TELEVISION BROADCAST CHANNELS The band of frequencies used for video and audio signal transmission is called a television *channel.*

Each TV station is assigned a 6-MHz-wide channel with a specific carrier frequency by the Federal Communications Commission (FCC). As shown in Table 1-1, all the television channels fall within three bands:

1. Lowband very high frequency (VHF) channels: 2 to 6
2. Highband VHF channels: 7 to 13
3. Ultra high frequency (UHF) channels: 14 to 83

Remember that the range is 30 to 300 MHz for VHF and 300 to 3000 MHz for UHF.

In all three bands, each TV channel is 6 MHz wide. This bandwidth is needed to accommodate the modulation with video frequencies up to 4 MHz, including the 3.58-MHz chroma signal for color television. Note the 3.58 MHz for color. The FM sound signal is also in the channel.

Furthermore, the picture and sound RF carrier frequencies are always separated by exactly 4.5 MHz in all channels. The value of 4.5 MHz is called the *intercarrier sound frequency.*

The following comments apply to Table 1-1. When television first started, channel 1 was broadcast at 44 to 50 MHz, but now this band is assigned to other services. Between channels 4 and 5, the frequencies of 72 to 76 MHz are used for other radio services, including air navigation. The commercial FM broadcast band of 88 to 108 MHz is just above the band for TV channel 6, but this radio service is not related to television broadcasting. In 1952 the UHF channels 14 to 83 were added to create more television stations. No assignments have been made for UHF channels 69 to 83 because these frequencies are used for mobile radio. All the TV channels are listed in App. A.

At the receiver, the RF tuner is used to select the desired station by tuning to its 6-MHz band. With two rotary-action tuners, one for VHF and the other for UHF, the receiver is capable of tuning both the VHF and the UHF channels. The channel 1 position on the VHF tuner is used to turn on the UHF tuner.

TABLE 1-1
TELEVISION CHANNELS

CHANNEL NUMBER	FREQUENCY BAND, MHz	DESCRIPTION
1	Not used	
2	54–60	Lowband VHF channels
3	60–66	
4	66–72	
5	76–82	
6	82–88	
	88–108	FM band
7	174–180	Highband VHF channels
8	180–186	
9	186–192	
10	192–198	
11	198–204	
12	204–210	
13	210–216	
14–83	470–890	UHF channels

In the VHF and UHF bands, the signals are propagated by line-of-sight transmissions from the transmitting antenna to the receiving antenna. The radiated signals do not normally follow the curvature of the earth, and there are no reflections from the ionosphere, such as occurs for radio signals at lower frequencies. Line-of-sight transmission makes the antenna height important in order to get good coverage of TV broadcast signals.

The FCC assigns the television channels and maintains strict technical standards. Each station must meet FCC specifications and serve the needs of the community. Licenses are reviewed at regular intervals, and the public is invited to participate in the renewal process.

Test Point Questions 1-2

Answers at End of Chapter

a. Is the vidicon a camera tube or a picture tube?

b. What is the chroma subcarrier signal frequency?

c. At what frequencies is TV channel 2 broadcast?

d. Is the maximum beam current in the picture tube used for white or black in the picture?

1-3 TELEVISION STUDIO OPERATIONS

In the early days of television, most programs were "live," and each station used studio cameras to generate its own programming. Network "feeds" provided programs to cover different areas throughout the country. The major networks are the Columbia Broadcasting Company (CBS), the American Broadcasting Company (ABC), and the National Broadcasting Company (NBC), which is owned by RCA. The distribution of network programs is handled by Bell Telephone facilities. Microwave links and wideband cable are used. Now more networks of stations are using satellite TV. The details of satellite television are explained in Chap. 11.

Additional television program sources are provided by the use of 35-mm film. A television film camera converts the optical image to a video signal from a camera tube.

Today, most television programs are produced and stored on tape. The magnetic video tape recorder (VTR) does for video programs what audio tape and phonograph records do for audio programs. The main advantage is that the program can be taped at one time and stored for broadcasting at a later date. Even the commercials are stored on videotape. Another advantage is that programs delivered by microwave or satellite can be recorded during off-peak hours and then broadcast at the best time for the station.

STUDIO-TRANSMITTER LINK (STL) Usually the studio where the video and audio signals originate and where the tape machines are housed is located in a midtown area convenient to the people producing the program. Or the program may originate outside the studio. The transmitter is at a remote location, however, usually at the highest building available. The baseband video and audio signals are delivered to the transmitter by microwave links or by wideband cable systems provided by Bell Telephone. In many cases the transmitter has its own microwave link, which is the STL. The transmitter uses microwave antennas, set up at the studio and transmitter sites. The microwave dish shown on the tower in Fig. 1-8 serves this purpose. STL systems operate in the bands of 2 and 12 gigahertz (GHz), which are assigned to the station by the FCC.

ELECTRONIC NEWS GATHERING (ENG) When the video cassette recorder (VCR) was upgraded to meet minimum broadcast requirements, the electronic news-gathering system developed. It

Fig. 1-8 Microwave antenna dishes used for television studio-transmitter link.

includes a portable TV camera and VCR. The camera is designed for extreme compactness. Both the camera and the VCR operate from a storage battery pack built into a belt worn by the camera operator. This system takes the place of portable film cameras. The signal from the ENG unit is available immediately. The tape can be delivered to the studio for later playback, or the baseband video and audio signals can be relayed by a microwave link for on-the-scene live coverage.

ELECTRONIC FIELD PRODUCTION (EFP) The EFP system uses the same type of compact, portable video equipment as the ENG application. However, the purpose of EFP is to generate an entertainment program at different locations away from the studio. One example is a documentary program or an interview at someone's home.

SWITCHING AND MIXING All the cameras and videotape machines are locked in by a master synchronizing generator, so that the scanning is the same for all the sources. This method permits electronic switching among VTR programs, line feeds, and the special cassette machines that store the commercials. There is no disturbance as you view the picture because the switching is done in the vertical blanking interval. The screen is black during this time, while the electron scanning beam retraces from the bottom to top of the frame. The vertical blanking time is relatively long, approximately 1300 μs.

In small studios, the switching is done manually at a central control console. For large network operations, though, the switching is entirely computer-controlled, even for the insertion of commercials. It is common practice to use a pair of machines playing identical tapes for the on-the-air feed. If one VTR fails, the other is switched in automatically.

ELECTRONIC EDITING Motion-picture film is edited mechanically by cutting the film and splicing the two ends at the frame junction. Videotape, however, is edited electronically. The tape is never cut physically; it is edited electronically by erasing and then recording over a particular segment. A VCR machine for editing videotape is shown in Fig. 1-9. The control console can be located elsewhere in the building, but the two recorders are controlled from the editing console. One tape machine is the player—feeder or source. The other is the recorder that makes the electronic splice. Electronic editing enables a complete program on tape to be made from a number of separate pieces of video tape.

SPECIAL-EFFECTS GENERATOR (SEG) Producing special effects in the picture is another task performed in the studio. The unit shown in Fig. 1-10 is used to switch and fade between video signals from separate sources, such as cameras or tape machines. Additional visual effects can be produced by changing from one source to another.

Fig. 1-9 Equipment for electronic editing of videotape. (*Sony Corporation*)

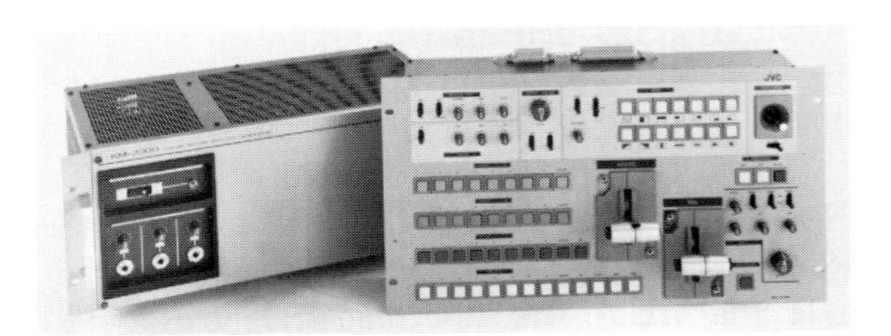

Fig. 1-10 Special-effects generator for television studio operations. (*U.S. JVC Corp.*)

There are special methods of signal switching. One method uses a *fade to black* for the signal switched out. A pair of controls on the switching console can be used to make one signal fade to black while the other comes out of black. Or either source can be made to go to black individually.

Switching can be used in the picture area to create special visual effects. In the split-screen effect, the video from one source can be shown at the left or the right of another signal source, or both signals can be shown at the left or the right. Furthermore, a "wipe" control can move the switching point horizontally or vertically.

Another option of the SEG is the corner insert. For instance, the commentator's face may be shown at the corner of a news scene. Other effects include insertions of various shapes, such as a diamond or circle, at any part of the screen. A very sophisticated SEG employs frame storage with a digital memory. The SEG can store the picture, reduce the size for playback, and superimpose the small picture over part of another scene.

In color transmission, *chroma keying* is another SEG function that allows a person to be superimposed on another scene. Assume that a performer stands in front of a highly saturated blue background. The blue video signal from the camera tube has a switching pattern at all points where the image borders on the blue background. So this switching pattern can be used to key the image into another scene. A common application is to superimpose the person giving the weather forecast onto the picture showing the weather information.

Test Point Questions 1-3
Answers at End of Chapter

What are the abbreviations for the following types of equipment?

a. Special-effects generator.
b. Studio-transmitter link.
c. Electronic news gathering.

1-4 VIDEO TAPE RECORDERS

A video signal can be recorded on magnetic tape, just as an audio signal can. The basic system is illustrated in Fig. 1-11. The tape consists of a coating of fine particles of iron oxide, which is

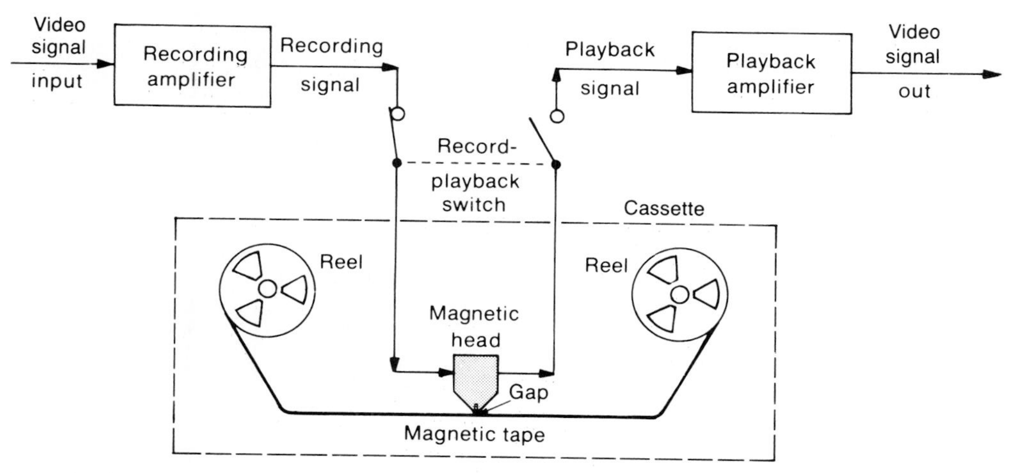

Fig. 1-11 Essential functions of a tape recorder. Tape reels shown in a cassette holder.

magnetic, on a plastic base. The transport mechanism pulls the tape past the record-playback head. Since the head has many turns of fine wire, its magnetic field reacts with the magnetic tape. On the recording position, the signal current in the head magnetizes the tape. During playback, the moving magnetic field induces a signal current in the head.

The problem with video recording is the very wide range of alternating-current (ac) signal frequencies, approximately 30 Hz to 4 MHz. Frequences lower than 30 Hz can be considered a change in direct-current (dc) level. This problem can be solved by recording the video component as an FM signal with a carrier frequency of about 8 MHz. The modulated signal has a much smaller frequency range in octaves. To record signal frequencies in the megahertz range, rotating heads are used. The speed of the rotating head allows a fast *writing speed,* or relative head-to-tape speed. These methods are analyzed in detail in Chap. 10, which discusses video cassette recorders for home use. For studio operation, the video tape recorders shown in Figs. 1-12 and 1-13 are generally used.

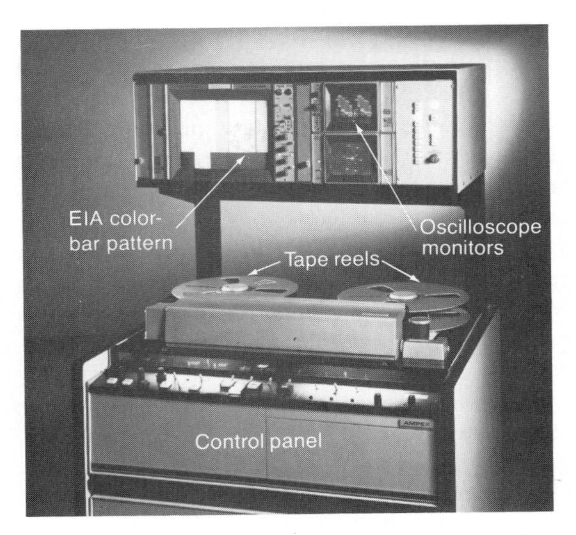

Fig. 1-12 Video tape recorder for studio operations. Four rotating heads are used with 2-in. tape. (*Ampex Corporation*)

QUADRAPLEX TAPE RECORDER The first video tape recorders for studio use, introduced by Ampex, had four heads. The heads moved across the 2-in.-wide tape, as shown in Fig. 1-12. The tape is molded into the radius of the head wheel by a vacuum shoe. The wheel rotates at 240 revolutions per second (rps). Writing speeds greater than 1000 inches per second (ips) are achieved. The recording has a segmented format, in that each head records only part of the image. Because of its good picture quality, this type of tape recorder, known as the *quadraplex* (or *quad*) *machine,* has been the mainstay of video recording in the studio.

Fig. 1-13 Type C video tape recorder, using two rotating heads and 1-in. tape. Width of unit is 19 in. [482.6 mm]. (*Sony Corporation*)

TYPE C VIDEO TAPE RECORDER The machine shown in Fig. 1-13 is being phased into studio operations because of its smaller size and reduced cost. The specifications of the type C recorder represent a compromise between the Ampex and Sony designs and the standards of the Society of Motion Picture and Television Engineers (SMPTE). The tape is 1 in. wide, compared with 2 in. for the quad recorder and ½ in. for home video cassette recorders. Like the home VCR, the type C machine uses two rotating heads that produce slanted tracks across the tape. Two tracks represent a complete field. Actually, one track also shows the image, but every other scanning line forms one of the two fields in a television frame. This operation with a nonsegmented picture is very useful for editing purposes because each field can be viewed in slow motion or as a still picture.

TIME-BASE CORRECTOR Even in studio tape recorders timing errors can be caused by mechanical vibrations. Shock waves can be created on the tape as the heads press into the tape passing the gap. A precise, uniform speed for the tape and recording heads is extremely critical for signal frequencies around 5 MHz, not only for recording but also to allow playback on another machine. The timing jitter causes a weaving effect, jitter in the picture, and color errors.

To eliminate timing jitter, the digital time-base corrector (TBC) shown in Fig. 1-14 is used. First, the TBC converts the analog signal to digital form. Then, the digital output is converted back to the conventional analog video signal. The time-base correction is used in the editing process and in the playback feed line for on-the-air signal transmission.

Test Point Questions 1-4

Answers at End of Chapter

Answer True or False.

a. Rotating heads increase the writing speed for video recording.

b. Video frequencies are much lower than audio frequencies.

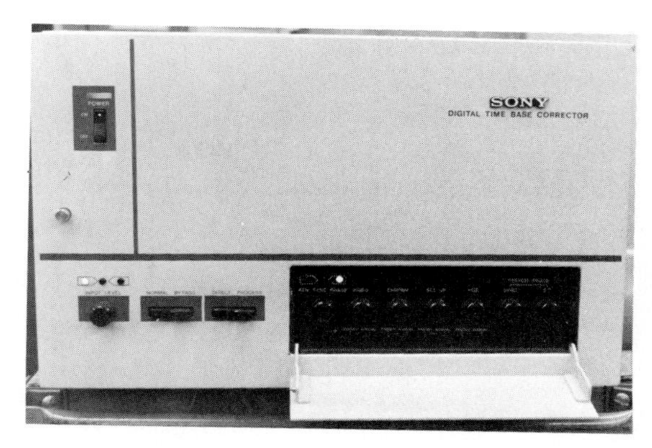

Fig. 1-14 Digital time-base corrector for video tape recorders.

c. The type C video recorder produces two slanted tracks on the tape for each picture field.

1-5 CABLE TELEVISION (CATV)

In addition to wireless transmission by broadcast stations, the cable TV system provides a distribution system with coaxial cable. Cable television is similar to a wired telephone system, but it is used for TV programs. The RF carrier signals are supplied so that a tuner can be used to select the desired channel. The cable signals are supplied to the antenna terminals of the TV receiver.

Cable TV has become very popular because more channels are provided and strong signals can be supplied for areas in which the antenna signal is not good enough. The cost for basic service with 28 channels is typically \$5 to \$12 per month. Actually, 30 or more channels can be supplied, with an extra charge for special channels offering premium programs. The details of cable television systems, including two-way cable communications, are given in Chap. 15, but the main features are summarized here. The basic cable distribution system is shown in Fig. 1-15.

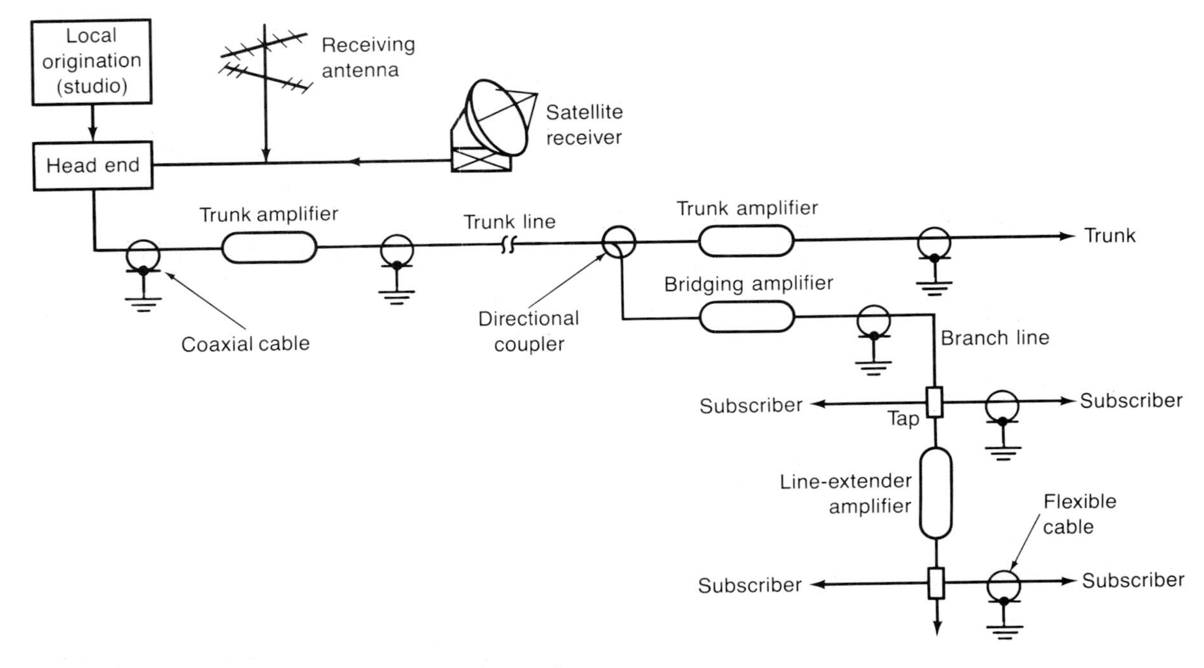

Fig. 1-15 Block diagram of cable TV distribution system.

CABLE CHANNELS Each cable channel is 6 MHz wide, like the broadcast channels, for the AM picture signal and the FM sound signal. However, the cable signals are not radiated. Therefore, the frequencies in between channels 6 and 7 can be used without interfering with other services. These *midband cable channels* range from 88 to 176 MHz. Also all the lowband VHF channels (2 to 6) and highband VHF channels (7 to 13) are used for cable TV. The channels used by broadcast stations usually are provided on their assigned channel numbers. Those VHF channels not assigned in a given area are utilized for special cable programs or to feed programs from TV stations in another city. In larger cable systems, *superband cable channels* above channel 13 also are used. However, the UHF channels from 470 to 890 MHz are converted to VHF channels for cable distribution. The cable TV channels are listed in App. B.

THE HEAD END As shown in the block diagram of a CATV system in Fig. 1-15, the head end provides the program signals for all channels. Local and distant broadcasts are picked up by an antenna which is mounted on a very high tower, in order to extend the line-of-sight distance (Fig. 1-16). These signals may be distributed as the original channel number or heterodyned to different channel frequencies. The studio also can be used for local origination (LO) of news and community service programs.

The premium services distribute signals to the cable systems by microwave or satellite relay links. At the head end, the signals are converted for a VHF cable channel. It is here that the picture is usually scrambled so that the subscriber can be charged for special programs.

CABLE DISTRIBUTION The RF losses in coaxial cable are high, especially in the 36-channel sys-

Fig. 1-16 Antenna to supply program sources for head end of a cable TV system.

tem that operates in the CATV superband. However, the line losses are made up by using wideband RF amplifiers that are spaced along the cable network, as shown in Fig. 1-15.

In the distribution system, the main line is the *trunk*. From the trunk, branch lines extend out for groups of subscribers. The line for each subscriber is called a *drop*.

Each trunk line amplifier has a gain equal to the line loss for the distance between amplifiers. A typical value is 40 decibels (dB), or a voltage gain of 100.

Although the cable distribution system does not involve radiation of TV signals, the FCC has stringent requirements to prevent accidental radiation and to maintain minimum operating standards. In many cases, one channel in the CATV superband is dedicated to a special signal used just for the detection of radiation. The channel chosen is usually in the FM broadcast band of 88 to 108 MHz, so a simple FM portable radio can be used to detect any possible radiation.

CABLE TV CONVERTER A typical cable TV converter is shown in Fig. 1-17. The output from the converter is connected to the antenna terminals of the TV receiver. The input originates in the cable system. The converter heterodynes all cable channels to the frequencies for an unused lowband VHF channel, usually channel 3, 4, or 5. The TV tuner is set to this channel only. All channel selection is done at the cable converter.

Many TV receivers now have "cable-ready" tuners which can be used to choose the cable channels directly, without the need for a converter. However, there is an extra requirement to convert the scrambled signals on the premium channels. The cable converter usually contains the circuits needed to unscramble the signal. From a practical viewpoint, then, a cable-ready receiver may not really be ready for the scrambled pay-TV channels.

Fig. 1-17 Cable converter for TV receiver with remote unit. (*Sylvania Electric Products*)

MASTER ANTENNA TELEVISION (MATV) The MATV system uses a smaller cable distribution network, in applications for a hotel, a motel, or an office building. Some larger hotels and motels have their own satellite earth station receiver to supply programs for the MATV system. Video cassette recorders also are a source for programs. In addition, cable television channels can be inserted into the MATV system.

Test Point Questions 1-5

Answers at End of Chapter

a. To which TV channel is your receiver set for cable input in a 36-channel system?
b. Does the head end feed the trunk or the branch line?
c. Is the line drop at the subscriber branch or at the head end?

1-6 CLOSED-CIRCUIT TELEVISION (CCTV)

The ability to put a television "eye" almost anywhere has facilitated the development of many industries and services that use a TV camera to "see" the scene without the need for a human observer or operator. TV cameras are used in traffic control, banks, building surveillance, the teaching of multiple classes, group business meetings, underseas exploration, the monitoring of dangerous industrial processes, and remote guidance of military weapons. These applications generally use baseband video, without a modulated carrier, in a closed-circuit cable system. The picture can be in monochrome or color. Without the need for broadcast quality, the video equipment is relatively inexpensive and very compact, especially for a black-and-white picture.

SURVEILLANCE the main components of a surveillance camera are a TV camera and a monitor

Fig. 1-18 Small monochrome camera with vidicon for closed-circuit TV. Length of case is 11 in. [279.4 mm] (*Jerrold Electronics Corporation*)

to show the picture, connected by a 75-Ω coaxial cable. Figure 1-18 illustrates a typical surveillance camera. It is extremely compact and can be mounted anywhere. The typical vidicon camera tube has a faceplate diameter of only ⅔ in. [18 mm]. Special vidicons can be used for some applications. One type is an infrared vidicon that detects intruders in the dark by their heat radiation.

A lens with a long focal length is used to make distant objects look close, much like a telephoto lens. The lens screws into a C mount, which is standard for optical cameras. The same lenses as those in 16-mm film cameras are generally used. For remote control, special lenses are fitted with a motor to control both optical focusing and the iris opening.

The aperture, or *f* number, can be controlled automatically in some cameras. A higher level of video signal output causes the iris to close when necessary, to prevent overload distortion.

Another remote-control accessory is the pan-and-tilt mount shown in Fig. 1-19. It has two motors. One can be controlled from a remote

Fig. 1-19 Pan and tilt mount for remote position control of surveillance camera. Height is 8 in. [203.2 mm]. (*Panasonic*)

position to "pan" the camera, or to sweep the view across the scene. The other motor, for tilt, swings the camera up or down.

An additional accessory for surveillance cameras is a weatherproof outdoor housing, equipped with a remote-control window wiper. Also a fully sealed housing for underwater cameras can be used.

In multiple-camera surveillance systems, each camera feeds its own black-and-white monitor, and all the monitors are grouped so that they can be viewed by a single operator. In other systems, an automatic sequence is used to switch the video signal from several cameras to a single monitor at a preset rate.

TIME-LAPSE VIDEO TAPE RECORDER A permanent record can be made of the surveillance operations. In this type of VTR, the tape is pulled at a fraction of its normal speed. The video head is gated on to record a single view and to ignore the next 60, or it can be set for any other chosen value. Since the tape moves so slowly, this machine can record up to 200 h on a standard video tape cassette.

A character generator may be used as an accessory to superimpose the date and time onto the picture. In addition, the machine can be made to change the picture rate, giving more detailed coverage when an alarm signal is triggered.

Another device detects motion in the scene by continuously comparing new images with the preceding signals. Any change, such as an intruder moving through an aisle or corridor where nobody should be, is detected by the video comparator, which then produces the alarm signal.

INFRARED TELEVISION The infrared spectrum of light is invisible because of its long wavelengths compared with those of visible light. Frequencies for infrared are just below 2×10^5 GHz, approximately, for red light. Heat energy produces infrared radiation. For infrared TV, a special vidicon camera tube is used that has an image plate sensitive to this spectrum of light. In addition, the optical system uses filters that allow infrared to pass but block visible light.

When the camera signal is used to reproduce a picture, the peak white parts of the signal are a function of temperatures in the scene. Such cameras are used for surveillance where visible illumination is not wanted. Another application is in heat-loss surveys. The points of a building with greatest heat loss show up as bright parts of the infrared picture. In some systems, the temperature ranges can be reproduced in different colors.

SLOW-SCAN TELEVISION It is the motion in television pictures that requires fast scanning and high video frequencies, up to approximately 4 MHz, in a 6-MHz broadcast channel. With slower scanning for a still picture, however, the video frequencies are lowered considerably. As a result, slow-scan TV can be used to transmit still pictures, such as documents and drawings, over narrowband telephone lines.

FACSIMILE This system is an important application of slow-scan TV. An optical scanner is used to mechanically scan a photograph or document, and there is a printer at the receiving end. Typically, the facsimile image has 360 scanning lines per minute. Compare this slow-scan system with 15,750 lines scanned per second by an electron beam for broadcast television.

The facsimile system is used widely to transmit weather maps in the U.S. weather service. Another application is facsimile mail service between different cities. Similar devices are used in business and industry to transmit pictures, drawings, or other important documents when written records are necessary.

SPACE-PROBE TELEVISION Perhaps the most exciting application of slow-scan TV, combined with digital techniques, is the superb pictures sent back by the *Voyager* space probe of Mars, Jupiter, and Saturn. The pictures taken by the TV cameras in the probe were stored in digital form until they were read out.

Another use of slow-scan TV was seen in the moon-landing pictures. The motion of the astronauts appeared disjointed because of the slow-scan TV. In this case, the slow-scan images were stored and used for transmission at the normal scanning rate for television broadcasting.

Test Point Questions 1-6

Answers at End of Chapter

Answer True or False.

a. Surveillance cameras must use slow-scan TV.
b. Facsimile pictures generate low video frequencies, compared with those for TV broadcasting.
c. An infrared vidicon camera tube can show differences of temperature in the scene.

1-7

VIDEO HOME ENTERTAINMENT CENTER

This rather long descriptive term refers to the TV receiver with the addition of optional accessory equipment. Examples include a cable TV converter, video cassette recorder or disk player, video games, and possibly a home computer. The word *video* is commonly used to describe any electronic equipment that can provide pictures, but the baseband video signal is seldom used for interconnections at the receiver. Most TV receivers do not have input jacks for the video amplifier. The reason is that distribution of video signals is not as simple as that of audio signals because of their bandwidth. The baseband video and audio signals, instead of being used for the receiver input, are distributed as modulated RF carrier signals, usually on channel 3 or 4.

Figure 1-20 shows a typical modulator unit from a video cassette recorder. The modulator is like a miniature TV transmitter, but the output is connected to the antenna input terminals on the receiver. A switch on the modulator is set for either channel 3 or 4. Then the receiver can

Fig. 1-20 VHF modulator unit for video cassette recorder. RF output on either channel 3 or 4.

be set to the selected channel for the modulator output signal.

The distribution level of RF signals is typically 1 to 3 millivolts (mV) at the antenna input terminals. When a baseband video signal is used, the standard level is 1 V, peak to peak, with negative sync polarity.

FCC RULES ON RADIATION The modulator is a potential source of interference because it generates RF output on channel 3 or 4. The RF signal may radiate from the antenna connections, producing interference in other receivers. To minimize this interference, the modulator output is limited to a maximum of 3 mV across a 75-Ω load such as coaxial cable or to 6 mV across a 300-Ω load for twin-lead antenna lines. These FCC rules apply for all class 1 television devices, which include the VCR, video disk player, video games, and home computers that use a TV receiver for the display.

HOME VIDEO ORGANIZER When there is more than one video accessory for the TV receiver, there can be a problem in switching the equipment in and out from one accessory to another. Furthermore, the switched signals are radio frequencies on channel 3 or 4. The solution is to organize all the accessory equipment in a switch box, as shown in Fig. 1-21. This unit has six inputs and two outputs. One output is for the TV receiver, and the second is for a video cassette recorder. The inputs are provided for antenna input or cable TV channels, VCR playback, a subscription cable TV channel, a video game, and two auxiliary jacks for extra equipment such as a personal computer.

Any of the six inputs can be switched to the antenna input terminals of the receiver. Also, all the inputs except the video game and the second auxiliary jack can be switched to the tape recorder. As a result, any of the six input signals can be observed on the TV receiver while one of the four inputs is recorded. The viewer can record the program being watched or a different program.

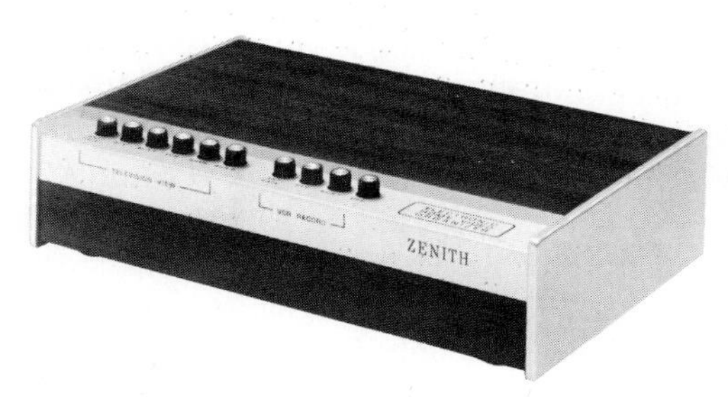

Fig. 1-21 Video home organizer. (*Zenith Radio Corporation*)

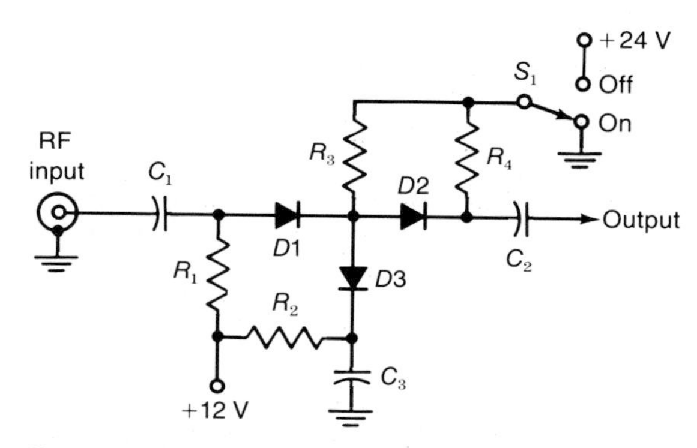

Fig. 1-22 RF switching circuit with diodes for the unit in Fig. 1-21. Each R is 2.7 kΩ and $C = 0.001\ \mu$F. Pushbutton switch S_1 is set to allow CR1 and CR2 to pass input signal to output.

The RF signals are chosen by diode-switching circuits, as in Fig. 1-22. Note that S_1 is one of the pushbutton switches on the unit in Fig. 1-21. When diodes $D1$ and $D2$ are in the on position shown, the RF input signal passes through to the output terminal. Remember that a forward-biased diode is like a short circuit with very low resistance. A reverse-biased diode, like an open circuit, has high resistance.

In Fig. 1-22, S_1 in the down position disconnects the diodes from the 24-V dc supply, placing 12 V on the anode of $D1$ through resistor R_1.

Positive voltage at the anode with respect to the cathode forward biases the diode. The 12-V supply also forward biases $D2$ and places the 12 V at the cathode of $D3$ through resistor $R2$, making $D3$ reverse-biased. As a result, $D1$ and $D2$ are forward biased with low resistances in the series path for the input signal to the output. In the shunt path, though, $D3$ has high resistance to prevent short-circuiting the signal to chassis ground.

When S_1 is in the up position (off), the 24-V dc supply is applied to the cathode of $D2$, through R_4 and at the cathode of $D1$ through R_3. Since the 24 V fed to the cathodes of $D1$ and $D2$ is more positive than the 12 V used for the anodes of $D1$ and $D2$, the diodes are considered reverse-biased. This condition blocks all input signals from the output. Furthermore, $D3$ has forward bias in the shunt path to short-circuit any input signal.

Test Point Questions 1-7

Answers at End of Chapter

a. Is the channel 3 signal a baseband video or a modulated RF signal?

b. Is the maximum RF signal at the antenna input terminals from a video game 3 mV or 5 V?

c. In Fig. 1-22, should diode $D3$ be in the on or off condition to pass the input signal?

1-8 VIDEOTEXT DATA TERMINAL

Usually we think of a video signal being used for pictures, but it can be used for digital data also. The system of distributing computer-stored data over the public telephone network is called *videotext*. A television receiver can be used for the display. Several applications offer access to news services and the latest Dow Jones stock prices and an ability to play video games. Note that commercial services offering access to computers charge a fee.

The videotext data terminal in Fig. 1-23 includes the following components, as numbered in the illustration:

1. The data terminal itself, with a built-in modem.

2. Power converter, connected to the 120-V ac line. The data terminal operates with lower voltage.

3. Switch box for antenna terminals of the receiver. The A and B positions are for data input and TV reception.

4. Modular T adapter for plugging into the telephone line.

5 and **6.** These are connecting cables.

A *modem* unit combines a *modulator* and a *demodulator*. It modulates the video signal on an RF carrier wave, for either channel 3 or channel 4, and it can demodulate the RF signal for video output. The data terminal also has baseband audio and video signals for a TV monitor. A monitor is like a TV receiver with a picture tube and associated circuits for displaying the image, but the monitor lacks the RF and IF sections.

The audio signal is used for frequency-shift keying with different frequencies for mark and space in the data code. In addition, sound effects are provided with video games. Different audio tones generate electronic music.

The modem is rated for a data speed of 300 baud (Bd). One baud is one bit of pulse information per second. A bit is *high* for binary digit 1 and *low* for binary digit 0.

The *high* and *low* indicate voltage levels of the pulse signals. A specific group of bits makes a *word*. An 8-bit word is called a *byte*.

The data code used is the American Standard Code for Information Interchange, generally called *ASCII*. It uses 128 combinations of 7 bits to indicate letters, numbers, punctuation marks, parentheses, and arithmetic operations. Also 3

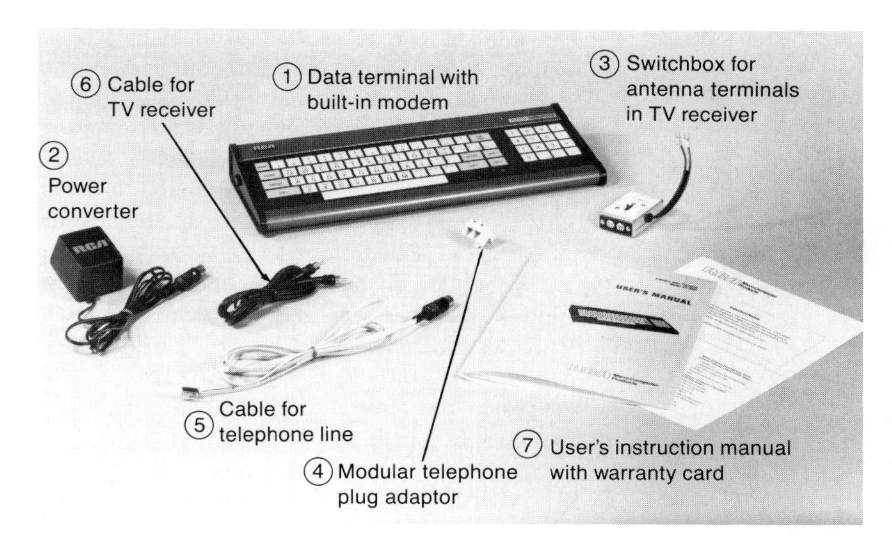

Fig. 1-23 Videotext data terminal. Length is 17 in. [431.8 mm]. (*RCA Microcomputer Products*)

bits can be added to make a 10-bit word with more information. One bit at each end gives stop and start instructions, and 1 bit is for parity. The *parity bit* can be used to check the data to protect against communications errors in the binary information.

Test Point Questions 1-8

Answers at End of Chapter

Answer True or False.

a. The videotext terminal in Fig. 1-23 cannot be used with a TV receiver.

b. A modem unit has two functions: modulation and demodulation.

c. The ASCII code uses 128 combinations of 7 bits for alphanumeric information.

1-9 DEVELOPMENT OF TELEVISION BROADCASTING

Television broadcasting began in 1945 when the FCC assigned the VHF channels 2 to 13 now used. Channel 1 was broadcast at 44 to 50 MHz, but now these frequencies have been assigned to mobile radio services because of interference problems.

The first popular TV receiver was RCA model 630 TS, marketed in 1946 at about $400. It used 30 vacuum tubes, including a monochrome picture tube with a 10-in. round screen (see Fig. 1-24*a*). Two important circuits first used in this receiver were the flyback high-voltage supply fed from the horizontal output circuit and the automatic frequency control (AFC) for synchronization of the horizontal scanning.

Because of the flyback high-voltage supply at the anode of the picture tube, there is no light on the screen unless the horizontal deflection circuits are operating normally. In modern receivers, the horizontal output circuit also feeds low-voltage supplies to the amplifiers. The benefit is less power consumption for greater efficiency.

With the AFC, the loss of horizontal synchronization makes the picture break into diagonal segments with diagonal black bars. The AFC has the advantage of being almost immune to noise-pulse interference.

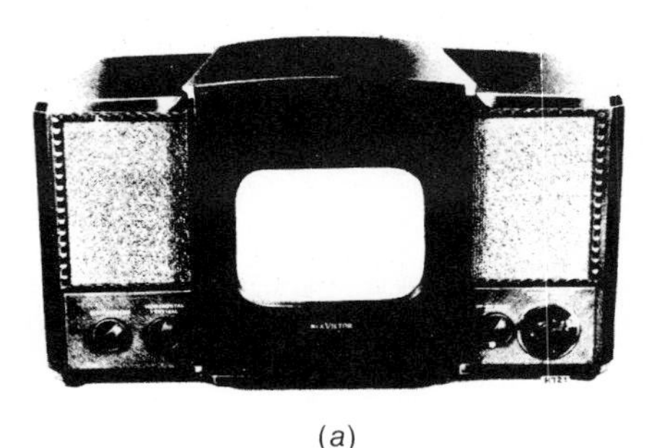

(*a*)

(*b*)

Fig. 1-24 The old and the new in television. (*a*) RCA model 630-TS monochrome receiver with 10-in. screen. (*b*) VCR on a 19-in. color receiver. Compartment door is open and shows hidden controls. (*General Electric Company*)

These circuits are still used in all television receivers for monochrome or color. A comparison of the old and new equipment in television is illustrated in Fig. 1-24.

COLOR SYSTEMS Color television broadcasting developed from early systems which had the disadvantages of a mechanical scanning wheel, incompatible scanning standards, and too much bandwidth for a 6-MHz channel. In 1949 experimental systems were created by CBS and RCA. The CBS system used a rotating color wheel, with scanning frequencies different from those of the monochrome standards. The RCA system was all electronic and used compatible scanning frequencies. In 1954 the FCC adopted a revised color system prepared by the National Television Systems Committee (NTSC) of the Electronic Industries Association (EIA). Its basic feature is a 3.58-MHz chroma subcarrier signal that is multiplexed on the main picture carrier signal. More details are given in Chap. 8, "Color Television Circuits and Signals." The NTSC system is used in the United States, Japan, and many countries in North and South America.

UHF CHANNELS In 1952 channels 14 to 83, broadcast at 470 to 890 MHz, were assigned to create more television broadcast stations. Receivers with a rotary-action station selector have two tuners, one for VHF and the other for UHF. The channel 1 position on the VHF tuner is used to turn on the UHF tuner.

WORLDWIDE TELEVISION In 1962 television transmission around the world was first made possible by using a satellite above the earth. Otherwise, line-of-sight transmission is limited to about 100 mi [161 km]. The satellite serves as a relay station, linking the ground transmitter to an earth-station receiver. Now there are dozens of satellites in orbit. More details are given in Chap. 11, "Television Transmission."

Test Point Questions 1-9

Answers at End of Chapter

a. Does the flyback high voltage depend on vertical or horizontal scanning?

b. Is AFC used for vertical or horizontal synchronization?

c. Is channel 14 a VHF or UHF channel?

SUMMARY

The main facts about video and television equipment can be summarized by the following definitions of technical terms:

Baseband signal A video or an audio signal that can be used directly to reproduce the picture and sound. Or the baseband signal can modulate an RF carrier wave for transmission.

Cable television (CATV) The modulated RF picture and sound carrier signals are distributed in a cable network, instead of by wireless transmission.

Camera tube Converts light input to video signal output.

Channel For television the channel is a 6-MHz band for the modulated picture and sound RF carrier signals.

Chroma signal A 3.58-MHz subcarrier signal for color in television.

Closed-circuit television (CCTV) The baseband video signal is distributed by cable.

Editing For videotape, segments are joined by electronic erasing and recording to create a single program.

Electronic news gathering (ENG) System used in television field operations to make on-the-spot video tape recordings using portable TV cameras and VTRs.

Flyback high voltage Anode voltage for the picture tube, developed from the output of the horizontal deflection circuit.

Head end Source of programs for the cable television system.

Horizontal automatic frequency control (HAFC) Synchronizes the horizontal line structure of the picture.

Infrared television Uses invisible infrared light to produce an image from temperature variations.

Intercarrier frequency Has value of 4.5 MHz, which is equal to the difference between the picture and sound RF carrier frequencies in a 6-MHz TV channel.

Master antenna television (MATV) A small cable system, usually with its own antenna.

Modem Modulator and demodulator unit.

Pay (Subscription) TV System exacting an extra charge for premium channels in cable TV or microwave systems.

Picture signal An RF carrier wave that is amplitude-modulated by the baseband video signal.

Satellite TV A satellite orbiting the earth is used as a relay link between transmitting and receiving earth stations.

Scanning Covers the entire picture area in a sequence of horizontal lines.

Slow-scan TV Provides narrowband signal for still pictures.

Sound signal An RF carrier wave that is frequency-modulated by the baseband audio signal.

Special-effects generator (SEG) Device used for television studio operations.

Studio-transmitter link (STL) Can use microwave transmission or a cable system.

Surveillance camera Observes operations from a remote location in a closed-circuit TV system.

Sync Synchronization of the scanning of a television picture, both horizontal and vertical.

UHF channels TV channels 14 to 83 in UHF band.

VHF channels TV channels 2 to 13 in VHF band.

Video cassette recorder (VCR) Used for recording and playback. Tape reels are in a cassette to eliminate threading by hand.

Video signal Baseband signal of electrical variations that can reproduce the visual information.

Video tape recorder (VTR) Recorder, generally with open reels, that can record and play back both picture and sound.

Videotext System of distributing computer data over a public telephone network.

Writing speed For video tape recorders, the relative speed between the video heads and the tape surface.

SELF-EXAMINATION

Answers at Back of Book

Match the letters at the right with the numbers at the left.

1. Vidicon	**a.** RF picture carrier signal
2. Baseband signal	**b.** 54 to 60 MHz
3. TV channel bandwidth	**c.** Brightness
4. Channel 2 frequencies	**d.** 8 bits
5. Amplitude modulation	**e.** 75 Ω
6. Frequency modulation	**f.** Video signal
7. Picture frames per second	**g.** RF sound carrier signal
8. Horizontal lines per frame	**h.** 4.5 MHz
9. Cable television	**i.** 3.58 MHz
10. Special-effects generator	**j.** VCR RF output
11. Channel 3 or 4	**k.** Camera tube
12. Infrared TV	**l.** 30
13. Facsimile	**m.** 525
14. Coaxial cable impedance	**n.** Head end
15. Chroma signal	**o.** Closed-circuit TV
16. Byte	**p.** 6 MHz
17. Intercarrier frequency	**q.** SEG
18. Anode high voltage	**r.** Slow-scan TV

ESSAY QUESTIONS

1. Compare video and audio signals. What is the frequency range for each?
2. Compare baseband and modulated RF carrier signals. Give some examples.
3. What are the frequencies for TV channels 2, 6, 7, 13, and 14?
4. Are the picture and sound RF carrier signals AM or FM?
5. Explain briefly the function of a vidicon.
6. Describe briefly two types of picture tubes.
7. What do the following values represent? 3.58 MHz, 4.5 MHz, 30 frames, 525 lines.
8. Give an example of a digital word with 8 bits of 0 or 1.
9. Why are synchronizing pulses used?
10. Spell out the following abbreviations: FCC, EIA, NTSC, CATV, CCTV, AFC, ENG, and SEG.
11. Name four video accessories that can be connected to a TV receiver.
12. Give two examples of closed-circuit TV used for surveillance.
13. Refer to the diode-switching circuit in Fig. 1-22. Which diodes are biased on for passing the input signal to the output?

14. What is meant by the visual transmitter and the aural transmitter?
15. Describe briefly how videotape is edited.
16. Why are rotating heads used in video tape recorders?
17. What is meant by slanted-track recording in a VCR?
18. Give an advantage and a disadvantage of cable TV compared with television broadcasting.
19. How can interference be produced by the VHF modulator used with video accessory equipment?
20. What is meant by the midband and superband channels for cable television?
21. What is the function of a video text data terminal?
22. How is a video home organizer used as a switching unit?

SPECIAL QUESTIONS

1. Give at least one example of video equipment you have seen connected to a TV receiver. Describe the connections.
2. Describe briefly one example of closed-circuit TV that you have seen.
3. Name one similarity and one difference between the VCR and an audio cassette player.
4. Why is the VCR output on TV channel 3 or 4 instead of using baseband video signal?
5. What is the basic monthly service charge for cable television in your area?

ANSWERS TO TEST POINT QUESTIONS

1-1 **a.** Loudspeaker
b. Video and audio
c. Video

1-2 **a.** Camera tube
b. 3.58 MHz
c. 54 to 60 MHz
d. White

1-3 **a.** SEG
b. STL
c. ENG

1-4 **a.** T
b. F
c. T

1-5 **a.** 3, 4, or 6
b. Trunk
c. Subscriber branch

1-6 **a.** F
b. T
c. T

1-7 **a.** Modulated RF
b. 3 mV
c. Off

1-8 **a.** F
b. T
c. T

1-9 **a.** Horizontal
b. Horizontal
c. UHF

2

THE TELEVISION PICTURE

Television is basically a system for reproducing a still picture such as a snapshot. However, the pictures are shown one over the other fast enough to give the illusion of motion. One picture frame by itself is just a group of small areas of light and shade. This structure can be seen in Fig. 2-1*b,* which is a magnified view to show the details of the still picture in Fig. 2-1*a.* All the details with varying light and dark spots provide the video signal for the picture information.

We consider black-and-white, or monochrome, pictures first because these requirements apply for color also. A color television picture has black-and-white outlines with color filled in for the main areas of the scene. More details about the television picture are described in the following topics:

(a)

(b)

Fig. 2-1 (*a*) Still picture illustrates picture information. (*b*) Magnified view shows individual picture elements.

2-1 PICTURE ELEMENTS

A still picture is fundamentally an arrangement of many small dark and light areas. In a photographic print, fine grains of silver provide the differences in light and shade needed to reproduce the image. When a picture is printed from a photoengraving, there are many small black, printed dots that form the image. Looking at the magnified view in Fig. 2-1*b,* we can see that the printed picture is composed of small elementary areas of black and white. This basic structure of a picture is evident in newspaper photographs. If they are examined closely, the dots will be seen because the picture elements are relatively large.

Each small area of light or shade is a *picture detail,* or *picture element.* For short, it is called a *pixel,* or a *pel.* All the elements together contain the visual information in the scene. If these elements are transmitted and reproduced in the same degree of light or shade as the original and in proper position, then the picture is reproduced.

As an example, suppose that we want to transmit an image of a black cross on a white background, at the left in Fig. 2-2, to the right side of the figure. The picture is divided into the elementary areas of black and white shown. Picture elements in the background are white, and the pixels forming the cross are black. When each

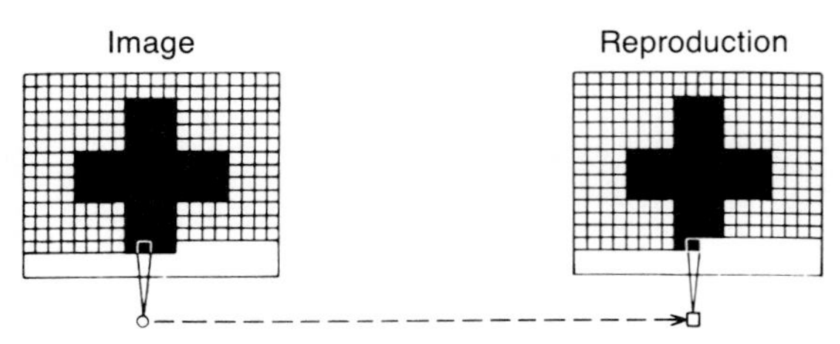

Fig. 2-2 Reproducing a picture by duplicating its picture elements.

picture element is transmitted to the right side of the figure and reproduced in the original position with its shade of black or white, the image is duplicated.

Test Point Questions 2-1
Answers at End of Chapter

Answer True or False.

a. One picture element is a pixel.
b. A still picture has many picture elements.
c. The position of a picture element is not important in the reproduction.

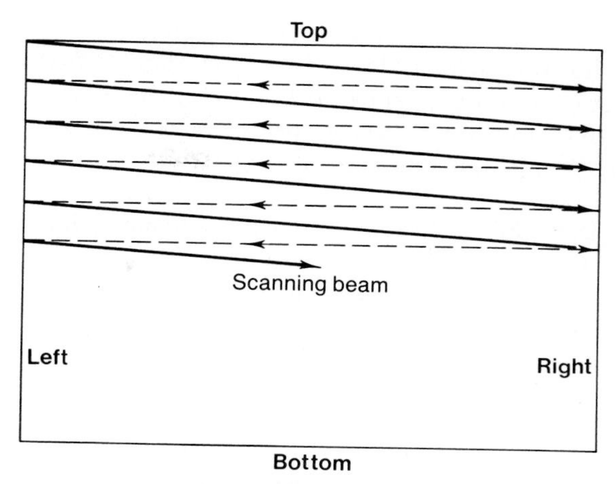

Fig. 2-3 How horizontal linear scanning is done.

2-2 HORIZONTAL AND VERTICAL SCANNING

The television picture is scanned in a sequential series of horizontal lines, one under the other, as shown in Fig. 2-3. This scanning makes it possible for one video signal to include all the elements for the entire picture. At one instant of time, the video signal can show only one variation. In order to have one video signal for all the variations of light and shade, all the picture details are scanned in a sequential order of time.

The scanning makes reproduction of a television picture different from that of a photographic print. In a photograph, the entire picture is reproduced at one time. In television, the picture is reassembled line after line and frame after frame. This time factor explains why a television picture can appear with the line structure torn apart in diagonal segments and the frames rolling up or down the screen.

The TV picture is scanned in the same way as you would read a text page to cover all the words in one line and all the lines on the page. Starting at the top left in Fig. 2-3, all the picture elements are scanned in successive order, from left to right and from top to bottom, one line at a time. This method is called *horizontal linear scanning.* It is used in the camera tube at the transmitter to divide the image into picture elements and in the picture tube at the receiver to reassemble the reproduced image.

The sequence for scanning all the picture elements is as follows:

1. The electron beam sweeps across one horizontal line, covering all the picture elements in that line.
2. At the end of each line, the beam returns very quickly to the left side to begin scanning the next horizontal line. The return time is called *retrace,* or *flyback.* No picture information is scanned during retrace because both the camera tube and the picture tube are blanked out for this period. Thus the retraces must be very rapid, since they are wasted time in terms of picture information.
3. When the beam has returned to the left side, its vertical position is lowered so that the beam will scan the next line down and not repeat the same line. This is accomplished by the vertical scanning motion of the beam, which is provided in addition to horizontal scanning.

As a result of the vertical scanning, all the horizontal lines slope downward slightly from top to bottom. When the beam is at the bottom, vertical retrace returns the beam to the top to start the scanning sequence again.

LINES PER FRAME The number of scanning lines for one complete picture should be large in order to include the greatest number of picture elements and thus more detail. However, other factors limit the choice, and it has been standardized at a total of 525 scanning lines for one complete picture or frame. This is the optimum number of scanning lines per frame for the standard 6-MHz bandwidth of the television broadcast channels.

FRAMES PER SECOND Note that the beam moves slowly downward as it scans horizontally. This vertical scanning motion is necessary so that the lines will not be scanned one over the other. The horizontal scanning produces the lines left to right, while the vertical scanning spreads the lines to fill the frame from top to bottom.

The time for one complete frame with 525 scanning lines is $\frac{1}{30}$ s. Then the picture repetition rate equals 30 frames per second.

Test Point Questions

Answers at End of Chapter

a. How many complete picture frames are scanned in 1 s?

b. How many horizontal scanning lines are there in one frame?

2-3 VIDEO SIGNAL INFORMATION

In a video signal, the voltage or current amplitude changes with respect to time, just like an audio signal, but the video signal variations correspond to visual information. An example of a video signal is shown in Fig. 2-4. Consider this signal as the result of the scanning shown in Fig. 2-3 for the image in Fig. 2-2. This video signal shows the black-and-white information for one horizontal scanning line at the center of the cross. At the left side, the information is white. Then the information is black for a longer time at the center. Finally, the information becomes white again for the end of a line at the right side. A video signal is produced in this way for the horizontal lines scanned across the picture.

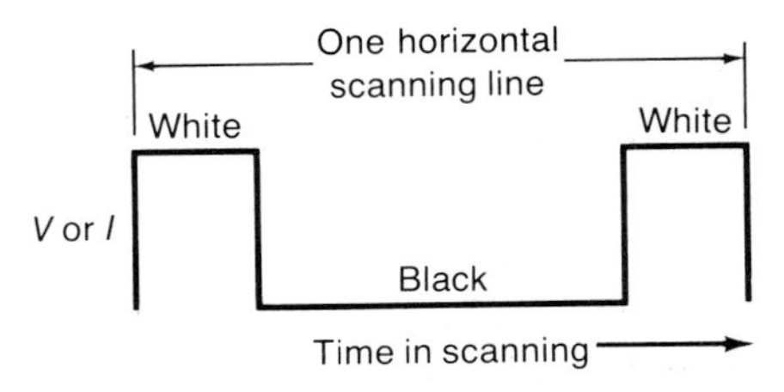

Fig. 2-4 Video signal information for one horizontal line of scanning.

The total of 525 lines makes one frame. All 525 lines are scanned in $\frac{1}{30}$ s. Therefore, the frames are repeated at the rate of 30 Hz. Note that 30 Hz is one-half the ac power-line frequency of 60 Hz.

The video signal amplitudes can have white up for positive polarity and black down for negative polarity, or with opposite polarities, depending on the application. Either way, the main effect is that white and black are represented by opposite voltage polarities in an ac video signal.

The video signal is produced by a camera tube. This pickup device converts picture information in the form of light variations to electrical variations in the video signal. The camera tube includes a photoelectric image plate for the conversion of light. Also, the electron beam is made to move across the image plate to scan all the picture elements. Actually, the waveshape in Fig. 2-4 is for a camera signal.

For the opposite effect, a picture tube is able to reconstruct the picture on its fluorescent screen. The video signal varies the beam intensity, corresponding to the picture information. Maximum beam current produces white. Black corresponds to zero beam current. Also, the deflection yoke around the neck of the tube provides scanning to fill the screen with the entire picture.

The video signal is the means by which picture information can be conveyed from one location to another. The main requirement is to get the picture information from the output of the camera to the input of the picture tube. Common methods include the following:

1. Closed-circuit television
2. Video recording, on magnetic tape or record disks
3. Television broadcasting
4. Cable television
5. Satellite television

The first method uses the baseband video signal directly, without modulation of an RF carrier wave. The others require modulated RF signals.

Test Point Questions 2-3

Answers at End of Chapter

In Fig. 2-4, is the video signal information black or white at the

a. Left side?
b. Center?

2-4 MOTION PICTURES

With all the picture elements in the frame televised by means of the scanning process, it is also necessary to present the picture to the eye in such a way that any motion in the scene appears on the screen as a smooth, continuous change. In this respect, the television system is very similar to motion-picture practice.

Figure 2-5 shows a strip of motion-picture film. Note that it consists of a series of still pictures with each picture frame differing slightly from the preceding one. Each frame is projected indi-

Fig. 2-5 Still picture frames in a strip of motion-picture film.

vidually as a still picture. However, the frames are shown one after the other in rapid succession to produce the illusion of continuous motion.

In standard commercial motion-picture practice, 24 frames are shown on the screen for every second during which the film is projected. A shutter in the projector rotates in front of the light source. The shutter allows the light to be projected on the screen when the film frame is still, but blanks out any light while the next film frame is being moved into position. As a result, a rapid succession of still film frames is seen on the screen. The only time you see the film is when it is not moving.

PERSISTENCE OF VISION The impression made by any light seen by the eye persists for a small fraction of a second after the light source is removed. Therefore, if many views are presented to the eye during this interval of persistence of vision, the eye will integrate them and the viewer has the impression of seeing all the images at the same time. It is this persistence effect that makes possible the televising of one basic element of a picture at a time. When the elements are scanned rapidly enough, they appear to the eye as a complete picture.

In addition, to create the illusion of motion, enough complete pictures must be shown during each second. This effect can be produced by having a picture repetition rate greater than 16 per second. The repetition rate of 24 pictures per second used in motion-picture practice is sufficient to produce the illusion of motion on the screen.

FLICKER IN MOTION PICTURES The rate of 24 frames per second, however, is not rapid enough to allow the brightness of one picture to blend smoothly into the next when the screen is black between frames. The result is a definite flicker of light as the screen is made alternately bright and dark. This flicker is worse at higher illumination levels.

In motion-picture films, the problem of flicker is solved by running the film through the projector at 24 frames per second but showing each frame twice, so that 48 pictures are flashed on the screen during each second. A shutter is used to blank out light from the screen not only when each frame is being changed but also once between. Then each frame is projected twice on the screen.

There are 48 views of the scene during each second, and the screen is blanked out 48 times per second, although there are still the same 24 picture frames per second. As a result of the increased blanking rate, flicker is eliminated.

Test Point Questions 2-4

Answers at End of Chapter

Answer True or False.

a. Motion is shown by a rapid succession of still pictures.

b. Flicker results when the blanking rate is too fast.

2-5 FRAME AND FIELD FREQUENCIES

A process similar to motion-picture film is used in television to reproduce motion in the scene. Not only is each picture broken down into its many individual picture elements, but also the scene is scanned rapidly enough to provide enough complete pictures or frames per second to give the illusion of motion. Instead of the rate of 24 frames per second used in commercial motion-picture practice, however, the frame repetition rate is 30 per second in the television system. This repetition rate provides the required continuity of motion.

The picture repetition rate of 30 per second is still not rapid enough to overcome flicker at the light levels produced by the picture tube screen. Again, the solution is similar to that in motion-picture practice. Each frame is divided into two parts, so that 60 views of the scene are presented to the eye during each second. However, the division of a frame into two parts cannot be accomplished simply by a shutter as in film, because the picture is reproduced one element at a time in television. Instead, the same effect is obtained by interlacing the horizontal scanning lines in two groups, one with the odd-numbered lines and the other with the even-numbered lines. Each group of odd or even lines is called a *field.*

The repetition rate of the fields is 60 per second, as two fields are scanned during one frame period of $\frac{1}{30}$ s. In this way, 60 views of the picture are shown during 1 s. This repetition rate is fast enough to eliminate flicker.

The frame repetition rate of 30 is chosen in television because most homes in the United States are supplied with 60-Hz ac power. When the frame rate is 30 per second, the field rate equals the power-line frequency of 60 Hz. In countries where the ac power-line frequency is 50 Hz, the frame rate is 25 Hz, which makes the field frequency 50 Hz. Television standards for the United States and other countries are compared in App. D.

Test Point Questions 2-5
Answers at End of Chapter

a. How many scanning fields are there in one picture frame?
b. How many fields are scanned in 1 s?

2-6 HORIZONTAL AND VERTICAL SCANNING FREQUENCIES

The field rate of 60 Hz is the vertical scanning frequency. This is the rate at which the electron beam completes its cycles of vertical motion, from top to bottom and back to top again. Therefore, vertical deflection circuits for either the camera tube or the picture tube operate at 60 Hz. The time of each vertical scanning cycle for one field is $\frac{1}{60}$ s.

The number of horizontal scanning lines in a field is one-half the total 525 lines for a complete frame, since one field contains every other line. This yields $262\frac{1}{2}$ horizontal lines for each vertical field.

Since the time for a field is $\frac{1}{60}$ s and since it contains $262\frac{1}{2}$ lines, the number of lines per second is

$$262\tfrac{1}{2} \times 60 = 15{,}750$$

Or, considering 525 lines for a successive pair of fields, which is a frame, we can multiply the frame rate of 30 by 525, which gives the same 15,750 lines scanned in 1 s.

This 15,750-Hz frequency is the rate at which the electron beam completes its cycles of horizontal motion, from left to right and back to left again. Therefore, horizontal deflection circuits for either the camera tube or the picture tube operate at 15,750 Hz.

HORIZONTAL LINE TIME The time for each horizontal (H) scanning line is $\frac{1}{15{,}750}$ s. In terms of microseconds,

$$H \text{ time} = \frac{1{,}000{,}000}{15{,}750}\ \mu\text{s} = 63.5\ \mu\text{s} \qquad \text{(approx.)}$$

This time in microseconds indicates that the video signal for picture elements within a horizontal line can have high frequencies, on the order of megahertz. Remember that frequency f is equal to $1/T$. If there were more lines, the scanning time would be shorter, resulting in higher video frequencies. Actually, in our 525-line system, the highest video frequency is limited to approximately 4 MHz because of the 6-MHz restriction for the commercial television broadcast channels.

Test Point Questions 2-6

Answers at End of Chapter

a. What is the horizontal scanning frequency, in hertz?
b. What is the time for scanning one horizontal line, in microseconds?
c. What is the vertical field-scanning frequency, in hertz?

2-7 HORIZONTAL AND VERTICAL SYNCHRONIZATION

The time spent in scanning corresponds to distance in the image. As the electron beam in the camera tube scans the image, the beam covers different elements and provides the corresponding picture information. Therefore, when the electron beam scans the screen of the picture tube at the receiver, the scanning must be exactly timed in order to assemble the picture information in the correct position. Otherwise, the electron beam in the picture tube could be scanning the part of the screen where a person's mouth should be while the picture information being received at that time corresponds to the person's nose. To keep the transmitter and receiver scanning in step, special synchronizing signals must be transmitted with the picture information for the receiver. These timing signals are rectangular pulses that are used to control both camera and receiver scanning.

The synchronizing pulses are transmitted as a part of the complete picture signal for the receiver, but they occur during the blanking time when no picture information is transmitted. The picture is blanked out for this period while the electron beam retraces.

A horizontal synchronizing pulse at the end of each line determines the start of horizontal retrace. Note that the synchronization is at the start of retrace or end of trace, and not at the start of trace. Horizontal retrace of the electron scanning beam begins from the right side of the picture.

Vertical synchronizing at the end of each field determines the start of vertical retrace. At this time the electron scanning beam is at the bottom of the picture.

Without the vertical field synchronization, the reproduced picture at the receiver does not hold vertically—it rolls up or down on the picture tube screen. If the scanning lines are not synchronized, the picture does not hold horizontally—it slips to the left or right and then tears apart into diagonal segments.

In summary, the horizontal line-scanning frequency is 15,750 Hz. The frequency of the horizontal synchronizing pulses is also 15,750 Hz. The frame repetition rate is 30 per second, but the vertical field-scanning frequency is 60 Hz. The frequency of the vertical synchronizing pulses is also 60 Hz.

Note that the scanning frequencies of 15,750 and 60 Hz are exact for monochrome but only approximate for color television. In color broadcasting, the horizontal line-scanning frequency is exactly 15,734.26 Hz, and the vertical field-scanning frequency is 59.94 Hz. These exact scanning frequencies are used to minimize interference between the color subcarrier signal at 3.579545 MHz and the luminance (monochrome) signal. This technique is explained in Chap. 8, "Color Television Circuits and Signals." However, the horizontal and vertical scanning frequencies can be considered generally as 15,750 and 60 Hz, because the deflection circuits are automatically synchronized at the required scanning frequencies for both monochrome and color broadcasting.

Test Point Questions 2-7

Answers at End of Chapter

a. What is the frequency of horizontal synchronizing pulses for every line, in hertz?

b. What is the frequency of vertical synchronizing pulses for every field, in hertz?

2-8 HORIZONTAL AND VERTICAL BLANKING

In television, *blanking* means "going to black." As part of the video signal, the blanking voltage is at the black level. Video voltage at the black level cuts off beam current in the picture tube to blank out light from the screen. The purpose of the blanking pulses is to make invisible the retraces required in scanning. Horizontal pulses at 15,750 Hz blank out the retrace from right to left for each line. Vertical pulses at 60 Hz blank out the retrace from bottom to top for each field.

The time needed for horizontal blanking is approximately 16 percent of each horizontal (H) line. The total horizontal time is 63.5 μs, including trace and retrace. The blanking time for each line, then, is $63.5 \times 0.16 = 10.2$ μs. This H blanking time means that the retrace from right to left must be completed within 10.2 μs, before the start of visible picture information during the scan from left to right.

The time for vertical (V) blanking is approximately 8 percent of each V field. The total vertical time is $\frac{1}{60}$ s, including the downward trace and upward retrace. The blanking time for each field, then, is $\frac{1}{60} \times 0.08 = 0.0013$ s. This V blanking time means that within 0.0013 s the vertical retrace must be completed from bottom to top of the picture.

The retraces occur during the blanking time because of synchronization of the scanning. The synchronizing pulses determine the start of the retraces. Each horizontal synchronizing pulse is inserted in the video signal within the time of the horizontal blanking pulse. Also each vertical synchronizing pulse is inserted in the video signal within the time of the vertical blanking pulse.

In summary, first a blanking pulse puts the video signal at the black level; then a synchronizing signal starts the retrace in scanning. This sequence applies to blanking both the horizontal and the vertical retraces.

Test Point Questions 2-8

Answers at End of Chapter

a. Is the television screen blanked out 30 or 60 times per second?
b. What is the frequency, in hertz, of H blanking pulses for every line?

2-9 THE 3.58-MHz COLOR SIGNAL

The system for color television is the same as for monochrome except that the color information in the scene is used also. This is accomplished by considering the picture information in terms of red, green, and blue. When the image is scanned at the camera tube, separate video signals are produced for the red, green, and blue picture information. Optical color filters separate the colors for the camera. For broadcasting in the standard 6-MHz television channel, however, the red, green, and blue video signals are combined to form two equivalent signals, one for brightness and the other for color. Specifically, the two transmitted signals are as follows:

1. *Luminance signal.* This signal contains only brightness variations of the picture information, including fine details, as in a monochrome signal. The luminance signal is used to reproduce the picture in black and white, or *monochrome.* It is generally labeled the *Y signal* (not for yellow).
2. *Chrominance signal.* This signal contains the color information. It is transmitted as the modulation on a subcarrier. The subcarrier

frequency is exactly 3.579545 MHz, which is generally considered as 3.58 MHz. Therefore 3.58 MHz is the frequency for color. It is generally labeled the *C signal* for chrominance, or chroma.

In a color television receiver, the color signal is combined with the luminance signal to recover the original red, green, and blue signals. Then these are used to reproduce the picture in color on the screen of a color picture tube. The color screen has phosphors that produce red, green, and blue. All colors can be produced as mixtures of red, green, and blue. A typical color television picture is shown in color plate I.

In monochrome receivers, the *Y* signal reproduces the picture in black and white. The 3.58-MHz color signal is just not used.

As a result, the color and monochrome systems are completely compatible. When a program is televised in color, the picture is reproduced in color by color receivers and in black and white by monochrome receivers. Moreover, programs televised in monochrome are reproduced in black and white by both monochrome and color receivers. The tricolor picture tube also can reproduce white by combining red, green, and blue.

Keep in mind that the color information starts with red, green, and blue at the camera and finishes with red, green, and blue at the picture tube, because these are the primary colors for television. Other color signals are just encoded information used for convenience in transmission. Methods of encoding the color information are explained in Chap. 8, "Color Television Circuits and Signals."

Test Point Questions 2-9

Answers at End of Chapter

Answer True or False.

a. The *Y* luminance signal is for black-and-white picture information.

b. The chrominance signal for color is at 3.58 MHz.

c. The chrominance signal includes red, green, and blue picture information.

2-10 PICTURE QUALITIES

Assuming it is synchronized to stay still, the reproduced picture also should have high brightness, strong contrast, sharp detail, and the correct proportions of height and width. These requirements apply for both monochrome and color. In addition, the color picture should have strong color, or saturation, with the correct tints or hues.

BRIGHTNESS *Brightness* is the overall, or average, intensity of illumination, and it determines the background level in the reproduced picture. Individual picture elements can vary above and below this average brightness level. Brightness on the screen depends on the amount of high voltage for the picture tube and its dc bias in the grid-cathode circuit. In television receivers, the brightness control varies the dc bias of the picture tube.

The fluorescent screen of the picture tube is illuminated on only one small spot at a time. Thus the brightness of the complete picture is much less than the actual spot illumination. The bigger the screen is, the more light is needed from the spot to produce enough brightness.

CONTRAST By *contrast* we mean the difference in intensity between black parts and white parts of the reproduced picture. The contrast range should be great enough to produce a strong picture, with bright white and dark black for the extreme intensity values.

The amount of ac video signal determines the contrast of the reproduced picture. The ac signal amplitude determines how intense the white will be, compared with black parts of the signal. In television receivers, the contrast control varies the peak-to-peak (p-p) amplitude of the ac video signal coupled to the grid-cathode circuit of the picture tube.

Actually, black in the picture is the same light level you see on the picture tube screen when the set is shut off. In a picture, this level looks black in contrast to the white fluorescence. However, the black cannot appear any darker than the room lighting reflected from the picture tube screen. So the surrounding illumination must be low enough to make black look dark. At the opposite extreme, the picture appears washed out, with little contrast, when it is viewed in direct sunlight because so much reflected light from the screen makes it impossible to have dark black.

DETAIL The quality of detail, which is also called *resolution,* or *definition,* depends on the number of picture elements that can be reproduced. With many small picture elements, the fine detail of the image is evident. Therefore, as many picture elements as possible should be reproduced to create a picture with good definition. This quality makes the picture clearer. Small details can be seen, and objects in the image are outlined sharply. Good definition also gives apparent depth to the picture by bringing out background details. The improved quality of a picture with more detail can be seen in Fig. 2-6, which shows how more picture elements increase the definition.

(*a*)

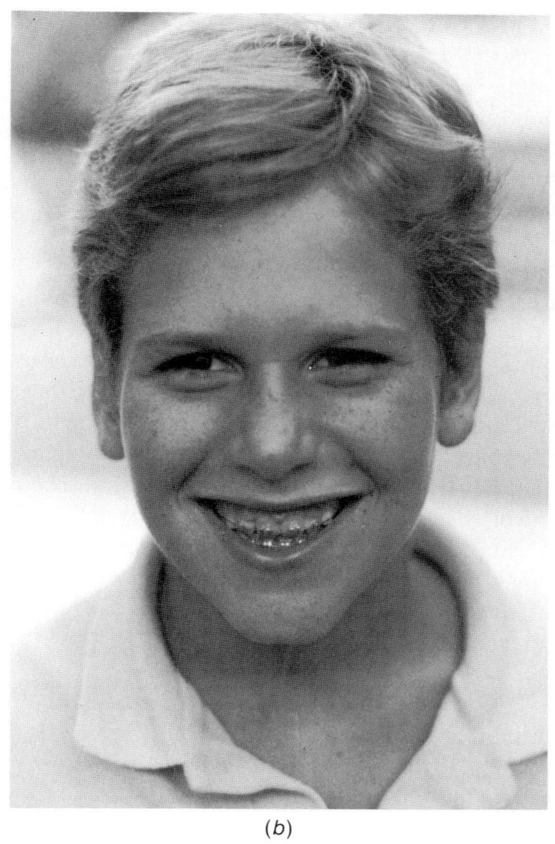

(*b*)

Fig. 2-6 Picture quality improves with greater detail. (*a*) Coarse structure with few details. Definition, or resolution, is poor. (*b*) Fine details for good quality.

In our commercial television broadcasting system, the picture reproduced on the screen is limited to a maximum of approximately 150,000 picture elements if we count all details horizontally and vertically. Such definition allows about the same detail as in 16-mm film. This maximum applies to any size frame, from a small 4 × 3 in. [102 × 76 mm] picture to a projected image 20 × 15 ft [6.1 × 4.6 m]. The reason is that the maximum definition in a television picture depends on the number of scanning lines and on the bandwidth of the transmission channel.

COLOR LEVEL In effect, the color information is superimposed on a monochrome picture. How much color is added depends on the amplitude of the 3.58-MHz chrominance signal. The amount of color, or *color level,* is varied by controlling the gain, or level, for the *C* signal. In color television receivers, this control is called *color, chroma,* intensity, or *saturation.* The color control should vary the picture from no color, to pale and medium colors, up to vivid, intense colors.

HUE What we generally call the color of an object is more specifically its *hue,* or *tint.* For instance, grass has a green hue. In the color television picture, the hue, or tint, depends on the phase angle of the 3.58-MHz chrominance signal. This phase with respect to a color synchronizing signal is varied by the hue, or tint, control. The control is set for the correct hue of any known color in the scene, such as blue sky, green grass, or pink flesh tones. Then all other hues are correct, for the color synchronization holds the hues in their proper phase.

ASPECT RATIO The width-to-height ratio of the picture frame is called the *aspect ratio.* Standardized at 4:3, this aspect ratio makes the picture wider than its height by a factor of 1.33. Approximately the same aspect ratio is used for the frames in conventional motion-picture film. Making the frame wider than it is tall allows for motion in the scene, which is usually in the horizontal direction.

Only the proportions are set by the aspect ratio. The actual frame can be any size, from a few square inches to 20 × 15 ft [6.1 × 4.6 m], as long as the correct 4:3 aspect ratio is maintained. If the picture tube does not reproduce the picture with this proportion, people in the scene look too thin or too wide.

The rectangular picture tube screen has the proportions of 4:3, approximately, for width to height. Thus when the horizontal scanning amplitude just fills the width of the screen and the vertical scanning amplitude just fills the height, the reproduced picture has the correct aspect ratio.

VIEWING DISTANCE Close to the screen, we see all the details. However, the individual scanning lines are visible. Also, we may see the fine grain of the picture reproduction. In television, the grain consists of small white speckles, called *snow,* that are produced by noise in the video signal. So the best viewing distance is a compromise, about four to eight times the picture height.

Test Point Questions 2-10

Answers at End of Chapter

a. Does more video signal increase the contrast or the resolution in the picture?

b. Is the average screen illumination its brightness or its contrast?

2-11 THE 6-MHz TELEVISION BROADCAST CHANNEL

The group of frequencies assigned by the FCC to a broadcast station for transmission of its signals is called a *channel.* Each television station has a 6-MHz channel within one of the following bands allocated for commercial television broadcasting:

1. Lowband VHF channels 2 to 6 from 54 to 88 MHz
2. Highband VHF channels 7 to 13 from 174 to 216 MHz
3. UHF channels 14 to 83 from 470 to 890 MHz

In all the bands, each TV channel is 6 MHz wide. For example, channel 3 is broadcast at 60 to 66 MHz. The picture and sound RF carrier signals are both included in each channel.

These channels were summarized in Table 1-1. All channels are listed in App. A, along with their carrier frequencies. How each channel is used for the picture and sound signals is illustrated in Fig. 2-7.

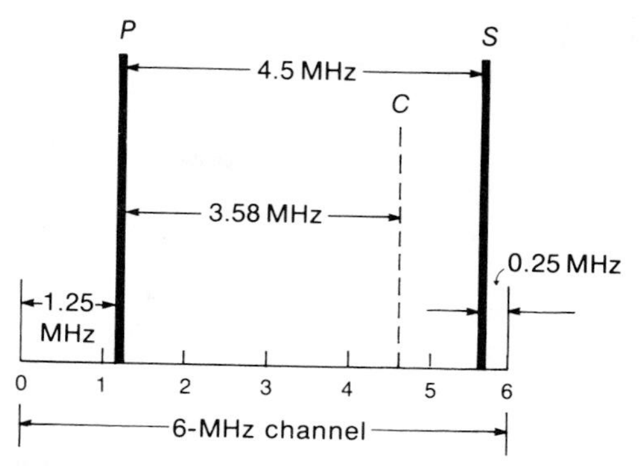

Fig. 2-7 How the frequencies are used in the standard 6-MHz television broadcast channel. *P* is picture carrier; *S* is sound carrier; *C* is color subcarrier.

VIDEO MODULATION The 6-MHz bandwidth is needed mainly for the picture carrier signal. The amplitude of this carrier signal is modulated by the video signal with a wide range of video frequencies up to approximately 4 MHz. The highest video modulating frequencies of 2 to 4 MHz correspond to the smallest horizontal details in the picture.

CHROMINANCE MODULATION For color broadcasts, the 3.58-MHz chrominance signal contains the color information. This color signal is combined with the luminance signal to form one video signal that modulates the picture carrier wave for transmission to the receiver.

THE FM SOUND Also included in the 6-MHz channel is the sound carrier signal for the picture, which is called the *associated sound.* The sound carrier is an FM signal modulated by audio frequencies in the range of 50 to 15,000 Hz. This audio frequency range is the same as that for stations in the commercial FM broadcast band of 88 to 108 MHz. In the TV sound signal, the maximum frequency swing of the carrier is ±25 kilohertz (kHz) for 100 percent modulation. This swing is less than the ±75 kHz for 100 percent modulation in the commercial FM broadcast band. However, the television sound has all the advantages of FM compared with AM, including less noise and interference.

Note that AM is better for the picture signal because the ghosts resulting from multipath reception are less obvious. With AM, the ghosts stay still, but with FM the ghosts would flutter.

CARRIER FREQUENCIES Figure 2-7 shows how the different carrier signals fit into the standard 6-MHz channel. The picture carrier frequency, labeled *P,* is always 1.25 MHz above the low end of the channel. At the opposite end, the sound carrier frequency, labeled *S,* is 4.5 MHz above the picture carrier signal, or 0.25 MHz below the high end of the channel. This spacing of the carrier frequencies applies for all TV channels in the VHF and UHF bands, whether the broadcast is in color or monochrome.

Note that the picture carrier frequency is not at the center of the 6-MHz channel, because this arrangement allows more space for the upper sidebands of the modulated picture carrier signal.

To apply the standard spacing to actual RF carriers, consider channel 3 as an example. This channel is broadcast at 60 to 66 MHz, which is a band 6 MHz wide. The picture carrier frequency is $60 + 1.25 = 61.25$ MHz. The sound carrier frequency is $66 - 0.25 = 65.75$ MHz.

INTERCARRIER SOUND The RF sound carrier also can be figured as 4.5 MHz above the picture carrier because these two frequencies are always separated by exactly 4.5 MHz. This frequency difference is important because all television receivers use 4.5 MHz for the sound intermediate-frequency (IF) signal. The 4.5 MHz signal is called the *intercarrier sound signal.* In the receiver, the sound signal is made to beat with the picture carrier, to make the frequency difference always equal to exactly 4.5 MHz. The intercarrier sound method makes it much easier for the receiver to tune in the sound associated with the picture, especially for the UHF channels. Note that the 4.5-MHz sound is still an FM signal with its original audio modulation.

Test Point Questions 2-11

Answers at End of Chapter

a. What is the width, in megahertz, of a television broadcast channel?
b. What is the intercarrier sound frequency, in megahertz?
c. What is the maximum frequency deviation for the FM sound signal?
d. Calculate the picture carrier frequency for channel 4 at 66 to 72 MHz.

2-12 STANDARDS OF TRANSMISSION

Mainly because scanning must be synchronized, the receiver depends on the transmitter for proper operation. Therefore, it is necessary to establish standards for the transmitter, so that a receiver will work equally well for all stations. The FCC has specified a list of transmission standards.[1] Several points in the standards are mentioned here to summarize briefly the main requirements of the television system:

1. It is standard to scan at uniform velocity in horizontal lines from left to right, progressing from top to bottom of the image, when the scene is viewed from the camera position.
2. The number of scanning lines per frame period is 525.
3. The frame repetition rate is approximately 30 Hz, or exactly 29.97 Hz.
4. The color subcarrier signal has the exact frequency of 3.579545 MHz.
5. The aspect ratio of the frame is 4 units horizontally to 3 units vertically, or 1.33.
6. The width of the channel assigned to a television broadcast station is 6 MHz. This bandwidth applies to VHF and UHF channels, either for monochrome or for color.
7. The picture carrier signal is amplitude-modulated by both the picture signal and the synchronizing signal. They have different amplitudes on the transmitted AM picture carrier. The AM transmitter for the picture signal is called the *visual transmitter.*
8. The associated sound is transmitted as an FM signal. The maximum frequency swing is ±25 kHz for 100 percent modulation. The frequency of the sound carrier is 4.5 MHz above that of the picture carrier, within the 6-MHz broadcast channel. The FM transmitter for the sound signal is called the *aural transmitter.*

[1] "Rules Governing Radio Broadcast Services, Part 73, Rules Governing Television Broadcast Stations." This also lists channel assignments by state and city.

Test Point Questions 2-12

Answers at End of Chapter

a. What is the aspect ratio for a television picture?
b. Is the picture carrier signal AM or FM?
c. Is the sound carrier signal AM or FM?
d. Is 3.58 MHz the frequency for the chrominance or for the sound signal?

SUMMARY

1. The smallest area of light or shade in the image is a picture element, called a *pixel*, or *pel*.
2. Picture elements are converted to an electric signal by a camera tube at the studio. This signal becomes the video signal to be broadcast to receivers. The picture tube in the receiver converts the video signal back to visual information.
3. The electron beam scans all the picture elements from left to right in one horizontal line and all the lines in succession from top to bottom. There are 525 lines per picture frame.
4. The complete picture frame is scanned 30 times per second.
5. Blanking means going to black so that retraces cannot be seen.
6. For vertical scanning, the 525 lines in each frame are divided into two fields, each with 262½ lines. The odd lines are scanned separately; then the even lines are scanned. This procedure is called interlaced scanning.
7. The vertical scanning frequency is the field rate of 60 Hz.
8. The horizontal scanning frequency is 15,750 Hz.
9. Synchronization is necessary to time the scanning with respect to picture information. The synchronizing pulse frequencies are 15,750 and 60 Hz, respectively, the same as horizontal and vertical scanning frequencies.
10. Brightness is the average, or overall, illumination. On the picture tube screen, brightness depends on high voltage and dc grid bias for the picture tube.
11. Contrast is the difference in intensity between black parts and white parts of the picture. The peak-to-peak ac video signal amplitude determines contrast.
12. Detail, resolution, or definition is a measure of how many picture elements can be reproduced. With many fine details, the picture looks sharp and clear.
13. The aspect ratio specifies 4:3 for the ratio of width to height of the frame.
14. A standard commercial television broadcast channel is 6 MHz wide. This includes the AM picture carrier signal 1.25 MHz above the low end of the channel and the FM sound carrier signal 0.25 MHz below the high end. The two carrier frequencies are separated by 4.5 MHz.
15. In color television broadcasting, red, green, and blue video signals corresponding to the picture information are converted into luminance and chrominance signals for transmission in the standard 6-MHz broadcast channel. The luminance signal has the black-and-white picture information; the chrominance signal provides the color.
16. The color subcarrier frequency is approximately 3.58 MHz.
17. The amount of color in the picture, or color intensity, is the color level, chroma level, or saturation. It depends on the amplitude of the modulated chrominance signal.
18. The tint of the color is its hue. The hue depends on the phase angle of the chrominance signal. See Table 2-1.

TABLE 2-1
PICTURE QUALITIES

QUALITY	PICTURE	SIGNAL
Contrast	Range between black and white	Amplitude of ac video signal
Brightness	Background illumination	DC bias on picture tube
Resolution	Sharpness of details	Frequency response of video signal
Color saturation	Intensity or level of color	Amplitude of 3.58-MHz chroma signal
Hue	Tint of color	Phase angle of 3.58-MHz chroma signal

SELF-EXAMINATION

Answers at Back of Book

Fill in the missing word or number in the following statements:

1. Picture frames are repeated at the rate of _______ per second.
2. The number of scanning lines is _______ per frame.
3. The number of fields is _______ per frame.
4. The number of scanning lines is _______ per field.
5. The number of scanning lines is _______ per second.
6. The horizontal line-scanning frequency is _______ Hz.
7. The vertical field-scanning frequency is _______ Hz.
8. Video signal amplitude determines the picture quality called _______.
9. Light is converted to video signal by the _______ tube.
10. Video signal is converted to light by the _______ tube.
11. The bandwidth of a television channel is _______ MHz.
12. The type of modulation on the picture carrier signal is _______.
13. The type of modulation on the sound carrier signal is _______.
14. The assigned band for channel 3 is _______ MHz.
15. The difference between the picture and sound carrier frequencies for channel 3 is _______ MHz.
16. Scanning in the receiver is timed correctly by _______ pulses.
17. Retraces are not visible because of _______ pulses.
18. Black on the picture tube screen results from _______ beam current.
19. The color subcarrier frequency is approximately _______ MHz.
20. The amount of color saturation in the picture depends on the amount of _______ signal.

ESSAY QUESTIONS

1. Why is the television system of transmitting and receiving the picture information called a sequential method?
2. Why is vertical scanning necessary in addition to the horizontal line scanning?
3. Define aspect ratio, contrast, brightness, and resolution.
4. Name the two signals transmitted in color television.
5. How is flicker eliminated by using interlaced scanning?
6. How would the reproduced picture look if it were transmitted with the correct aspect ratio of 4:3 but the frame on the picture tube screen at the receiver were square?
7. What is the difference between color level and hue?
8. Name two ways in which color and monochrome television broadcasting are compatible.
9. Name three applications for the picture information in the video signal.
10. Why are blanking pulses used in the video signal?

PROBLEMS

Answers to Odd-Numbered Problems at Back of Book

1. A picture has 400 horizontal and 300 vertical picture elements. Calculate the total number of details in the picture.
2. Show calculations for the horizontal blanking time of 10.2 μs as 16 percent of H.
3. How long does it take to scan 2 picture elements when 400 are scanned in 50 μs?
4. At what frequencies are channels 2, 6, 7, 13, and 14 broadcast?
5. Calculate the time of one horizontal scanning line for: **(a)** frames repeated at 60 Hz with 525 lines per frame for progressive scanning without interlacing; **(b)** frames repeated at 25 Hz with 625 interlaced lines per frame (for European standards).

SPECIAL QUESTIONS

1. Which picture quality do you think is more important, contrast or resolution?
2. Name one similarity and one difference between television pictures and motion pictures on film.
3. Why is the number of pixels in television the same for any size picture?

ANSWERS TO TEST POINT QUESTIONS

2-1 **a.** T
b. T
c. F

2-2 **a.** 30
b. 525

2-3 **a.** White
b. Black

2-4 **a.** T
b. F

2-5 **a.** 2
b. 60

2-6 **a.** 15,750
b. 63.5
c. 60

2-7 **a.** 15,750
b. 60

2-8 **a.** 60
b. 15,750

2-9 **a.** T
b. T
c. T

2-10 **a.** Contrast
b. Brightness

2-11 **a.** 6
b. 4.5
c. ±25 kHz
d. 67.25 MHz

2-12 **a.** 4:3
b. AM
c. FM
d. Chrominance

3

TELEVISION CAMERAS

The video signal for the picture starts in the camera. The optical image is focused on a light-sensitive target plate in the camera tube. By means of the photoelectric effect, the light variations are converted to corresponding electric signals. The vidicon shown in Fig. 3-1 or a similar camera tube is generally used.

Conversion of the entire picture area to a video signal is accomplished by the scanning process. The electron scanning beam in the camera tube "looks" at each picture element from left to right in each horizontal line, line by line top to bottom. As the scanning continues in this sequential order, the light values for every point in the image are converted to the signal output. The basic system is the same for color or monochrome TV. For color, though, separate signals are produced for the red, green, and blue picture information.

Figure 3-2 shows a small, portable camera televising a scene. The camera includes a camera tube, such as the vidicon, with associated circuits for the scanning and signal processing. To avoid confusion of terms, the camera tube itself is generally called a *pickup tube.* The entire package with the scanning and signal circuits is a *TV camera,* or *video camera.* More details are explained in the following sections:

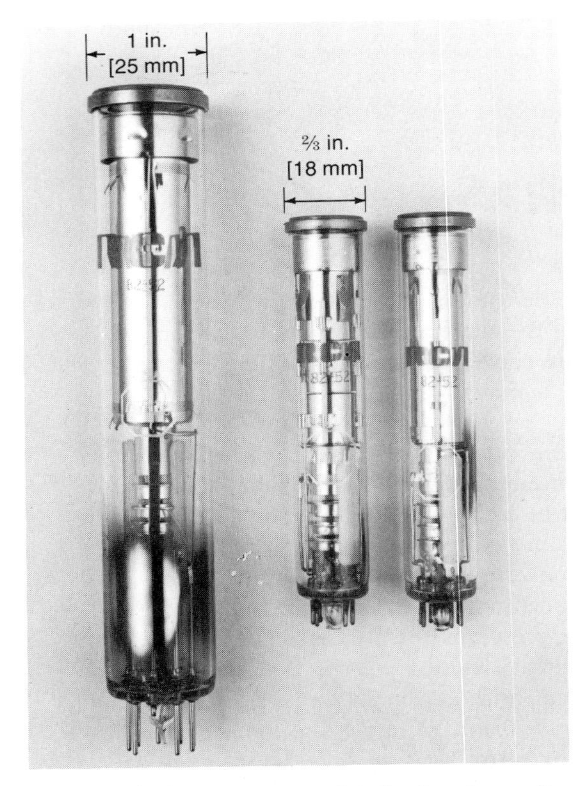

Fig. 3-1 Vidicon camera tubes. Smaller size also available has faceplace diameter of ½ in. [12.7 mm]. Missing pin is the index for base and socket connections.

3-1 BASIC OPERATION OF A TV CAMERA

Television is so common now that we tend to take it for granted, but the ability to convert a picture to a video signal is a fantastic technical achievement. This is especially true for portable TV cameras, which can be smaller than film cameras. An important advantage of TV cameras is that you see the picture immediately, instead of waiting for film processing.

An overall idea of the function of the TV camera is illustrated in Figs. 3-2 and 3-3. In Fig. 3-2, the camera is aimed at the scene so that

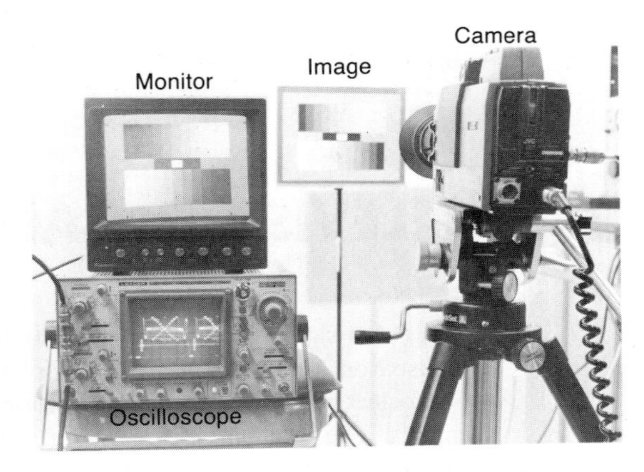

Fig. 3-2 TV camera setup shooting a black-and-white reflectance chart. Oscilloscope waveform shows video signal output.

the optical image can be focused on the target plate of the pickup tube. If you could look in, you would see the optical image. The resulting video signal is shown by the oscilloscope waveform at the bottom left of the figure. Above the oscilloscope is the monitor, which shows the reproduced picture.

More details of the video signal waveform are shown by the block diagram in Fig. 3-3. First, blanking pulses are added to the camera signal. They make the signal amplitude go to the black level so that the retraces in scanning will not be visible. Then the synchronizing (sync) pulses are inserted. Synchronization is needed to time the horizontal and vertical scanning.

The camera signal with blanking and sync is called a *composite video signal.* Sometimes, the term *noncomposite video signal* is used to identify the camera signal with blanking but without sync. The standard output level of the composite video signal from the camera is 1 V peak to peak (p-p), with the sync pulses in the down position for negative polarity.

OPTICAL IMAGE In Fig. 3-3, a vidicon camera tube is used. The optical image is focused on

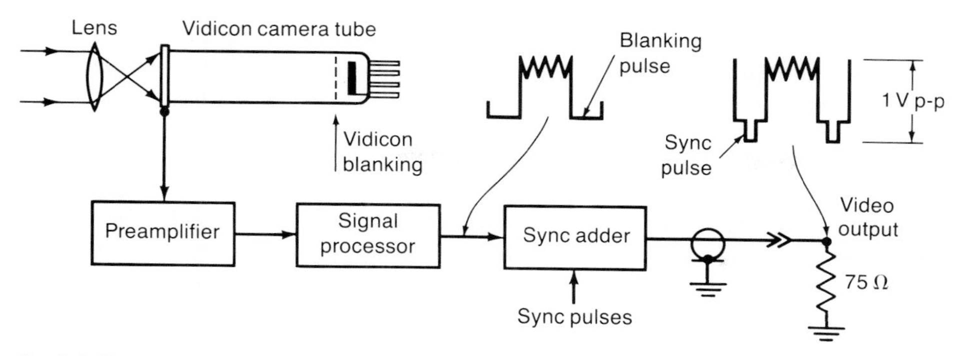

Fig. 3-3 Block diagram of how TV camera supplies composite video signal output. Deflection and focusing for the camera tube are not shown here.

the front glass faceplate. Since the glass is transparent, the light strikes the photoelectric image plate on the inside surface. The optical lens produces an inverted image of the scene on the rectangular area scanned by the electron beam. An inverted image is reversed right to left and bottom to top. Any convergent lens produces an inverted image. In this way, the lens functions exactly as in a film camera, except that the focal plane is the vidicon faceplate instead of a film surface.

In addition to forming the optical image, the lens regulates the light by a mechanical iris built into the lens housing. The iris adjusts the opening, or *aperture,* to determine how much light goes through the lens. Just as in a film camera, the iris opening is calibrated in *f* stops. In low-priced cameras for consumer use or industrial applications, the iris opening is adjusted manually for the required *f* stop. The light can be set automatically, though, in more advanced cameras.

PHOTOELECTRIC CONVERSION Inside the camera tube, the light image is converted to an electric charge pattern. The amount of charge for each picture element varies directly with the amount of light. This charge pattern is scanned sequentially in time by the electron beam that sweeps over the image plate. Scanning here is done from right to left and from bottom to top. Remember that the image in the camera tube is inverted by the lens.

The function of the electron scanning beam is to discharge each point in the charge pattern of the image. This discharge produces the signal current from the output electrode of the camera tube. As the entire charge pattern is scanned, the signal current is produced for the picture.

SIGNAL PROCESSING The signal current from the camera tube is extremely small, a few tenths of a microampere. Therefore, the first stage in Fig. 3-3 shows a preamplifier for the low-level camera signal. This stage represents a high-gain, low-noise amplifier, fully shielded to prevent pickup of electrical interference. The preamplifier is located as close as possible to the output terminal of the camera tube.

The electron scanning beam is cut off during the retrace intervals for the horizontal lines and during the vertical retraces. This blanking during retrace is necessary so that the beam can swing back to its starting position without being visible. Retrace is also called *flyback* because it is much faster than trace. The blanking level establishes a reference for the black level.

Following the preamplifier in Fig. 3-3 are the

functions of the signal processor and sync adder. The signal processing corrects undesired shading in the picture and provides the desired contrast ratio. Shading is produced because the characteristics of the photosensitive image plate are not perfectly uniform over the entire surface.

It is necessary to obtain the desired contrast ratio, called the *gamma correction,* to compensate for the fact that the picture tube emphasizes white in reproducing the image. The correction is comparable to the idea of volume compression and expansion with an audio signal.

Final processing includes clamping of the blanked parts of the video signal to some reference voltage level, followed by insertion of the synchronizing pulses. In effect, the blanking level is a pedestal level at which the sync is added.

The final result is the composite video signal, including camera signal variations, blanking pulses, and sync pulses. The standard output level is 1 V p-p, as shown at the right in Fig. 3-3, across 75 Ω. Camera output circuits are designed to drive 75-Ω coaxial cable.

BEAM CONTROL Included in the camera are provisions to control the amount of beam current, focusing, and deflection in the camera tube. The beam focus is critical because the size of the moving spot determines the overall resolution, or sharpness, of the resulting picture.

It is important to realize that the TV camera has two focus adjustments. The optical focus brings the light image into sharp focus on the surface of the pickup tube. The electrical focus sharpens the electron beam into a tiny spot on the photosensitive surface being scanned. Otherwise, details are lost as the beam straddles the picture elements.

The electron scanning beam is deflected by coils in an external yoke that fits over the camera tube. The linear scanning current for uniform deflection is provided by current-ramp, or sawtooth, generators for both *H* and *V* scanning. They are driven from a master timing source called a *sync generator.* In studio cameras, the sawtooth generators are supplied with *H drive* and *V drive* signals from a master generator which provides the same drive to all other cameras in the system. Then all cameras scan in synchronism. The standard drive signal is a negative 4-V pulse, with its leading edge coincident with the start of blanking, for *H* and *V* scanning. However, in small, portable cameras, the deflection circuits are driven from an internal sync generator.

CAMERA HEAD AND CAMERA CONTROL UNIT (CCU) Studio cameras are divided into two major sections, the head and the control unit. The camera head is the business end. It contains the pickup tube (or tubes in color cameras), deflection circuits and other circuits needed for the camera tube, and the preamplifier.

The CCU is the master control unit, located in the control room console. In the CCU are interface connections with the master sync generator, provision for remote control of the iris opening on the camera lens, circuits for setting the black level, and other signal processing needs.

The CCU supplies current to a *tally lamp* mounted on the camera to let the operator know which camera is taking the picture. Also, the CCU has intercom connections with a headset jack on the camera, which allows voice communications with the camera operator. When the camera is under control of the CCU, the operator has only to aim the picture and zoom and to focus.

Test Point Questions 3-1

Answers at End of Chapter

Answer True or False.

a. The lens inverts the optical image on the faceplate of the camera tube.

b. The composite video signal includes the camera signal and sync but not blanking.

c. The standard composite video signal from a camera is 1 V p-p with negative sync.

3-2
TYPES OF CAMERA TUBES

Camera pickup devices have come a long way since the early days of mechanical scanning with the *Nipkow disk.* In this system, a photoelectric tube is used with a rotating wheel punched with small holes spiraling in toward the center to scan the picture elements. The first all-electric pickup devices were the *image dissector* and the *iconoscope.* Improved types were the image iconoscope and the orthicon. The name *orthicon* indicates a linear relation between light input and signal output. These early camera tubes were used in television broadcasting from about 1932 to 1945. Another pickup device used then was the *flying-spot scanner.* In this method, the spot of light from the screen of a CRT is used as the light source to scan a film slide.

The image orthicon (IO) camera tube developed in 1945 became the standard workhorse of television for many years because of its high sensitivity, compared with the older types. However, this camera tube is relatively large and expensive because of its complex structure. Now the vidicon is employed in practically all TV applications, including broadcasting, small portable cameras, surveillance cameras, and industrial uses. These are the main types:

Vidicon See Fig. 3-1. Note the small size of the vidicon, with its faceplate diameter of ⅔, 1, or 1.2 in. [16.9, 25.4, or 30.5 mm]. In this basic camera tube, the photosensitive target, or image plate, is made of antimony trisulfide.

Plumbicon This name is a trademark of N. V. Philips. The camera tube is similar to the basic vidicon, but the image plate of the Plumbicon is made of lead oxide (PbO). Its sensitivity is better for blue light than for red.

Saticon This name is a trademark of Hitachi Ltd. The image plate is made of selenium, arsenic, and tellurium.

Silicon vidicon A silicon semiconductor junction is used for the target material in the silicon vidicon. The advantage is the extremely high sensitivity for low-light applications.

Chalnicon This name is a trademark of Toshiba Electric Co. Ltd. The target is a complex multilayer arrangement consisting of tin oxide, cadmium selenide, and arsenic trisulfide. This camera tube has very high sensitivity.

Newvicon This name is a trademark of Matsushita Electric. The target is made of an amorphous zinc-selenium layer backed by antimony trisulfide. *Amorphous* means a physical state that is not in a definite form, equivalent to a solid liquid. The advantages of the Newvicon are its extremely high sensitivity and a spectral response that extends into the long light wavelengths for infrared.

All these camera tubes are similar in construction to the vidicon, but different materials are used for the target plate to obtain the desired photoelectric characteristics. High sensitivity is desired so that less light is needed for the camera signal. The spectral response determines the relative sensitivity for various colors.

Test Point Questions 3-2
Answers at End of Chapter

Answer True or False.

a. The diameter of the vidicon image plate is about 5 in. [127 mm].

b. The plumbicon camera tube uses a silicon target plate.

3-3
VIDICON

Details of the vidicon construction are shown in Fig. 3-4. The vidicon consists of a glass envelope with an optically flat faceplate at the end to receive the light input. On the rear surface of the faceplate, inside the evacuated envelope, is the photosensitive material that serves as the

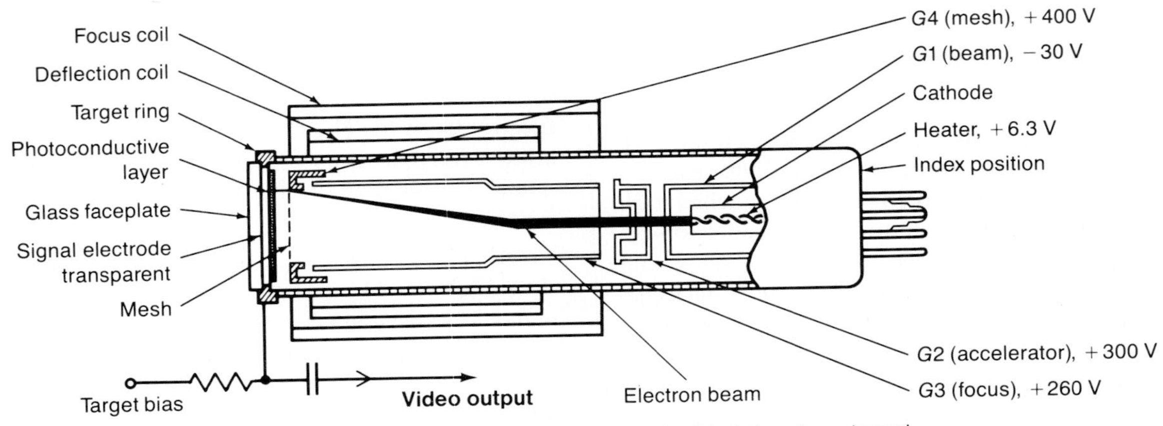

Fig. 3-4 Internal construction of vidicon camera tube. Signal output is taken from target ring at left. External beam-alignment magnets are shown in Fig. 3-14.

target plate, or image plate. The plate has two layers. To the front, facing the light, is a thin coating that is transparent to light but is electrically conductive. This layer is made of tin oxide (SnO). Electric connection is made to this layer by a metal *target ring* surrounding the tube. The target ring is the signal output terminal.

The back of the target plate, facing the electron gun, has a coating of photosensitive material, usually antimony trisulfide. This layer is photoconductive. Its resistance decreases with increasing light. As a result, variations of light intensity can be converted to electric signal variations.

The scene is focused by an optical lens onto the vidicon target. Light passes through the glass faceplate and internal conductive surface to the photoconductive image plate that is scanned by the electron beam. The resulting camera signal is taken from the target ring. Generally vidicons come in three sizes, according to faceplate diameter: 1.2 in. [30.5 mm], 1 in. [25.4 mm], and ⅔ in. [18 mm]. The length is 5 to 8 in. [127 to 203 mm].

ELECTRON BEAM IN THE VIDICON The electrons originate at the cathode, which is heated for thermionic emission, as in typical vacuum tubes. The heater voltage is 6.3 V at 95 milliamperes (mA).

Electrons from the cathode are attracted to the target by the positive accelerator grid *G*2 at 300 V. However, the control grid *G*1 next to the cathode controls the space charge next to the cathode. Note that *G*1 is at −30 V, with reference to the grounded cathode. This bias voltage controls the density of the electrons, or the amount of beam current. The *G*1 bias voltage is adjusted by the *beam control.* Both *G*1 and *G*2 are small metal cylinders with an aperture through which the electron beam can pass.

After *G*2 is the long focus-grid electrode *G*3 at 260 V. Next is a wire mesh for *G*4, close to the target plate. The *G*4 potential is 400 V with respect to the cathode.

BEAM FOCUS Electrons are made to converge to a narrow beam by the electrostatic lens in the gun and by an external coil for magnetic focusing. Note that the focus grid *G*3 at 260 V is less positive than the accelerator grid at 300 V. The result is deceleration of the electrons. Slowing the electrons makes them converge to the center of the beam. In addition, the current in the magnetic focus coil can be adjusted. The focus coil surrounds the deflection coils in the yoke assembly around the tube.

BEAM DEFLECTION For scanning the image, the electron beam is made to move from side to side at the horizontal line rate and vertically at the field repetition rate by current in the deflection coils. Each set of coils, two for *H* deflection and two for *V* deflection, is wound in the form of a saddle, in a yoke assembly to fit around the glass envelope.

The electron beam moves at right angles to the direction of the magnetic field. As a result, the *H* deflection coils are mounted above and below the tube. This magnetic field is in the vertical plane to deflect the beam horizontally. Similarly, the vertical deflection coils are located on either side of the tube.

BEAM LANDING At the front of grid *G*3, near the target plate, the wire mesh for *G*4 serves as the muzzle of the electron gun. Grid *G*4 is a disk of very fine wire mesh. Its potential is 400 V with respect to the cathode. However, the target is at a much lower potential, typically 50 V. Therefore, the target plate is negative compared with *G*4. The result is that the electrons are slowed down and the beam reaches the target with very low velocity.

In addition, the electric field between the target and the mesh is perpendicular to the surface of the target. As a result, electrons approach at right angles to the target, for all points on the surface, the center as well as the corners and sides of the image plate. The perpendicular beam landing allows more uniform focus at all points on the surface. Another advantage of having the scanning beam at low velocity is the absence of secondary emission of electrons from the target, which can interfere with the photoconductive effect for the image.

PHOTOCONDUCTOR ACTION The antimony trisulfide layer is a semiconductor, which is sensitive to light. The layer behaves as an insulator at very low temperatures and without any light input. There are very few free electrons in the covalent bond structure of semiconductors. Absorption of light raises the energy levels of atoms in the crystalline structure, however. As a result, electrons raised to the conduction level are free to migrate to the positive tin oxide layer. This action causes charge to be displaced from front to back of the target plate. The positive charge is on the inside surface, toward the electron gun.

In effect, the target plate has a charge image that corresponds to the optical image. White in the picture is the most positive.

The charge displacement does not form a signal current, though, until the electron beam sweeps past each picture element. The low-energy beam deposits just enough electrons on the target plate to discharge each point to zero potential. This discharge current, taken from the connection at the target ring, is the signal current which provides the camera signal.

As shown in Fig. 3-5, the discharge current for the camera signal output flows in a series circuit consisting of the target, the external load resistance R_L, the target voltage supply, the grounded cathode, and the electron beam itself. In this circuit the target acts as a variable resistance. Its resistance *R* ranges between 20 megohms (MΩ) for no light and 2 MΩ with strong light.

Typical response curves for the light transfer characteristics of the vidicon are shown in Fig. 3-6. Each curve corresponds to a specific value of the *dark current,* which is the current for zero light input, when the lens is capped. The dark current is increased by raising the target voltage. Greater target voltage improves the camera's sensitivity, which is needed when there is less light in the scene. However, the problem of image lag on the target plate is worse with a higher target voltage.

SPECTRAL RESPONSE To produce a suitable monochrome picture, the photoconductor must

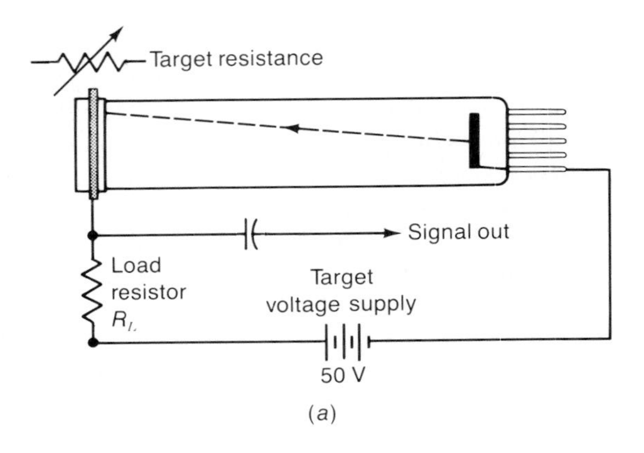

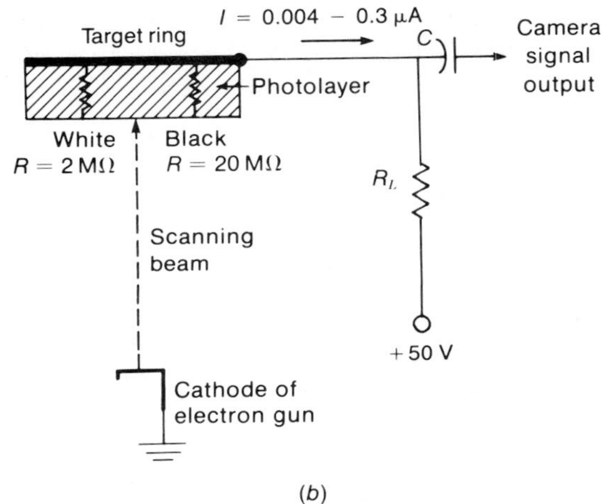

Fig. 3-5 How the vidicon produces signal current for the camera signal output. (*a*) Circuit arrangement. (*b*) Schematic diagram.

have a spectral response for light of different colors similar to the response of the eye. Different wavelengths correspond to different colors, or hues. The human response is not uniform throughout the visible spectrum, but peaks for the yellow-green wavelength at about 560 nanometers (nm). (One nanometer is equal to 1×10^{-9} m.) The spectral responses of the human eye and the vidicon are illustrated in Fig. 3-7.

If we were to view light of various hues, each radiating the same light energy, then yellow and

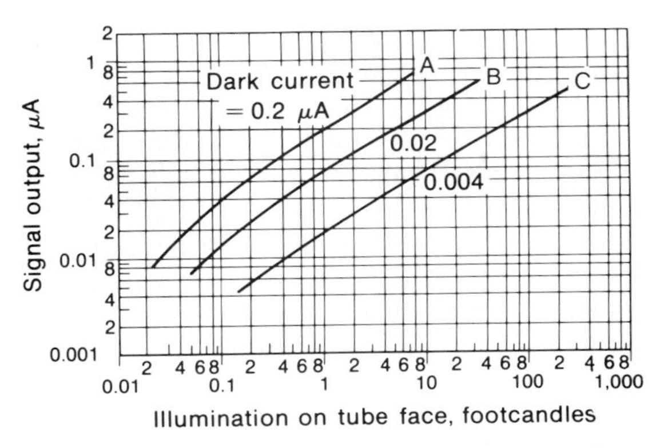

Fig. 3-6 Light-transfer characteristic curves for vidicon camera tube. (*RCA*)

green would appear brightest. To form a natural-looking gray scale from black through gray to white, therefore, the camera tube must have a response that also peaks in the yellow-green wavelengths. A camera tube sensitive only to blue, for example, would produce a black-and-white picture in which highly saturated yellows, greens, and reds would appear black or very dark gray.

Note that camera tubes that are sensitive to infrared are used for special applications. These cameras can "see in the dark," because infrared wavelengths are not in the visible light spectrum.

IMAGE LAG The migration of free electrons, as the charge carriers in the light-sensitive target plate, is variable. It depends on the plate's thickness, the crystalline structure, and the target voltage. At high target voltages, a fraction of the total charge carriers released by light can arrive at the tin oxide layer too late. This effect causes a slow fading of the image. In severe cases, the image on the target is retained for a few seconds after the camera is panned to a new scene. *Panning* is the moving of the camera across the scene horizontally.

Because of the image lag, an x-ray effect can be seen. For example, when a performer steps

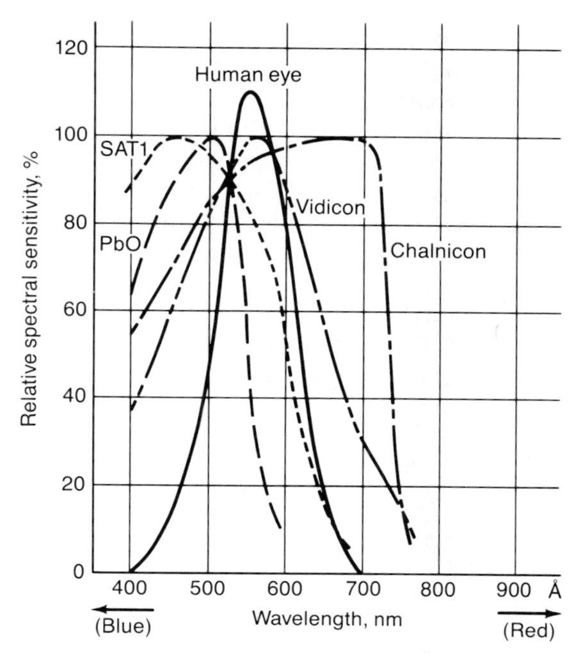

Fig. 3-7 Spectral response of camera tubes, compared with response of the human eye. PbO is lead oxide for Plumbicon. Wavelengths are in nanometers (1 nm = 10^{-9} m). Shorter wavelengths for blue light are at left end of scale.

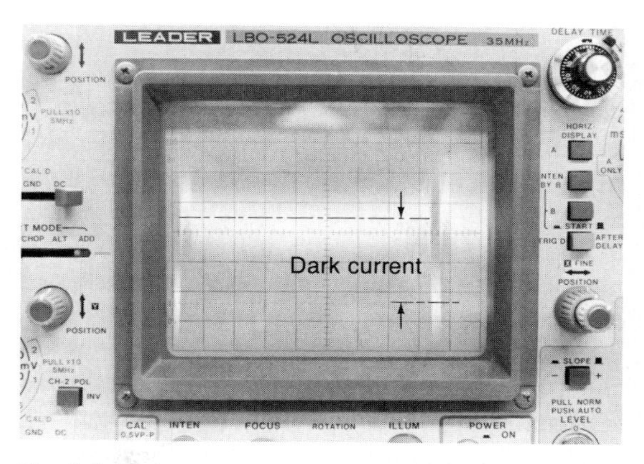

Fig. 3-8 Dark-current waveform of vidicon, obtained with the lens capped.

in front of a table, the table continues to appear as though the actor's body were transparent.

In less severe cases of image lag, bright moving objects in the picture show a tail or a smear that trails off, away from the direction of movement.

To evaluate the amount of image lag, the camera is tested with a swinging pendulum or with a scene that has white chips on a rotating platform.

DARK CURRENT Current carrier signals are liberated in the target layer even when it is completely shielded from light. The resulting current in the output is the dark current. The dark current is similar in many respects to the leakage current in semiconductors, for the current tends to increase with temperature. The dark current forms the "floor," or the lowest level, for the total signal swing when the camera is in use. This floor of the dark signal is subtracted from the total output signal.

It is common practice to adjust the target voltage for a specified dark current, usually a fraction of a microampere. The adjustment is made with the lens cap in place and the video signal monitored at the output of the preamplifier. Here the dark current is checked in terms of the signal voltage. This voltage is measured with respect to blanking, which corresponds to zero target current as the electron beam is cut off. Figure 3-8 shows a video signal waveform and identifies the voltage span caused by the dark current.

IMAGE BURN Prolonged exposure to very bright, high-contrast scenes can damage the target material. A negative of the image, burned into the target, remains for a time following exposure. In some cases, the image burn can be corrected by operating the camera with the lens focused on a flat, white card or on a clear section of the sky. However, the camera should never be pointed at the sun or any other very bright source of light. In severe cases, when the burned-in image cannot be removed by these procedures, the camera tube must be replaced.

RESOLUTION AND BEAM APERTURE The ability to resolve picture elements depends on the diameter of the electron beam at the point where it lands on the target. Ideally, this should be a dimensionless point, but this is not realizable in electron guns. The beam diameter, called the *aperture,* is responsible for a loss of resolution and a degradation in rise time as the beam scans across abrupt light transitions on the target.

The effect of beam aperture is illustrated in Fig. 3-9. Here the beam scans from a dark area to a bright area in which the transition is abrupt. But the signal current does not rise in zero time. It begins slowly as part of the beam moves into the bright area, reaches the halfway mark as the beam is half-eclipsed between the bright and dark zones, and finally reaches the peak white value when the beam is fully into the bright area.

The limitations of the beam aperture impose a finite limit to the resolution and to the overall video-frequency response. The amplitude response falls off at some frequency (5 to 10 MHz) in the same way as the response of a wideband video amplifier falls. But there is a difference, because the fall-off in frequency response resulting from aperture effects is not accompanied by the phase shift associated with wideband amplifiers. In many cases, the high-frequency response of signal processing amplifiers is compensated to offset the results of the aperture effect. This type of equalization is called *aperture correction.*

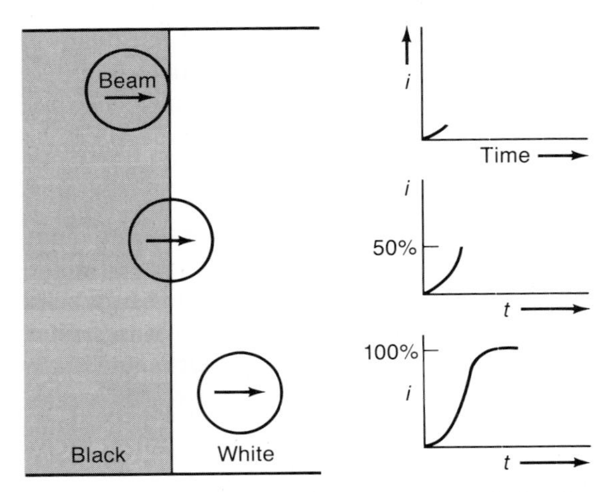

Fig. 3-9 Aperture effect of electron beam limits the rise time and video bandwidth of camera signal.

Test Point Questions 3-3

Answers at End of Chapter

a. Are signal variations produced by the target plate or the wire mesh for *G*4?

b. Does the photoconductive layer have less or more resistance with increasing light?

c. Is the dark current checked when the lens cap is on or off?

d. Is image lag a problem of the beam aperture or of the target plate?

3-4 PLUMBICON

This camera tube is similar to the vidicon, except that the target has a different construction. Some Plumbicons intended for studio cameras are a little larger than vidicons. Others are the same size as 1-in. [25.4-mm] vidicons and are interchangeable with vidicons and similar camera tubes.

Figure 3-10 shows the structure of the Plumbicon faceplate. It consists of a conducting, transparent film of tin oxide just inside the glass. Deposited on this film is a layer of lead oxide (PbO) that has been doped with trace elements in the same way as silicon is doped during manufacture to form PN junctions. The N zone is closest to the faceplate, the central zone is undoped to form an intrinsic (I) layer, and the layer toward the electron gun is doped to form the P layer.

The PIN junction so formed acts very much as a semiconductor diode. The voltage field gra-

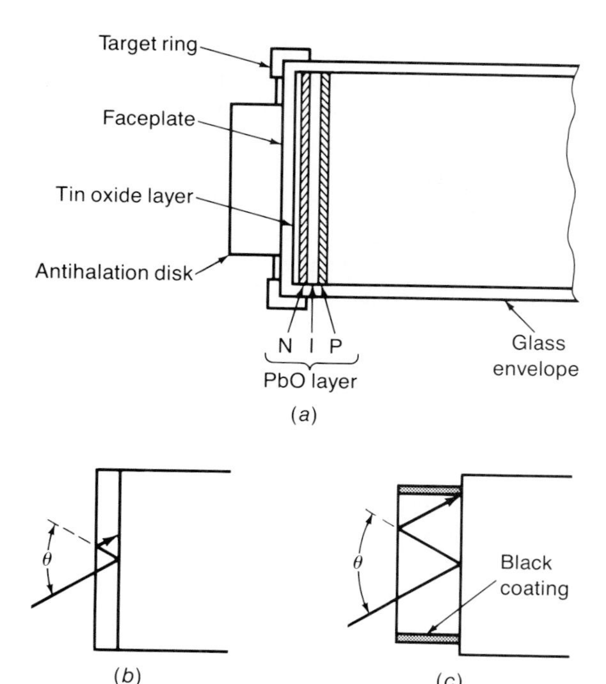

Fig. 3-10 Construction of image plate in Plumbicon camera tube. (*a*) Lead oxide layer. (*U.S. JVC Corp.*) (*b*) Cause of halation or light scattering. (*c*) Action of antihalation disk.

dient set up in the intrinsic layer is quite high, so that all carrier signals released owing to the absorption of light are swept across the target plate to establish the image charge pattern on the gun side. As a result, the mechanism that causes lag in the vidicon is essentially absent. The Plumbicon has the lowest lag of all camera tubes.

Also the dark current is extremely low and practically unaffected by temperature. The spectral sensitivity of the Plumbicon is similar to that of human vision. These factors make the Plumbicon a frequent choice for the performance demanded of broadcast and other high-quality studio operations.

One drawback of the Plumbicon is the orange color of the target material itself. It reflects light in this part of the spectrum back to the faceplate. Light hitting at an angle is reflected from the faceplate back to the target to form a halo (also called *flare*) of the optical image. The antihalo device is a glass disk with a black coating on its circumference. The thickness of this coating is designed so that light reflected from the target is absorbed by the coated walls of the antihalo disk. Refer to Fig. 3-10*b* and *c*.

Test Point Questions 3-4
Answers at End of Chapter

Answer True or False.

a. The Plumbicon uses a lead oxide layer for the target plate.
b. Image lag is the biggest problem with the Plumbicon.

3-5 SATICON

The first three letters in the name *Saticon* identify the materials used for the target: selenium, arsenic, and tellurium. Selenium, long known for its photoelectric properties, was one of the first chemical elements tried in TV pickup tubes. However, these tubes suffered from chemical instability and crystallization, which quickly degraded their performance. The Saticon uses arsenic as a doping agent, which yields long-term stability and prevents crystallization. In addition, the target layer is doped with tellurium in a narrow band close to the faceplate, to increase sensitivity in the red (long-wavelength) end of the visible spectrum.

The basic structure of the target is shown in simplified form in Fig. 3-11. As in other tubes, a transparent tin-oxide layer forms the target terminal. A thin layer of antimony trisulfide on the gun side of the target is applied to suppress secondary electron emission.

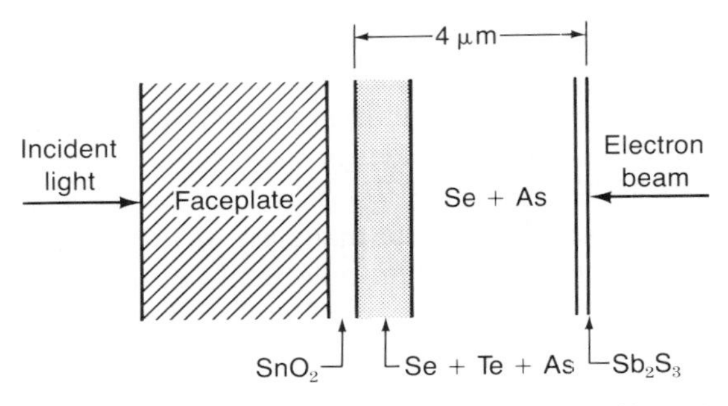

Fig. 3-11 Faceplate of Saticon camera tube. (Chemical symbols: Se = selenium, Te = tellurium, As = arsenic, Sb_2S_3 = antimony trisulfide, SnO_2 = tin dioxide.)

Saticons can be produced at a relatively low cost, and they perform in the same class as Plumbicons. One advantage of the Saticon is its almost black target material which reflects little light. The result is very little light dispersion inside the material. This factor helps reduce flare and improves resolution. Although dark current varies with temperature, it is so low that the effect is negligible. Lag could be objectionable were it not for bias lighting.

BIAS LIGHTING One method of minimizing the image lag in the Saticon is to keep a minimum and steady light, for bias lighting, on the target. This light ensures that there is enough signal current to permit rapid charge and discharge of the layer's capacitance.

The bias lighting assembly consists of a ring of light-emitting diode (LED) units surrounding the faceplate of the camera tube. This steady light raises the black level slightly in the camera signal. However, the steady level can be subtracted electrically from the video signal in the signal processor circuit, so that the full signal swing between black and peak white is obtained.

The use of bias lighting for the Saticon results in a lag performance almost as good as that for the Plumbicon. The Plumbicon also has some lag that is caused by the target's capacitance, but it is much smaller. Bias lighting may be used in some Plumbicon cameras, though, to prevent even small amounts of lag. The image lag is especially noticeable in color, for a colored tail can be seen following a moving bright object.

A recent development in electron guns is the use of a different control-grid cup design. The purpose is to reduce the dynamic beam resistance, which reduces the image lag. An electron gun of this type is known as a *diode gun.*

Test Point Questions 3-5

Answers at End of Chapter

Answer True or False.

a. The target of the Saticon is constructed in the same way as that of the Plumbicon.

b. The use of bias lighting reduces the image lag.

3-6 CAMERA ADJUSTMENTS

Basic camera adjustments include target voltage and beam-current adjustment, beam alignment, optical and electrical focus, and deflection. In color cameras that contain two or three pickup tubes, the adjustments must be performed for each tube.

TARGET VOLTAGE Often camera tubes are supplied with a specification sheet that includes the recommended target voltage. For vidicons, operation at the recomended target voltage provides optimum performance in terms of sensitivity and lag. In the absence of a specification sheet, conventional practice for vidicons is to set the target voltage at the value that will yield the recommended dark current. This current is not measured directly. It is given as a specified signal voltage, usually at the output of the preamplifier, measured with respect to the signal level when the beam is blanked. Refer to Fig. 3-8 for an oscilloscope photograph of the dark current.

The dark current is independent of the target voltage when the target behaves as a semiconductor junction. This feature applies to Plumbicons and Saticons. Here the target voltage is set to a recommended value that applies to all tubes of a given type. If the target voltage is set too low, the sensitivity is decreased somewhat. If the target voltage is set too high, there is danger of electrical breakdown in the target material and permanent damage. The target voltage is seldom higher than 50 V.

The target voltage is always measured with respect to the cathode. When positive beam-blanking pulses are applied to the cathode, the target voltage must be measured between the target and cathode without the blanking pulses.

BEAM CURRENT There must be sufficient beam current to discharge the target at the brightest parts of the charge image. Insufficient beam current results in a low video signal output as well as whites that are saturated. Then white is clipped off by the beam-current limitation. The peaks of the output waveform appear flat, and bright parts of the picture appear as white blobs, without detail. Figure 3-12*a* shows a TV picture that has insufficient beam current. The normal picture is shown in Fig. 3-12*b*.

Excessive beam current produces geometric distortion and defocusing of the image as a result of the accumulation of electron space charge in the mesh-target area. Standard practice is to adjust the video signal output level by using a recommended lens opening and a test pattern illuminated with the recommended incident light. Then the lens is opened an additional two stops, and the beam is adjusted for a specified video signal output level. Opening the lens ensures sufficient beam current for highlights that are just higher than those expected in normal use.

High-performance cameras employ either automatic beam control (ABC) or dynamic beam stretching (DBS) to increase the beam current for abnormal picture highlights. In this sytem, the beam current is modulated by the *G*1-to-cathode voltage to boost the beam current for signals that approach peak white.

FOCUS There are two focus adjustments in a TV camera, optical and electrical. The optical focus matches the focal plane of the lens to the target plane of the vidicon. In essence, the optical

(*a*)

(*b*)

Fig. 3-12 Effect of beam-current adjustment. (*a*) Insufficient beam current. (*b*) Normal beam current.

focus sets the precise distance between the rear of the lens mounting and the vidicon faceplate. This adjustment is also known as *back focus*, or *flangeback*. The latter term refers to a mechanical reference at the rear of the lens assembly.

In most cases, the pickup tube with its deflection yoke and focus coil housing is moved back and forth along the tube axis until optical focus is achieved. Then the assembly is locked firmly in place.

In some cameras an adjustable flange is used at the lens mount. This flange can be threaded in or out to achieve the correct distance.

To make the optical focus adjustment, the lens focus ring is set to infinity and the camera is aimed at a distant subject, 30 ft [9.1 m] or more away. Then the pickup tube assembly, or the flange ring, is adjusted for a sharp image.

Electrical focus involves adjustment of a potentiometer. The camera is aimed at a test pattern, and the focus is set for the sharpest picture. The focus is set for best resolution of the vertical striped wedges in the test pattern.

In cameras that use magnetic focus, the image appears to rotate around the center as the electrical focus is adjusted. This is a result of the action of the focus field. See Fig. 3-13. The focus coil is a solenoid wound around the long axis of the pickup tube. Electrons that move along the central axis of the tube do not cross the flux lines and are not affected by them. However, electrons

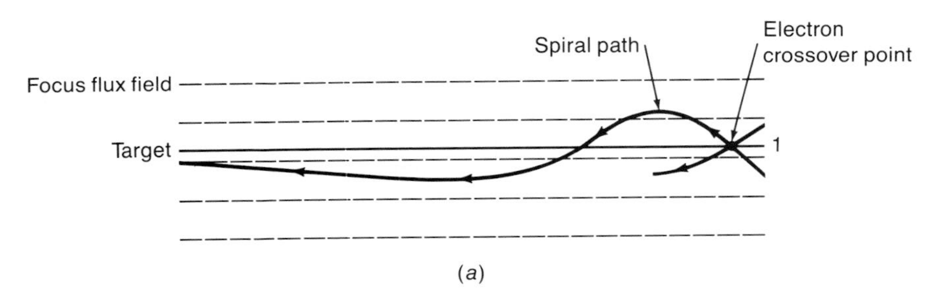

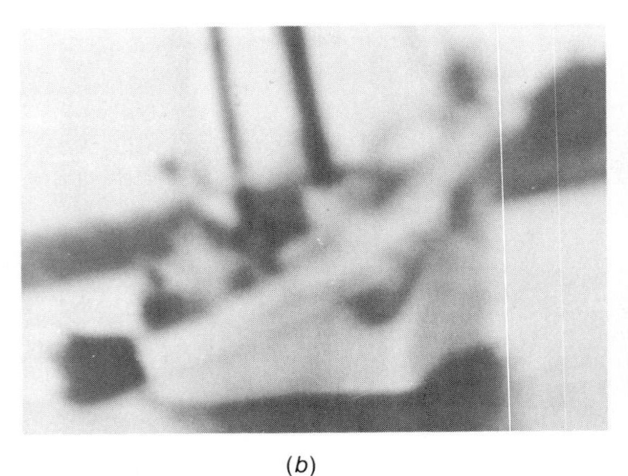

Fig. 3-13 Magnetic focus adjustment for camera tube. (*a*) Action of magnetic focus field. (*b*) Poor focus. (*c*) Sharp focus.

that are diverging toward the tube wall cross the flux of the magnetic field and are forced to move at right angles to the flux lines. The steeper the crossing angle, the greater the correcting force. The result is a spiral route, as shown in Fig. 3-13. All the electrons in the beam come together at a point, which is adjusted to be in the plane of the target plate.

Following magnetic focus adjustment, in which the picture rotates about its center, the picture may be tilted at the point of best focus. In that case, the mounts for the deflection yoke must be loosened and the yoke rotated until the picture position is correct.

BEAM ALIGNMENT An assembly is mounted on the pickup tube, at the rear of the deflection yoke assembly, to align the electron beam with the center of the deflection-focus axis. This beam magnet consists of two sets of coils having magnetic axes at right angles to the tube axis and at right angles to each other. In some cameras, a permanent-magnet assembly is used instead of coils. It consists of a pair of rings magnetized so that the flux lines cross the tube axis at right angles. Refer to Fig. 3-14. When the tabs on the rings are aligned, the flux fields from each ring are opposite and thus cancel. Spreading the tabs increases the field strength. The entire assembly can be rotated to point the flux field in the required direction. A similar device is used on TV picture tubes for centering the picture.

To adjust the beam alignment, the camera is pointed at a test pattern and the electrical focus is rocked back and forth. In cameras that use magnetic focusing, the picture appears to rotate. When the beam alignment is correct, the center of rotation stays in one spot—at the center of the monitor picture. Therefore, the beam alignment magnets are adjusted until the center of rotation remains stationary when the focus control is rocked.

A similar system is used for pickup tubes that employ electrostatic focus only. In this case, the picture does not rotate, but the center of the picture is displaced as the focus is rocked. The beam alignment currents, or rings, are adjusted until the center of the picture remains at the center of the monitor screen as the focusing control is rocked back and forth through best focus.

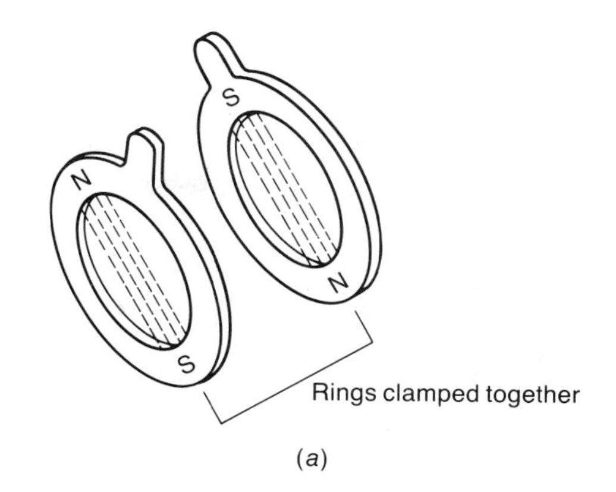

(*a*)

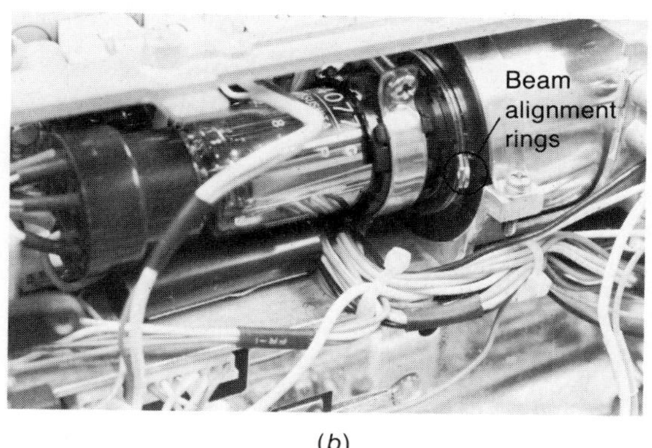

(*b*)

Fig. 3-14 Beam alignment magnets for camera tube. (*a*) Ring magnets. (*b*) Mounting on camera tube.

DEFLECTION The deflection size depends on the amplitude of the horizontal and vertical current ramps in the deflection coils. The width and height are adjusted to scan the full optical image on the target. In some cases, an opaque mask is affixed to the pickup tube faceplate, and the deflection is adjusted until the mask just becomes visible at the edges of the picture. A specially

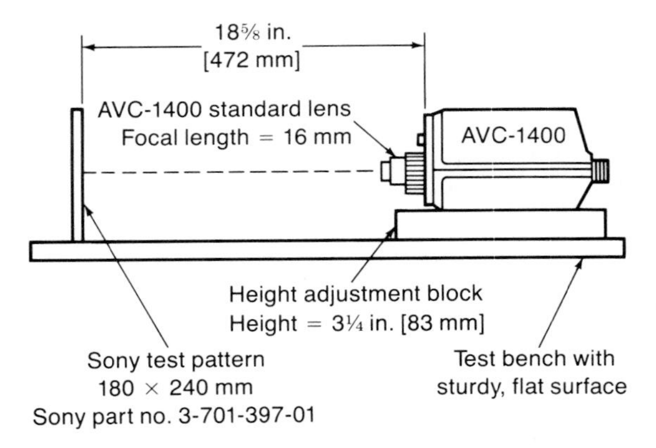

Fig. 3-15 Camera test setup for correct height and width of picture.

modified monitor is required for this purpose. The picture is underscanned so that the edges of the raster can be seen.

When a mask is not used, it is necessary to form an optical image of the correct dimension. The usual practice is to set up a test fixture such as the one shown in Fig. 3-15. The size of the test pattern and the distance to the camera are critical in this setup.

Test Point Questions 3-6

Answers at End of Chapter

Answer True or False.

a. The typical target voltage is less than 50 V.

b. Optical focus and electrical focus require essentially the same adjustments.

c. Beam alignment is similar to centering of the electron beam.

3-7 OPTICAL COLOR SEPARATION FOR RED, GREEN, AND BLUE

The color camera is really three cameras in one housing. A typical studio camera contains three pickup tubes, one for each primary color. An optical separator, behind the main lens (called the *taking lens*), breaks incoming light into its red, green, and blue values. Separate preamplifiers and processors handle these *R, G,* and *B* signals.

The correct percentages of the signals are added, so that the resultant closely resembles the gray scale produced by a black-and-white camera. This resultant signal is called the *Y,* or *luminance, signal.* It is essentially the same as the video signal produced by a black-and-white camera.

The percentages taken of each primary signal are adjusted to match the luminance, or brightness, sensation of human vision. The equation is

$$Y = 30\% \text{ red} + 59\% \text{ green} + 11\% \text{ blue}$$

Remember that human vision peaks at the yellow-green wavelengths. Therefore, a larger percentage is used for the green primary signal. The *Y* signal produces a normal gray scale on a black-and-white TV set.

A simple optical separator with color filters is shown in Fig. 3-16. Incoming light from the taking lens is split into three parts by partially silvered mirrors. The mirrors pass part of the light and reflect the remainder. In front of each pickup tube is an optical color filter. These filters

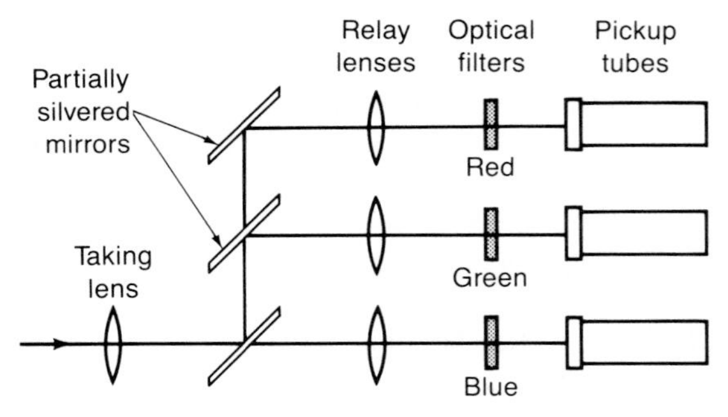

Fig. 3-16 Separator using optical red, green, and blue filters for color TV camera.

are selected to pass a narrow band of wavelengths centered on the red, green, and blue primary signals. The filters block unwanted light. The blue filter, for example, passes blue but blocks red and green. The problem with this simple scheme is excessive light loss. Only one-third of the light passed by the taking lens reaches each pickup tube.

DICHROIC MIRRORS Dichroic mirrors solve the light-loss problem because they pass certain wavelength bands and reflect others. The basic arrangement is shown in Fig. 3-17. The first mirror reflects blue light but passes the remainder. The blue light is totally reflected from a front-silvered mirror into a relay lens, which forms an image of the blue components of the picture onto the target plate of the blue (*B*) pickup tube at the bottom of the figure.

The light that passes through the first dichroic mirror then impinges on a second mirror. Here the red component is reflected, and the remainder passes through. What is left is white minus red and blue, which is essentially green. Very little of the red-green-blue component is lost. The light that reaches the red pickup tube is a very large

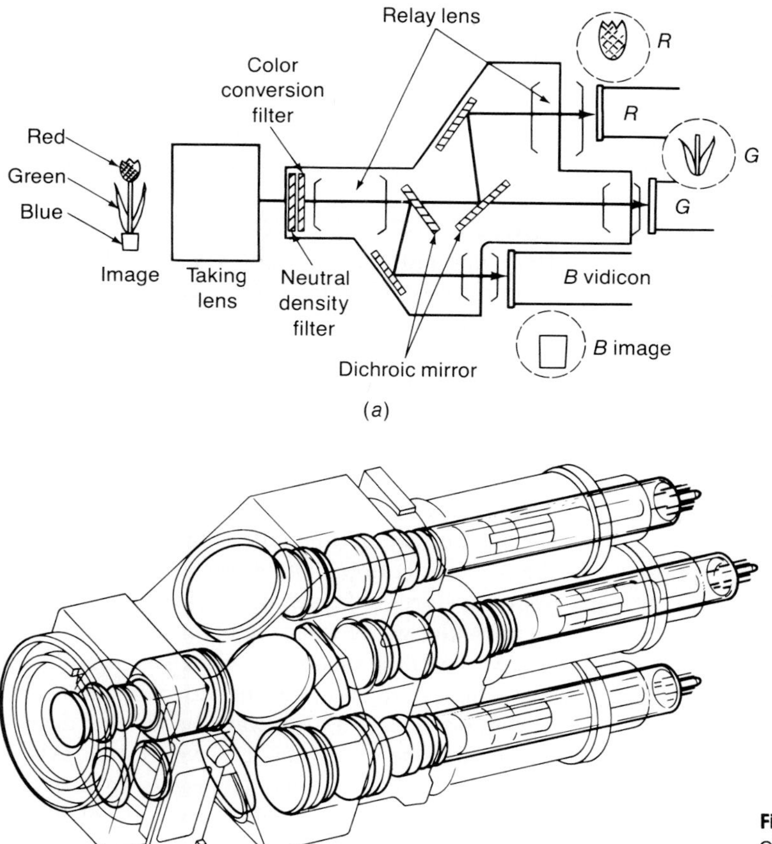

Fig. 3-17 Color separator using dichroic mirrors. (*a*) Simplified view showing separation of red, green, and blue. (*b*) Phantom drawing of actual camera. (*U.S. JVC Corp.*)

fraction of the total red light leaving the taking lens. A dichroic mirror system is shown in color plate XIV.

The key to the action of dichroic mirrors is an extremely thin, accurately controlled transparent layer on one surface. The layer thickness is controlled in manufacture, and so at certain wavelengths light reflected from the front and rear surfaces is additive, or in phase, in a given direction. By varying the layer thickness both the direction and the wavelength can be altered.

A variation of the dichroic mirror system makes use of prisms, as shown in Fig. 3-18. Here the controlling layers are deposited on surfaces of the prisms. There is no glass-to-air interface inside the prism system, resulting in less light loss as a result of scattering. Thus prism systems offer greater light sensitivity. In photographic terms, prisms are said to be "faster" and have a lower f stop rating. Note that the pickup tubes in the prism system are not parallel, but are grouped around the prism at angles dictated by the angles at which the designated primary colors emerge. This arrangement gives the prism color camera a characteristic shape that often can be recognized from the appearance of the housing.

Dichroic cameras, though somewhat less efficient in terms of light loss, have the advantage that all pickup tubes are parallel in space. Hence, any magnetic influence, such as the earth's magnetic field, tends to affect the electron beams in all three pickup tubes in the same way.

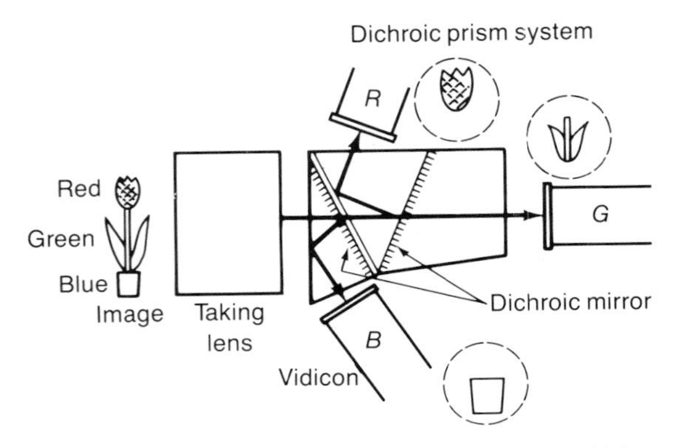

Fig. 3-18 Prism beam splitter for red, green, and blue light.

DYNAMIC COLOR SHADING The dichroic mirrors work as described when light passes down the optical paths shown in Fig. 3-17. These simplified diagrams represent light at the center of the optical image. However, light from the top and bottom of the image passes through the mirrors at slightly different angles, and so the action of the mirror is altered somewhat. The result is a green-magenta shading from top to bottom in the picture. This effect is offset in the signal processor by altering the gain of the green channel at the vertical scan rate. A sawtooth voltage developed from the vertical deflection circuit is used to control the gain. This form of correction is called *dynamic color shading.*

STATIC COLOR SHADING Shading also results from nonuniform dark current in each of the pickup tubes. This form of background shading shows up as a brightness variation in the black level of black-and-white cameras. It is far more noticeable in color cameras, however, because variations in background color produce color-shading effects. Shading from right to left in the pickup tube shows up as a tilt or parabolic shape in the dark-current waveform when it is viewed at the horizontal line rate. Similarly, shading from top to bottom can be seen in the dark-current waveform by adjusting oscilloscope controls to view the waveform at the vertical scan rate.

To correct the shading, sawtooth and parabolic waveshapes are added to the video signal in the signal processor. These waveshapes are developed from the deflection scan waveforms. Also, they are applied to phase inverters to provide both sawtooth and parabolic waveforms of either polarity. See Fig. 3-19. The variable R controls are adjusted to make the dark-current waveform flat. A studio-type camera has H sawtooth, H

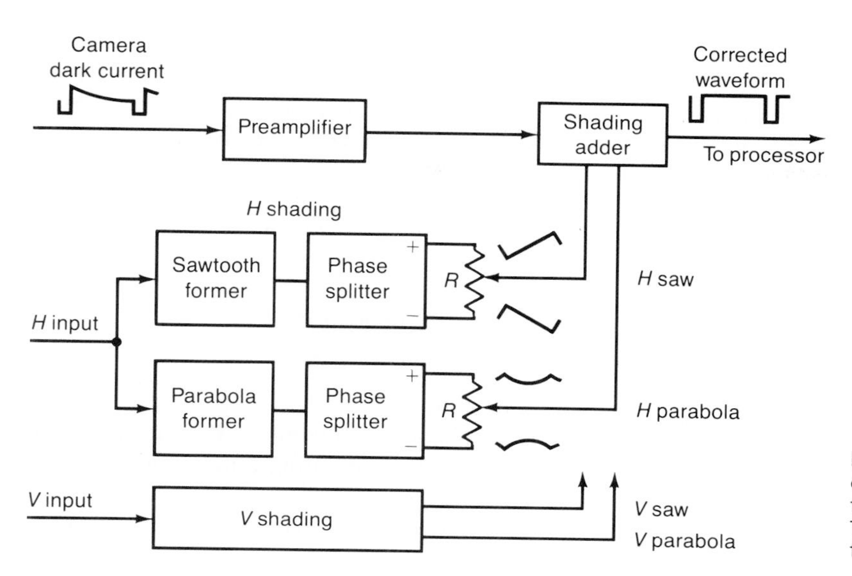

Fig. 3-19 Block diagram of circuits for static shading correction of dark-current waveform. The *V* shading box duplicates the *H* shading circuits.

parabola, *V* sawtooth, and *V* parabola for four controls for each pickup tube. Three-tube cameras, therefore, have a total of 12 static shading adjustments.

WHITE BALANCE The camera is balanced for white when it shows a picture of a white card as neutral white, and not some identifiable hue. Human vision corrects for differences in illumination quite automatically. A shirt, for example, is accepted as white both indoors under incandescent lighting and outdoors under natural light. Film and TV cameras are not self-adjusting in that sense. A color TV camera is considered balanced for a particular reference white when a neutral white card is illuminated with the lighting to be used for shooting and the red, green, and blue channels provide *equal* output levels. Neutral white has no color: the color saturation is zero. As explained in Chap. 8, "Color Television Circuits and Signals," the 3.58-MHz color subcarrier signal disappears when neutral white, gray, or black is scanned. Therefore, the camera operator notes the disappearance of the color subcarrier signal on that part of the signal representing the white card.

If the light source is changed, such as in going from the studio to an outdoor setting, the camera must be rebalanced. The gains of the three channels must be readjusted to provide the same output on the white card with the new source of light (in this case, the sun). The usual practice is to hold the gain of the green channel fixed and alter the red and blue gain to match the red and blue amplitude to the green amplitude.

Many cameras now are automatic in that the red and blue amplitudes are matched to the green amplitude by automatic gain control circuits at the touch of the AUTO WHITE button. The procedure is to point the camera at a white card under the light to be used for shooting, to frame the card so that it occupies the entire picture, and to press the AUTO WHITE button. It takes a fraction of a second to achieve white balance. Many cameras are equipped with memory circuits that store the gain factors of the red and blue channels so the camera will remain balanced for a particular light source.

REGISTRATION In multitube cameras, the video image of all three channels must *register,* or *superimpose,* in every respect. This means that the size and centering as well as the deflection linearity must be identical for all three channels. For example, if horizontal deflection in the blue pickup tube were narrower than that in the other two, the picture would show blue outlines at the edges of vertical lines near the sides of the picture.

To register all three pictures, the scan size, centering, and scan linearity are adjusted precisely. Here again, green is taken as the reference. Its scan size, linearity, and centering are set in much the same way as in a black-and-white camera. Then blue and red are made to register with the green.

To facilitate registration adjustments with the small black-and-white monitors used in the camera viewfinder, a system using inverted green is employed. The inverted signal is negative, or minus green. The camera is pointed at a registration test pattern consisting of black crosshatched lines on a white background, and the viewfinder is set to display red and inverted green. The latter is a negative picture of black with a white crosshatched pattern. When the two equal but opposite signals are made to register at all points on the screen, the two signals cancel and the picture appears almost blank. The procedure is repeated with blue and minus-green signals.

Switches in the camera head permit blue, minus-green, and red-minus-green signals to be sent to the viewfinder. Remote control of centering also is provided at the camera control unit as well as monitor switching, so that touch-up registration adjustments can be made from the control console.

FOUR-TUBE CAMERAS Very small registration errors tend to blur the edges of objects in the picture because the three signals do not occur at exactly the same time. The overall effect is a drop in sharpness, or resolution, that may not be detected visually as color fringing. For this reason, cameras employing four pickup tubes have been developed. In this scheme the black-and-white signal, the *Y* signal, is provided by a separate black-and-white pickup tube that does not receive its light from the dichroic beam splitter. Three separate pickup tubes are used to develop the *R, G,* and *B* signals.

Test Point Questions 3-7

Answers at End of Chapter

Answer True or False.

a. Dichroic mirrors are more efficient than optical filters for separating red, green, and blue light.

b. Dynamic shading corrects for optical effects in the light splitter.

c. Static shading corrects for nonuniform dark current.

d. White balance is not necessary for color cameras.

3-8 GAMMA CORRECTION

A basic problem in the TV system is a nonlinear relationship called *gamma* between light values and signal voltage at both the input (pickup tube) and the output (picture tube) of the system. The biggest offender is the picture tube in the TV set. Because of the operating characteristic of the electron gun in the picture tube, the beam current and the resulting light output do not vary uniformly with the drive voltage. They almost follow the squaring law: Light output varies as the square of the video driving voltage. The overall effect is to compress blacks and stretch whites.

This problem is not severe in black-and-white cameras, but it is extremely serious in color cameras because errors in gamma produce serious errors in hue. To illustrate, a particular color may be made of one part red, two parts blue, and three parts green. If the system effectively squares these values, the resulting light output is one part red, four parts blue, and nine parts green, which produces a decidedly different color.

Gamma correction is one of the signal changes made in the signal processor. In color cameras it is applied to all three channels. The circuits use semiconductor diodes to compress whites just enough to offset the stretching that occurs in the picture tube.

The effect of gamma correction is illustrated in Fig. 3-20. The gamma of the picture tube is 2.2. Therefore, the gamma needed for correction has the inverse value 1/2.2, which is 0.4545. The gamma (γ) values are exponents of epsilon (ϵ), which is the natural base for logarithms or exponents in the expression ϵ^γ.

To adjust gamma, a special chart of graduated black-gray-to-white chips is used. One manufacturer provides a chart whose reflectance values vary at the exponential rate of 2.2, similar to the effect of the picture tube. This makes adjustment easy because the gamma correction circuit is set so that the stair-step pattern viewed on an oscilloscope appears to rise linearly (in a straight line) when the adjustment is correct. See the waveform in Fig. 3-20*d*. In color cameras, gamma is adjusted first in the green channel by using the chart for the neutral gray scale. Then

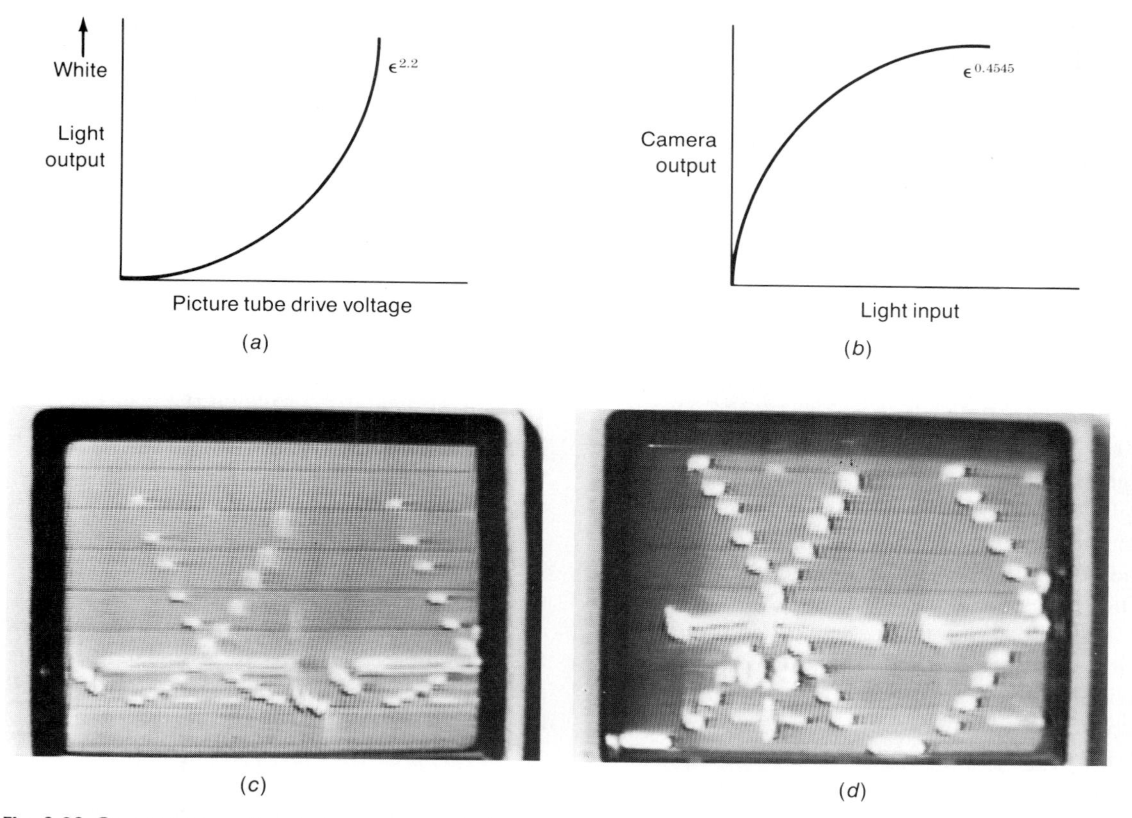

Fig. 3-20 Gamma correction. (*a*) Light characteristic curve of picture tube with gamma = 2.2. (*b*) Correction at camera tube with gamma = 1/2.2 = 0.4545. (*c*) Preamplifier output (no gamma correction). (*d*) Processor output (gamma corrected).

blue and red are set to match the green at each step.

Test Point Questions 3-8

Answers at End of Chapter

a. Is the gamma required for the camera tube 2.2 or 0.4545?

b. Is gamma correction more important for monochrome or for color?

c. Is white compressed or stretched by the picture tube?

3-9 SINGLE-TUBE COLOR CAMERAS

These cameras also break incoming light into the primary color components, but they do so in a time sequence. They make use, in some way, of the time taken for the beam to traverse each tiny area of the target.

SEPARATION WITH VERTICAL COLOR STRIPES

This system is an older method, but it is shown in Fig. 3-21 to illustrate the requirements. The camera actually used two vidicons, one for the *Y* signal and the other for the *R, G,* and *B* color signals. The arrangement in Fig. 3-21*a* shows light from the taking lens split into two paths for the vidicons. At the bottom, the vidicon with the color stripes is a single-tube *color dissector.* The stripes are shown in Fig. 3-21*b.*

The tube used for color separation is equipped with a mask made of groups of vertical color-stripe filters. Each group consists of a black (opaque) stripe, followed by a blue, red, and green stripe (Fig. 3-21*b*). A total of about 87 such groups appears from left to right across the target area. The time taken for one visible horizontal scan is about 53.5 μs. Therefore, the electron beam scans each stripe group in 53.5 μs/87 = 0.615 μs. Dividing this figure by four stripes gives 0.154 μs, or 154 ns, as the time needed for the beam to move between the centers of each stripe.

Separation of colors is accomplished by gated switches. The negative-going index pulse developed by the opaque stripe triggers the switches at the right time. For example, the input to the blue channel is a sample-and-hold gate that is switched on 154 ns after the index pulse. The delay is achieved by precision delay lines. A capacitor at the output of the sample-and-hold gate stores this "blue" information for the next gate. The red and green channels are switched in the same way at intervals of 308 and 462 ns, respectively, from the index pulse. Red, green, and blue signals developed in this way are processed just as they are in three-tube cameras.

The principle of color separation is simple enough, but there are practical considerations. First, the beam focus is extremely critical in all single-tube color dissectors. The spot must be small enough to resolve the light output of the individual stripes. Poor focus shows up first as a loss of color. In addition, the scanning width is extremely critical because it determines the time needed for the electron beam to move across each stripe. A camera using this system needs elaborate automatic control circuits to maintain a precise scanning width. Also the linearity of the horizontal deflection is critical, because a nonuniform scanning speed results in color shading from right to left in the picture.

OBLIQUE COLOR STRIPES This system is used in a JVC (Japan Victor Company) color camera, as illustrated in Fig. 3-22. The color-stripe filter is shown in Fig. 3-22*a,* the associated circuits are shown in Fig. 3-22*b,* and the red, green, and blue signal output is seen in Fig. 3-22*c.*

The oblique, or diagonal, stripes for the color dissector are crisscrossed. Cyan and white stripes slope downward from left to right in Fig. 3-22*a.* Yellow and white stripes have the opposite slope—upward from left to right. Yellow is a

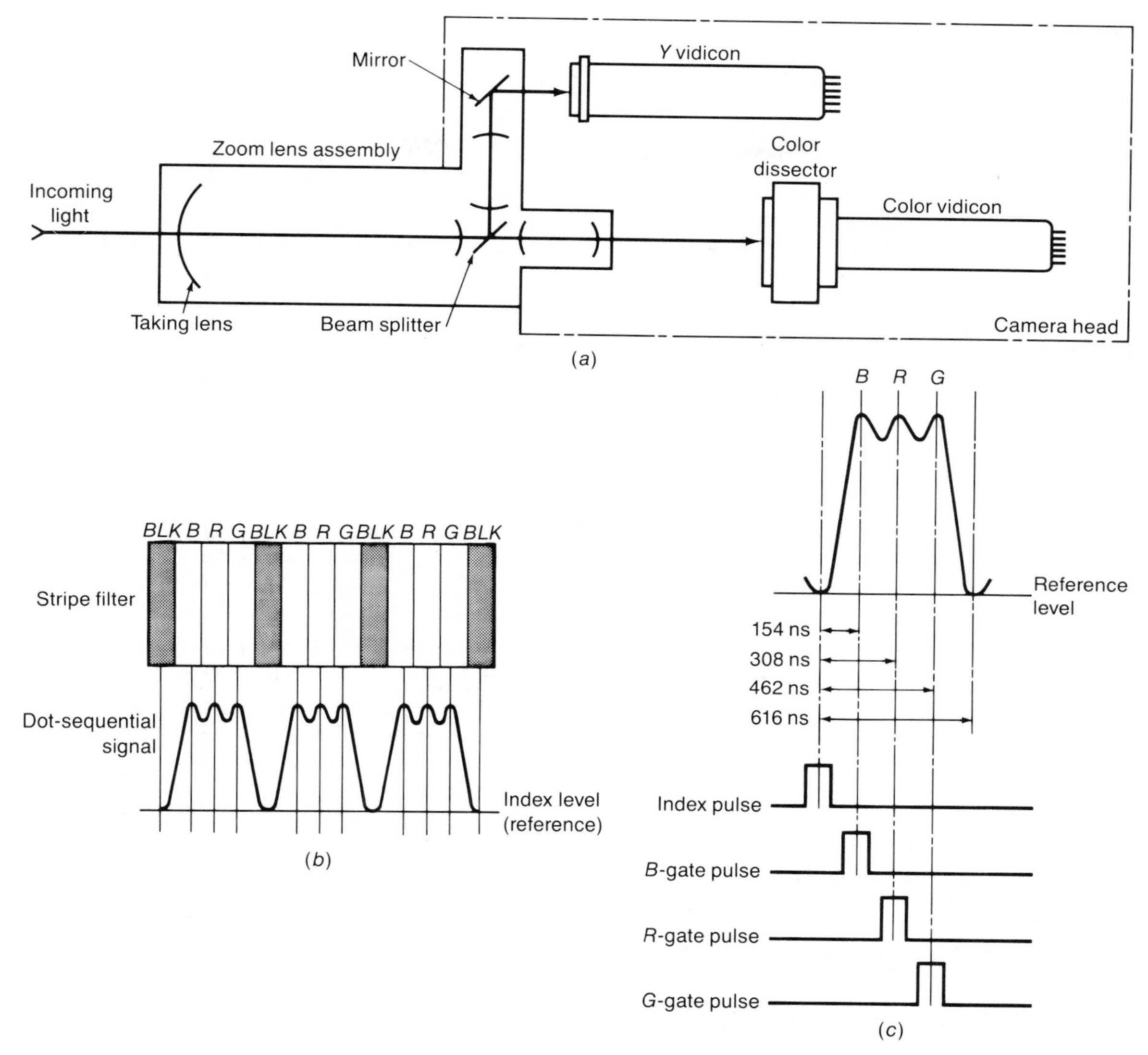

Fig. 3-21 An early color-stripe filter system for single-tube color camera. (*a*) Arrangement with vidicon for *Y* signal and color dissector for color vidicon. (*b*) Stripe filter of color dissector in front of color vidicon. (*c*) Gating pulses. (*Sony Corporation of America*)

color mixture that contains red and green. The cyan color mixture includes blue and green. Therefore, the green is in both of the color mixtures.

With light input, the white stripes pass red, green, and blue. Yellow passes only red and green. The cyan passes only blue and green. Where the color stripes cross, only green survives to pass through to the target plate of the camera tube.

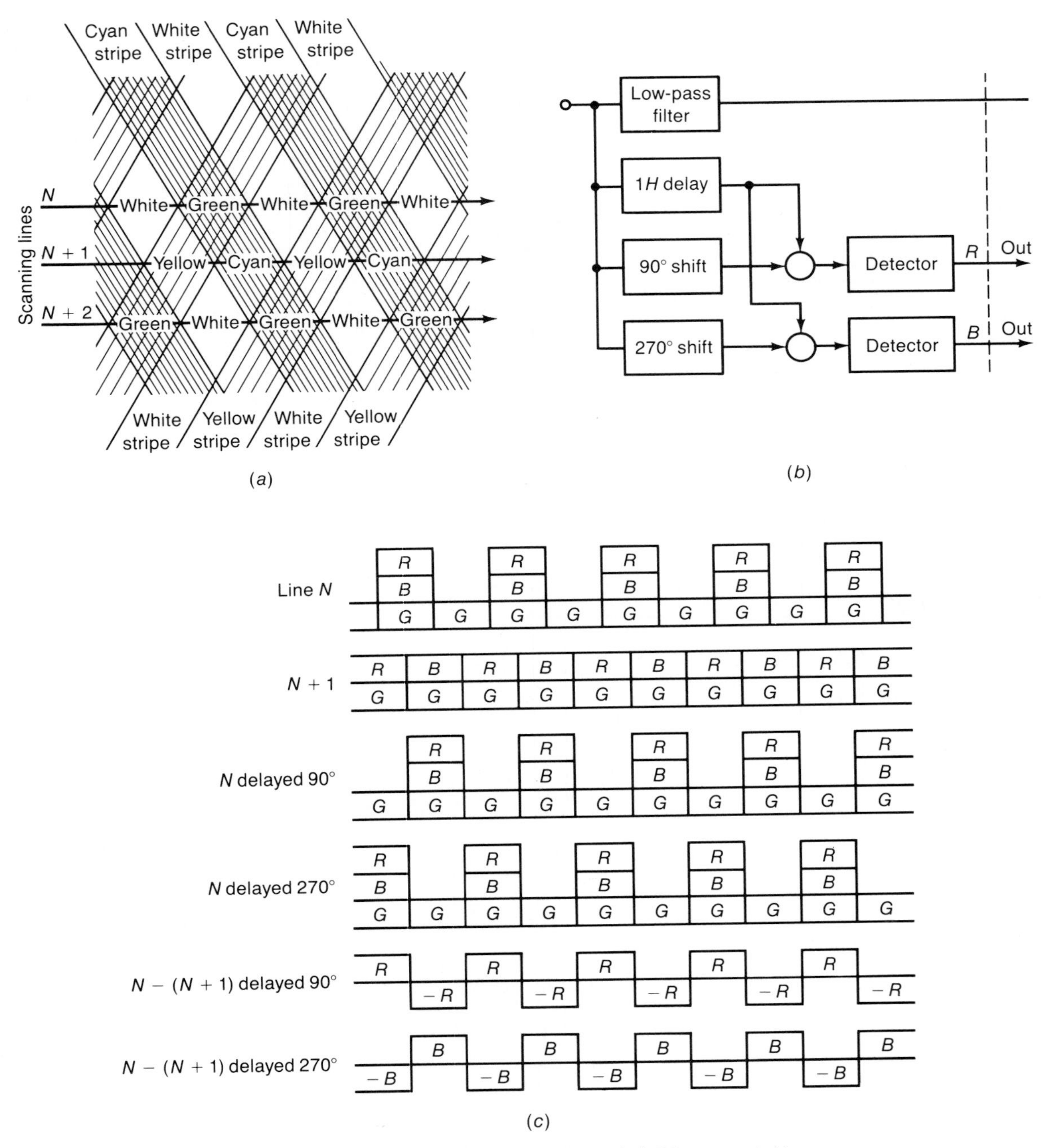

Fig. 3-22 System with oblique stripes for single-tube color camera. (*a*) Crisscrossed stripes of cyan, yellow, and white. (*b*) Block diagram of auxiliary circuits. (*c*) Waveforms of signal output from camera preamplifier. (*U.S. JVC Corp.*)

Consider one scanning line at the position labeled N in Fig. 3-22*a*. As the beam scans this line, it passes only white and green, which is where the cyan and yellow overlap. The white has red, green, and blue signals for the waveshapes in Fig. 3-22*c*.

On the next scan line, labeled $N + 1$, the beam passes yellow and cyan but no white. Yellow has red and green signals for the waveshapes in Fig. 3-22*c*, and cyan has blue and green signals. In the waveforms, there is about a 90° phase difference between the stripe-signal changes from line N to $N + 1$.

Decoding of the signal is accomplished by storing a full scanning line of information in a time-delay device that inserts a lag of 63.5 μs. This time H is the period of one full horizontal scan, including retrace. Then the signal output of the delay line can be compared with the signal from the scanning line that follows, since now they are lined up in time.

Delaying the phase of line $N + 1$ by 90° and subtracting it from the $1H$ delayed line yield the red signal. For the waveforms in Fig. 3-22*c*, compare line $N + 1$ in the second row with the line N delayed by 90° in the third row. In the first sequence at the left, green is subtracted from $R + G$, leaving only the $+R$ signal. For the next sequence to the right, RBG is subtracted from B and G, leaving only the $-R$ signal. The result of the subtraction is shown by the waveform in the fifth row.

The same sequence is followed for all the lines. As a result, the camera produces $+B$ and $+R$ signals from the individual color stripes. The G signal results from the color intersections. The monochrome signal for the Y video signal is obtained by filtering out the signal variations caused by the color stripes.

This camera also requires precise electrical focus. The effects of poor focus range from a green background to no color. Precise control of the scanning width is also essential. An added complication is the exact control of vertical deflection for the scanning height. The scanning lines must be spaced as shown in Fig. 3-22*a* with respect to the crossing of the stripes.

Test Point Questions 3-9

Answers at End of Chapter

Answer True or False.

a. The color dissector in Fig. 3-21 is used for the Y video signal.

b. The oblique color stripes for the camera tube in Fig. 3-22 are red, green, blue, and white.

c. The horizontal scanning width and the linearity affect the color video signal in a single-tube color pickup tube.

3-10 STUDIO AND FIELD APPLICATIONS

Studio operations have evolved steadily from the time when TV was "live" to now, when nearly all programs are recorded on videotape. The videotape permits careful editing of program material prior to actual airing. Even news programs are taped and edited before air time.

The constant improvement and the lower cost of videotape have resulted in a gradual return to operations more like those used in motion-picture production. That is, a single camera drives a single tape recorder. Actual assembly of the program from "cuts" made in this way is performed by videotape editors, who make an electronic splice between program cuts. Mechanical editing, the cut-and-splice system used for film, is not used in TV production. Instead, material to be deleted is just erased from the videotape. More details are given in Chap. 1.

However, many studio operations still use several cameras for TV productions. In this case, the switching between cameras is done live.

SYNCHRONIZED CAMERAS In a multiple-camera system, the *H* and *V* scan rates of all cameras must be synchronized precisely. There are two ways to do this. In the older system, a master synchronizing generator supplies the *H* and *V* drive to all cameras in the system. The video outputs of all cameras are brought together to a *switcher-fader* or, more common in modern operations, to a *special-effects generator* (*SEG*), which is also a production switcher. The switcher permits individual camera outputs to be switched to the *program line,* the final output of the system that is routed to a video tape recorder or the transmission system.

Switching is not done by a simple mechanical switch because a *glitch,* or a spurious pulse, would appear in the picture at the instant that the switch is made. Instead, an electronic switch is held off until the next vertical blanking period arrives. With *vertical-interval switching,* the change is made when all the monitors or receivers fed with the signal are blanked. The fader permits a simultaneous drop in the video feed from one camera while the video-designated camera is permitted to rise from black to the standard level.

SPECIAL-EFFECTS GENERATOR The SEG performs the functions of the switcher-fader and, in addition, provides electronic gating for special effects. Examples of the SEG's function are side-to-side and top-to-bottom wipes in which the video output signals from the two cameras share different parts of the picture area. Corner insertion is achieved by using *H* and *V* wipes simultaneously. Various modulation techniques are employed to achieve a center insertion of circular or diamond shapes, wipe effects that look like a backgammon board, and many others. An SEG unit is shown in Fig. 3-23.

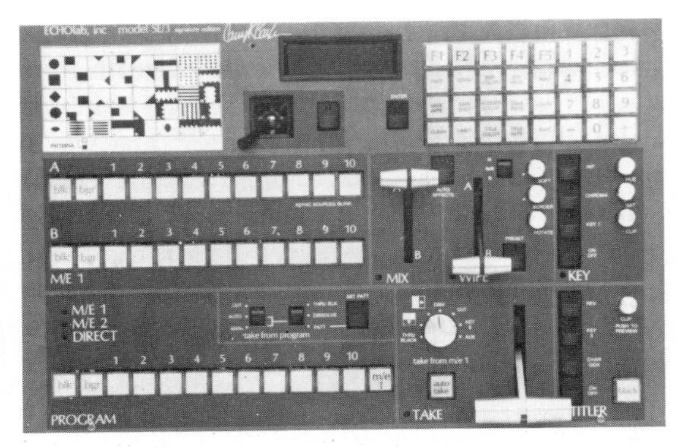

Fig. 3-23 SEG unit for special effects and production switcher. (*Echolab Inc.*)

GENERATOR LOCK Recent development of large-scale integrated circuits designed especially for sync generator applications has made it possible to build the master sync generator into the camera. In many cases it is in the camera head. Then the camera can function entirely on its own with internal sync, or can be switched to make its internal sync generator follow the *H* and *V* sync timing as well as the color subcarrier signal phase of any other source of video signals. This method is usually called *gen-lock.*

All that is needed to lock the sync generator of a camera so equipped would be a composite video signal feed from another source or a signal composed solely of color burst, blanking, and sync. The latter signal is called a *black burst.*

Figure 3-24 shows a camera setup where one camera is used as the master. A composite signal called *CVBS* (for composite video, burst, and sync) is obtained from the top camera. This feed is looped through the SEG camera 1 input connectors to the camera control units for the remaining cameras. The lower cameras are set to lock the sync generators. The upper camera is set to internal sync.

VIEWFINDERS Television cameras use a small-screen black-and-white TV monitor mounted in an assembly above the camera head. The viewfinder is intentionally underscanned so that the picture does not fill the mask. Then all four edges

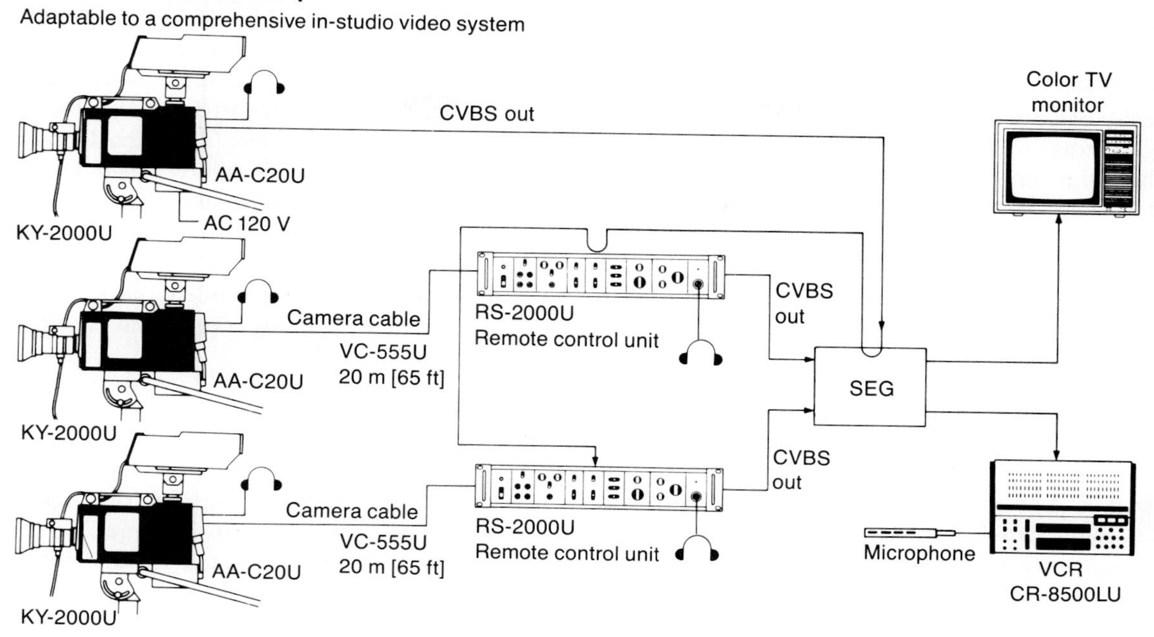

Fig. 3-24 Multiple-camera hookup using gen-lock system. CVBS means composite video with burst and sync. (*U.S. JVC Corp.*)

of the picture can be observed by the camera operator. The viewfinder is driven directly from the video output of the camera, which permits the operator to see what the camera sees for the purpose of subject framing and optical focus adjustment.

FILM-CHAIN CAMERAS Motion-picture film and still color slides are converted to a TV signal by specially adapted color cameras or by conventional color cameras with fixed-focal-length lenses mounted on an assembly known as a *film-chain island.* This equipment has an optical beam splitter with two or three optical input ports that receive light images supplied by a slide projector and one or two film projectors. The island is essentially a mounting base for all units. An achromatic beam splitter uses partially silvered mirrors and a relay lens to supply light to the camera. *Achromatic* means that the beam splitter does not favor any one color over others.

ADAPTING 24 FILM FRAMES TO 60 TV FIELDS

When commercial motion-picture films are televised, a special projector is necessary to convert from 24 to 30 frames per second. The film moves at 24 frames per second to keep the sound track normal, but an intermittent shutter projects 60 images per second.

Specifically, one film frame is projected for two television fields ($2/60$ s), but the next frame is scanned with three fields ($3/60$ s). The apertures in the revolving shutter have unequal spacings. After four film frames, the two extra fields make five television frames.

The time for four film frames is $4/24 = 1/6$, s. Similarly, the time for five television frames is $5/30$ s, or $1/6$ s. As a result, the scanning of 30 television frames in 1 s matches the 24 film frames.

PORTABLE CAMERAS Cameras intended for field operations, called *ENG* (electronic news gathering) or *EFP* (electronic field production), have the same basic aspects as the studio camera, but their emphasis is on portability. A typical setup is shown in Fig. 3-25.

Test Point Questions 3-10
Answers at End of Chapter

Answer True or False.

a. The SEG also can be used as a production switcher.
b. *CVBS* means "composite video signal without color burst."
c. Commercial movie film is run at 30 film frames per second for television.
d. Generator lock is used to synchronize multiple cameras.

3-11 LENSES AND LIGHT VALUES

The basic features of lenses chosen for all cameras are their focal length and *f* stop ratings. *Focal length* is the distance from the center of the lens to the point at which parallel rays from a distant object come to a common focal point. See Fig. 3-26*a*. The *f stop number* is the ratio of focal length to the diameter of the lens.

Fig. 3-25 Portable TV camera setup for electronic news-gathering (ENG) applications. (*U.S. JVC Corp.*)

The focal length determines the "taking angle" of the lens. Lenses with short focal lengths are used for wide-angle shots. Long-focal-length lenses are called *telephoto* lenses. Their taking angles are narrow, and they make distant objects look close. These effects are shown in Fig. 3-26*b* and *c*.

Camera lens mounts are often the standard screw-type mount used for 16-mm film cameras, called the *C mount.*

***f* STOP VALUES** The light-gathering ability of a camera is determined by the diameter of the lens. The larger the lens diameter, the greater the amount of light falling on the target. Lenses are rated at maximum diameter, for the biggest iris opening. The iris varies the opening for light to enter the lens. Specifically, the *f* rating is

$$f = \frac{F}{d} \tag{3-1}$$

where F is the focal length and d is the diameter of the lens with the iris fully open. A longer focal length means a higher value of f. However, a larger diameter corresponds to a smaller f stop.

The smaller the f rating, the more light the lens can take in. A low f number is needed when light is low in the scene. High f numbers can be used in bright sunshine.

A lens with a 13-mm diameter and a 25-mm focal length, for example, has an f rating of

$$f = \frac{F}{d} = \frac{25 \text{ mm}}{13 \text{ mm}} = 1.9$$

Such a lens would have 1.9 engraved on the iris ring which lines up with an index mark when the iris is fully open.

The light input is controlled by closing the iris. The iris ring is calibrated in f stops, such

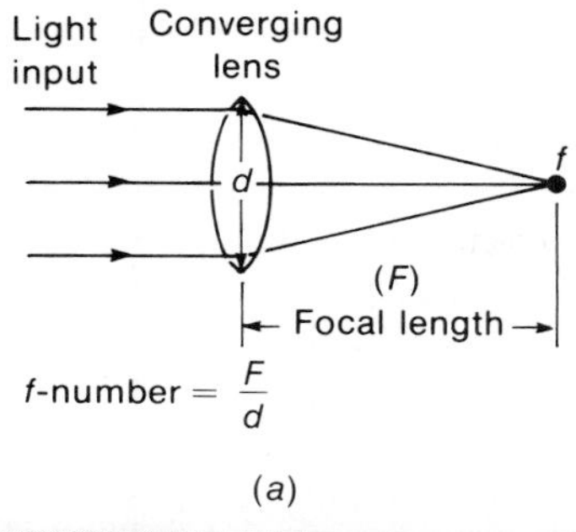

(a)

(b)

(c)

Fig. 3-26 (*a*) Focal length and *f* stop rating of an optical lens. (*b*) Photograph with 17-mm lens. (*c*) Photograph with 102-mm lens.

as 1.9, 2.8, 4, 5.6, 8, 11, 16, 22. Each of these calibration marks is called an *f* stop.

The *f* stop numbers increase in steps of $\sqrt{2}$, or approximately 1.414, so that each higher *f* stop allows one-half the light input of the previous *f* stop. Remember that the area of a circle is proportional to the square of its diameter. Making the aperture smaller by "stopping down" the iris to an effective diameter of $1/\sqrt{2}$ reduces the light by half. For example, an *f* stop of 2.8 multiplied by 1.4 equals 3.92, or 4, for the next higher *f* stop. An *f* stop of 4 allows half the light of the 2.8 *f* stop.

In practice, the lens on the TV camera is stopped down until the brightest object in the scene yields the standard 1-V p-p video output. In many cameras, the iris is servo-controlled to maintain this relationship.

DEPTH OF FIELD One important factor affected by the lens opening is the depth of field. No doubt, you have noticed that the background goes out of focus in a TV scene when the camera is focused on a performer close to the camera. The *depth of field* is the distance between the object in focus closest to the camera and that object farthest from the camera which remains in focus. Actually there is only one focal distance, but the depth of field is that distance which is discernible to the viewer.

At wide lens openings, the depth of field is poorest. This fact explains why lenses are stopped down to higher numbers to allow the desired depth of field when enough light is available.

Still-picture photographers have another variable to work with. They can increase the exposure time, trading exposure speed for depth of field, provided there is little or no movement in the picture. But the exposure time is fixed at the frame rate in both motion pictures and television. Therefore, the only variable left to manipulate is the lighting on the subject. If the depth of field is to be increased, the lens must be stopped down and the amount of light on the subject increased to compensate for the smaller aperture.

ZOOM LENSES The zoom lens has a continuously variable focal length. The use of zoom lenses is now almost universal in color productions, for they have replaced the optical turret of fixed-focal-length lenses found on older monochrome cameras. Figure 3-27*a* shows a power zoom lens from a portable camera having motorized zoom adjustment. The taking angle can be "zoomed in" to a closeup telephoto shot or zoomed out to a wide-angle view by pressing the rocker-type switch. The switch is under the operator's fingers when the hand is inserted into the hand grip. The unit has been disassembled in Fig. 3-27*b* to show the motors that drive both the zoom mechanism and the automatic iris.

Zoom lenses are rated by the ratio between minimum and maximum focal lengths. For example, the focal length of the lens used to take the pictures of Fig. 3-26*b* and *c* varies between 17 and 102 mm. The zoom range, then, is 102:17 = 6:1. Zoom lenses made for cameras used in home VCR operations are rated at 3:1 or 6:1. Those intended for commercial TV applications range from 10:1 to 15:1. The large zoom lenses, such as those used to cover sports events, are extremely expensive because they are "fast" lenses with low *f* stop ratings.

LIGHT VALUES The amount of light reflected from the subject into the camera is an important factor in achieving low noise for a snow-free picture and in making the best use of the depth of field. Although the camera works with *reflected* light, it has become traditional in TV operations to use *incident* light, the illumination falling on the subject. Meters that measure illumination are readily available.

Measurement of light values starts with the source. The standard reference for luminous intensity, although somewhat obsolete, has been the candle. The *candela* (cd) is a more recent unit based on electrically repeatable devices and is practically equal to the candle. For a practical comparison, the number 51 pilot lamp is rated at about one candlepower.

The light flux falling on a surface is directly proportional to the candlepower and inversely proportional to the square of the distance. The light flux on the surface is its *illumination.* One *footcandle* (fc) is the light flux intercepted by a one-foot-square surface that is one foot from a one-candlepower source. To calculate the illumination in footcandles, divide the candlepower of the source by the distance squared. For example, a 400-candlepower source that is 10 ft from a surface provides this illumination:

$$L = \frac{400}{10^2} = \frac{400}{100} = 4 \text{ fc}$$

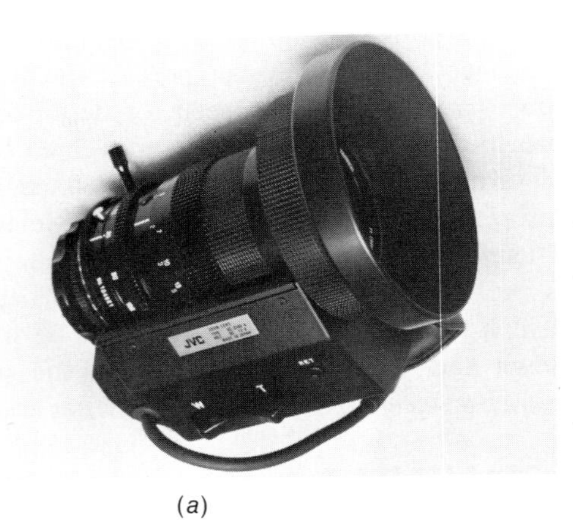

(*a*)

(*b*)

Fig. 3-27 (*a*) Power zoom lens. (*b*) Cover removed to show drive motor.

The unit used in the metric system for illumination is the candela-meter, called a *lux* (lx). If we use the same numbers but convert feet to meters, the answer comes out in lux units. For example, since 10 ft is about 3 m,

$$L = \frac{400}{3^2} = \frac{400}{9} = 44.4 \text{ lux}$$

The footcandle and the lux are both units of luminous flux, or illumination. Note that footcandles and lux differ by an approximate factor of 10. This ratio is important because specifications for foreign-made cameras often are rated in lux. To convert lux to footcandles, divide by 10 for approximate values (10.87, to be more exact). For these examples, 4 fc and 44 lux are approximately equal. The footcandle is the larger unit.

Cameras are rated in minimum illumination required for a usable picture. Also, the illumination required to meet certain performance specifications is usually given. For example, a representative 3-Saticon ENG camera specifies minimum illumination as 250 lux, or 23 fc on the camera tubes. Specifications for the signal-to-noise ratio, resolution, and other performance factors are given for a subject illumination of 2500 lux, or 230 fc. As a practical comparison of light flux, the desired illumination for reading is about 10 fc.

Test Point Questions 3-11

Answers at End of Chapter

a. Does a low *f* stop rating allow more or less light?

b. Is the depth-of-field improved with a lower or a higher *f* stop?

c. To how many lux units is the illumination of 3 fc approximately equal?

SUMMARY

1. Television cameras use the vidicon, or similar camera tubes, as the pickup device. The photoconductive target plate converts light input to camera signal output as an electron beam scans the target. In the vidicon, the target is made of antimony compounds. The Plumbicon uses a lead oxide target plate; selenium, arsenic, and tellurium are used in the Saticon.
2. The camera head contains the pickup tube(s) for color, coil assemblies for magnetic deflection and focus, preamplifiers for the camera signal, and the signal processor section. A signal with sync and blanking is called a composite video signal. Portable cameras contain an internal sync generator.
3. Color cameras require some means for separating light into its primary red, green, and blue components. This function is performed by light splitters in three-tube cameras or by color-stripe filters in single-tube color pickup tubes.
4. The dark current is the current that flows in the target circuit when the camera lens is capped for no light input.
5. The target voltage is set for a specified value, with respect to the cathode, to provide the desired amount of dark current.

6. The beam current is set to provide sufficient electrons in the scanning beam to discharge the target at white highlight areas of the picture.
7. Signal processing in color cameras includes correction for static and dynamic shading, gamma correction, white balance, and the addition of sync.
8. Gamma is an exponential value that specifies how white light values are expanded or compressed, and this affects the contrast ratio. Gamma correction is done in the camera to compensate for the nonlinear drive characteristics of the picture tube.
9. Image lag in the camera tube means that the old image remains too long after the picture information on the target plate has changed. This causes white tails in the picture and an x-ray effect. Image lag is most serious in vidicons, better in Saticons, and best in Plumbicons. Lag is reduced in Saticons through the use of bias lighting.
10. The focal length of a lens determines its taking angle for closeup views or long shots. A shorter focal length means a wider taking angle for closeups.
11. The *f* rating of a lens is its focal length divided by its diameter. A lens with a lower *f* rating is a faster lens that allows more light input.
12. Light flux for cameras usually is measured in footcandles. The *f* stop on the lens adjusts the iris to vary the light input.

SELF-EXAMINATION

Answers at Back of Book

Choose (a), (b), (c), or (d).

1. Which of the following camera tubes uses lead oxide (PbO) for the photoconductive target plate? (a) Vidicon, (b) Plumbicon, (c) Saticon, (d) image orthicon.
2. Camera signal output without sync is called (a) black burst, (b) generator lock video, (c) composite video, (d) noncomposite video.
3. A low-contrast picture in which white seems flat and lacking in detail suggests (a) low beam current, (b) high gain in the preamplifier, (c) excessive gamma, (d) insufficient scanning width.
4. Which of the following camera tubes has minimum lag? (a) Vidicon, (b) Plumbicon, (c) Saticon, (d) iconoscope.
5. The part of the visible spectrum where camera pickup tubes have the greatest output is (a) red, (b) blue, (c) yellow-green, (d) infrared.
6. Precise scanning size and linearity are most important in (a) a black-and-white camera, (b) a Plumbicon, (c) a single-tube color pickup, (d) a Saticon.

7. Beam alignment magnets for the camera tube are adjusted while rocking which control? (a) Optical focus, (b) electrical focus, (c) beam current, (d) shading.
8. Special effects and production switching are done by the (a) CCU, (b) ENG camera, (c) SEG, (d) sync generator.
9. The gamma of the picture tube is (a) 0.4545, (b) 1.0, (c) 1.4, (d) 2.2.
10. If the camera cannot be placed far away enough to include everything in the scene, change the lens to one with a (a) lower f rating, (b) higher f rating, (c) longer focal length, (d) shorter focal length.
11. A typical value of vidicon dark current is (a) 0.2 μA, (b) about 200 μA, (c) 8 mA, (d) 800 mA.
12. A lens has an 8-cm focal length and 4-cm diameter. Its f rating is (a) 2, (b) 4, (c) 8, (d) 32.

ESSAY QUESTIONS

1. List the main parts of a vidicon camera tube and the function of each.
2. Compare the types of target plate used in the vidicon, Plumbicon, and Saticon.
3. What is meant by *image lag* in the camera tube?
4. List the three components of a composite video signal.
5. Why is gamma correction necessary for the camera signal?
6. Define CCU, ENG, EFP, SEG, and CVBS.
7. Explain how 24 film frames are televised with 60 television fields.
8. What is a tally lamp?
9. Explain how the resistance of a photoconductive material changes with the amount of light.
10. List two controls for the vidicon camera tube, and explain how they are adjusted.
11. Why is white balance important for color?
12. Describe one type of single-tube color pickup.
13. What are the percentages of red, green, and blue in the Y video signal?
14. What is a dichroic mirror?
15. Define the f number of an optical lens. What is the f number of a fast lens?
16. Describe the effect of focal length on the taking angle of the lens.
17. What is the purpose of a zoom lens?
18. Define the following light units: candle, candela, footcandle, and lux.

PROBLEMS

1. Calculate the candlepower needed for a light source to produce 25 fc at a distance of 10 ft [3.0 m].
2. Calculate the approximately constant ratio for the following *f* stop comparisons: 2/1.4, 2.8/2, 4/2.8, 5.6/4, and 8/5.6.
3. Calculate the diameter of an *f*/1.9 lens with a focal length of 100 mm, or 10 cm.
4. What is the diameter of an *f*/1.9 lens that has a focal length of 50 mm, or 5 cm?
5. Refer to Fig. 3-6. What is the vidicon signal current for a 20-fc illumination with a 0.02-μA dark current?

SPECIAL QUESTIONS

1. Which camera tube do you think is the best? Explain why.
2. Give some differences between studio and field cameras.
3. What is meant by *clamping* an ac signal to a dc level?

ANSWERS TO TEST POINT QUESTIONS

3-1 **a.** T
b. F
c. T
3-2 **a.** F
b. F
3-3 **a.** Target plate
b. Less
c. On
d. Target
3-4 **a.** T
b. F

3-5 **a.** F
b. T
3-6 **a.** T
b. F
c. T
3-7 **a.** T
b. T
c. T
d. F
3-8 **a.** 0.4545
b. Color
c. Stretched

3-9 **a.** F
b. F
c. T
3-10 **a.** T
b. F
c. F
d. T
3-11 **a.** More
b. Higher
c. 30

4

PICTURE TUBES

The picture tube is a cathode-ray tube (CRT) with an electron gun and a phosphor screen inside the evacuated glass envelope, as shown in Fig. 4-1. In the narrow neck of the tube, the electron gun produces a beam of electrons. The beam is accelerated to the screen by the positive anode voltage. To form the screen, the inside of the wide glass faceplate at the front is coated with a luminescent material that produces light when excited by electrons in the beam. Magnetic deflection is used with external coils around the neck of the tube to make the electron beam scan the entire picture area. Picture tubes are used in TV receivers and monitors.

A monochrome picture tube has one electron gun and a continuous phosphor coating that emits white light. In color picture tubes, the screen is formed with dot trios or vertical stripes of red, green, and blue phosphors. There are three electron beams, one for each phosphor color. More details are given in the following sections:

4-1 Picture Tube Construction
4-2 Anode High Voltage
4-3 Screen Phosphors
4-4 Electron Gun
4-5 Electrostatic Focus
4-6 Magnetic Deflection
4-7 Tricolor Picture Tubes
4-8 Shadow Mask
4-9 Methods of Phosphor Masking
4-10 Television Projection Systems
4-11 Picture Tube Precautions
4-12 Problems with Picture Tubes

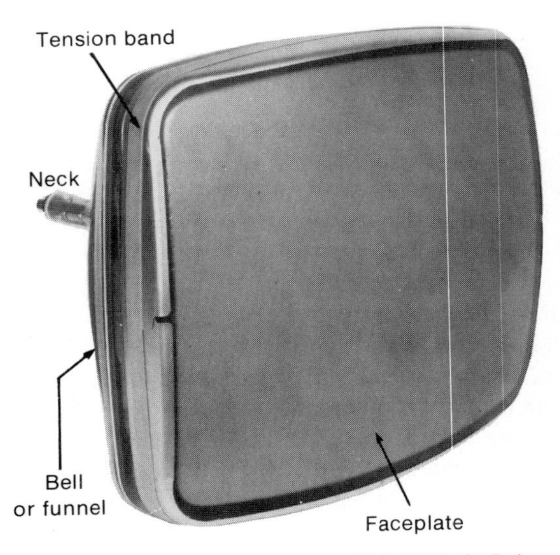

Fig. 4-1 Color picture tube, type 19VHBP22. (*RCA*)

4-1 PICTURE TUBE CONSTRUCTION

The size of a picture tube ranges from the smallest with about a 1-in. screen, measured diagonally, to large, direct-view tubes with a diagonal screen of 30 in. or more. The 1-in. tube is a monochrome type for the viewfinder in portable TV cameras. Most common screen sizes are 5, 7, 9, 10, 12, 13, 15, 17, 19, 21, 23, and 25 in. For larger picture sizes, optical projection systems are used.

The Federal Trade Commission (FTC) requires that all screen sizes be advertised as the diagonal measurement of the viewable screen area. With a 4:3 aspect ratio the diagonal is about 25 percent greater than the width.

The type number of a picture tube starts with a number that gives the screen size in the EIA system. For the 19VHBP22 in Fig. 4-1, for example, the screen diagonal measures 19 in., give or take ½ in. If the screen size is a whole number plus exactly 0.5 in., the next higher number is used.

Type numbers of foreign picture tubes begin with a number specifying the screen diagonal in millimeters (mm). For example, a Japanese type number such as 330WB22 has a diagonal screen measurement of 330 mm [approximately 13 in.]. One inch equals 25.4 mm.

At the end of the type designation is a P or B number that specifies the phosphor screen. The phosphor number is P4 or B4 for black-and-white picture tubes. For color picture tubes the number is P22 or B22. This screen has red, green, and blue phosphors.

A new worldwide system of type designation numbers for all types of CRTs has been developed, starting in 1982. The details are given in App. E.

HEATER VOLTAGE AND CURRENT These values are not specified in the type number for picture tubes. However, the heater voltage is generally 6.3 V. Current ratings are 450 or 600 mA for monochrome tubes and 800 to 1800 mA for color tubes. Special small monochrome picture tubes for battery-operated TV receivers may use a lower heater voltage of 2 to 4 V.

In most color picture tubes, the three heaters for the electron guns are connected in series internally. The leads are brought out to the two end pins, on either side of the socket key on the base. The 6.3-V rating is for the three heaters in series. Note that if one of the series heater circuits becomes open, the circuit for all three is open. However, an open-circuit heater is not a common problem in color picture tubes. In some cases, the three heaters may be connected in parallel.

INSTANT-ON OPERATION As receivers have been converted to solid state, the picture tube remained the only vacuum tube, and so it became the major cause of waiting for warmup to see the picture. Then a system was developed to keep the picture tube heater near the emission temperature but at a reduced heater voltage when the TV set was switched off yet plugged into the ac power outlet. The heater was partially on, but it had only one-half power. When the TV set was turned on, full power was applied to the heater and the picture appeared within a fraction of a second. This system is called the *instant-on operation.*

However, in the interest of conserving energy, the instant-on circuit is no longer used. Today, nearly all picture tubes have quick-heating cathodes. Special materials are used that provide good heat conduction from the heater to the cathode but that offer the required electric insulation.

FACEPLATE The phosphor screen coats the inner surface of the glass faceplate to form the viewing screen. The glass must be thick enough to withstand the air pressure that exerts a force against the vaccum inside the envelope.

Because the envelope is evacuated (that is, there is a vacuum), there is a danger of a violent collapse, called an *implosion,* which scatters the glass dangerously. Two systems are used to minimize the danger of implosion. In one method, the glass faceplate is actually a heavy laminate of thick glass layers. A transparent, resinous panel is mounted between the layers, somewhat like automobile safety glass. In the second method, a prestressed steel band is mounted around the circumference of the faceplate. In the event of a crack or puncture in the glass envelope, the steel band forces the faceplate to remain intact. Picture tubes must pass rigid implosion tests by Underwriters Laboratories (UL) to merit the UL seal.

DEFLECTION ANGLE The maximum angle that the electron beam can be deflected without striking the sides is called the *deflection angle.* Typical values are 70, 90, 110, and 114°. The deflection angle is the total angle. For instance, a tube with a 110° deflection angle has a maximum deflection of 55° to either side of the center axis.

A trend toward larger deflection angles has reduced the depth of the cabinet for TV receivers, because a tube with a larger deflection angle has a shorter length for the same screen size.

But the trend toward larger deflection angles has been reversed because of the need to conserve energy. More deflection power is needed for a very wide angle. This power is the major part of the load current that a modern TV receiver takes from the ac power line. So the deflection angle has been kept small to achieve a higher operating efficiency. Most picture tubes now have a deflection angle of 90°.

Some special picture tubes made especially for portable TV receivers have a narrow deflection angle. The tube is long, but there is less current drain in order to conserve the battery.

The deflection angle of the deflection yoke matches the angle of the picture tube. A 90° tube takes a 90° yoke.

Note that different screen sizes can be filled with the same deflection angle. For instance, a 90° yoke will fill the screens of 17-, 19-, or 21-in. picture tubes if they all have the same deflection angle of 90°. The reason is that bigger tubes with the same deflection angle are longer.

Test Point Questions 4-1

Answers at End of Chapter

a. What is the diagonal screen size for the 19CP4 picture tube?

b. To what deflection angle does a maximum deflection angle of 45° either side of center correspond?

c. What is the usual heater voltage for picture tubes?

4-2 ANODE HIGH VOLTAGE

The second anode for the electron gun has the positive high voltage needed to accelerate electrons to the screen for the desired brightness. *Ultor* is the general term used for all the electrodes that have the maximum accelerating voltage. Typical values are as follows:

3 kV for 1-in. monochrome picture tube

10 kV for 12-in. monochrome picture tube

20 kV for 19-in. monochrome picture tube

30 kV for 25-in. color picture tube

These voltages are too high for a connection at the socket pins. Instead, the ultor, or anode, connection is a recessed cavity on the wide bell of the glass envelope. This connection is sometimes referred to as the *anode button.*

The anode connection passes through the envelope and makes contact with a conductive coating inside the glass bell which reaches back into the neck of the tube. The coating is a black graphite material called *Aquadag.* "Fingers" in the ultor at the muzzle of the electron gun make a spring contact with the inner Aquadag coating in the neck. This is how the high voltage is applied inside the tube. The entire inner surface of the tube forward of the electron gun and including the phosphor screen is at the potential of the applied high voltage. Note that the positive potential completely surrounds the electron beam, so that electrons are not attracted to the sides of the tube.

The ultor cavity on the bell of the picture tube has a diameter of about ¼ in. [6.4 mm]. The connecting lead from the high-voltage supply is held in the cavity by a spring clip. A rubber suction cup of about 1-in. [25.4-mm] diameter covers the cavity to protect against contact with the high voltage. In the case of the Sony Trinitron, though, the ultor connector is a coaxial fitting that has two high-voltage values. One is the ultor voltage, and the other is used for a set of static convergence plates.

EXTERNAL CONDUCTIVE COATING The outside surface of the glass bell is also coated with Aquadag. This coating is connected to chassis ground by spring clips or a bare-wire harness, usually mounted on the metal frame that holds the deflection yoke. A small, circular area around the ultor connection is left clear without the external coating.

The grounded outer coating on the picture tube minimizes radiation of electric interference at the vertical and horizontal scanning frequencies. For example, an open-circuit ground here can cause a buzzing sound because the vertical scanning output is picked up in the audio circuits.

ANODE CAPACITANCE The glass envelope acts as a capacitor, formed by the inner and outer coatings with glass as the dielectric. This construction is similar to the original Leyden jar. The anode capacitance is quite high, with a typical value being 2000 picofarads (pF) for a 25-in. tube, because of the large surface area. Also, the thickness of the glass provides a very high rating for the breakdown voltage.

This anode capacitance forms the filter capacitor of the high-voltage supply. A flyback supply is used, with the high-voltage induced during horizontal retrace time. Since the nominal horizontal scanning frequency equals 15,750 Hz, the ripple frequency is also 15,750 kHz. At this frequency, the anode provides enough capacitance for filtering.

The anode capacitor of the glass has extremely low leakage. It can hold a charge a long time, possibly for a few months. Whenever you handle the picture tube, first discharge the anode capacitor. Do this by short-circuiting the outer conductive coating to the ultor button.

Test Point Questions 4-2

Answers at End of Chapter

a. Is 10 or 30 kV a typical anode voltage for a 25-in. color picture tube?

b. Is the anode capacitance typically 2 or 2000 pF?

c. The anode connection is the end pin on the tube socket. True or False?

4-3 SCREEN PHOSPHORS

Most common are the P1 green phosphor for oscilloscope tubes, the P4 white phosphor for monochrome picture tubes, and the P22 phosphor for color tubes. They are listed in Table 4-1.

The phosphor chemicals are generally light metals such as zinc and cadmium in the form of sulfide, sulfate, and phosphate compounds. For the green P1 phosphor, a form of zinc silicate called *willemite* is generally used. The P4 white phosphor usually combines compounds of zinc sulfide, cadmium sulfide, or zinc silicate. This phosphor is actually a combination of yellow and blue, since no single phosphor can produce white. For color screens, the P22 phosphor includes zinc sulfide for blue, zinc silicate for green, and rare-earth elements such as europium and yttrium for red.

The phosphor material is processed to produce very fine particles which are applied to the inside of the glass faceplate. This very thin coating that will form the screen is a uniform layer for monochrome tubes. For color tubes, though, the phosphor is deposited in dots or vertical lines for each color. You can see the individual color dots or lines with a small, portable microscope of 50× power held against the screen while the picture is on.

In terms of molecular structure, the phosphors are crystals to which an activator material such as manganese or silver can be added to distort the crystal lattice. Then high-velocity electrons excite the phosphor, causing it to emit light. Electrons within the atoms of the phosphor are forced to move to a higher energy level. As these electrons fall back to a lower level, energy is radiated. The radiation of light from the screen as it is excited by the electron beam is called *luminescence.* When the light is extinguished after excitation, the screen is *fluorescent.* Also, *phosphorescence* is the continued emission of light following excitation of the screen.

SCREEN PERSISTENCE The time that it takes for light emitted from the screen to decay to 1 percent of its maximum value is called the *screen persistence.* Medium persistence is desirable, because it increases the average brightness and reduces flicker. However, the persistence must be less than $\frac{1}{30}$ s for picture tubes so that one frame does not persist into the next, causing the objects in motion to be blurred.

The decay time for picture tubes is approximately 0.005 s, or 5 ms, which is a medium-short persistence. The P1 green phosphor for oscilloscope tubes generally has a longer persistence—0.05 s.

ALUMINIZED SCREEN Practically all picture tubes today have a very thin layer of aluminum on the inside surface of the phosphor screen, toward the electron gun. There are several advantages to this. First, the aluminum coating is transparent to the electron beam but still can reflect

TABLE 4-1
COMMON SCREEN PHOSPHORS FOR CATHODE-RAY TUBES

PHOSPHOR NUMBER	COLOR	PERSISTENCE	USE
P1	Green	Medium	Oscilloscope
P4	White	Medium-short	Monochrome picture tube
P22	Red, green, blue	Medium	Tricolor picture tube
P31	Green	Medium-short	Oscilloscope

light from the screen. Then the light emitted in the phosphor is not directed back toward the gun, but is reflected forward toward the viewer. The result is a substantial increase in brightness compared with nonaluminized screens.

Second, the aluminized layer acts as a trap to block the heavy-ion charges that are an inescapable by-product of electron emission at the cathode. Since these heavy ions are not deflected as much as electrons, the ions tend to be concentrated at the center of the screen. This effect can create a brown spot, called *ion burn,* which is caused by chemical action in the phosphor. Before aluminized screens were used, the solution was to mount a small magnet, called an *ion trap,* or *beam bender,* onto the neck of the tube. The electron gun was aimed off the screen, but the magnet deflected the electrons to the center axis but not the ions. However, this technique is no longer needed with aluminized tubes.

Third, the aluminum backing collects secondary electrons emitted from the phosphor screen when it is excited by the beam. As a result, the screen can charge to the ultor potential. Then the phosphor screen actually has the positive anode potential to attract the electron beam.

Aluminizing is done by evaporation. A link of pure aluminum is evaporated by a high surge of current in a vacuum chamber. The screens are grouped around the link, and the aluminum vapor condenses on the back of the phosphor layer. The glass faceplate is complete after aluminizing. Then the faceplate is heat-sealed to the bell of the tube with a layer of ceramic called *frit cement.*

Test Point Questions 4-3

Answers at End of Chapter

a. What are the phosphor numbers, respectively, for monochrome and color picture tubes?

b. Aluminized tubes do not need an ion-trap magnet. True or False?

c. What is the color of the P1 phosphor?

4-4 ELECTRON GUN

Figure 4-2 is a simplified diagram of an electron gun. The cathode is a small metallic oxide disk placed at the end of the narrow tube that covers the heater. Although the cathode is heated to produce thermionic emission, it is electrically insulated from the heater. Next along the tube axis is the control-grid cylinder, labeled *G*1. The grid almost completely covers the cathode cylinder, but a small aperture in *G*1 allows electrons to pass through. The negative bias voltage at the control grid with respect to the cathode enables *G*1 to control the space charge of electrons emitted from the cathode. As a result, the beam cur-

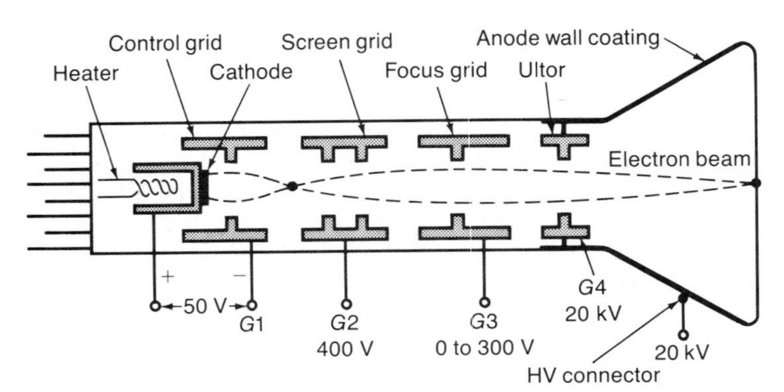

Fig. 4-2 Basic structure of an electron gun that uses electrostatic focus and magnetic deflection.

rent can be varied and the brightness modulated by the video signal voltage that is applied between $G1$ and the cathode.

The screen grid $G2$ is also considered the first anode. It accelerates electrons in the beam because of its positive voltage. The $G2$ cylinder contains internal baffles to restrict the beam to a narrow path. Following $G2$ is the focus cylinder $G3$, which forms an electrostatic lens with $G2$ to force electrons into paths that come to a point at the phosphor screen.

All the cylinders are made of nickel or a nickel alloy. They are supported by glass or ceramic insulating rods that are parallel to the gun axis. Connections to all the elements are made at the base pins, except for $G4$, which is part of the ultor. This cup has metallic spring fingers that make contact with the inner Aquadag coating for the anode voltage. Figure 4-3 shows a typical electron gun from a small-screen, monochrome picture tube.

Very little current is drawn by the $G2$, $G3$, and $G4$ elements, even though they are positive. Most electrons in the beam pass through the small apertures in each cylinder because their circular structure provides a symmetric accelerating field on all sides of the beam. Thus the beam moves straight ahead to the screen, as though the electrons were ejected from the gun as a point source. The aperture in $G4$ at the end can be considered the "muzzle" of the electron gun.

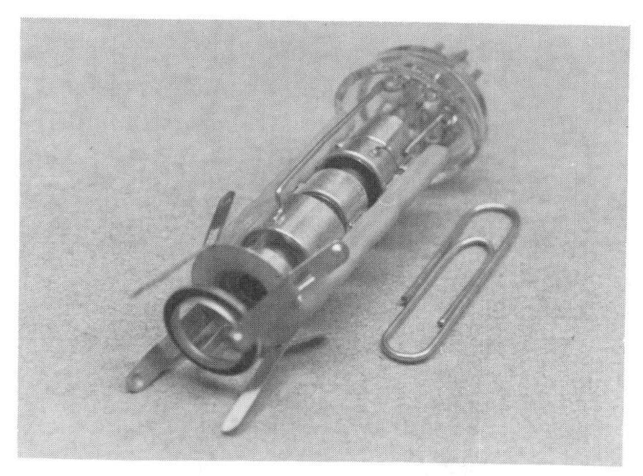

Fig. 4-3 Actual electron gun from a small-screen monochrome picture tube that uses an Einzel lens for low-voltage electrostatic focusing. Length of the gun is 3 in. [76.2 mm]. Diameter is ½ in. [12.7 mm].

A complete circuit for the electron beam is formed between the cathode and the anode connection for high voltage. Secondary electrons released in the phosphor screen are collected by the aluminum backing, which is connected to the inner Aquadag coating and the high-voltage supply. The picture tube can be considered as a series circuit with the high-voltage supply. A path from the cathode to the phosphor screen is formed by the electron beam. Typical values of beam current range from 300 to 800 μA for one electron gun. This beam current is the load current for the high-voltage supply connected to the anode.

Test Point Questions 4-4

Answers at End of Chapter

a. Which is the most negative (or least positive) electrode in the electron gun, the cathode or the control grid?

b. Which is the most positive element in the electron gun?

c. Most of the electrons in the beam flow out of which terminal?

4-5 ELECTROSTATIC FOCUS

Electrons emitted from the cathode tend to diverge because they repel one another. However, the electrons can be forced to converge by an electric or magnetic field. This action is similar to the focusing of a beam of light by optical lenses. Therefore, the term *focusing* is used for the producing of a narrow beam, where the focusing system is an electron lens. Two electron lenses

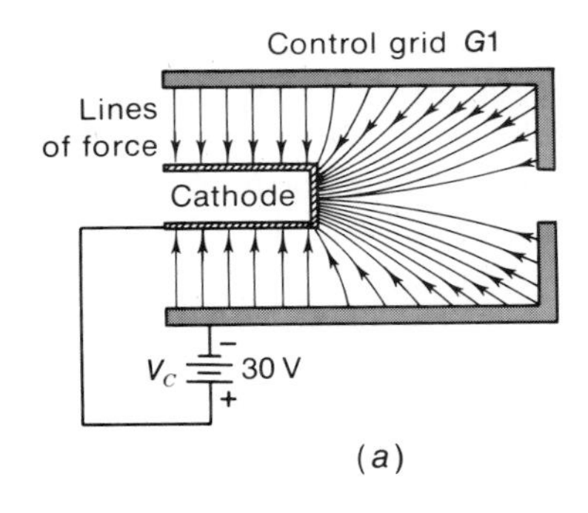

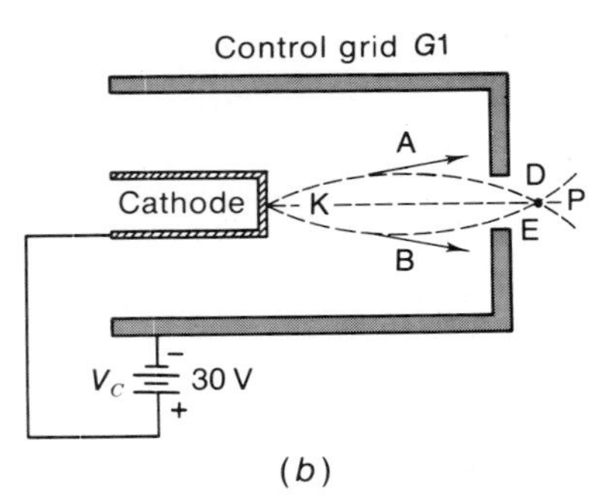

Fig. 4-4 Electrostatic focus for the first electron lens between cathode and control grid *G*1. (*a*) Electric lines of force between *G*1 and cathode. The electron beam is not shown here. (*b*) Effect on electron beam. Diverging electrons from point K are focused at crossover point P. The lines of force are not shown here.

are used. The first is the electrostatic field between the cathode and the control grid which is produced by their difference in potential. This voltage causes the beam to converge to a spot called the *crossover point,* located just beyond the control grid at point P in Fig. 4-4. The second lens may be either an electrostatic field or a magnetic field, and it focuses the beam just before the point of deflection. As a result of the action of the two electron lenses, the beam is focused to a small, sharp spot of light on the screen.

CROSSOVER POINT The first electron lens, which is formed by the electrostatic field between the cathode and the control grid, is illustrated in Fig. 4-4. The lines of force in Fig. 4-4*a* tend to push electrons back to the cathode because the control grid is negative. The lines of force are straight where the cathode and the grid are parallel. Such straight lines indicate a uniform change of potential in the space between the grid and the cathode. However, where the grid is not uniformly distant from the cathode, the lines of force curve. Notice that the curved lines of force follow the direction of electrons pushed back toward the center axis. Electrons diverging the most have the greatest force toward the center.

Remember, now, that the positive *G*2 voltage and the anode voltage provide a forward accelerating force. The net result is that diverging lines of force are bent so that the electrons go through the grid aperture (Fig. 4-4*b*). Then the diverging beam is focused at point P just beyond the control grid. Note that electrons emitted in the direction KA are made to follow the curved path KDP. Similarly, electrons from path KB are forced into path KEP. Electrons in a straight path KP along the center axis continue in this direction.

The focal point P is the crossover point produced by the first electron lens. Point P is a point source of electrons that will be imaged onto the screen by the second electron lens to make a sharp spot of light. A fine focus can be produced in this way because the crossover point is much smaller than the cathode area supplying electrons for the beam.

SECOND ELECTRON LENS Either of two methods can be used. For the high-voltage focus system in Fig. 4-5, the focusing voltage is generally one-fifth of the anode voltage. For example, if the anode voltage is 25,000 V for a 19-in. color picture tube, then the voltage for the focus grid

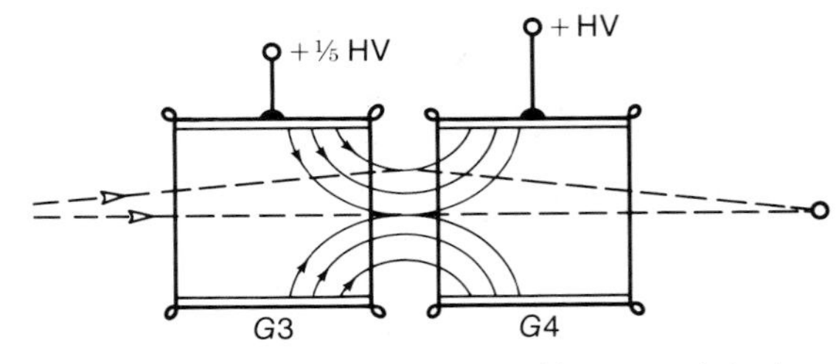

Fig. 4-5 High-voltage focus method for second electron lens.

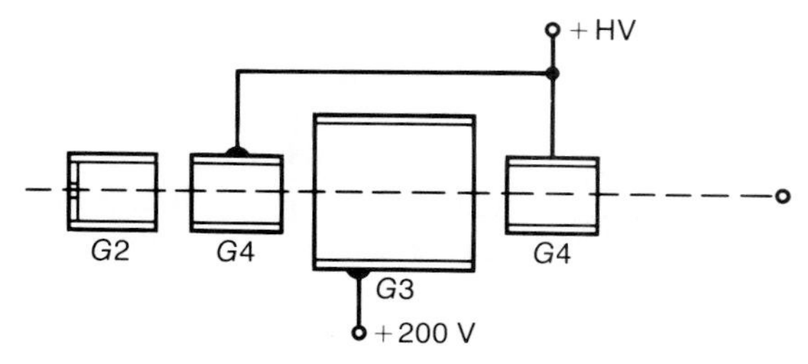

Fig. 4-6 Low-voltage focus method for second electron lens, using Einzel or unipotential lens.

is approximately ⅕ × 25,000 = 5000 V. For the low-voltage method in Fig. 4-6, the focus grid has a much lower potential, typically about 0 to 400 V.

HIGH-VOLTAGE FOCUS In Fig. 4-5, the *G*3 and *G*4 cylinders have the same diameter. Grid *G*4, with its full high voltage, is part of the ultor. However, *G*3 is the focus grid with a voltage of several kilovolts, or one-fifth the anode voltage. The electric lines of force are shown by the curved lines with arrows. These lines are more dense, or bulge, toward the center axis because of the field gradient between the surfaces. In the gap from *G*3 to *G*4, therefore, the electric field forces diverging electrons to move toward the center axis.

This focus system with its *G*3 and *G*4 cylinders of uniform diameter is common in electron guns in most tricolor picture tubes. The *G*3 voltage is about one-fifth, or 20 percent, of the high voltage applied to *G*4. A variable control is usually provided for the *G*3 voltage to permit precise focus adjustment. The focus control is set for the sharpest scanning lines in the raster and small details in the picture.

LOW-VOLTAGE FOCUS The system shown in Fig. 4-6 uses for the focus grid a larger cylinder set between two smaller cylinders which are at the ultor potential. Actually, the small cylinders form the ultor *G*4 but split into two parts, before and after *G*3. The focus grid *G*3 is at a low voltage, between 0 and 400 V. As a result, the electron beam enters a decelerating field, approaching *G*3, which converges electrons to the center axis.

This focus system is known as a *unipotential,* or *Einzel,* lens. It is used in most black-and-white picture tubes and in the Sony Trinitron color picture tube. The focusing is not critical in the Einzel system. Adjustment is made by selecting one of several fixed voltages available from the low-voltage power supply.

Test Point Questions 4-5

Answers at End of Chapter

a. Is the crossover point for focusing formed by the first or second electron lens?

b. Is a *G*3 voltage of 200 V used for the low-voltage or high-voltage focus method?

c. For most color picture tubes, the *G*3 focus voltage is an adjustable value of several kilovolts. True or False?

4-6 MAGNETIC DEFLECTION

All picture tubes, either color or monochrome, use magnetic deflection with *V* and *H* scanning coils in an external yoke around the neck of the tube, rather than electrostatic deflection with internal deflection plates. The electrostatic deflection plates take sawtooth voltage. For the magnetic scanning coils, sawtooth current is required.

Deflection is much easier for magnetic scanning, especially with the very high anode voltage used for picture tubes. In electrostatic scanning, the deflection angle is inversely proportional to the amount of high voltage. For example, increasing the anode voltage nine times reduces the deflection angle by one-ninth. For magnetic scanning, however, the deflection angle is inversely proportional to the square root of the high voltage. Thus, increasing the anode voltage by nine times reduces the deflection angle only by one-third. The conclusion is, then, that a picture tube with electrostatic deflection would have too small a deflection angle and the tube would be much too long.

In magnetic scanning, two pairs of deflection coils are used (see Fig. 4-7) which are mounted externally around the neck of the tube just before the bell. The pair of coils above and below the beam axis produces horizontal deflection; the coils to the left and right of the beam produce vertical deflection. This perpendicular displacement results because the current in each coil has a magnetic field that reacts with the magnetic field of the electron beam. The resulting force deflects the electrons at right angles to both the beam axis and the deflection field.

To analyze the deflection, remember that the reaction between two parallel fields always exerts a force toward the weaker field. Consider first the horizontal deflection coils in Fig. 4-7. The windings are in a horizontal plane above and below the beam axis. By the left-hand rule, the thumb points in the direction of the field inside a coil when the fingers curve in the direction of the electron flow around the coil. Therefore, the deflection field for the horizontal windings is downward. When the direction of the electron beam is into the paper, as indicated by the cross in the center, the magnetic field of the beam has lines of force counterclockwise around the beam in the plane of the paper. To the left of the beam axis, the magnetic field of the beam is downward, in the same direction as the deflecting field; to the right of the beam axis, the magnetic field of the beam is upward, in the direction opposite that of the deflecting field. The electron beam is deflected to the right, therefore, as the resultant force moves the beam toward the weaker field. In a similar manner, the vertical deflection coils deflect the electron beam downward. Deflecting currents for both sets of coils are applied simultaneously, forcing the beam to the lower right in this example.

The actual deflection coils are wound in the form of a saddle, and the four coils in one assembly are called the *deflection yoke*. Figure 4-8

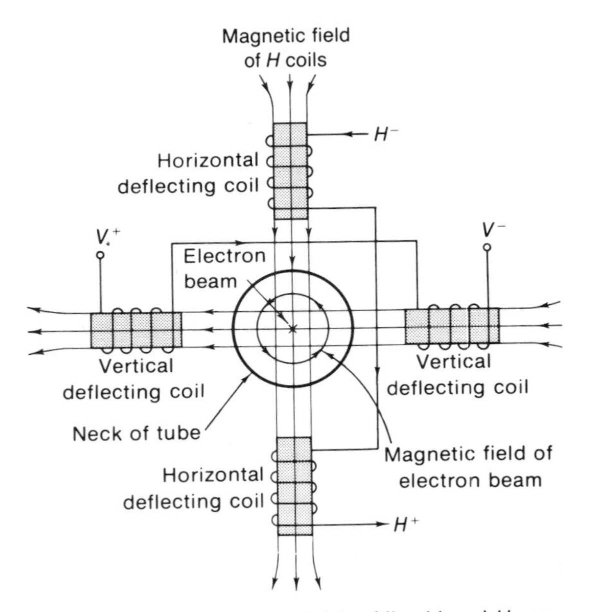

Fig. 4-7 How the magnetic fields of the V and H scanning coils produce deflection. The electron beam is deflected down and to the right for the electron flow shown in the coils.

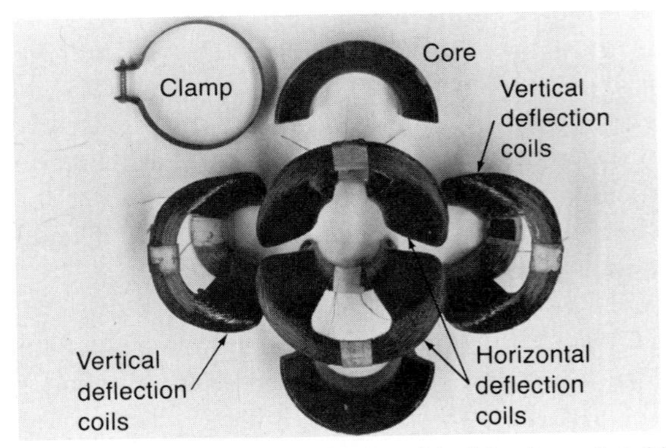

Fig. 4-8 Deflection yoke disassembled to show the V and H scanning coils.

shows the coils from a typical yoke; they are separated for inspection but are in the correct relative position. A ring formed of two segments of ferrite core material is clamped around the outside of the coils. This ring completes the external path for magnetic flux lines so that the total reluctance of the magnetic circuit is minimized. The largest air-and-vacuum gap in the magnetic circuit is formed by the neck of the picture tube itself.

One mark of progress in picture tubes has been the trend toward a narrower neck, made possible by improved electron guns. A narrower neck results in a shorter gap, which means reduced reluctance in the magnetic path. A higher flux density is produced for a given amount of current in the coils, resulting in greater deflection sensitivity. These advantages can be used for a large deflection angle to shorten the picture tube, to conserve the deflection power, or to do both.

CENTERING ADJUSTMENTS Owing to tolerances in the design and mounting of the electron gun in the picture tube, usually there is a method of shifting the static position of the beam at zero deflection so that the center of the raster coincides with the center of the screen. In early TV receivers, the centering was accomplished by rheostat control of direct current flowing in both the vertical and horizontal windings. In this method, power is taken from the dc supply. Today, though, for monochrome tubes centering is done with a pair of permanent-magnet (PM) rings mounted just behind the deflection yoke. The centering magnets function in the same way as the beam-alignment rings for cameras (see Fig. 3-14*a*).

Centering controls usually are not found in modern color receivers. The reason is that the adjustment can change the color purity and convergence of the three beams. However, the beam-landing adjustments for color purity are used to produce precise centering of the electron beams. These adjustments also are made with two magnetic rings.

PINCUSHION DISTORTION For a wide deflection angle, the raster tends to stretch out at the corners, resembling a pincushion. This same effect can be seen with optical projectors that use a wide-angle lens.

The pincushion distortion is corrected in monochrome receivers by means of small permanent magnets embedded in the front part of the housing of the deflection yoke. These magnets cannot be used for color tubes, however, because distortion of the deflection field affects the color purity and convergence. Instead, the deflection current waveform is modified to correct for pincushion distortion.

YOKE POSITION As the electron beam enters the magnetic field of the yoke, the beam is deflected, and this continues until the beam emerges from the forward edge of the field. If we could look back along the path of the electrons, they would appear to fan out from a single point, the deflection center, as shown in Fig. 4-9*a*. It is important that this point be far enough forward that the electrons do not strike the neck of the tube at the extreme angles of deflection.

Shadowed corners, called *neck shadow,* indicate that the deflection center is too far back toward the tube socket. An extreme case is shown in Fig. 4-9*b*, where a circular raster results because the yoke is too far back.

To avoid neck shadow, usually the yoke is pushed up against the wide bell of the picture tube and then clamped in place. In color receivers, though, the yoke position is more critical. Yoke position adjustment is actually one of the setup adjustments for color purity in the picture tube.

Finally, it is important to note the following practical features of the yoke and its effect on the scanning raster:

1. If the yoke is tilted, left or right, the raster and picture will be tilted the same way.
2. The symmetry of the rectangular raster results from the balanced deflection coils in the yoke.

In terms of troubles, remember that when the raster is not straight, the yoke must be adjusted. Also, if the raster does not have parallel edges, left and right or top and bottom, the trouble must be a defect in the deflection yoke itself.

Test Point Questions 4-6

Answers at End of Chapter

a. Do the small magnets embedded in the yoke housing correct for pincushion distortion or for centering?
b. Are the coils above and below the electron beam for V or H scanning?
c. Two permanent-magnet (PM) rings just behind the yoke are used for centering the beam in monochrome receivers. True or False?
d. Does neck shadow result when the deflection yoke is too far back or too far forward?

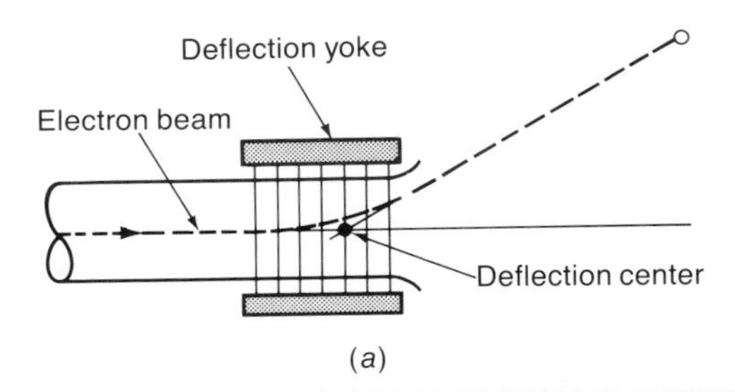

(*a*)

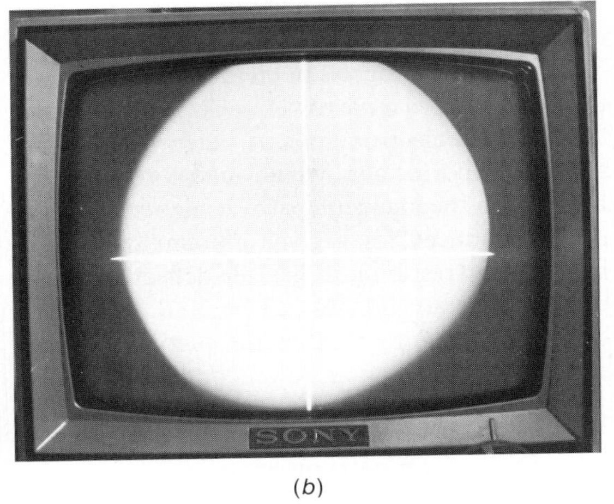

(*b*)

Fig. 4-9 (*a*) Deflection center at the muzzle of the electron gun, where the beam starts deflection. (*b*) Circular raster with shadowed corners, caused by deflection center being too far back. The yoke must be moved forward.

4-7 TRICOLOR PICTURE TUBES

The screen has red, green, and blue phosphors, and three electron beams are used, one for each primary color. There are essentially three picture tubes in a single envelope, as shown in Fig. 4-10. One gun controls electrons that strike only the red phosphor, the second is for the green phosphor, and the third is for the blue phosphor. Trios of dots are formed by the color phosphors in Fig. 4-10, but trios of red, green, and blue vertical lines are used in many color picture tubes. An example is shown in Fig. 1-1.

Separation of the colors is maintained by the shadow-mask principle. The mask is a perforated steel sheet mounted on the back of the screen. The holes, or apertures, can be made for phosphor dots or phosphor lines. Only the electrons that converge at the proper angle can strike the phosphor screen to produce the correct color. Other electrons are blocked by the mask. About 20 to 30 percent of the beam current actually is used in exciting the screen phosphors. For this reason, color picture tubes need a much higher anode voltage and have a larger value of beam current, compared with monochrome tubes.

Figure 4-11 shows the external components mounted on the neck of the color picture tube:

1. *Deflection yoke.* The V and H scanning coils deflect all three beams to form the scanning raster.

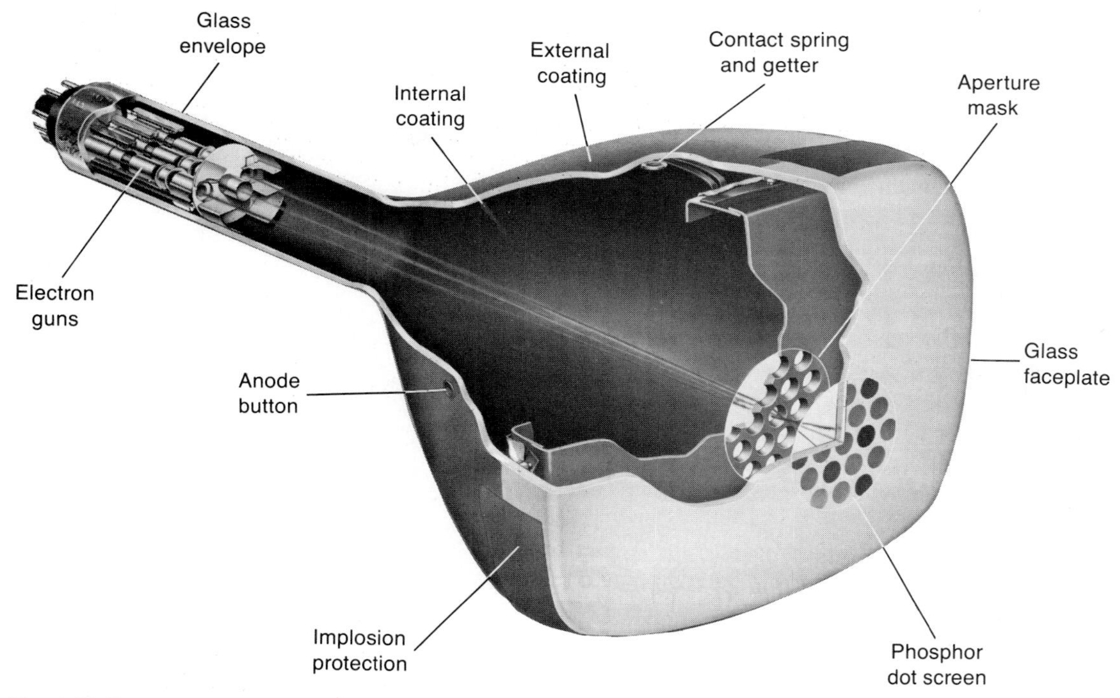

Fig. 4-10 Structure of tricolor picture tube with three in-line electron guns for red, green, and blue phosphor dots. Aperture mask has holes over entire area. (*General Electric*)

2. *Convergence yoke.* This magnetic yoke has individual adjustments for each color to make the beams converge through the openings in the shadow mask.
3. *Color purity magnetic rings.* These rings are adjusted for beam landing at the screen, to obtain good color purity. The two magnetic rings are moved as a centering adjustment for all three electron beams.

The details of how to make the color purity and convergence adjustments are explained in Chap. 5.

DELTA GUNS The first shadow-mask tubes, produced by RCA, used the delta-gun arrangement shown in Fig. 4-12*a*. The three electron guns are mounted at the corners of an equilateral triangle, forming a delta (Δ). This system allows maximum diameter for the focus electrode in the individual guns, within the neck of the tube, and offers the best ratio of gun-to-neck diameter. However, the ability to maintain registration of the three beams at all points on the screen is complicated by the fact that no combination of guns can be in the same vertical or horizontal plane.

IN-LINE GUNS Improvements in gun design have led to the in-line system generally used today. All three guns are in one horizontal plane on a diameter of the tube neck, as shown in Fig. 4-12*b*. Green is usually at the center. Although some sacrifice in gun diameter must be made, the design still enables excellent focus to be maintained with a small spot size for high resolution in the picture. Color convergence is much easier

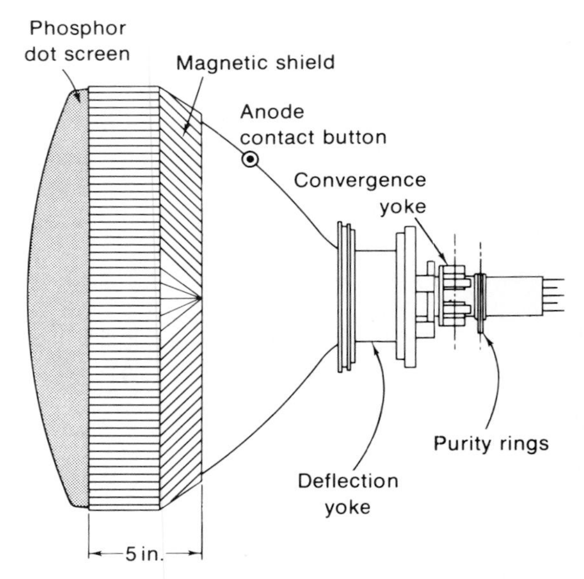

Fig. 4-11 External magnetic components mounted on neck of picture tube for deflection and color convergence.

with in-line guns because one gun is at the center and the other two are in the same horizontal plane.

SONY TRINITRON GUN This system, shown in Fig. 4-12*c*, is a unique approach to the focusing system. All the electrodes are in a single electron gun, but with three cathodes. The *G*1 cup and the accelerating grids have three holes to accommodate the three beams. All three beams emerge from *G*1, toward the crossover point. Then the beams pass through a large-diameter Einzel lens that focuses all three with a common electric field by low-voltage electrostatic focusing.

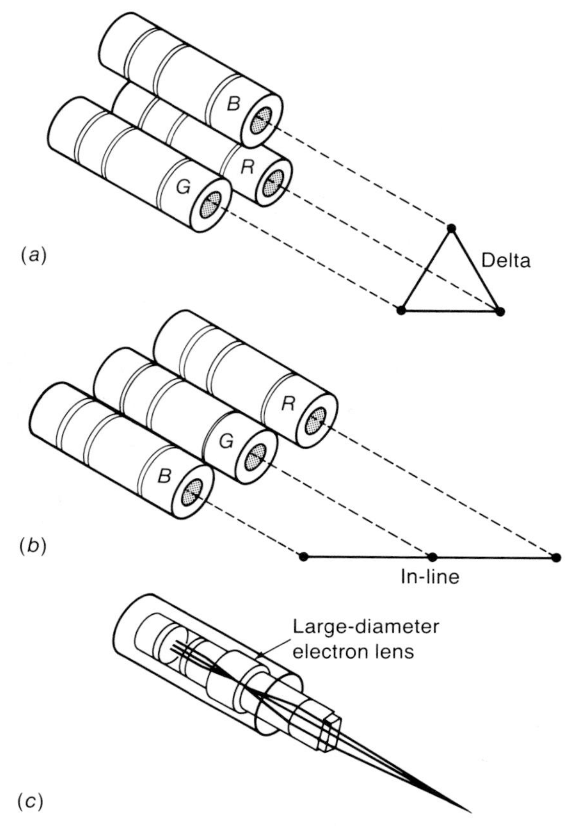

Fig. 4-12 Methods of having three electron guns in one picture tube. (*a*) Delta guns. (*b*) In-line guns. (*c*) Trinitron gun, with three in-line cathodes for a single-gun assembly.

Test Point Questions 4-7

Answers at End of Chapter

Answer True or False.

a. Separation of the beams for the red, green, and blue colors is accomplished by the shadow mask.
b. The deflection yoke is for the green beam only.
c. Delta guns have two beams in the same plane.
d. In-line guns are easier than delta guns in making the convergence adjustments.

4-8 SHADOW MASK

In a tricolor picture tube, red, green, and blue are kept separate by the shadow mask. The principle of having each beam for just one color is illustrated in Fig. 4-13. If we were to suspend a light source above a perforated plate, with holes like a sieve, then light from source A would pass through the holes as shown. Assume these illuminated points are painted red. Then light from the source at point A illuminates only the red-painted spots. Next, consider light source B. Because of its position, source B illuminates only the blue-painted spots. The same idea can be applied to a third light source for green. Note that each source itself is not a primary color; the mask makes one beam serve for red, blue, or green. It is the relative position of the light sources with respect to the mask that determines the separate colors.

Now consider electron beams, specifically the deflection center for each beam, instead of the light sources. Also, replace the painted spots with color phosphors. The result is the shadow-mask tricolor picture tube.

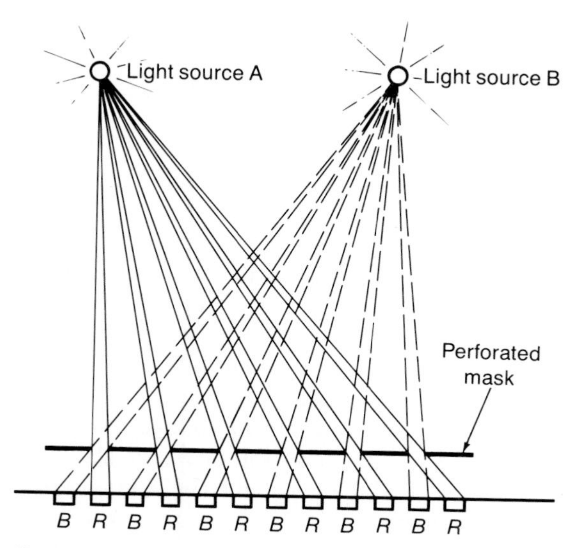

Fig. 4-13 Shadow-mask principle illustrated with two light sources.

This simplified illustration is not much different from the actual method of producing the tube. First, the shadow mask, which is not a master but actually the mask to be used in that particular tube, is fixed correctly to the phosphor screen. The screen is coated with a photosensitive material. The mask is a thin spherical or cylindrical sheet of steel that has been photo-etched with 300,000 or more holes.

Second, the screen is exposed, through the shadow mask, to light from a special point source called a *lighthouse tube.* This should not be confused with a UHF amplifier tube of the same name.

One set of phosphor dots will be located where the light hits the screen through a hole. Then the film on the screen is etched to remove both the exposed areas and the phosphor deposited in the resulting cavities. This sequence is followed for one color. Then the process is repeated for the remaining primary color phosphors, by mechanically indexing the location of either the lighthouse tube or the faceplate assembly. The glass faceplate is a separate unit until it is bonded to the envelope.

When the picture tube is put into service, the deflection center for each electron beam must be put in the precise location of the lighthouse tubes used when the phosphor screen was made. This adjustment is called *beam landing,* or *color purity.* The correct result produces pure red, green, and blue rasters when the guns are activated in that sequence.

Practically all tricolor picture tubes work according to this shadow-mask principle. The holes in the mask may be round, rectangular, lozenge-shaped, or continuous slots. The basic principle is the same for all, and the fabrication techniques using lighthouse tubes and photo-etching are similar.

The shadow mask is a thin steel sheet, but it is supported by a heavy internal frame to maintain its rigidity. Figure 4-14 shows a mask assembly removed from the picture tube. The mask

Fig. 4-14 Shadow mask removed from a color picture tube to illustrate transparency of the mask. Partial view through the mask.

is somewhat transparent to either electrons or light, as you can see. About 300,000 holes are provided. Still, only 20 to 30 percent of the electrons pass through to the phosphor screen.

The holes are acid-etched from one side, away from the electron gun, to make them conical instead of cylindrical. Figure 4-15 shows a photograph taken through a 50X microscope. The purpose of the conical shape is to prevent secondary

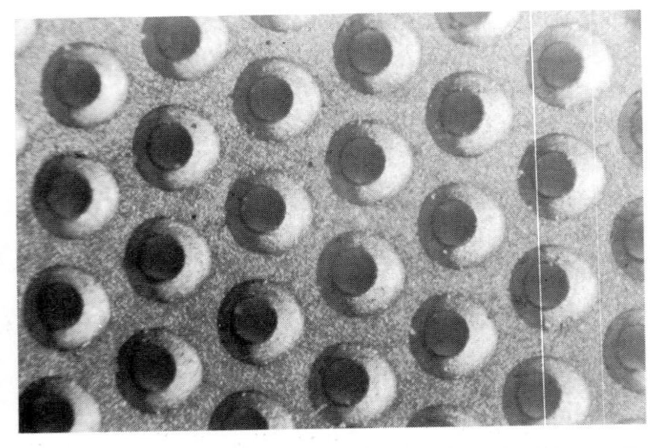

Fig. 4-15 Microscope photograph of conical holes in the shadow mask, faceplate side.

emission from the mask itself. The conical holes present a knife edge at the gun side, so that electrons approaching at an oblique angle do not bounce off the inside surface of the hole. If such secondary emission occurred, a white halo would surround the bright parts of the picture.

A different approach is taken for the Sony Trinitron, which has vertical color stripes on the phosphor screen. In this case, the mask is perforated with continuous vertical slots. The steel mask is a cylindrical surface stretched between the upper and lower members of a heavy steel frame. Four thin wires run horizontally across the mask to dampen any mechanical motion of the vertical "tapes" forming the mask. You can see these wires if you look closely at a stationary picture such as color bars.

Test Point Questions 4-8

Answers at End of Chapter

Answer True or False.

a. A shadow mask has about 300,000 holes.

b. Figure 4-14 shows that the shadow mask is somewhat transparent.

c. The mask is designed to increase secondary emission of electrons.

4-9 METHODS OF PHOSPHOR MASKING

Efforts are continually being made to increase both the brightness and the contrast of the tricolor picture tube, so that the picture will not appear washed out by ambient lighting from the room in which the screen is viewed. The ultor high voltage and screen-grid voltage have been raised to partially offset the fact that about 70 to 80 percent of the beam current is intercepted by the shadow mask. Also, improvements in electron gun design have reduced the spot size, so that the beam density is greater where the elec-

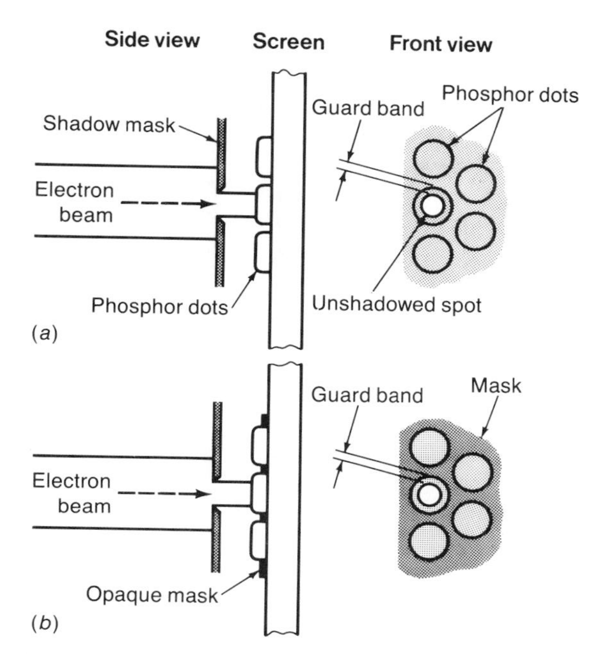

Fig. 4-16 Example of opaque (black) masking for the screen phosphor to increase picture contrast. (*a*) Phosphor dots without any masking. (*b*) Screen masking between phosphor dots.

trons strike the screen. All these factors create a whiter white in the reproduced picture.

Other improvements operate in the opposite direction, to improve contrast by making the black appear blacker. The problem is ambient lighting, which limits the ability to remove all light. The method involves reducing the reflectivity of the phosphor screen surface to ambient light. An early system used a tinted, or smoked, glass panel in front of the faceplate. Room light reflected from the phosphor screen travels twice through the glass, and is attenuated twice, whereas light emitted from the phosphors is attenuated only once.

More recent improvements deal with the phosphor screen itself. Early phosphor screens have a pale gray color, when viewed in room lighting without a picture on the screen. The entire phosphor surface is quite reflective. Furthermore, not all the phosphor area is illuminated by the electron beam. The reason is that the diameter of each dot is a little larger than the diameter of the beam through the hole in the shadow mask.

When the beam-landing adjustments are made correctly and the deflection centers are placed in the same relative positions as the lighthouse tubes used in production, the beams illuminate only the centers of the dots, as shown in Fig. 4-16*a*. Note that there is room for error. The beams can be off center by the distance identified as the *guard band,* before the electrons are off the spot.

In Fig. 4-16*b,* the screen has a black mask added to the areas between phosphor dots. Now there is a substantial opaque area on the screen that does not reflect light. The mask is located by using the same photographic techniques that locate the phosphor dots.

Test Point Questions 4-9

Answers at End of Chapter

Answer True or False.

a. Ambient room lighting makes black on the screen appear lighter.

b. Opaque phosphor masking improves contrast by making black appear darker.

4-10 TELEVISION PROJECTION SYSTEMS

The method used in TV projection systems is just the reverse of that in a three-tube color camera with separate pickup tubes. To reproduce the picture, separate red, green, and blue images are registered on a common reflecting screen. The viewer sees the resulting light mixtures as a big, beautiful color picture. Screen sizes are 2×3 and 4×5 ft [0.6×0.9 and 1.2×1.5 m], up to 9×12 ft [2.7×3.7 m], as big as a movie screen.

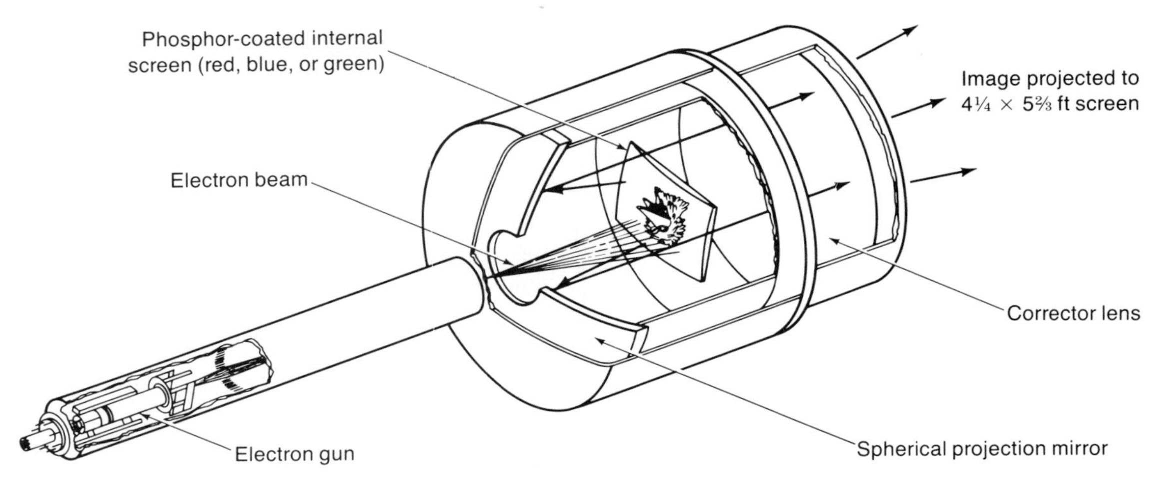

Fig. 4-17 Light-guide picture tube for the Advent TV projection system (*Advent Corporation*)

The advantage of projection is that the picture is much larger than that in direct-view tubes. A big picture looks real. However, the problem with TV projection is the production of enough brightness. When the picture area is increased 10 times, then 10 times more light is needed to achieve the same overall brightness. Another factor is that the larger picture still has the same number of scanning lines and the same maximum resolution with a 4-MHz video signal. In our standard television system, the horizontal scanning lines are easily visible. Also, the image does not look as sharp as a picture on a small screen that contains the same number of details and has stronger contrast. New systems are being considered with satellite television, though, that could provide a very high definition (VHD) picture for projection systems. More scanning lines and a wider frequency range for the signal are planned, in special transmission channels.

TV projection systems use small-screen picture tubes built to produce very intense light output. The screen size is generally 1 to 5 in., and the anode high voltage is 30 to 80 kV. The height, width, and scanning linearity for the raster are critical. Each tube has its own deflection system, and the three rasters must match precisely so that the images will remain in register at all points on the screen.

ADVENT SYSTEM One interesting example of TV projection is the Advent system. One of the three projection tubes is shown in Fig. 4-17 to illustrate the general requirements. The phosphor screen is a small, rectangular but spherical surface inside a relatively large envelope which also contains a spherical mirror to reflect the optical image from the screen. The small screen area of the picture tube requires a deflection angle only 14°, which minimizes problems with deflection linearity. Three such tubes are used, one each for red, green, and blue, to project the color picture on a screen 4¼ × 5⅔ ft [1.3 × 1.7 m].

SCHMIDT OPTICAL SYSTEM Many TV projection receivers use this method, which is adapted from the Schmidt astronomical camera. The two major advantages are high efficiency for maximum brightness and relatively small size for com-

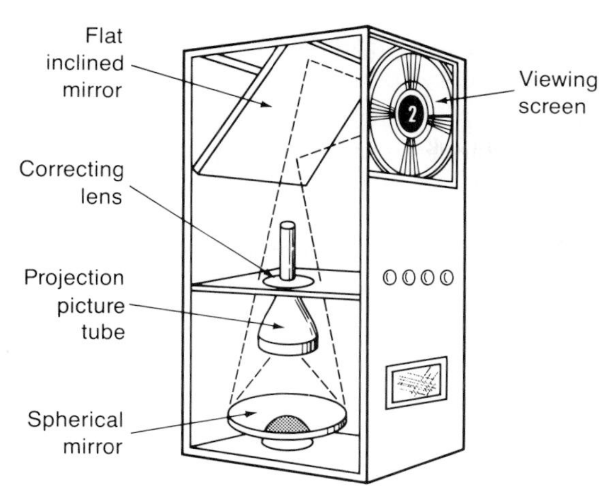

Fig. 4-18 Folded Schmidt-type projection system.

pactness. As shown in Fig. 4-18, the projection distance is folded back on itself by the use of a spherical mirror, instead of a diverging lens. The spherical shape reflects an enlarged image. A corrector lens is used to reduce optical aberrations at the edges of the image.

Test Point Questions 4-10
Answers at End of Chapter

Answer True or False.

a. A TV projection picture shows more detail than the image on a direct-view picture tube.
b. The typical anode voltage for projection tubes is 30 to 80 kV.

4-11 PICTURE TUBE PRECAUTIONS

The picture tube is extremely dangerous because it is a large, evacuated glass bulb. A crack or puncture results in a violent inrush of air called an *implosion,* but the kinetic energy of the broken glass causes a subsequent explosion. You should always wear eye protection, such as goggles or a face shield, when handling a picture tube. Also, wear heavy gloves that provide a secure grip.

In large-screen sets, the picture tube can be extremely heavy and awkward to handle. In this case, it is better to put the set face down on a blanket or carpet and lift or lower the picture tube vertically into place. Never handle the picture tube by its neck. Be sure the delicate neck does not strike the cabinet or any chassis bracket while you are installing or removing the picture tube.

HIGH-VOLTAGE PRECAUTIONS The glass dielectric for the anode capacitance of the picture tube has extremely low leakage. Out of the set, the anode can retain a charge of several thousand volts for weeks at a time. Accidental contact with the ultor button of a charged picture tube, in itself, seldom gives a dangerous electric shock. However, the person's physical reaction may cause the tube to be dropped, and the consequences can be disastrous.

Always discharge the picture tube before removing it. To do this, connect a clip lead between the chassis ground and the metal shank of a plastic-handled screwdriver. Then, holding the screwdriver by its plastic handle, touch the ultor button under the rubber cap of the high-voltage connector. You will hear a snap when the tube is discharged.

Do not trust picture tubes that are stored temporarily out of the set. Ground the ultor button, using the clip-lead and screwdriver technique, but hold the end of the clip lead against the outer Aquadag coating before and during contact of the blade with the ultor button.

X-RADIATION X-rays are invisible radiation with wavelengths much shorter than those of visible light. Prolonged exposure to x-rays can be harmful. The x-rays are produced when a metal anode is bombarded by high-velocity electrons, generally with an anode voltage above 16 kV.

Color picture tubes with an anode voltage of 20 to 30 kV can produce soft x-rays. This radiation is easier to shield than hard x-rays which are produced with much higher accelerating voltages—up to 100 kV. Lead and leaded glass are used for shielding against x-ray penetration in general. For soft x-rays, some attenuation is provided by wood, cardboard, pressed paper, metals, and glass.

The main sources of x-rays in a television receiver are the picture tube (especially from the metal shadow mask) and the high-voltage rectifier tube, if used. However, when solid-state devices are used for the high-voltage supply, they do not produce x-rays. Picture tubes with an improved faceplate for x-ray shielding may have the letter V in the type designation or the prefix letters XR. Always make sure that an exact replacement tube is used, so that a set that requires a leaded-glass faceplate is not used with a CRT made of conventional glass.

Television receivers are designed to limit the x-ray level below the value set by the U.S. Department of Health, Education, and Welfare. The limit is 0.5 milliroentgen per hour (mR/h) as measured at a point 2 in. [51 mm] from any surface of the receiver. This dosage is extremely small, just above the normal background level.

HOLD-DOWN CIRCUIT For protection against x-ray radiation from color picture tubes, the main problem is not allowing the anode voltage to exceed the recommended value. The receiver should not be able to produce a viewable picture when the high voltage exceeds a specified limit. In one method, the high voltage is cut off, resulting in no brightness. In another method, the horizontal sweep frequency is increased. This effect makes the picture be out of horizontal sync and reduces the high voltage. Either system is called a *hold-down circuit* because it limits the amount of high voltage. A typical hold-down circuit is explained in Fig. 16-27.

Test Point Questions 4-11

Answers at End of Chapter

Answer True or False.

a. When a picture tube is being discharged, the ground end of the clip lead should be connected first.

b. Hold-down circuits limit the amount of color saturation.

4-12 PROBLEMS WITH PICTURE TUBES

A natural and eventual cause of picture tube failure is loss of emission at the cathode. The result is a dim picture. In a color set, the gray-scale imbalance identifies the weak gun. For example, a cyan picture points to a weak red gun. Remember that the addition of cyan and red makes white.

Although video circuit troubles can cause similar symptoms, the picture tube gives a few more clues. First, in cases of low emission, the weak cathode takes a long time to warm up to produce any emission at all. A tube that takes a half hour to give a reasonable picture is definitely bad.

Second, the picture starts off cyan, instead of black and white, but then gradually balances to produce a neutral gray scale after 20 to 30 min. A monochrome picture can be created by turning down the color control. A long warmup time for balanced white and gray is a definite sign of weak emission from the red gun. An unbalanced gray scale also results from weak emission by the green or blue gun.

A third clue to low emission is the saturation limiting of the beam current. The weak cathode cannot supply enough electrons for the highlight areas of the picture. When either the brightness or the contrast control is advanced, the whites appear to wash out. Faces become featureless, gray blobs, and the overall picture takes on a

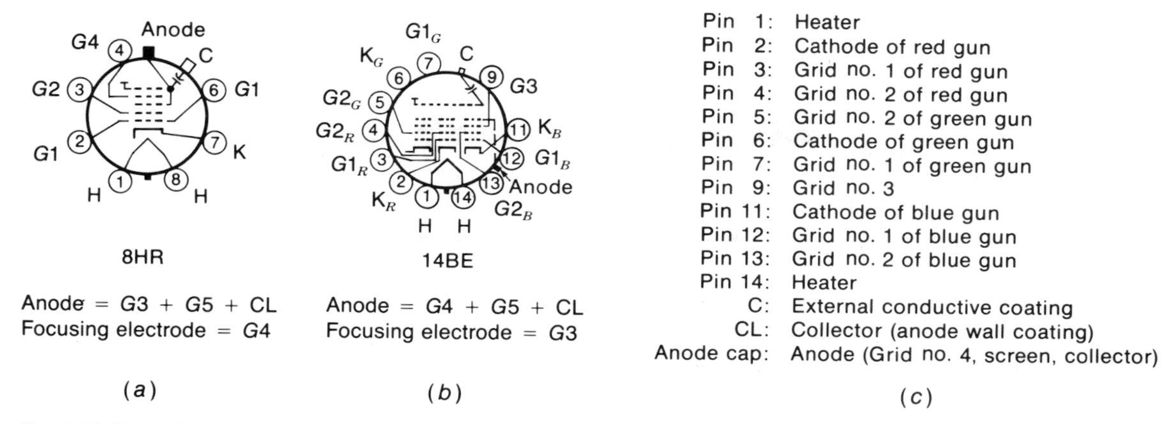

Fig. 4-19 Examples of base-pin connections for picture tubes. (*a*) An 8-pin base 8HR for monochrome tubes. (*b*) A 14-pin base 14BE for color tubes with delta guns. (*c*) Listing of electrodes for base 14BE.

silvery look. This effect is shown in color plate XIII for the case of weak emission and saturation limiting in the red gun. It is necessary to cut off the other two guns to view the picture produced by only the suspected gun.

When a picture tube is replaced, either a new or a rebuilt tube can be used. Rebuilt picture tubes cost less because they use the old glass envelope, or "dud," but the internal parts are all new. For some black-and-white types, a rebuilt tube must be used because there are no new tubes for replacement.

Two examples of picture tube sockets are shown in Fig. 4-19. Note that the heaters are end pins 1 and 8 in Fig. 4-19*a* or end pins 1 and 14 in Fig. 4-19*b*. The keyway for inserting the socket is between the end pins.

PICTURE TUBE RESTORATION Sometimes emission can be restored by overheating the cathode and operating the grids at a positive potential to force contaminants off the cathode surface. The unit shown in Fig. 4-20 is designed for that purpose. It will test each gun and process the cathode to restore emission. The method is somewhat violent for the tube, though, which can result in its complete failure. However, if the emission is weak, the tube must be replaced anyway. The rejuvenator also can be used to clear internal short circuits between electrodes in the gun system.

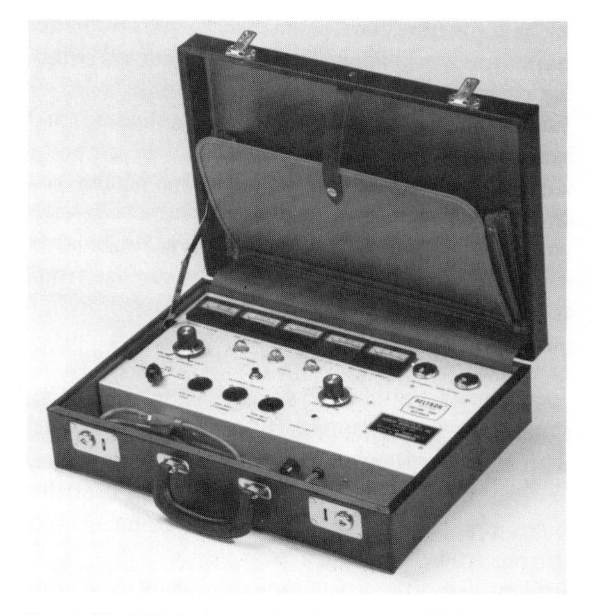

Fig. 4-20 CRT tester and rejuvenator. (*Edtron Instruments, Inc.*)

GRID-CATHODE SHORT CIRCUIT A short circuit between the cathode and control grid $G1$ is a common problem. As a result, there is no picture, but there is a bright raster, and the brightness control has no effect. The reason for the bright raster is that the short circuit has reduced the picture tube bias to zero.

In some cases, the beam current is so great that the high-voltage supply might be excessively loaded. Then the symptom is no raster, with little or no high voltage. However, the high voltage will return if the ultor lead is disconnected from the picture tube.

CATHODE-HEATER SHORT CIRCUIT This short circuit also can reduce the bias on the affected gun to zero. The bias is grounded through the heater circuit.

INTERNAL ARCING The arcing between electrodes in the picture tube can be both seen and heard. Frequently, the associated transistor amplifiers may be damaged by high-voltage arcs in the picture tube. For protection, generally neon lamps and spark gaps are used in circuits feeding the picture tube cathode, $G1$, $G2$, and $G3$.

In some circuits, a dc bias is applied to the heater to keep its potential close to the cathode voltage. The purpose is to minimize arcing between the cathode and the heater.

A new picture tube may arc a few times after it is installed, especially if there is a change from cold to warm temperature. If the internal arcing persists, however, the picture tube must be replaced.

GAS AND LOSS OF VACUUM A cracked seal, with the resulting loss of vacuum, can produce very subtle symptoms. When the amount of the gas is small, a blue or purple glow forms around the electrodes in the electron gun.

Complete loss of vacuum as a result of a *slow* leak causes a no-raster condition. The set may behave as though it had no high voltage. The reason is that the high-voltage supply has an excessive load current and often fails as a result. When the high-voltage supply is repaired, the trouble will recur, though, unless the picture tube problem is corrected.

A clue to the problem is that the heaters draw filament current but do not glow visibly. To be sure, check the high-voltage supply with the picture tube disconnected. If the high voltage drops when the picture tube is connected, you can suspect that the tube is the source of the trouble.

OPEN-CIRCUIT HEATER The result of an open-circuit heater is no brightness and no raster. This problem can be checked visually by looking at the base of the gun inside the glass neck to see whether the filament is lighted. In most three-gun color picture tubes, the three heaters are connected in series. Then an open circuit in one heater causes all three to be dark. Oddly enough, though, an open-circuit heater is not a common problem in picture tubes.

SCREEN BURN The phosphor does change gradually with use. Then the screen takes on a brown stain. Since the discoloration is uniformly distributed, it is seldom noticed. Generally other troubles will require picture tube replacement before screen burn is a problem. However, in some studio applications in which a single test pattern, such as color bars, is held on the screen for long periods every day, screen burn may be seen as a faint pattern even when other signals are displayed. There is no cure for this problem other than picture tube replacement.

CONTINUING SPOT This luminous spot remains at the center of the screen for a few seconds after the receiver is turned off. *Afterglow* results because the ultor voltage remains on the anode filter capacitance. This spot normally does not damage the screen, though, because it is on for a short time. One way to eliminate afterglow is to turn up the brightness control for maximum beam current just before the receiver is turned off. Then the high voltage can discharge quickly.

Test Point Questions 4-12

Answers at End of Chapter

Answer True or False.

a. Weak emission from the cathode of the electron gun causes saturation limiting, with the picture appearing silvery gray where it should appear white.

b. No picture, with a bright, blank raster and no control of brightness, may indicate a short circuit between the cathode and the control grid in the picture tube.

c. A yellowish brown monochrome picture slowly balancing to a neutral gray scale indicates weak emission in the blue gun.

SUMMARY

1. The picture tube is a CRT containing an electron gun, which produces a beam of electrons accelerated to a fluorescent screen that emits light. Monochrome picture tubes have one electron gun for the white phosphor screen. Color picture tubes have three guns for red, green, and blue phosphors.
2. High voltage is applied to the anode, or ultor, of the picture tube to achieve sufficient brightness. The positive dc voltage is typically 25 kV for a 19-in. color picture tube and 10 kV for a 12-in. monochrome tube. The anode connection is made in a recessed cavity on the wide bell of the glass envelope.
3. Focusing of the electron beam produces a sharp spot of light. Picture tubes use electrostatic focusing.
4. The electron beam is deflected horizontally and vertically to fill the screen area. Magnetic deflection is used for picture tubes.
5. A permanent-magnet ring on the neck of the tube is used for centering.
6. In a type number such as 19VDCP22, the first digits give the diagonal screen size—19 in.—and P22 is the phosphor number. The heater voltage is not indicated, but usually it is 6.3 V. The two end pins on the tube base are generally for the heater.
7. The most common screen phosphors are P1 for a green screen, P4 for white, and P22 for red, green, and blue in color picture tubes.
8. Picture tubes have two black conductive coatings made of Aquadag. One is on the inside for the anode. The other is on the wide bell of the glass envelope and is connected to the chassis ground for shielding.
9. The deflection angle of the picture tube is the total angle that the beam can be deflected without touching the sides of the envelope. The deflection angle of the yoke should match that of the tube.
10. Color picture tubes have a screen with red, green, and blue phosphors arranged in dot trios or vertical stripes. Each of the three electron beams is used for one color.

11. The shadow mask next to the tricolor screen has apertures that allow each beam to excite its corresponding color, while blocking electrons that approach at the wrong angle. A mask for dot trios has about 300,000 holes.
12. Convergence adjustments cause the three electron beams to excite the correct colors on the screen. Incorrect convergence shows as color fringing at the edges of objects in the picture.
13. The beam-landing, or color purity, adjustment causes the beams to strike the center of each phosphor dot or line, without contamination from other colors. Poor color purity shows up as patches of color in a white raster.
14. Black masking is used around the phosphor dots to make a darker black which improves contrast in the picture.
15. TV projection systems use small-screen picture tubes that produce intense light output for optical projection. The anode high voltage is 30 to 80 kV. The main problem is the production of sufficient brightness in the enlarged image.
16. Picture tubes should be handled with extreme care because of the danger of implosion.
17. Picture tubes with an anode voltage of 20 to 30 kV can emit x-rays. Lead and leaded glass provide the best shielding. The letters XR or V in the type designation indicate an improved glass faceplate for shielding of x-rays.
18. Weak emission from one cathode in a tricolor picture tube causes a weak picture, a long warmup time, and color imbalance in the raster and picture.

SELF-EXAMINATION

Answers at Back of Book

Answer True or False.

1. The 19VBLP22 is a color picture tube with a 19-in. screen.
2. The typical heater voltage for picture tubes is 19 V.
3. The anode voltage for a 25-in. color picture tube is usually 25 to 30 kV.
4. When the raster is tilted, it can be straightened by turning the deflection yoke.
5. The centering magnet is an adjustable permanent magnet.
6. The typical focusing voltage for an Einzel lens is 5 kV.
7. The outside wall coating on a picture tube forms one side of the anode capacitance.
8. An aluminized screen does not need an ion-trap magnet.
9. The shadow mask in a color picture tube is part of the electron gun.
10. Lead and leaded glass are used for x-ray shielding.
11. The picture tube is a vacuum tube.

12. The deflection yoke has four coils in two pairs for horizontal and vertical scanning.
13. A picture tube with deflection angle of 110° needs a yoke with a 70° angle.
14. The anode connection is usually the end pins of the tube base.
15. A cathode-to-heater short circuit in one gun usually causes a weak picture.

ESSAY QUESTIONS

1. Give an example of a type number for a color picture tube, and explain what the numbers and letters indicate.
2. What functions do the following parts of an electron gun serve? Heater, cathode, control grid ($G1$), screen grid ($G2$), and focus grid.
3. What functions do the phosphor screen and the shadow mask in a color picture tube serve?
4. Describe two types of phosphor screens for color picture tubes.
5. How is the anode or ultor high voltage applied to accelerate the electron beam to the screen?
6. Define deflection angle, crossover point, and afterglow for a picture tube.
7. What is the difference between magnetic and electrostatic focusing?
8. Name two methods of electrostatic focusing.
9. What is the difference between magnetic and electrostatic deflection?
10. Give some applications of the P1, P4, and P22 phosphors.
11. Explain briefly the purpose of convergence and color purity adjustments for a color picture tube.
12. Describe briefly an arrangement for projection television. Why is brightness the main problem?
13. Compare the delta and in-line types of electron gun for color picture tubes.
14. Why can the anode retain its high voltage after the set is turned off?
15. How would you correct the problem of **(a)** tilted raster, **(b)** a raster that is off center?
16. What two precautions should you take when installing a picture tube?
17. What is meant by *neck shadow?*
18. List two differences between the Sony Trinitron and a delta-gun color picture tube.
19. What are two possible causes of no brightness on the screen of the picture tube?
20. What is meant by *phosphor masking?* How does it improve the picture contrast?
21. List two signs of weak cathode emission.
22. Name two problems with picture tubes other than weak emission.

SPECIAL QUESTIONS

1. What is the difference between an implosion and an explosion?
2. Explain how you would check a picture tube for an open-circuit heater.
3. Name one advantage and one disadvantage of projection television.
4. List at least three ways in which a picture tube is different from a loudspeaker and one way they are similar.

ANSWERS TO TEST POINT QUESTIONS

4-1 **a.** 19 in.
b. 90°
c. 6.3 V

4-2 **a.** 30 kV
b. 2000 pF
c. F

4-3 **a.** P4 and P22
b. T
c. Green

4-4 **a.** Control grid *G*1
b. Ultor, or anode
c. Ultor, or anode

4-5 **a.** First
b. Low-voltage focus
c. T

4-6 **a.** Pincushion distortion
b. *H* scanning
c. T
d. Too far back

4-7 **a.** T
b. F
c. T
d. T

4-8 **a.** T
b. T
c. F

4-9 **a.** T
b. T

4-10 **a.** F
b. T

4-11 **a.** T
b. F

4-12 **a.** T
b. T
c. T

5

SETUP ADJUSTMENTS FOR COLOR PICTURE TUBES

Figure 5-1*a* shows a typical mounting assembly for a color picture tube in the receiver cabinet. This example is for a delta-gun tube with a phosphor-dot screen. The external magnetic components on the neck of the tube have to be adjusted to set up the picture tube. Included are the deflection yoke against the wide bell; the convergence magnet assembly for red, green, or blue; and the color purity magnetic rings. All these components are adjusted for correct color purity and convergence. An example for in-line guns is shown in Fig. 5-1*b*.

Also shown is the external magnetic shield with a wrap-around degaussing coil. The shield reduces the effect of the earth's magnetic field on the electron beams. The degaussing coil is used to demagnetize the steel elements in the picture tube, particularly the shadow mask. More details of the setup adjustments needed for proper operation of color picture tubes are explained in the following sections:

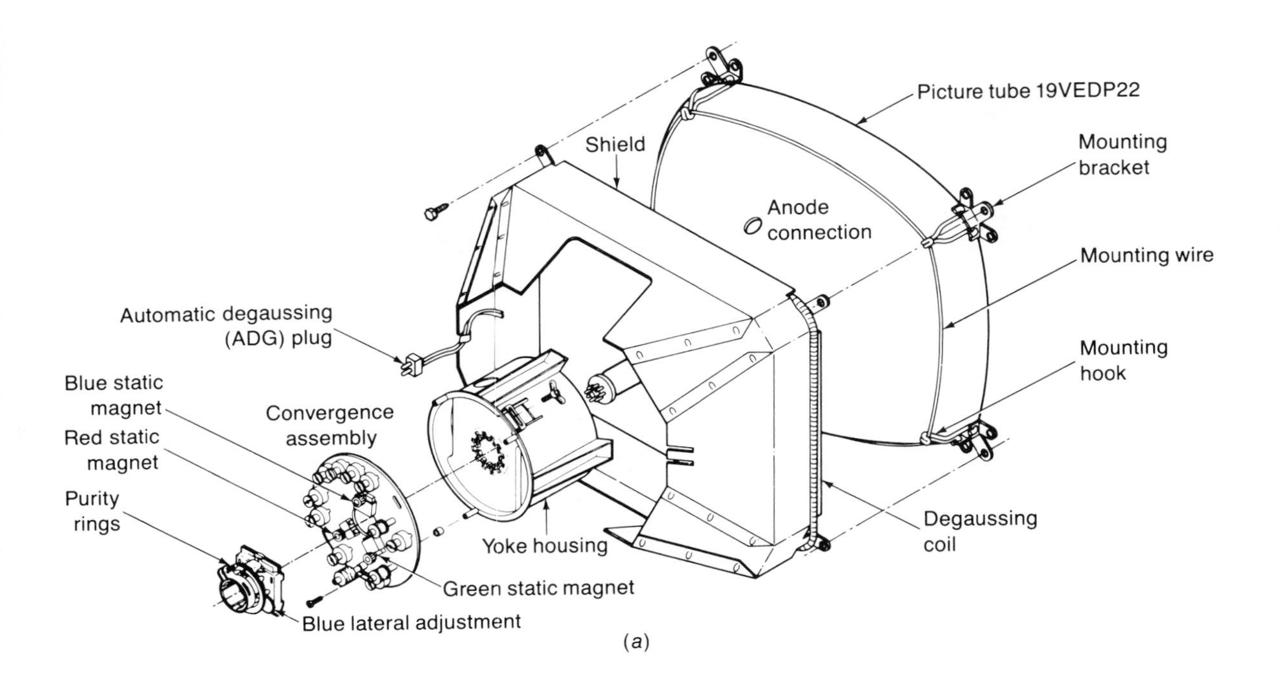

(*a*)

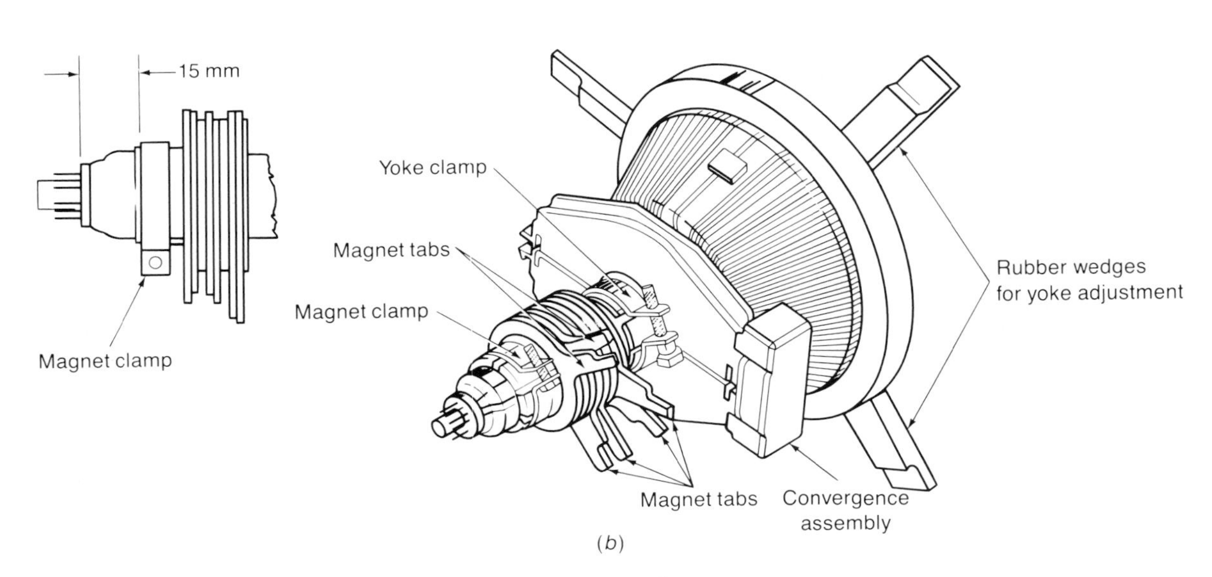

(*b*)

Fig. 5-1 Mounting assembly for color picture tubes. (*a*) Tube with delta guns and phosphor-dot trios. (*b*) Assembly for tube with in-line guns.

5-1 BEAM-LANDING ADJUSTMENTS FOR COLOR PURITY

The beam-landing adjustments are made to locate the deflection centers for all three electron beams at the precise points used for the lighthouse tubes (see Sec. 4-7) at the time of manufacture of the picture tube. When the beam landing is correct, the electrons from the gun designated as red strike only the red phosphor, for example, for the red primary. With the other two guns biased out of operation, you see a pure red raster. There is no contamination of other colors at any point on the screen. Bear in mind that the terms *red gun, green gun,* and *blue gun* are for identification only. The guns all look the same, and all electrons are the same, without any color. The designation *red gun* only identifies the electron gun that produces light from the red phosphor on the screen.

When the color purity adjustments are correct, activating the red, green, and blue guns in sequence will produce pure red, green, and blue rasters. With all three guns on and the beam currents balanced correctly, the raster is a uniform, neutral white.

There are two basic steps in setting the beam-landing adjustment correctly: moving the color purity magnet and moving the deflection yoke.

1. First, the electron beams are aimed by the color purity magnet. It is mounted behind the yoke toward the tube socket. The magnetic field of the rings acts as a centering control, so that all three beams can be aimed at their correct deflection centers.
2. Second, the deflection yoke is moved along the long axis of the tube to place the deflection centers at the exact correct distance from the shadow mask.

Note that good color purity will be difficult—and maybe impossible—to achieve unless the static convergence is approximately correct and the picture tube is demagnetized.

TURNING OFF THE GUNS Only one electron gun is on, usually for red, when the color purity adjustments are made. To turn off the other two guns temporarily, consult the service manual, since different methods are used.

If separate screen-grid voltage controls are provided for each gun, they can be used to turn off the guns. Without *G*2 voltage, the gun does not produce the beam current.

Older receivers could use the gun-killer switches provided with some color-bar generators. These switches bias off the control-grid to kill the beam current. However, they should not be used for newer receivers in which the *G*1 connections are common to all three guns.

Some receivers have separate plug connectors for the three cathode leads. One connector can be opened to turn off the electron gun.

Some newer color-bar generators provide blank raster signals for the three primary colors. These can be used with any receiver.

CENTERING THE RED CLOUD Red is the color often used to make the initial color purity adjustments. The reason is that red has been the least efficient phosphor, requiring a much larger beam current to bring it up to balance with blue and green light output. Thus an error in red would show up more readily because of the higher beam current. Today, though, green or blue may be suggested by the manufacturer for color purity adjustments. With in-line guns, the logical choice is the color for the center beam, usually green.

To minimize trial-and-error adjustments between the color purity magnet and yoke settings, first the yoke is set to the extreme position of its range. It is pushed either all the way forward against the bell of the tube or all the way back toward the socket. Often there are slotted openings at the sides of the plastic yoke housing with wing nuts on the protruding studs. The yoke inside the housing can be moved along the slots. A clamp on the assembly must be loosened to allow the yoke to slide forward or backward.

The large error in yoke position creates huge errors in beam landing at the edges of the screen. At the center, however, where the deflection current is going through zero, the beam landing is not affected by the yoke position at all. Therefore, only the center of the screen is watched for this part of the adjustment. A red cloud should appear near the middle of the screen, as shown in color plate III. The cloud is approximately circular. Second, the color purity neck magnet is adjusted to move the red cloud to the center of the screen.

The color purity assembly has two magnetic rings, which can be turned with the tabs shown in Fig. 5-2, to center all three beams. When the tabs are together, there is no net magnetic field to shift the position of the beam. Spreading the tabs produces a stronger field for a greater effect in positioning. You can turn either ring or both together to move the beams up or down or diagonally.

The color purity magnetic rings are adjusted to move the red cloud to the precise center of the screen. This procedure for the beam-landing adjustment is independent of the yoke position.

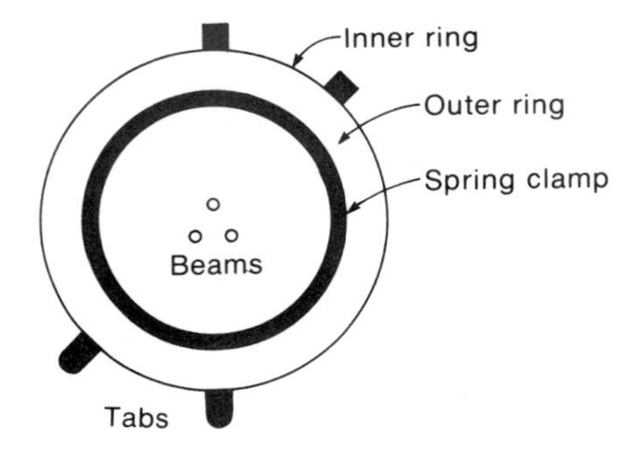

Fig. 5-2 Construction of color purity magnet.

RESETTING THE YOKE This step is the final adjustment for color purity. Move the yoke opposite to the direction in which it was purposely misadjusted. Locate the position where the cloud spreads out to fill the screen uniformly with the one color. Check the color purity for the other two colors by activating the guns, one at a time. Usually, when the red purity is good, the purity of the other colors is even better. Then all clamps may be tightened to hold the adjustments at the correct position.

Note that many types of in-line picture tubes have a special deflection yoke that is part of the convergence setup. These adjustments are explained in Sec. 5-3.

CHECKING COLOR PURITY WITH COLOR STRIPES The color purity adjustments are basically the same for all tricolor picture tubes, but the observations can be different. In the Sony Trinitron, for example, there is little beam-landing error in the vertical direction, since the slots and stripes are continuous from top to bottom. A vertical error in beam landing still puts the unshadowed beam on the same stripe, but just a little higher or lower. Then when the deflection yoke is displaced, a central vertical bar of the selected primary color appears, instead of the circular cloud. Next the color purity magnet is set to center the bar, left to right. Color plate IV shows this adjustment for green.

SUMMARY OF COLOR PURITY ADJUSTMENTS In short, there are just two definite steps:

1. With the deflection yoke too far back or too far forward, turn the color purity magnet to center the red cloud on the screen.
2. Set the yoke to the position where the red cloud fills the screen uniformly over the entire area.

This procedure applies exactly to the case of red purity with a phosphor-dot screen.

Test Point Questions 5-1

Answers at End of Chapter

Answer True or False.

a. The color purity magnet serves as a centering adjustment.

b. The color purity and beam-landing adjustments are the same.

c. The color purity magnet moves only the red beam.

d. The color purity is adjusted for the raster, one color at a time.

5-2 DEGAUSSING COLOR PICTURE TUBES

Degaussing means "demagnetizing." The name comes from the gauss unit, which measures flux density. The purpose of degaussing is to remove the magnetic flux from metals that have become magnetized. In color receivers, the steel chassis and its supports, the internal frame that holds the shadow mask, and the mask itself are all subject to induced magnetism. These local magnetic fields can affect the path of electrons in the picture tube, causing errors in beam landing that result in contamination of the color purity. For this reason, loudspeakers, toys, and other devices containing magnets should be kept away from a color receiver. However, one PM field is unavoidable—the earth's magnetic field in which we are all immersed. Terrestrial magnetism is the main reason why degaussing is necessary for color picture tubes.

With a monochrome picture tube, magnetization is no problem. For color tubes, though, the magnetization affects the color purity and convergence for the three electron beams. Before these adjustments are made, the set should be degaussed manually by using the type of coil shown in Fig. 5-3.

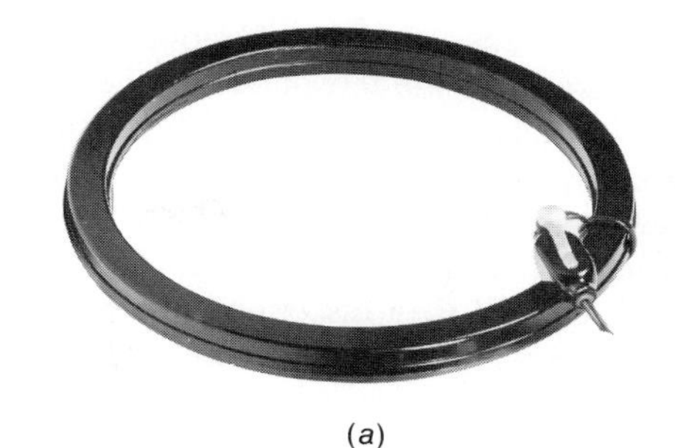

(*a*)

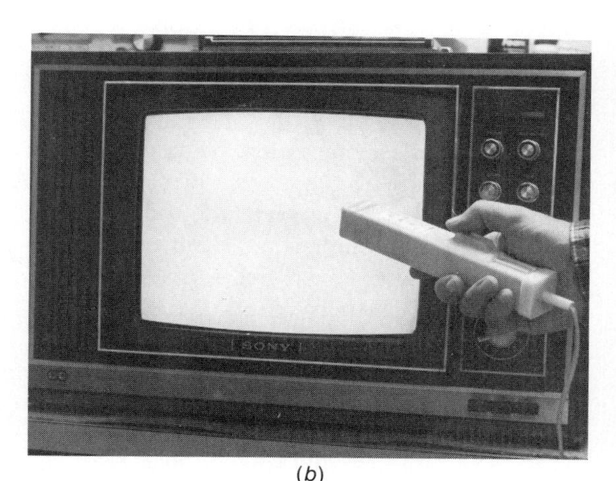

(*b*)

Fig. 5-3 Degaussing coil. (*a*) Ring type. (*b*) Iron-core type being used to degauss picture tube.

In the degaussing technique, a strong ac field is produced by 60-Hz current from the power line. In general, the principle is to provide a varying magnetic field, which has an average value of zero, and then slowly remove the field.

The requirements for degaussing are typically a 2-A current through 450 turns of No. 20 wire, with a coil diameter of 12 in. [305 mm], as in Fig. 5-3*a*. This coil produces a magnetomotive force of 900 ampere-turns. The type shown in Fig. 5-3*b* produces a stronger field, but it is more concentrated.

USING A DEGAUSSING COIL Plug the coil into an ac outlet, and turn on the switch. Hold the coil close to the screen and move it around slowly, parallel to the screen and to the top and sides of the cabinet. Do this a few times to cover the entire area. Then, to reduce the field to zero gradually, withdraw the coil from the set, as far as the power cord will reach. Lay the coil flat on the floor, and then disconnect the power.

Under no conditions should the power be cut off while the coil is near the shadow mask of the picture tube. The current might be interrupted at or near its peak value. Then a strong magnetic field would be induced in the shadow mask by the sharp drop in current, which is the opposite of what you want.

The receiver can be either off or on during the degaussing. With the set on, you see beautiful color patterns on the screen as the coil is moved.

Degaussing does more than remove the previously induced field. It also builds in a local magnetic field that partially offsets the effect of the earth's field. For this reason, the receiver should be degaussed while it is facing in the same direction as that used for actual viewing. Otherwise, the built-in field would be a hindrance if the receiver were turned 90° after it had been degaussed.

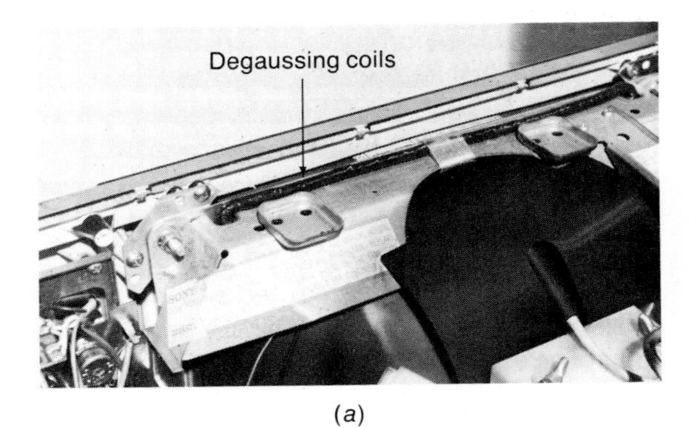

(*a*)

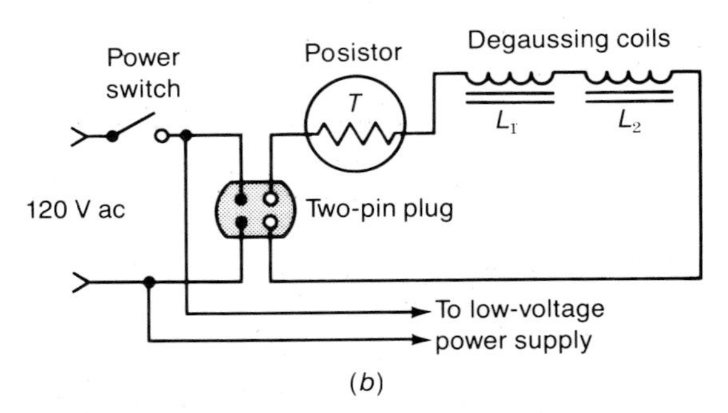

(*b*)

Fig. 5-4 Automatic degaussing (ADG) system. (*a*) Coils around wide bell of picture tube. (*b*) ADG circuit connected to ac power line. The posistor is a temperature-dependent resistor with a large positive temperature coefficient.

AUTOMATIC DEGAUSSING (ADG) The ADG circuit is designed to compensate for the earth's magnetic field, no matter which way the set is facing. By this method the picture tube is demagnetized automatically each time the receiver is turned on. A set of degaussing coils is built into the tube support harness, at the top, bottom, and sides of the screen. See Fig. 5-4*a*. A strong current from the ac input passes through these coils when the set is first turned on. Then the current decreases rapidly to a negligible value in a fraction of a second.

Control of the degaussing current is achieved by a special temperature-dependent resistor called a *posistor* in series with the coils, as shown in the ADG circuit in Fig. 5-4*b*. The posistor is practically a short circuit when cold but has a high *R* when it is heated by the degaussing current. As a result, there is a high value of *I* for a burst of degaussing current and then a small idling current. Since the resistor is very hot to the touch, it is mounted on the tube shield, away from other components.

Usually you can hear the degaussing action taking place when a color TV set is first turned on. There is a short "chung" sound like the buzz of iron-core laminations that last for a fraction of a second. The effects are not visible on the screen because degaussing is finished long before the cathodes of the picture tube reach the emission temperature.

Test Point Questions 5-2

Answers at End of Chapter

a. Should degaussing be done before or after the color purity adjustments?
b. Is the degaussing done with direct current or 60-Hz alternating current?
c. Does the ADG circuit have a high or low current when the receiver is first turned on?

5-3 CONVERGENCE ADJUSTMENTS

The color purity magnet adjusts all three beams at the same time to obtain pure red, green, and blue colors. However, a refinement is needed to aim each beam individually so that the three beams meet at the same point on the screen. These adjustments to achieve the registration of the three colors to produce white are called *convergence.*

Poor convergence shows up as color fringes at the edges of objects in the picture, as shown in color plate II. The fringes can be at the left or right and top or bottom. Misconvergence will not be seen on a blank raster unless the edges are visible.

As a comparison of color purity and convergence adjustments, note that the color purity adjustment is for solid color in the raster and the background in the picture. Convergence is for the picture only. The color purity magnet adjusts all three beams, but convergence adjustments are provided for each color individually. The final test of good convergence is the presence of white dots without color fringing. Actually, all the setup adjustments for a color picture tube are made for good white. The white is the most difficult color of all because it is made with red, green, and blue.

White dots or lines on a black background, provided by a signal generator such as the one shown in Fig. 5-5, are best for checking convergence error. This test instrument is called a *pattern generator,* or *color-bar generator.* It provides signals for:

1. Small, white dots in horizontal rows and vertical columns
2. A crosshatch pattern of horizontal and vertical white lines
3. Ten vertical color bars

This generator also can produce a single dot or cross at the exact center of the picture. This pattern is useful in locating the midscreen area for beam-landing adjustments.

The reason for color fringing is the lack of registration of the three primary colors. Misconvergence of a single primary color results in two color fringes on a white dot. For example, if red is displaced to the right, the right edge of the white dot will show a red fringe. Also, the left edge of the dot will be missing red, which shows as cyan. The cyan fringe equals white minus red. Also the fringes can be above and below the white dot.

The convergence control for individual beam

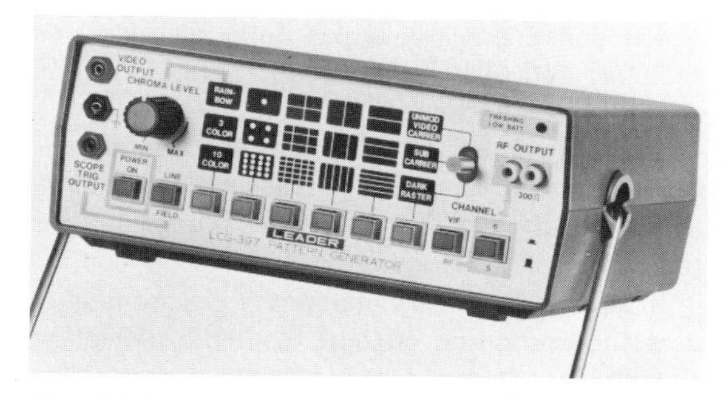

Fig. 5-5 Signal generator provides dot, crosshatch, and color-bar test signals for TV servicing. Modulated RF output on channel 5 or 6. (*Leader Instruments Corp.*)

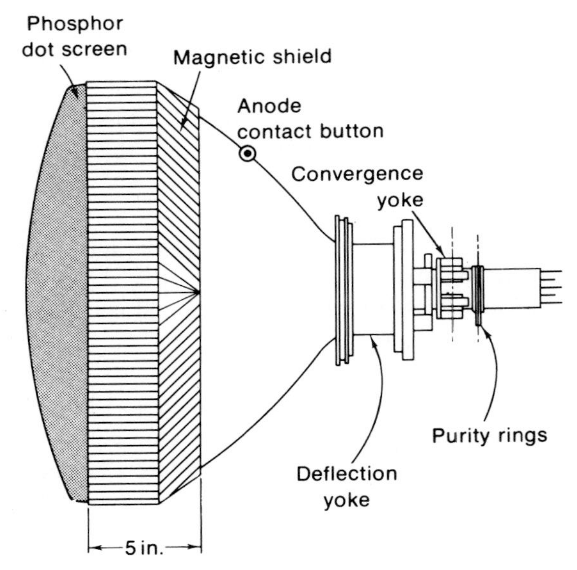

Fig. 5-6 Convergence components on neck of picture tube.

alignment is achieved magnetically, by internal magnetic pole pieces built into the gun assembly. Magnetic flux is coupled into these internal pole pieces, through the glass neck, from an external magnetic assembly called the *convergence yoke.* It is mounted just behind the deflection yoke and forward of the color purity magnet, as shown in Figs. 5-1 and 5-6.

The convergence yoke has three magnets, one each for red, green, and blue. Blue is usually at the top or bottom of the delta.

The adjustment of the permanent magnets is called *static convergence,* because the magnetic field is steady. Static convergence is adjusted for the center of the picture.

In addition, each coil magnet or electromagnet uses the correction current from the deflection circuits for *dynamic convergence.* The current can be varied by controls on a separate convergence board. Dynamic convergence is adjusted for the top, bottom, and left and right edges of the picture.

Test Point Questions 5-3

Answers at End of Chapter

a. Is a solid red raster a check for good color purity or for convergence?

b. Are small, white dots in the picture used for color purity or convergence adjustments?

c. Is color fringing on the edges of the picture a sign of misconvergence or an insufficient video signal drive?

5-4 STATIC CONVERGENCE

Figure 5-7 shows the triple electron gun for a delta tube. The internal pole pieces for convergence are mounted on the forward surface of the *G*4 ultor cup. The external convergence yoke that is mounted over the internal pole pieces is shown in Fig. 5-8. The three magnets in a delta are shown in Fig. 5-8*a,* and Fig. 5-8*b* is a simpli-

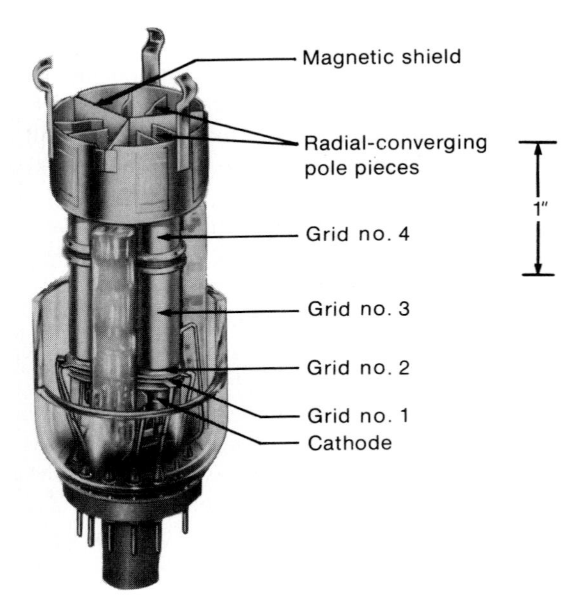

Fig. 5-7 Three electron guns in delta assembly. (*RCA*)

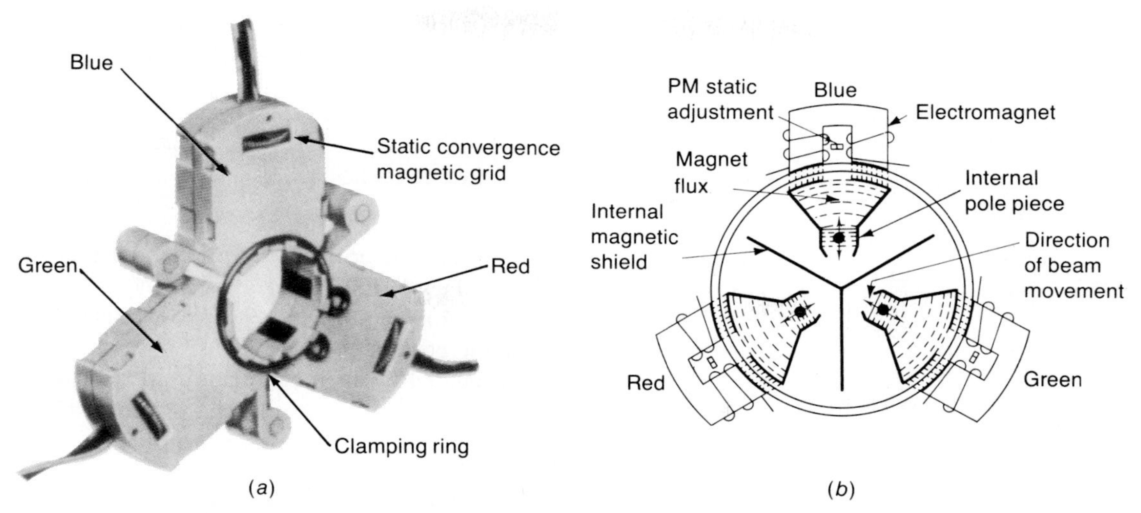

Fig. 5-8 External convergence yoke for a delta-gun picture tube. (*a*) Red, green, and blue magnets around opening for glass neck of picture tube. (*b*) Simplified cross section showing flux lines of magnets.

fied cross-sectional drawing which illustrates the magnetic flux lines. Note the direction of flux shown where the dotted lines cross the black dots representing the electron beams. Each beam moves at right angles to the magnetic field lines. Therefore, the top beam for blue moves up and down as the field is varied or reversed in polarity. The other two beams move in a line 30° from the horizontal, as shown by the diagonal arrows.

It is much simpler to converge picture tubes with in-line guns because all three beams are in the same horizontal plane. However, a system of internal and external magnets still must be used. These magnets are mounted on the forward surface of the gun assembly. The magnetic assembly is designed to have minimum effect on the central beam, usually green. Figure 5-9 shows the external convergence yoke for a typical in-line tube. Two rotatable PM magnets on either side couple a variable magnetic flux to the internal pole pieces. These adjustments for red and blue bend the outer beams to converge with the green beam, for horizontal convergence. In addition, two magnets at the top couple a horizontal magnetic field into the vicinity of the outer beams. These adjustments move the beams vertically to compensate for a beam that is above or below the common horizontal plane.

The Sony Trinitron is an in-line tube that uses an electrostatic method for bending the outer beams to converge with the central beam. A po-

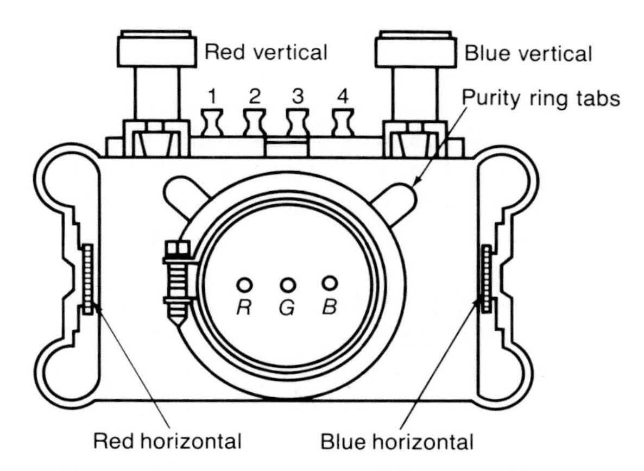

Fig. 5-9 Convergence yoke and color purity assembly for an in-line picture tube. *R*, *G*, and *B* indicate electron beams.

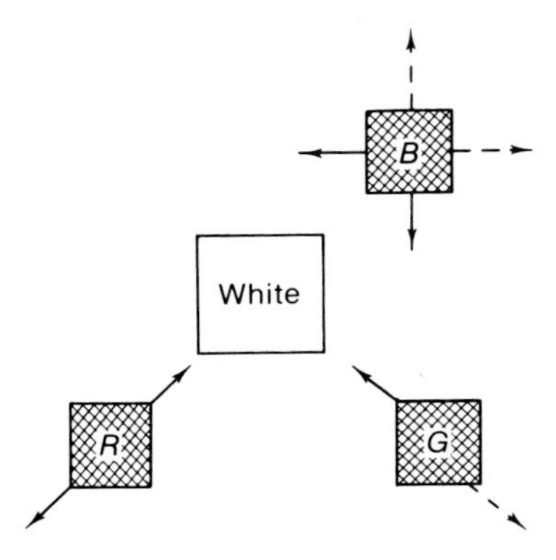

Fig. 5-10 Effect of static convergence magnets in moving color dots to produce white.

tentiometer control varies the voltage on the outer deflection plates. Additional trim adjustments permit fine control of the vertical beam alignment. In some cases, a coil mounted on the neck of the tube imparts a twist to the outer beams that causes them to rotate about the central green beam. Current in this "neck-twist" coil is set to put all three beams in a plane parallel to the horizontal axis. The adjustment is made for best convergence on a horizontal white line through the center of the picture.

In general, the adjustments for static convergence are made by using white dots or a crosshatch pattern for the picture and confining attention to the center of the screen only. For delta-gun tubes, red and green are adjusted first, to form a yellow dot. The diagonal motion is illustrated in Fig. 5-10. The blue is lowered or raised vertically to register perfectly with yellow, to make a white dot at the center, without any color fringes.

However, another degree of freedom in motion is needed. If blue is not directly over or under the yellow dot, the blue static magnet will not be able to achieve the convergence for a white dot. Therefore, one more adjustment, called the *blue lateral magnet,* is provided. This external magnet is mounted close to the tube socket to move the blue beam horizontally. By adjusting all the static magnets, perfect convergence can be produced for the white dot at the center of the screen.

Test Point Questions 5-4

Answers at End of Chapter

a. Is static convergence done for the center or the edges of the screen?

b. Are permanent magnets used for static or dynamic convergence?

c. In Fig. 5-10, which color is moved vertically?

5-5 DYNAMIC CONVERGENCE

Once the beams have been converged at midscreen, a fixed convergence distance has been set up between each electron gun and the screen. As the beams are deflected from center, this fixed distance forms a spherical surface in which convergence is maintained. However, this sphere has a larger curvature than that of the screen itself. Therefore, as the beams are deflected toward the edges of the screen, they converge short of the screen, cross one another, and hit the screen misconverged. The result is shown by the crosshatch pattern in Fig. 5-11.

To correct this misconvergence, it is necessary to spread the beams, so that they converge at a longer distance with more deflection toward the screen edges. The correction is made by modulating the static convergence magnetic fields with an ac component at both the vertical and horizontal scan rates. The ac field is provided by current in the windings of the convergence yoke. Refer to Fig. 5-8 to see the construction. Two coils are used on each pole piece, one for V deflection signals at 60 Hz and the other for H deflection signals at 15,750 Hz.

The waveform for the convergence correction current is parabolic. It is clamped to zero at midscreen, to prevent alteration of the static adjust-

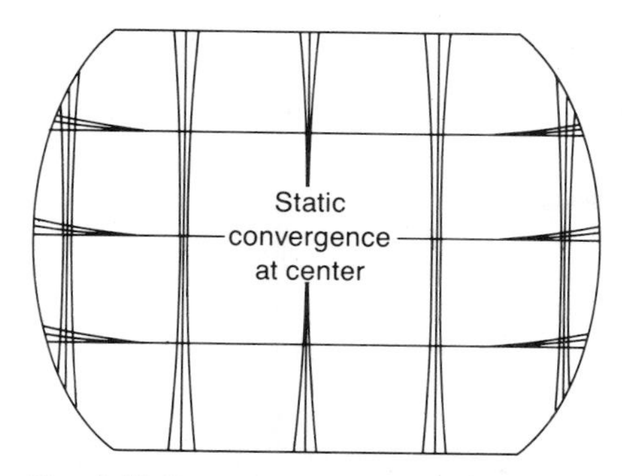

Fig. 5-11 Correct static convergence at center of screen but there is no dynamic convergence correction.

ments. A parabolic waveform is ideal because it is symmetric at both ends.

In addition, a variable sawtooth component is added to the parabolic waveshape. This effect "tilts" the waveform, to pile up more correction at one end at the expense of the other end. The tilt corrects for the fact that all three beams are not on a common axis. For example, the blue beam in a delta gun must travel farther than the other beams to reach the bottom of the screen. Furthermore, the tilt adjustment also can correct for a faceplate that is not precisely at a right angle to the long axis of the picture tube. Figure 5-12 shows how the sawtooth waveshape added to a parabola can tilt the combined waveform.

A similar waveform developed from the horizontal deflection circuits is used for side-to-side dynamic convergence. In practice, a sine wave is used, because it is easier to generate and close enough to the parabolic waveshape.

The dynamic convergence is quite complex for delta-gun tubes because there are so many adjustments. There are 12 controls total for amplitude and tilt, vertical and horizontal, for all three guns. All the controls are on a convergence board assembly, as shown in Fig. 5-13. They are adjusted while the observer watches the crosshatch pattern, to converge the lines at the top, bottom, and left and right edges of the screen. The controls are usually in a bridge circuit, to make the adjustments a little easier. One end of the pattern can be converged without affecting the other end too much. An example of how convergence controls are used is shown in Fig. 5-14.

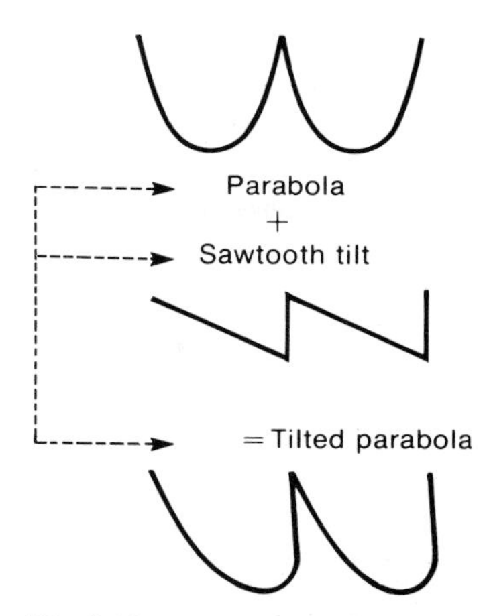

Fig. 5-12 How tilted parabolic waveform is produced for dynamic convergence correction.

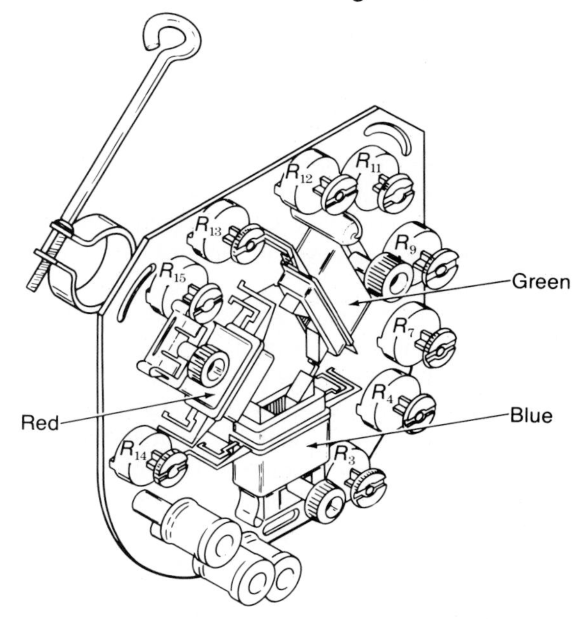

Fig. 5-13 Convergence yoke and board assembly that mounts on neck of picture tube.

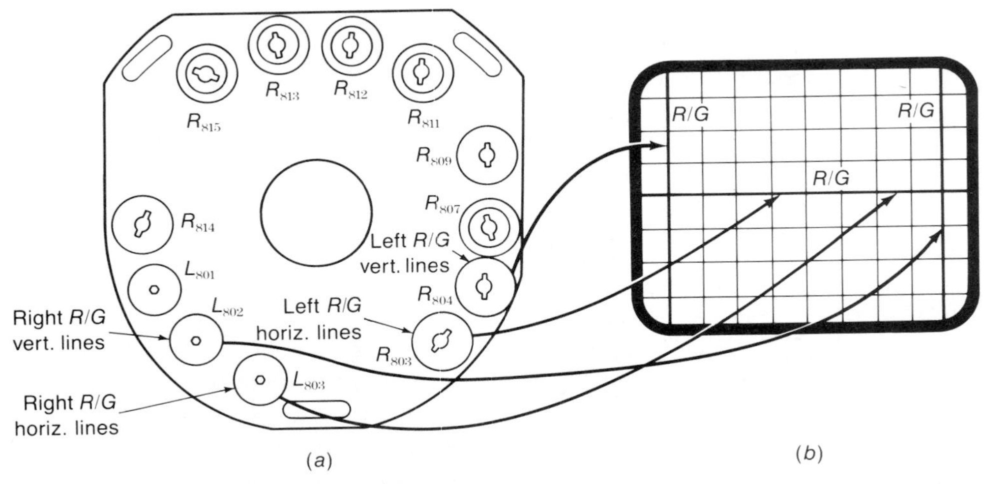

Fig. 5-14 (*a*) Controls for dynamic convergence. (*b*) Effect on crosshatch pattern. (*RCA*)

In practice, red and green are adjusted first, and blue is turned off to avoid confusion. When a good yellow crosshatch pattern is achieved, the blue is activated and adjusted to form a converged crosshatch of white lines. Note that the blue gun is usually at the top or bottom of the delta.

Dynamic convergence for in-line guns is much simpler to achieve. Again, parabolic or sine waveforms are used, but to spread only the outer two beams. In some cases, only horizontal dynamic convergence is necessary. Convergence in the vertical direction is achieved by shaping the vertical deflection field.

In some receivers, a special deflection yoke includes features for dynamic convergence. No electrical adjustments are provided, but the yoke position is critical. Clamps or wedges are used to align the magnetic field of the yoke with respect to the electron-beam axis. The yoke is tilted to achieve the correct alignment while the crosshatch pattern at the edges of the screen is observed. An example is shown in Fig. 5-1*b*.

The general procedure for setting up a picture tube with in-line guns is as follows:

1. Set the static convergence at midscreen.
2. Set the color purity.
3. Reset the static convergence.
4. Set the *H* dynamic amplitude and tilt controls for best convergence at the sides.
5. Set the *V* dynamic amplitude and tilt controls, if they are used, for best convergence at top and bottom.
6. Set the yoke tilt, if provision is made for this adjustment, for best convergence at the edges of the screen.
7. Reset the static convergence if necessary.

Test Point Questions 5-5

Answers at End of Chapter

Answer True or False.

a. The crosshatch pattern in Fig. 5-11 shows good dynamic convergence.

b. The basic waveform for dynamic convergence is the parabola or half a sine wave.

c. In Fig. 5-14, the control R_{804} is for vertical dynamic convergence.

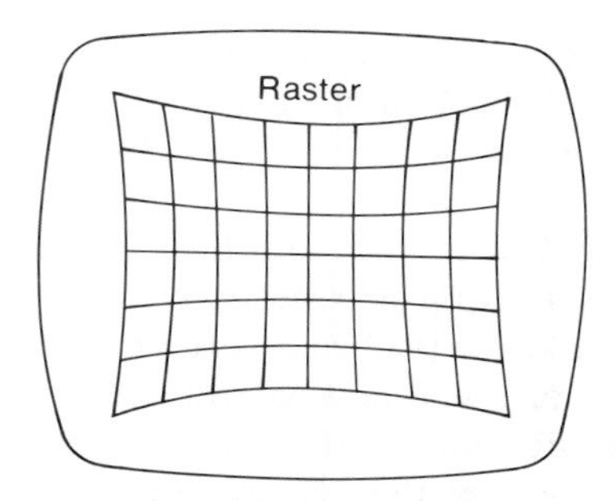

Fig. 5-15 Pincushion distortion of the raster.

5-6 PINCUSHION CORRECTION

The pincushion shape of the raster is shown in Fig. 5-15. The reason for this distortion is that the corners of the screen are farther from the deflection center for the electron beams, compared with the midscreen. Then the beams are moved more horizontally and vertically at the extreme angles of deflection for the corners. The pincushion distortion is more severe with wide-angle tubes of 90° or more.

In monochrome picture tubes, the pincushion effect is corrected by small, permanent magnets mounted on the housing of the deflection yoke. These pincushion magnets cannot be used with color picture tubes, however. They would affect the three beams by different amounts, creating more problems with color purity and convergence. Therefore, the dynamic pincushion correction is used with color picture tubes.

The pincushion correction signals, labeled PIN, are applied to the deflection yoke. The horizontal scanning coils use the correction current to straighten the sides of the raster. Also, the top and bottom are straightened by the PIN correction current in the vertical scanning coils.

Usually there are no adjustments for the side pincushion correction. The vertical PIN controls, marked TB for top and bottom, are factory-set and seldom need adjustment. If necessary, though, the adjustments can be made on a cross-hatch pattern. Adjust the PIN phase control to move any curvature of the horizontal lines to the middle. Then adjust the PIN amplitude control for straight horizontal lines at the top and bottom of the raster.

Note that design improvements in deflection yokes and picture tubes have been effective in reducing the amount of pincushion distortion. Therefore, little correction is required in modern receivers.

Test Point Questions 5-6

Answers at End of Chapter

a. Are pincushion magnets used for monochrome or color picture tubes?

b. Is the abbreviation TB for vertical or horizontal pincushion correction?

5-7 VIDEO SIGNAL DRIVE

For any picture tube, the beam current and the resultant light output are controlled by the voltage applied between *G*1 and the cathode. This effect can be seen from the characteristic curve shown in Fig. 5-16 for a typical electron gun. On the horizontal axis, the control-grid voltage for *G*1 is marked with values from 0 to −80 V. These voltages indicate the potential difference between *G*1 and the cathode. The anode current, corresponding to the beam current, goes up to 1.5 mA on the vertical axis. The curve shows how much beam current is produced by various grid voltages. The high voltage for the anode is fixed at its specified value.

For typical values, a negative *G*1 potential of −80 V cuts off the beam current. This cutoff corresponds to black in the picture.

For −60 V at *G*1, the beam current is about 0.1 mA. This condition is indicated by the bias

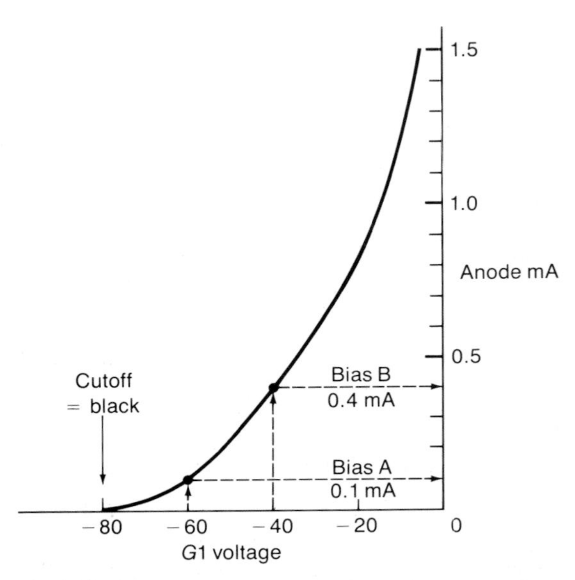

Fig. 5-16 The dc bias *B* at −40 V produces more beam current and higher brightness than bias *A* at −60 V.

value A in Fig. 5-16. Reducing the bias to −40 V raises the beam current to about 0.4 mA, as shown for the bias value B. More beam current produces more light output for white picture information. Note the following characteristics:

1. Decreasing the negative *G*1 voltage increases the beam current.
2. For a change of only about 33 percent in the *G*1 voltage, the beam current is four times greater, changing from 0.1 to 0.4 mA.

The curve becomes steeper (has a sharper slope) as the negative *G*1 voltage is decreased toward zero. This characteristic accounts for the gamma distortion of stretched whites which is introduced by the picture tube in reproducing the image.

It is important to realize that it is the voltage between *G*1 and the cathode that determines the beam current. Either element can be used as the reference, but the control grid must be negative with respect to the cathode. For example, *G*1 can be at +100 V with respect to the chassis ground, but if the cathode is at +140 V, the control grid is still 40 V more negative. The potential difference for V_{GK} is 100 − 140 = −40 V.

The overall effect in reproducing the picture information is to supply the ac video signal drive on a dc bias axis to vary the beam current. The dc bias is varied by the brightness control, usually located on the front panel of the receiver. The ac video signal is varied by the contrast or picture control.

BRIGHTNESS CONTROL This dc bias adjustment may supply negative voltage at *G*1, as shown in Fig. 5-17*a*, or positive voltage at the cathode, as in Fig. 5-17*b*. In both cases the grid-cathode bias equals −40 V. The same bias can be produced as the difference between two positive potentials, as in Fig. 5-17*c*. Here the grid-cathode bias is also −40 V, which is the difference in potential between 120 and 160 V.

The brightness control is set correctly when the blanking level of the composite video signal produces visual cutoff, or black, for the picture tube. Visual cutoff depends, to some extent, on room lighting. The brightness of the picture should be greater to compensate for ambient light shining on the screen. For this reason, some receivers have an automatic brightness circuit. A photosensitive device on the cabinet senses the amount of ambient light and automatically sets the dc bias on the picture tube for the correct brightness.

COLOR VIDEO DRIVE For a long time, the usual method of driving the tricolor picture tube was as follows:

1. The *R* − *Y*, *G* − *Y*, and *B* − *Y* signals were applied to the three control grids in positive polarity.
2. The −*Y* signal, for negative polarity, was applied to all three cathodes.

Then the picture tube served as a matrix circuit

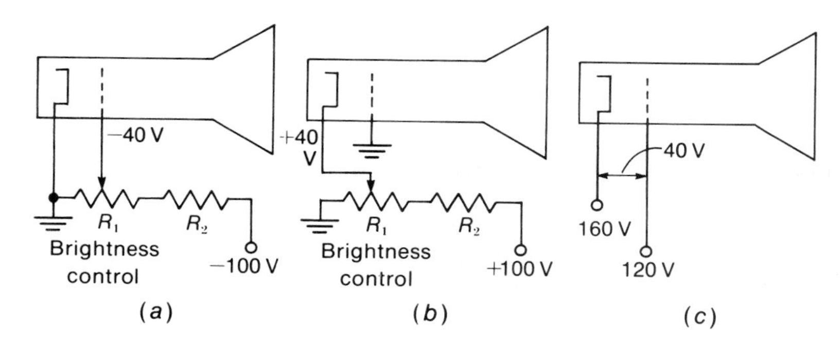

Fig. 5-17 Methods of dc bias adjustment for grid-cathode circuit of picture tube. (*a*) Negative grid bias of −40 V. (*b*) Positive cathode bias of +40 V. (*c*) Potential difference of 40 V, with grid negative with respect to cathode.

to produce the effect of red, green, and blue in the picture, in addition to the luminance information.

In newer receivers, though, color video and luminance signals are added in the video drive circuits. The output is negative *R, G,* and *B* signals applied to the three cathodes of the picture tube. The purpose is to keep the video signal circuits off the *G* 1 electrode. Internal arcing can be produced at the control grid because it is the most negative electrode.

A comparison between the cathode drive and the *G*1 drive for the picture tube is shown in Fig. 5-18. In Fig. 5-18*a,* the white video signal amplitudes make the control grid more positive or less negative. In Fig. 5-18*b,* the white video signal makes the cathode more negative. For both cases, peak white produces maximum beam current.

The actual amount of ac video signal drive required depends on the characteristics of the electron gun and the voltage applied to the screen grid (*G*2). As the *G*2 voltage is increased, the cutoff voltage of the electron gun also increases. Typical drive voltages range from 30 V p-p for a small-screen monochrome picture tube to 200 V p-p for large-screen color tubes using high values of *G*2 voltage.

INTERNAL BLANKING Retrace blanking is provided by the blanking level of the composite video signal. The blanking level should be at cutoff for black. In addition, though, practically all receivers use internal retrace blanking circuits. Pulses are developed from the vertical and horizontal deflection circuits to blank out the vertical and horizontal retraces. Because of internal blanking, normally you never see any retrace lines regardless of the brightness setting.

In one method of retrace blanking, positive blanking pulses are added to the composite video signal that is applied to the cathode in the picture tube. In another method, negative blanking pulses are used at the control grid. Both polarities cut off the beam current during retrace time. For those color tubes in which the control grid is common to all three guns, often the internal blanking is applied to the common *G*1 connection.

Test Point Questions 5-7

Answers at End of Chapter

a. Is a typical dc grid bias for a 19-in. picture tube −4 or −60 V?

b. Is a typical ac signal drive for a 19-in. picture tube 8 or 140 V p-p?

c. Does the brightness control vary the dc bias or the ac signal drive for the picture tube?

5-8 GRAY-SCALE TRACKING

In color picture tubes, the light output for red, green, and blue must be balanced to produce a

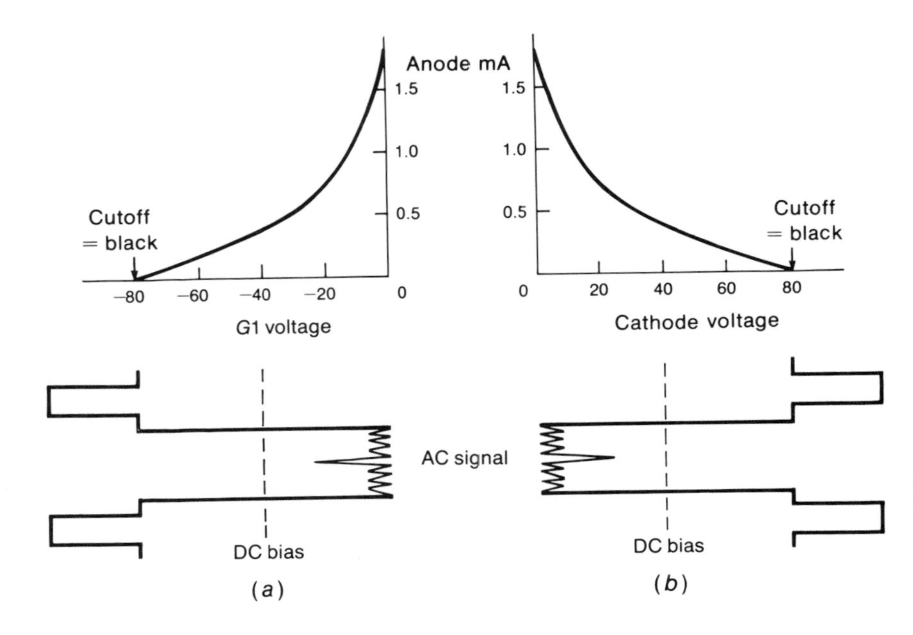

Fig. 5-18 How ac video signal varies beam current to reproduce the picture information. (*a*) Negative sync and positive white at the control grid. (*b*) Positive sync and negative white at the cathode.

neutral white, with the color signal turned off. Furthermore, the ratio of *RGB* needed to produce white must be maintained from high to low brightness values. This ability to keep the correct proportions from highlights to dark parts of the picture is called *gray-scale tracking.* If the tracking is not right, the color on the screen will change as the brightness control is varied. For instance, the raster may look a little too yellow at one brightness level and a little too blue at another brightness level. Furthermore, when the video signal is applied, the highlights of white in the picture might be a different color than the lowlights.

The gray-scale setup is also called the *color-temperature adjustment.* This term is based on the idea of producing white that corresponds to 9300 on the Kelvin temperature scale.

The results of the tracking adjustments are checked visually by observing the screen. Some experience is required to produce perfect tracking, but keep in mind the following:

1. The dc voltages are for the raster.
2. The ac signal voltages are for the picture. Remember that the monochrome picture is made with *R, G,* and *B* video signals.
3. Lowlights of dark gray in the picture depend on the cutoff characteristics of the electron guns, which are determined by dc voltages.
4. Highlights of white in the picture depend on the maximum beam current produced by the *R, G,* and *B* video drive signals.

The location of the *R, G,* and *B* drive controls on the rear apron of the chassis, for older receivers, can be seen by referring to Fig. 5-19. These controls adjust the proportions of the ac video signal for the three electron guns. Also shown in Fig. 5-19 are the *R, G,* and *B* screen-grid *G*2 controls. These adjustments vary the dc voltages to set the gun cutoff characteristics.

***R, G,* AND *B* CONTROLS FOR *G*1 AND *G*2** Older receivers with separate *G*1 and *G*2 controls can be made to track easily. First, all three guns are made to produce visual cutoff, at the minimum setting of the brightness control.

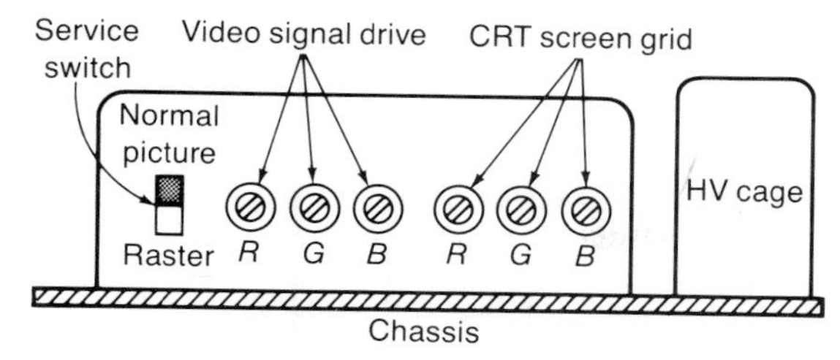

Fig. 5-19 *RGB* drive and screen-grid controls on rear apron of chassis.

These receivers usually have a NORMAL-SETUP switch on the rear apron of the chassis. In the SETUP position, vertical deflection is disabled and the video signal is removed to provide just a horizontal line on the screen. With the raster compressed into just one line, even a small amount of beam current produces visible light. Second, set the *R, G,* and *B* screen controls to produce a line that is barely visible for each primary color. This is the procedure for setting the cutoff characteristics.

Third, move the switch to NORMAL, for a full raster and video signal. Also turn up the brightness and contrast controls to normal. Set the *R, G,* and *B* video drive controls for neutral white in the highlights of the picture. One drive control, usually red, should be at maximum while you adjust the other two. In many cases, only two drive controls are provided, with the third fixed at maximum.

BACKGROUND CONTROLS Many picture tubes now have common connections for *G*1 and *G*2. In this case, each gun cannot be set independently for cutoff. Instead, the grid-cathode bias for two or three of the guns is trimmed at low settings of the *master brightness control,* which adjusts the common screen-grid (*G*2) voltage. The bias trimmers are the background controls.

To achieve gray-scale tracking, the color signal should be off and the brightness and contrast controls turned all the way down. Then set the master (*G*2) screen control to produce a dim monochrome picture. Trim the background controls for a neutral, colorless gray. If the picture appears purple, for instance, it needs more green. Either advance the green background or turn back the others.

Next, set the brightness and contrast for a normal picture. Adjust the video drive controls for neutral white in the highlights. To achieve good gray-scale tracking, some readjustments may be needed between the background and video drive controls for a neutral tone from the darkest to the lightest parts of the picture.

Test Point Questions 5-8

Answers at End of Chapter

a. Are the *R, G,* and *B* screen-grid adjustments set for visual cutoff or white highlights in the picture?

b. Are the *R, G,* and *B* video drive controls set for dark gray or white?

c. Are the background controls for the dc bias or the ac video signal?

d. Does the *G*2 master screen control vary the dc voltage or the ac video signal?

5-9 OVERALL SETUP ADJUSTMENTS

This general procedure indicates the sequence to follow in making the color purity, convergence, and gray-scale tracking adjustments.

1. Check the picture size and linearity, top to bottom and left to right. Make sure the focus is good and the centering is correct. Any changes will affect the dynamic convergence, so all these adjustments should be correct at the start.
2. Degauss the receiver.
3. Make a preliminary setting of static convergence at the center of the screen.

4. Set the color purity.
5. Reset the center static convergence.
6. Make the dynamic convergence adjustments.
7. Reset the center static convergence.
8. Using the background and screen controls, balance the lowlights in the picture for white.
9. Using the drive controls, balance the highlights for white in the picture.
10. Repeat steps 8 and 9, if necessary, for a neutral monochrome picture.

The receiver comes from the manufacturer with all the setup adjustments for the picture tube properly made. Once they are set, the adjustments are stable and seldom need to be changed, except when a new picture tube is installed.

Test Point Questions 5-9

Answers at End of Chapter

Answer True or False.

a. Degaussing is usually the last step in the setup adjustments.

b. The color purity is adjusted before the dynamic convergence.

c. Once the static convergence has been set, readjustments are never necessary.

SUMMARY

1. The color purity, or beam-landing, adjustment is made for uniform color in the raster.
2. Convergence adjustments are made with a signal generator that produces a picture with white dots or a crosshatch pattern. Poor convergence produces color fringes in the picture. See color plate II.
3. Static convergence adjustments are made by permanent magnets. The magnets adjust convergence at the center of the picture.
4. Dynamic convergence adjustments vary the correction current in the coils of the convergence yoke. The convergence at the edges of the picture is adjusted.
5. Degaussing means demagnetizing the picture tube with 60-Hz alternating current from the power line. The automatic degaussing (ADG) circuit demagnetizes the picture tube each time the receiver is turned on.
6. Pincushion correction signals can be inserted in series with the *V* and *H* coils of the deflection yoke, to straighten the edges of the raster.
7. Gray-scale tracking, or color-temperature, adjustments maintain neutral white from low to high levels of brightness.
8. Internal blanking is used in addition to the blanking pulses in the composite video signal.
9. A background control varies the dc bias for the picture tube.
10. The *R, G,* and *B* drive controls vary the amount of ac signal for the picture tube.
11. The NORMAL-SETUP switch removes the picture for adjustments on the raster alone, or just a horizontal line.
12. A color picture tube generally has *R, G,* and *B* video signals at the three cathodes, with positive sync polarity.

SELF-EXAMINATION

Answers at Back of Book

Answer True or False.

1. The color purity magnet usually is mounted against the wide bell of the picture tube.
2. Static convergence adjustments are made for the center of the picture.
3. A degaussing coil uses 15,750-Hz current from the horizontal output circuit.
4. A dot-bar generator can produce white dots, a white crosshatch pattern, and vertical color bars.
5. Internal blanking is not necessary in color receivers.
6. The *R*, *G*, and *B* screen controls affect the color of the raster.
7. A blue lateral magnet moves the blue in the horizontal direction.
8. A master brightness control adjusts the dc screen-grid voltage for the picture tube.
9. The gamma of 2.2 for the picture tube means that the white values are stretched.
10. The cathode drive for the picture tube requires a video signal with positive sync polarity.
11. A background control varies the amount of p-p video signal.
12. The screen controls adjust the cutoff characteristics of the red, green, and blue guns.

ESSAY QUESTIONS

1. Compare the color purity and convergence adjustments.
2. Compare static and dynamic convergence adjustments.
3. List three functions of a dot-bar signal generator.
4. What functions does the NORMAL-SETUP switch serve?
5. Why are convergence adjustments easier with the in-line gun than with a delta gun?
6. Why is degaussing done before making color purity and convergence adjustments?
7. What is the purpose of the ADG circuit?
8. What is the function of the *R*, *G*, and *B* screen-grid controls?
9. What is the function of the background control?
10. What are the functions of the *R*, *G*, and *B* drive controls?
11. What is meant by color-temperature adjustments?
12. How much video signal drive is needed for a 19-in. color picture tube?
13. Why are color video signals usually applied to the cathodes of the picture tube instead of to the control grids?

14. What polarity of video signal is needed for the cathode drive at the picture tube?
15. Refer to the picture tube characteristic curve in Fig. 5-16. **(a)** What is the grid-cathode cutoff voltage? **(b)** What is the gamma value for this curve?
16. Refer to the bias circuits in Fig. 5-17. What is the grid-cathode bias for all three circuits?
17. For a 19-in. color picture tube, list the typical values of heater voltage, heater current, grid-cathode bias, beam current, and anode voltage.
18. Compare the functions and required circuits for the contrast control and the brightness control.
19. Describe briefly how to make the gray-scale tracking adjustments.
20. What is the purpose of internal blanking? How is it applied to the picture tube?
21. The raster is tilted. What would you adjust?
22. The raster is too green. What would you adjust?
23. White lettering in the picture has blue fringes, always to the right. What would you adjust?
24. White in the picture does not remain neutral from low to high brightness levels. What adjustments are needed?

PROBLEMS

Answers to Odd-Numbered Problems at Back of Book

1. Refer to the picture tube characteristic curve in Fig. 5-16. **(a)** What is the value of the anode current for −20 V at $G1$? **(b)** What is it for −10 V at $G1$?
2. The cathode is at 240 V, and the control grid is at 190 V. Give the voltage and polarity of the bias from grid to cathode.
3. How much is the equivalent internal resistance of the electron beam with a 1.2-mA beam current at 25 kV?
4. How much p-p composite video signal will fit the graph in Fig. 5-16, with a blanking level of −80 V for $G1$ and peak white at 0 V?

SPECIAL QUESTIONS

1. Why is the effect of the earth's magnetic field important for color picture tubes but not monochrome tubes?
2. Explain the Kelvin scale for temperature measurements.
3. Compare the advantages and disadvantages of color picture tubes with an in-line gun or a delta gun.

ANSWERS TO TEST POINT QUESTIONS

5-1 **a.** T
b. T
c. F
d. T

5-2 **a.** Before
b. 60 Hz
c. High

5-3 **a.** Color purity
b. Convergence
c. Misconvergence

5-4 **a.** Center
b. Static
c. Blue

5-5 **a.** F
b. T
c. T

5-6 **a.** Monochrome
b. Vertical

5-7 **a.** −60 V
b. 140 V
c. DC bias

5-8 **a.** Visual cutoff
b. White
c. DC bias
d. DC voltage

5-9 **a.** F
b. T
c. F

6

SCANNING AND SYNCHRONIZING

The rectangular area of the picture tube screen scanned by the electron beam as it is deflected horizontally and vertically is called the *raster.* Figure 6-1 shows the illuminated scanning raster, without any picture information. With the video signal, the picture tube reproduces the picture on the raster.

In addition, the deflection for the raster must be synchronized with the picture. To time the scanning correctly, synchronizing pulses are included in the video signal. The total video signal has two parts—camera signal variations for the picture and synchronizing pulses for the scanning raster. Thus the video signal has the timing pulses needed to synchronize the picture information in terms of light, dark, and color values, with respect to the position on the screen in terms of horizontal and vertical deflection. More details are given in the following sections:

6-1 Sawtooth Waveform for Linear Scanning
6-2 Interlaced Scanning Pattern
6-3 Sample Frame of Interlaced Scanning
6-4 Flicker
6-5 Raster Distortions
6-6 Synchronizing Pulses
6-7 Scanning, Synchronizing, and Blanking Frequencies

Fig. 6-1 Scanning raster on screen of picture tube. The raster is not interlaced without *V* sync. The *V* retrace lines here are normally blanked out.

6-1 SAWTOOTH WAVEFORM FOR LINEAR SCANNING

As an example of linear scanning, consider the sawtooth waveshape in Fig. 6-2 as scanning current for an electromagnetic tube. This current can be for vertical or horizontal deflection. Let us assume that the peak value is 400 mA. If 100 mA is needed to produce a deflection of 5 in. [127 mm], then 400 mA will deflect the beam $4 \times 5 = 20$ in. [508 mm]. Furthermore, the linear rise on the sawtooth wave provides equal increases of 100 mA for each of the four equal time periods shown. Each additional 100 mA deflects the beam another 5 in. [127 mm].

HORIZONTAL SCANNING This linear rise of current in the horizontal deflection coils deflects the beam across the screen with a continuous, uniform motion for the trace from left to right. At the peak of the rise, the sawtooth wave reverses direction and decreases rapidly to its initial value. This fast reversal produces the *retrace,* or *flyback.*

The horizontal trace begins at the left edge of the raster. It ends at the right edge, where the flyback causes the beam to return to the left edge. See Fig. 6-3*a*. Note that "up" on the sawtooth wave corresponds to horizontal deflection to the right.

VERTICAL SCANNING This sawtooth current in the vertical deflection coils causes the electron beam to move from top to bottom of the raster. While the electron beam is being deflected horizontally, the vertical sawtooth deflection causes the beam to move downward with uniform speed. So the beam produces the horizontal lines one under the other.

The trace part of the sawtooth wave for vertical scanning deflects the beam to the bottom of the raster. Then the rapid vertical retrace returns

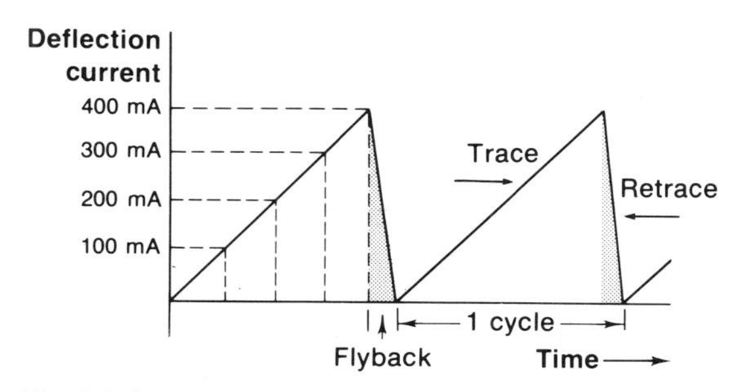

Fig. 6-2 Sawtooth scanning waveform, used for *H* and *V* deflection.

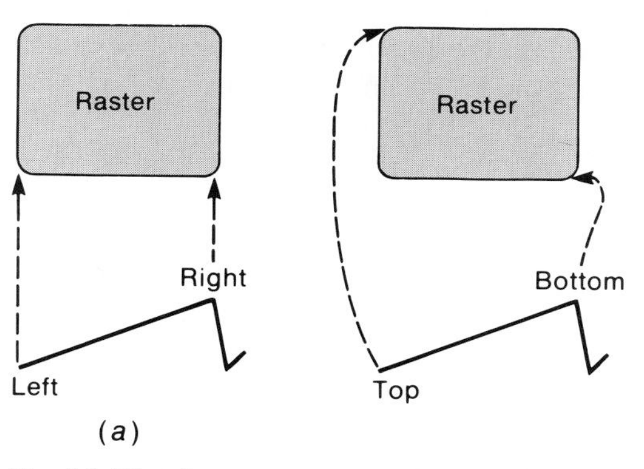

Fig. 6-3 Directions for trace and retrace on sawtooth scanning waveform. (*a*) *H* deflection. (*b*) *V* deflection.

the beam to the top. See Fig. 6-3*b*. Note that "up" on the sawtooth wave for vertical deflection corresponds to increasing current, which deflects the beam downward.

SCANNING FREQUENCIES Both trace and retrace are included in one cycle of the sawtooth wave. Since the number of complete horizontal lines scanned in 1 s is 15,750 for horizontal deflection, the frequency of the sawtooth waves is 15,750 Hz. For vertical deflection, the frequency of the sawtooth waves equals the 60-Hz field-scanning rate.

The vertical scanning motion at 60 Hz is much slower than the horizontal sweep rate of 15,750 Hz. As a result, many horizontal lines are scanned during one cycle of vertical scanning. We can consider that the vertical deflection makes the horizontal lines fill the raster from top to bottom.

RETRACE TIME During flyback, both horizontal and vertical, all the picture information is blanked out. Thus the retrace part of the sawtooth wave is made as short as possible, since retrace is wasted time in terms of picture information. For horizontal scanning, the retrace time is approximately 10 percent of the time needed for the total line. Since 63.5 μs is needed to scan a complete line, 10 percent of this value equals the 6.35-μs horizontal flyback time. Practical limitations in the circuits producing the sawtooth waveform make it difficult to produce a faster flyback.

The lower-frequency vertical sawtooth waves usually have a flyback time less than 5 percent of that needed for one complete cycle. For example, a vertical retrace of 3 percent of $\frac{1}{60}$ s is equal to 0.0005 s, or 500 μs. Although vertical retrace is faster than vertical trace, 500 μs is much longer than the time needed to scan a complete horizontal line, or 63.5 μs. Actually, in the 500-μs vertical retrace time, approximately eight lines can be scanned.

Test Point Questions 6-1

Answers at End of Chapter

a. Which is faster, the trace or retrace?

b. Which takes more time, the *H* trace or the *V* retrace?

6-2 INTERLACED SCANNING PATTERN

The scanning procedure that has been universally adopted employs horizontal linear scanning in an odd-line interlaced pattern. The FCC scanning specifications for U.S. television broadcasting provide a standard scanning pattern that includes a total of 525 horizontal lines in a rectangular frame having a 4:3 aspect ratio. The frames are repeated at a rate of 30 per second with two fields interlaced in each frame.

INTERLACING PROCEDURE Interlaced scanning can be compared with reading the interlaced lines written in Fig. 6-4. Here the information on the page is continuous if you read all the odd lines from top to bottom and then go back to the top to read all the even lines from top to bottom. If the whole page were written and read in this interlaced pattern, the same amount of information would be available as when it was written in the usual way, with all the lines in progressive order.

For the interlaced scanning, first all the odd lines are scanned from top to bottom, and the

The horizontal scanning lines are interlaced in
the odd lines are scanned, omitting the even lines.
the television system in order to provide two
Then the even lines are scanned to complete the
views of the image for each picture frame. All
whole frame without losing any picture information.

Fig. 6-4 An example of interlaced lines. Read the first and odd lines and then the second and even lines.

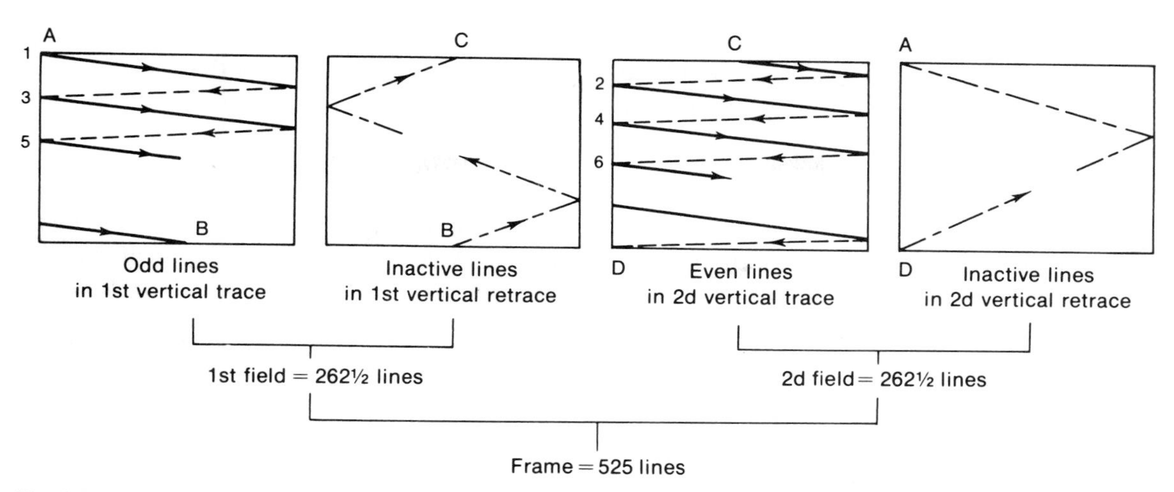

Fig. 6-5 Details of odd-line interlacing with two fields in one frame.

even lines are skipped. After this vertical scanning cycle, a rapid vertical retrace causes the electron scanning beam to return to the top of the frame. Then all the even lines that were omitted in the first scanning are scanned from top to bottom.

Each frame becomes divided into two fields. The first and all the following odd fields contain the odd lines in the frames. The second and all the even fields include the even scanning lines. Given two fields per frame and 30 complete frames scanned per second, the field repetition rate is 60 per second and the vertical scanning frequency is 60 Hz. In fact, doubling the vertical scanning frequency from the 30-Hz frame rate to the 60-Hz field rate is what makes the beam scan every other line in the frame.

ODD-LINE INTERLACING The geometry of the standard odd-line interlaced scanning pattern is illustrated in Fig. 6-5. Actually, the electron gun aims the beam at the center, which is where the scanning starts. For convenience, however, we can follow the motion by starting at the upper left corner of the frame at point A. For this line 1, the beam sweeps across the frame with uniform velocity to cover all the picture elements in one horizontal line. At the end of this trace, the beam retraces rapidly to the left side of the frame, as shown by the dashed line, to begin scanning the next horizontal line.

Note that the horizontal lines slope downward in the direction of scanning because the vertical deflection signal simultaneously produces a vertical scanning motion, which is very slow compared with horizontal scanning. Also note that the slope of the horizontal trace from left to right is greater than the slope during retrace from right to left. The reason is that the faster retrace does not allow the beam as much time to be deflected vertically.

After line 1 is scanned, the beam is at the left side, ready to scan line 3, omitting the second line. This line skipping is accomplished by doubling the vertical scanning frequency from 30 to 60 Hz. Deflecting the beam vertically at twice the speed necessary to scan 525 lines produces a complete vertical scanning period for only 262½ lines, with alternate lines left blank. The electron beam scans all the odd lines, then, finally reaching a position, such as point B in Fig. 6-5, at the bottom of the frame.

At time B the vertical retrace begins because of flyback on the vertical sawtooth deflection signal. Then the beam returns to the top of the frame to begin the second, or even, field. As shown in Fig. 6-5, the beam moves from point B up to C, traversing a whole number of horizontal lines.

This vertical retrace time is long enough for the beam to scan several horizontal lines. We can call these *vertical retrace lines,* meaning complete horizontal lines scanned during vertical flyback. Note that the vertical retrace lines slope upward, because the beam is moving up while it scans horizontally. The upward slope of the vertical retrace lines is greater than the downward slope of the lines scanning during vertical trace because the flyback upward is much faster than the trace downward. Any lines scanned during vertical retrace are not visible, though, because the electron beam is cut off by blanking voltage during the vertical flyback time. The vertical retrace lines are *inactive* because they are blanked out.

Horizontal scanning of the second field begins with the beam at point C in Fig. 6-5. This point is at the middle of a horizontal line because the first field contains 262½ lines. After scanning a half-line from point C, the beam scans line 2 in the second field. Then the beam scans between the odd lines—it scans the even lines that were omitted during the scanning of the first field. The vertical scanning motion is exactly the same as in the previous field, which means that all the horizontal lines have the same slope downward in the direction of scanning. As a result, all the even lines in the second field are scanned down to point D. Points D and B are a half-line away from each other because the second field started at a half-line point.

The vertical retrace in the second field starts at point D in Fig. 6-5. From here, vertical flyback causes the beam to return to the top. Since there are a whole number of vertical retrace lines, the beam finishes the second vertical retrace at A. The beam will always finish the second vertical retrace where the first trace started because the number of vertical retrace lines is the same in both fields. At point A, then, the scanning beam has just completed two fields, or one frame, and is ready to scan the third field.

All odd fields begin at point A. All even fields begin at point C. Since the beginning of the even-field scanning at C is on the same horizontal level as A with a separation of one-half line, and since the slope of all the lines is the same, the even lines in the even fields fall exactly between the odd lines in the odd fields. To achieve this odd-line interlace, the starting points at the top of the frame must be separated by exactly one-half line.

Test Point Questions 6-2

Answers at End of Chapter

a. Does interlaced scanning require an odd or an even number of horizontal lines?

b. How many horizontal lines are in an odd or an even field?

6-3 SAMPLE FRAME OF INTERLACED SCANNING

A complete scanning pattern is shown in Fig. 6-6, where the corresponding horizontal and vertical sawtooth waveforms illustrate odd-line interlaced scanning. A total of 21 lines in the frame is used for simplicity, instead of 525. The 21 lines are interlaced with two fields per frame. Each field contains half of the 21-line total, or 10½ lines. Of the 10½ lines in a field, we can assume that 1 line is scanned during vertical retrace to have a convenient vertical flyback time. So 9½ lines are scanned during vertical trace in each field.

In the entire frame, 2 × 9½, or 19, lines are scanned during vertical trace, in addition to the two vertical retrace lines.

Starting in the upper left corner, point A in Fig. 6-6, the beam scans the first line from left

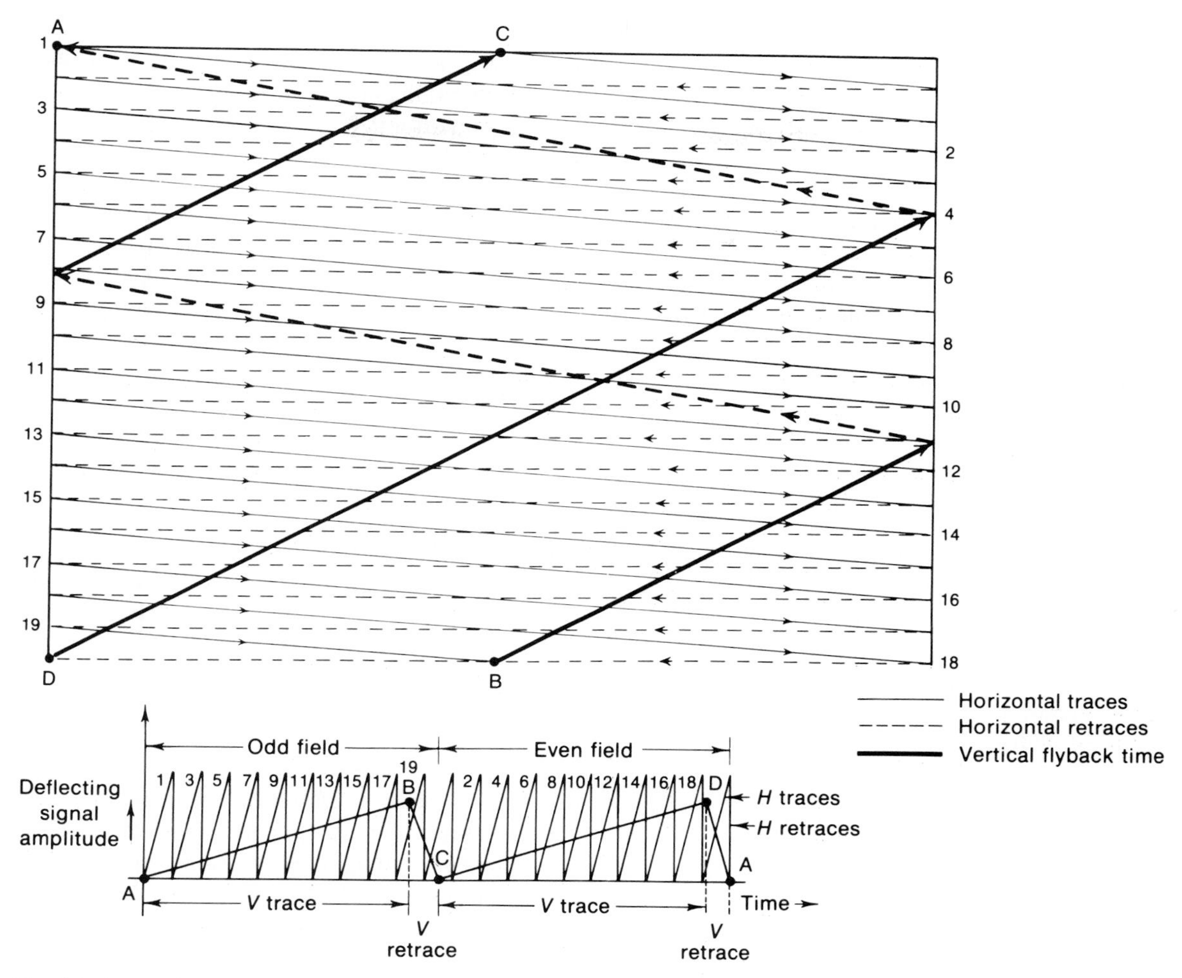

Fig. 6-6 A sample scanning pattern for 21 interlaced lines per frame and 10½ lines per field. The corresponding *H* and *V* sawtooth deflection waveforms are shown below pattern. Starting at point A, the scanning motion continues through B, C, and D and back to A again.

to right and retraces to the left to begin scanning the third line in the frame. Then the beam scans the third and all succeeding odd lines until it reaches the bottom of the frame. After scanning 9½ lines, the beam is at point B, at the bottom, when vertical flyback begins. Note that this vertical retrace begins in the middle of a horizontal line. Then one line is scanned during vertical retrace (this line consists of two half-lines in Fig. 6-6), and it slopes upward in the direction of scanning. During this vertical retrace the scanning beam is brought up to point C, which is separated from point A by exactly one-half line, so that scanning of the second field can begin.

Because of this half-line separation between points A and C, each line scanned in the even field falls exactly between two odd lines in the previous field. Then the beam scans 9½ even lines from point C to D, where the vertical retrace begins for the even field. This vertical retrace starts at the beginning of a horizontal line. The vertical retrace time is the same for both fields. So after one vertical retrace line in the second field, the beam goes from D at the bottom to A at the top left corner, where another odd field begins.

Note that the points at which vertical retrace and the downward scanning begin need not be exactly as shown in Fig. 6-6. All these points could be shifted by any fraction of a horizontal line without interfering with the interlaced pattern—as long as the half-line difference is maintained.

The half-line spacing between the starting points in alternate fields is produced automatically in both the sawtooth deflection signals and the scanning motion because there are an odd number of lines for an even number of fields. The proper interlacing results when the required frequencies of the horizontal and vertical sawtooth scanning signals are maintained precisely and the flyback time on the vertical sawtooth wave is constant for all fields.

Test Point Questions 6-3

Answers at End of Chapter

Refer to the scanning pattern in Fig. 6-6.

a. How many *H* lines are there in a complete frame?

b. How many *H* lines are there in each field?

c. How many *H* lines are there in each *V* retrace?

6-4 FLICKER

Interlaced scanning is used because the flicker effect is negligible when 60 views of the picture are presented each second. Although the frame repetition rate is still 30 per second, the picture is blanked out during each vertical retrace, or 60 times per second. So the change from black between pictures to the white picture is too rapid to be noticeable.

If progressive scanning were used instead of interlaced scanning—all the lines in the frame being scanned in progressive order from top to bottom—there would be only 30 blank-outs per second, and objectionable flicker would result. Scanning 60 complete frames per second in a progressive pattern also would eliminate flicker, but the horizontal scanning speed would be doubled, which would double the video frequencies corresponding to the picture elements in a line.

Although the increased blanking rate found in interlaced scanning largely eliminates flicker in the image as a whole, the fact that individual lines are interlaced can cause flicker in small areas of the picture. Any one line in the image is illuminated 30 times per second, which makes the flicker rate of a single line half of that for the interlaced image as a whole.

The lower flicker rate for individual lines may cause two effects in the picture—*interline flicker* and *line crawl.* Sometimes interline flicker is evident as a blinking of thin, horizontal objects in the picture, such as the roof line of a house. Line crawl is an apparent movement of the scanning lines upward or downward through the picture; it is a result of the successive illumination of adjacent lines. These effects may be noticed in bright parts of the picture because the eye perceives flicker more easily at high brightness levels.

Test Point Questions 6-4

Answers at End of Chapter

Answer True or False.

a. Flicker is caused by changes between black and white.

b. Increasing the vertical blanking rate makes the flicker worse.

6-5 RASTER DISTORTIONS

Since the picture information is reproduced on the scanning lines, distortions of the raster are in the picture also. A rectangular raster, correct proportions of width to height, and uniform deflection are required to get a good picture.

INCORRECT ASPECT RATIO Two cases of raster distortion are illustrated in Fig. 6-7. In Fig. 6-7*a*, the raster is not wide enough for its height, compared with the 4:3 aspect ratio used in the camera tube. So the people in the picture will look too tall and too thin—they will suffer from the same geometric distortion as the raster. This raster needs more width.

In Fig. 6-7*b*, the raster is not high enough for its width, and so the people in the picture will look too short. This raster needs more height.

In Fig. 6-7*a* or *b*, generally the trouble is caused by insufficient output from the horizontal or vertical deflection circuit.

PINCUSHION AND BARREL DISTORTION If deflection is not uniform at the edges of the raster, compared with its center, the raster will not have straight edges. The scanning lines bowed inward in Fig. 6-8*a* illustrate this effect, called *pincushion distortion.* And *barrel distortion* is shown in Fig. 6-8*b*.

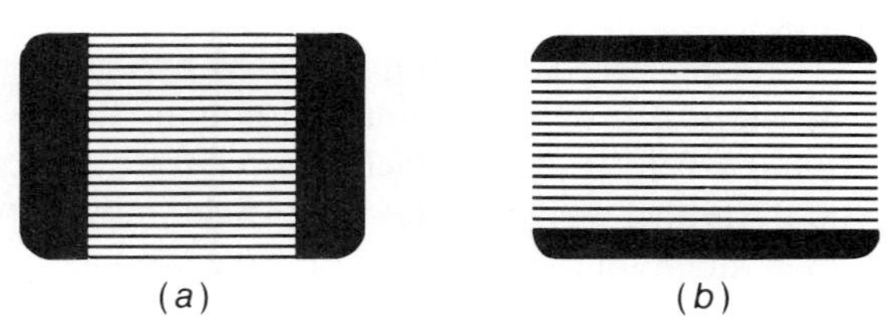

Fig. 6-7 Incorrect aspect ratio in raster. Black areas show areas of the screen not covered by the scanning lines. (*a*) Insufficient width. Too much black area at left and right sides. (*b*) Insufficient height. Too much black area at top and bottom.

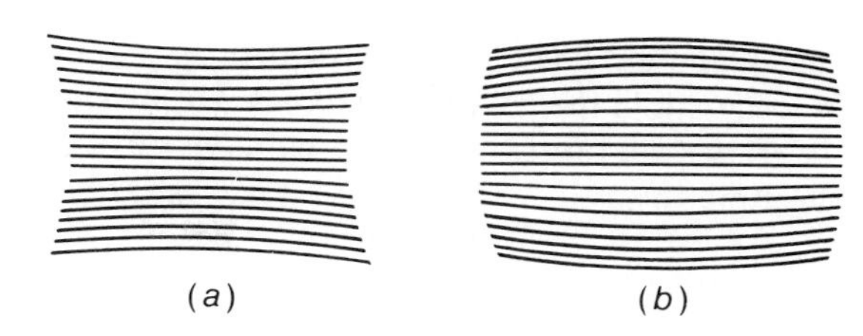

Fig. 6-8 (*a*) Pincushion effect in raster. (*b*) Barrel distortion.

Pincushion distortion is a problem with large-screen picture tubes. Since the faceplate is almost flat, the distance from the point of deflection to the corners of the screen is greater. The electron beam is deflected more at the corners than at the center, which gives a raster with stretched-out corners.

The pincushion distortion can be corrected, however, by a compensating magnetic field. Small permanent magnets are mounted on the deflection yoke in monochrome picture tubes. In color picture tubes, the deflection current in the yoke is modified by pincushion correction circuits, or specially designed yokes are used.

TRAPEZOIDAL DISTORTION In Fig. 6-9*a*, the scanning lines are wider at the top than at the bottom. This raster is shaped like a keystone, or a trapezoid. A trapezoid has two opposite edges that are not parallel. In the raster this effect is called *keystoning,* which is a form of trapezoidal distortion. The cause is nonsymmetric deflection, either left to right (as in Fig. 6-9*a*) or top to bottom (as in Fig. 6-9*b*). In picture tubes,

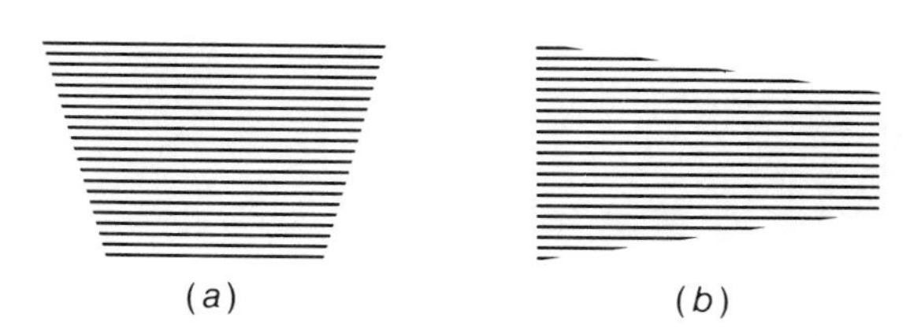

Fig. 6-9 Trapezoidal raster. (*a*) Keystoned sides caused by unsymmetric horizontal deflection. (*b*) Keystoning at top and bottom caused by unsymmetric vertical deflection.

the scanning symmetry is provided by the balanced coils in the yoke for scanning. The problem of trapezoidal raster is caused by a defective deflection yoke.

NONLINEAR SCANNING The sawtooth waveform with its linear rise for trace time produces linear scanning, since the beam is made to move with constant speed. With nonlinear scanning, however, the beam moves too slowly or too fast. If the spot being scanned moves too slowly at the receiver, compared with scanning in the camera tube, then the picture information is crowded together. Or, if the scanning is too rapid, then the reproduced picture information is spread out. Usually, nonlinear scanning creates both effects at opposite ends of the raster. Nonlinear scanning is illustrated in Fig. 6-10 for a horizontal line with picture elements spread out at the left and crowded at the right. When the same effect occurs for all the horizontal lines in the raster, the entire picture is spread out at the left side and crowded at the right side. When there are people in the picture, a person at the left appears too wide and someone at the right looks too thin.

The vertical scanning motion must be uniform also. Otherwise, the horizontal lines will be bunched at the top or bottom of the raster and spread out at the opposite end. This effect is illustrated in Fig. 6-11 for spreading at the top and crowding at the bottom. So a person in this picture will appear distorted, having a long head and short legs. Scanning nonlinearity is caused by amplitude distortion of the sawtooth waveform in the deflection amplifier circuits.

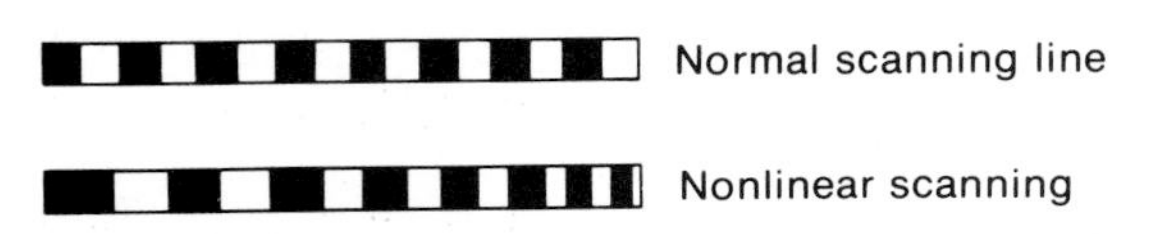

Fig. 6-10 Crowding at right side caused by nonlinear horizontal scanning.

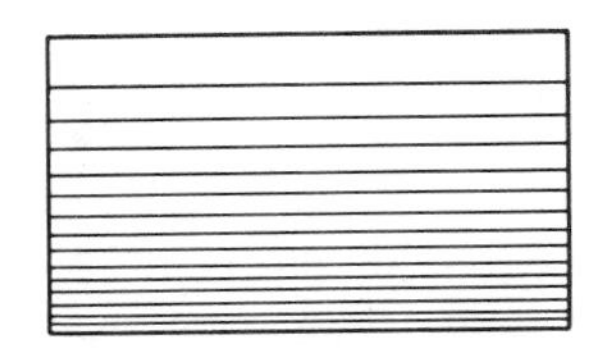

Fig. 6-11 Crowding at bottom caused by nonlinear vertical scanning.

POOR INTERLACED SCANNING In each field, the vertical trace must start exactly a half-line from the start of the previous field for odd-line interlacing. If the downward motion is slightly displaced from this correct position, the beam begins scanning too close to one of the lines in the previous field, instead of scanning exactly between lines. This incorrect starting position produces a vertical displacement between odd and even lines that is carried through the entire frame. As a result, pairs of lines are too close, and there is extra space between pairs. So you see too much space between the white scanning lines. This defect in interlaced scanning is called *line pairing.* In the extreme case, lines in each successive field are scanned exactly on the previous field lines. Then the raster contains only half of the usual number of horizontal lines.

When the picture has diagonal lines as part of the image, poor interlaced scanning makes them appear to be interwoven in the moiré effect shown in Fig. 6-12. This effect, also called *fishtailing,* is more evident in diagonal picture information, as the interlacing varies in successive frames.

Poor interlaced scanning is caused by inaccurate vertical synchronization. Although the period of a field is $\frac{1}{60}$ s, which is a relatively long time, vertical scanning in every field must be timed much more accurately to achieve good interlacing. If the vertical timing is off by 0.25 μs in one field compared with the next, then the interlaced fields are shifted the distance of one picture element.

Fig. 6-12 Example of faulty interlacing. The line divisions in horizontal wedges of test pattern are interwoven in a moiré effect.

Test Point Questions 6-5

Answers at End of Chapter

Refer to Figs. 6-7 to 6-11. Which figures show the following raster distortions?

a. Not enough height

b. Pincushion distortion

c. Crowding at the bottom

6-6
SYNCHRONIZING PULSES

In the picture tube, the scanning beam must reassemble the picture elements on each horizontal line with the same left-right position as the image at the camera tube. Also, as the beam scans vertically, the successive scanning lines on the picture tube screen must present the same picture elements as the corresponding lines at the camera tube. So a horizontal synchronizing pulse is transmitted for each horizontal line, in order to keep the horizontal scanning synchronized. And a vertical synchronizing pulse is transmitted for each field, to synchronize the vertical scanning motion. Thus the horizontal synchronizing pulses have a frequency of 15,750 Hz, and the frequency of the vertical synchronizing pulses is 60 Hz.

The synchronizing pulses are part of the video signal, but they occur during the blanking period, when no picture information is transmitted. This is possible because the synchronizing pulse begins the retrace, either horizontal or vertical, and so occurs during the blanking time. The synchronizing signals are combined in such a way that part of the video signal amplitude is used for the synchronizing pulses and the remainder is used for the camera signal. The term *sync* is used often to indicate the synchronizing pulses.

The form of the synchronizing pulses is illustrated in Fig. 6-13. Note that all pulses have the same amplitude but differ in pulse width or waveform. The synchronizing pulses shown include (from left to right) three horizontal pulses, a group of six equalizing pulses, a serrated vertical pulse, and six additional equalizing pulses, which are followed by three more horizontal pulses. There are many additional horizontal pulses after the last one shown, following each other at the horizontal line frequency until the equalizing pulses recur at the beginning of the next field. For every field there must be one wide vertical pulse. The serrations are cuts or openings in the pulse amplitude.

Each vertical synchronizing pulse extends over a period equal to six half-lines, or three complete horizontal lines, and so it is much wider than a horizontal pulse. This is done to give the vertical pulses an entirely different form from that of the horizontal pulses. Then the vertical pulses can be completely separated from the horizontal ones at the receiver. One part of the sync circuit provides vertical synchronizing signals alone while the other provides only the horizontal synchronization.

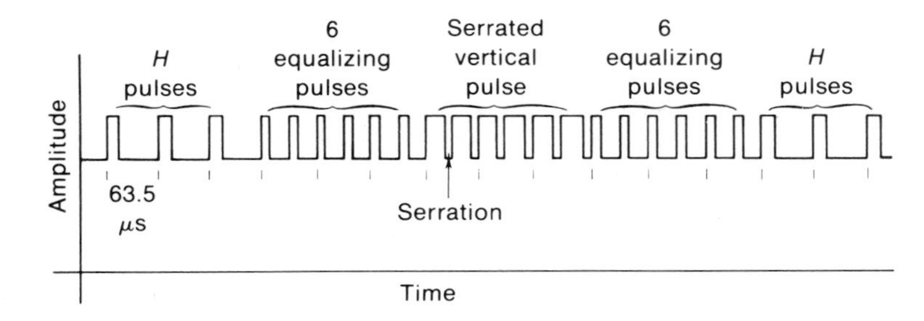

Fig. 6-13 Synchronizing pulses.

The five serrations are inserted in the vertical pulse at half-line intervals. The equalizing pulses also are spaced at half-line intervals. These half-line pulses can serve for horizontal synchronization, with alternate pulses used for even and odd fields. Since the equalizing pulses are repeated at half-line intervals, their repetition rate is $2 \times 15{,}750 = 31{,}500$ Hz.

The reason for using equalizing pulses, however, is related to vertical synchronization. Equalizing pulses provide identical waveshapes in the separated vertical synchronizing signal for even and odd fields, and so constant timing can be achieved for good interlaced scanning.

The synchronizing signals do not produce scanning. Sawtooth generator circuits are needed to deflect the electron beam which produces the scanning raster. However, the sync pulses time the scanning circuits. Therefore, the sync enables the picture information reproduced on the raster to remain still, in the correct position.

Without vertical sync, the picture reproduced on the raster appears to roll up or down the screen (Fig. 6-14). The reason is that successive picture frames are not superimposed exactly one on the next. The black bar across the picture in Fig. 6-14 corresponds to vertical blanking, which normally is at the bottom and top of the picture, off the screen.

Without horizontal sync, the picture drifts to the left or right, and then the line structure breaks into diagonal segments of the picture (Fig. 6-15). The groups of horizontal lines result because an AFC circuit is used for horizontal sync.

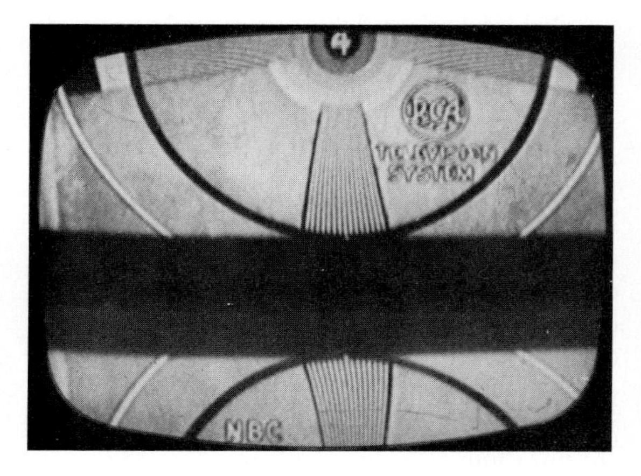

Fig. 6-14 Pictures rolling up or down without *V* sync.

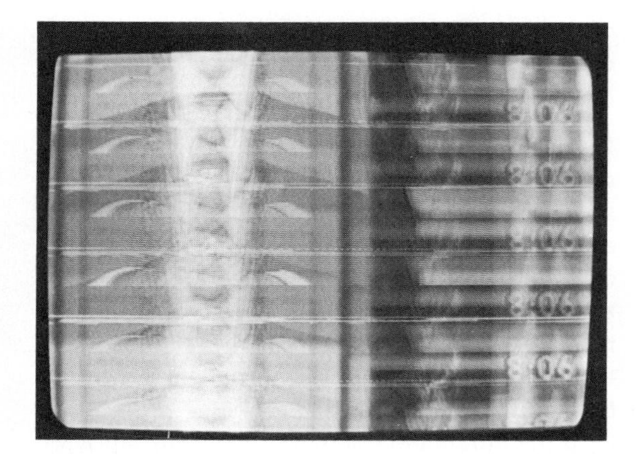

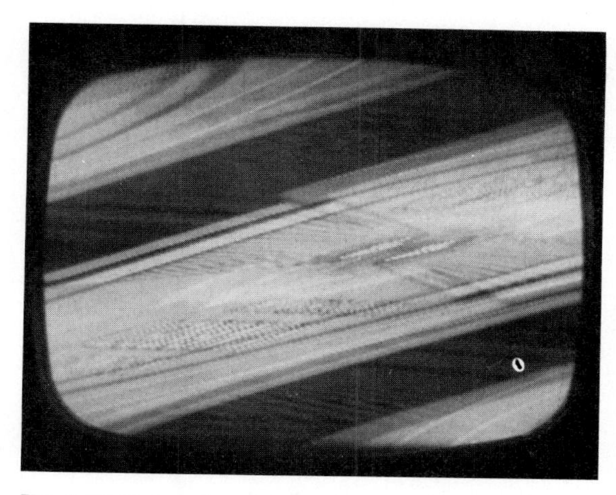

Fig. 6-15 Picture torn into diagonal segments without *H* sync.

The diagonal black bars in Fig. 6-15 are parts of the blanking bars normally located at the sides of the picture, off the screen.

Test Point Questions 6-6
Answers at End of Chapter

Answer True or False.

a. All synchronizing pulses have the same amplitude.
b. The frequency of the equalizing pulses is 30 Hz.
c. The *H* sync pulses have a higher frequency than the *V* sync pulses.

6-7 SCANNING, SYNCHRONIZING, AND BLANKING FREQUENCIES

The sync and blanking pulses always have the same timing as the scanning. These values are summarized in Table 6-1. In vertical deflection, the sawtooth scanning waveform has a frequency of 60 Hz because this value is determined by the *V* sync pulses repeated every $\frac{1}{60}$ s. The vertical retrace is blanked out because the flyback is triggered by the *V* sync pulse during the time of the *V* blanking pulse.

Similarly, in horizontal deflection, the sawtooth scanning waveform has a frequency of 15,750 Hz because this is the repetition rate of the *H* sync pulses. The *H* flyback is blanked out because *H* retrace occurs during *H* blanking.

The groups of equalizing pulses are repeated every $\frac{1}{60}$ s, but each pulse is spaced at half-line intervals with a frequency of 31,500 Hz. These pulses equalize the vertical synchronization in even and odd fields to achieve good interlaced scanning. However, there is no scanning or blanking at the equalizing-pulse rate of 31,500 Hz.

Note that in color television the *V* field frequency is exactly 59.94 Hz and the *H* line frequency is 15,734.26 Hz. These values are derived as submultiples of the exact color subcarrier frequency of 3.579545 MHz. The calculations are explained in Chap. 8, "Color Television Circuits and Signals." However, these frequencies are so close to 60 and 15,750 Hz that the deflection circuits can lock in easily for synchronized *V* and *H* scanning. In color television, when the

TABLE 6-1
SCANNING, SYNCHRONIZING, AND BLANKING FREQUENCIES

FREQUENCY, Hz	APPLICATION
60	*V* sync to time *V* field scanning
60	V scanning to make lines fill raster
60	V blanking to blank out *V* retraces
15,750	*H* sync to time *H* scanning
15,750	*H* scanning to produce lines
15,750	*H* blanking to blank out *H* retraces
31,500	Equalizing pulses

V and H scanning frequencies are shifted slightly, both the sync and blanking pulses are changed to the new frequencies also. A synchronized scanning circuit automatically locks into the sync frequency. In any case, the values in Table 6-1 can be considered the nominal values of scanning, sync, and blanking frequencies for television.

Test Point Questions 6-7

Answers at End of Chapter

a. What are the frequencies of V scanning, V sync, and V blanking?

b. What are the frequencies of H scanning, H sync, and H blanking?

SUMMARY

1. The sawtooth waveform for deflection provides linear scanning. The linear rise on the sawtooth is the trace part; the sharp drop in amplitude is for the retrace, or flyback. Both trace and retrace are included in one cycle.
2. The frequency of the sawtooth waveform for horizontal deflection is the 15,750-Hz horizontal line rate.
3. The frequency of the sawtooth waveform for vertical deflection is the field rate of 60 Hz. The vertical flyback time, 5 percent or less of $\frac{1}{60}$ s, is long enough for several complete lines to be scanned. The horizontal lines scanned during vertical retraces are the vertical flyback lines.
4. In odd-line interlaced scanning, an odd number of lines (525) are used with an even number of fields (60), so that each field has a whole number of lines plus a half-line. Each field is scanned a half-line away from the previous field to interlace the scanning of odd and even lines in the frame.
5. Interlaced scanning eliminates flicker because of the 60-Hz vertical blanking rate, while maintaining the 30-Hz rate for complete picture frames.
6. An incorrect aspect ratio can make people in the picture look too tall or too short, owing to incorrect height or width of the raster. See Fig. 6-7.
7. Distortions of the scanning raster include keystone, trapezoid, pincushion, and barrel effects. See Figs. 6-8 and 6-9.
8. Nonlinear scanning causes the picture information to be spread out or crowded at one end of the raster compared with the opposite end. This effect also distorts the shape of people in the picture. See Figs. 6-10 and 6-11.
9. The synchronizing pulses time the scanning with respect to the position of picture information on the raster. Horizontal sync pulses time every line at 15,750 Hz; vertical sync pulses time every field at 60 Hz. All the sync pulses have the same amplitude, but a much wider pulse is used for vertical sync. The equalizing pulses and the serrations in the vertical pulse occur at half-line intervals with the frequency of 31,500 Hz.

SELF-EXAMINATION

Answers at Back of Book

Choose (a), (b), (c), or (d).

1. In the sawtooth waveform for linear scanning, (a) the linear rise is for flyback, (b) the complete cycle includes trace and retrace, (c) the sharp reversal in amplitude produces trace, (d) the beam moves faster during trace than retrace.
2. Given a 635-μs vertical retrace time, the number of complete horizontal lines scanned during vertical flyback is (a) 10, (b) 20, (c) 30, (d) 63.
3. One-half line spacing between the start positions for scanning even and odd fields produces (a) linear scanning, (b) line pairing, (c) fishtailing, (d) exact interlacing.
4. The number of lines scanned per frame in the raster on the picture tube screen is (a) 525, (b) 262½, (c) 20, (d) 10.
5. In the frame for which interlaced scanning is used, alternate lines are skipped during vertical scanning because (a) the trace is slower than the retrace, (b) the vertical scanning frequency is doubled from 30 to 60 Hz, (c) the horizontal scanning is slower than vertical scanning, (d) the frame has a 4:3 aspect ratio.
6. If the horizontal flyback is 10 percent, this time equals (a) 10 μs, (b) 56 μs, (c) 6.4 μs, (d) 83 μs.
7. Which of the following is *not* true? (a) Line pairing indicates poor interlacing. (b) People look too tall and too thin on a square raster on the picture tube screen. (c) A person can appear to have one shoulder wider than the other because of nonlinear horizontal scanning. (d) The keystone effect produces a square raster.
8. The width of a vertical sync pulse with its serrations includes the time of (a) six half-lines, or three lines; (b) five lines; (c) three half-lines; (d) five half-lines.
9. Sawtooth generator circuits produce the scanning raster, but the sync pulses are needed for (a) linearity, (b) timing, (c) keystoning, (d) line pairing.
10. Which of the following frequencies is wrong? (a) 15,750 Hz for horizontal sync and scanning, (b) 60 Hz for vertical sync and scanning, (c) 31,500 Hz for equalizing pulses and serrations in the vertical sync pulse, (d) 31,500 Hz for the vertical scanning frequency.

ESSAY QUESTIONS

1. Draw the scanning pattern interlaced in two fields for a total of 25 lines per frame. Also show the corresponding sawtooth waveforms for horizontal and vertical scanning, as in Fig. 6-6. Assume one line is scanned during each vertical flyback.
2. Define **(a)** scanning raster, **(b)** the pincushion effect, **(c)** line pairing, **(d)** interline flicker, **(e)** the moiré effect.
3. Why are the lines scanned during vertical trace much closer together than lines scanned during vertical flyback?
4. Suppose the sawtooth waveform for vertical deflection has a trace that rises too fast at the start and flattens at the top. Will the scanning lines be crowded at the top or the bottom of the picture tube raster? How will people look in the picture?
5. Draw two cycles of the 15,750-Hz sawtooth waveform, showing the retrace equal to $0.08H$ to exact scale. Label the trace, retrace, and time of one cycle in microseconds.
6. Draw two cycles of the 60-Hz sawtooth waveform, showing the retrace equal to $0.04V$ to exact scale. Label the trace, retrace, and time of one cycle in microseconds.
7. Where is the electron scanning beam at the **(a)** start of linear rise in the *H* sawtooth waveform, **(b)** start of *H* flyback, **(c)** start of linear rise in the *V* sawtooth waveform, **(d)** start of *V* flyback?

PROBLEMS

Answers to Odd-Numbered Problems at Back of Book

1. How many flyback lines are produced during vertical retrace for each field and each frame when the retrace time is $0.03V$?
2. Compare the time in microseconds for horizontal flyback equal to $0.08H$ and vertical flyback equal to $0.03V$.
3. **(a)** How much time elapses between the start of one horizontal sync pulse and the next? **(b)** How much time passes between one vertical pulse in an odd field and the next in an even field?
4. Refer to the sawtooth waveforms in Fig. 6-16. For the opposite polarities in Fig. 6-16*a* and *b*, indicate trace and retrace on each *H* sawtooth, also, the corresponding left and right edges in the raster. For the opposite polarities in Fig. 6-16*c* and *d*, indicate trace and retrace on each *V* sawtooth, also, the corresponding top and bottom edges in the raster.
5. What frequencies correspond to the following times for one cycle? **(a)** $\frac{1}{60}$ s, **(b)** 63.5 μs, **(c)** 53.3 μs.

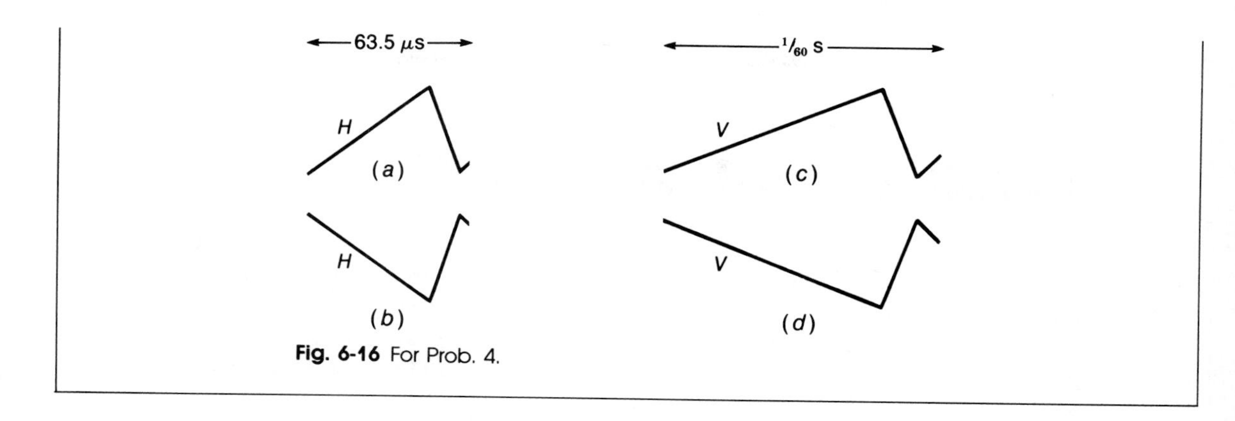

Fig. 6-16 For Prob. 4.

SPECIAL QUESTIONS

1. What makes a television picture roll up or down the screen?
2. Have you ever seen a scanning raster on the screen, without the picture?
3. Why do motion-picture films *not* have the problem of synchronizing horizontal scanning lines?

ANSWERS TO TEST POINT QUESTIONS

6-1 **a.** Retrace
b. *V* retrace
6-2 **a.** Odd
b. 262½
6-3 **a.** 21
b. 10½
c. One

6-4 **a.** T
b. F
6-5 **a.** Figure 6-7*b*
b. Figure 6-8*a*
c. Figure 6-11

6-6 **a.** T
b. F
c. T
6-7 **a.** 60 Hz
b. 15,750 Hz

7

VIDEO SIGNAL ANALYSIS

The three parts of the composite video signal, illustrated in Fig. 7-1, are (1) the camera signal corresponding to the variations of light in the scene; (2) the synchronizing pulses, or sync, to synchronize the scanning; and (3) the blanking pulses to make the retraces invisible. The camera signal in Fig. 7-1*a* is combined with the blanking pulse in Fig. 7-1*b*. Then sync is added to produce the composite video signal in Fig. 7-1*c*. The result shown here is the signal for one horizontal scanning line. For color television, the 3.58-MHz chrominance signal and color sync burst are added.

Given the signals for all the lines, the composite video contains all the information needed for the complete picture, line by line and field by field. The video signal is used in the picture tube to reproduce the picture on the scanning raster. More details about the composite video signal and how it affects picture reproduction are given in the following sections:

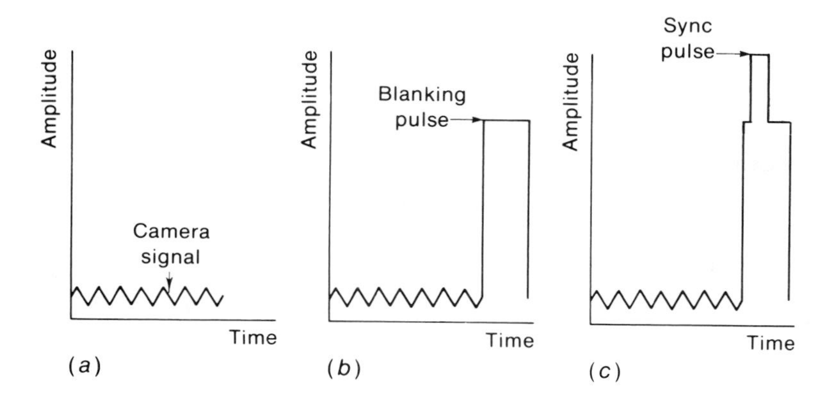

Fig. 7-1 Three components of composite video signal are camera signal variations, blanking pulses, and sync pulses. (*a*) Camera signal for one horizontal line. (*b*) *H* blanking pulse added to camera signal. (*c*) *H* sync pulse added to blanking pulse.

7-1 CONSTRUCTION OF THE COMPOSITE VIDEO SIGNAL

In Fig. 7-2, successive values of voltage or current amplitude are shown for the scanning of two horizontal lines in the image. As time increases in the horizontal direction, the amplitudes vary for shades of white, gray, or black in the picture. Starting at the extreme left, at zero time, the signal is at a white level and the scanning beam is at the left side of the image. As the first line is scanned from left to right, camera signal variations are obtained with various amplitudes that correspond to the required picture information. After horizontal trace produces the desired camera signal for one line, the scanning beam is at the right side of the image. Then the blanking pulse is inserted to bring the video signal amplitude up to the black level so that the retrace can be blanked out.

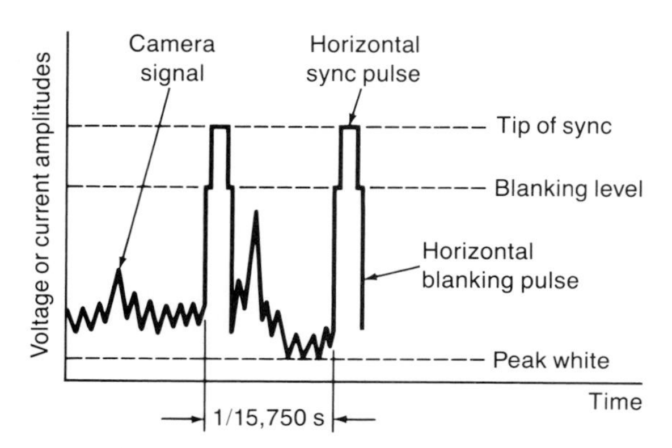

Fig. 7-2 Composite video signal for two horizontal lines.

After a blanking time long enough to include retrace, the blanking voltage is removed. Then the scanning beam is at the left side, ready to scan the next line. Each horizontal line is scanned successively in this way. Note that the second line shows dark picture information near the black level.

With respect to time, the signal amplitudes just after blanking in Fig. 7-2 indicate information corresponding to the left side at the start of a scanning line. Just before blanking, the signal variations correspond to the right side. Information exactly in the center of a scanning line is halfway in time between blanking pulses.

SYNC POLARITY IN THE COMPOSITE VIDEO SIGNAL The video signal can have two polarities:

1. A positive sync polarity, with the sync pulses in the up position, as in Fig. 7-2.
2. A negative sync polarity, with the sync pulses in the down position, as shown in Fig. 7-3.

The video signals shown in Figs. 7-2 and 7-3 both contain the same picture information. Video

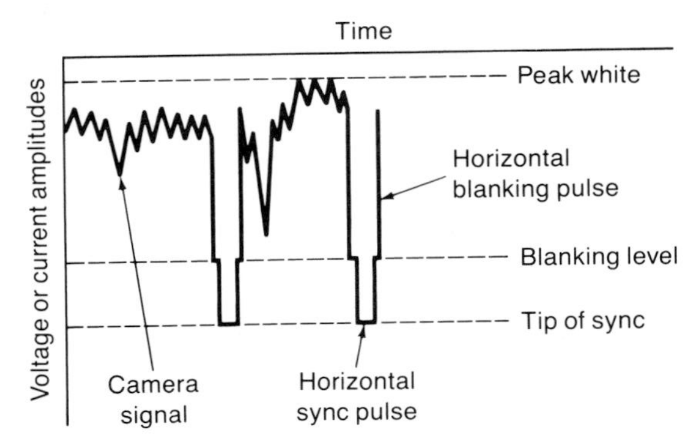

Fig. 7-3 Same video signal as in Fig. 7-2, but with negative sync polarity.

with negative sync polarity is needed at the control grid of the picture tube to reproduce the picture. Then the blanking level is negative to cut off the beam current for black. Video with positive sync polarity is needed at the cathode of the picture tube.

Furthermore, negative sync polarity is standard for signals into or out of video equipment such as the TV camera, video control equipment, and telephone distribution lines. The standard amplitude is 1 V p-p with sync negative.

For either polarity, remember that the white parts of the video signal are opposite to those of the sync pulses. The blanking level must be black. Sync amplitudes can be called *blacker than black.*

BLANKING The composite video signal contains blanking pulses to make the retrace lines invisible by changing the signal amplitude to black when the scanning circuits produce retraces. All picture information is cut off during blanking time. Normally the retraces are produced within the time of blanking.

As illustrated in Fig. 7-4, there are horizontal and vertical blanking pulses in the composite video signal. The horizontal blanking pulses are included to blank out the retrace from right to left in each horizontal scanning line. The repetition rate of horizontal blanking pulses, therefore, is the line-scanning frequency of 15,750 Hz. The vertical blanking pulses blank out the scanning lines produced when the electron beam retraces vertically from bottom to top in each field. So the frequency of vertical blanking pulses is 60 Hz for every field. Each blanking pulse changes the video signal to black during blanking time.

Test Point Questions 7-1

Answers at End of Chapter

a. What are the three parts of the composite video signal, for two horizontal lines in the picture, as in Figs. 7-2 and 7-3?

b. Is the video signal with negative sync polarity shown in Fig. 7-2 or 7-3?

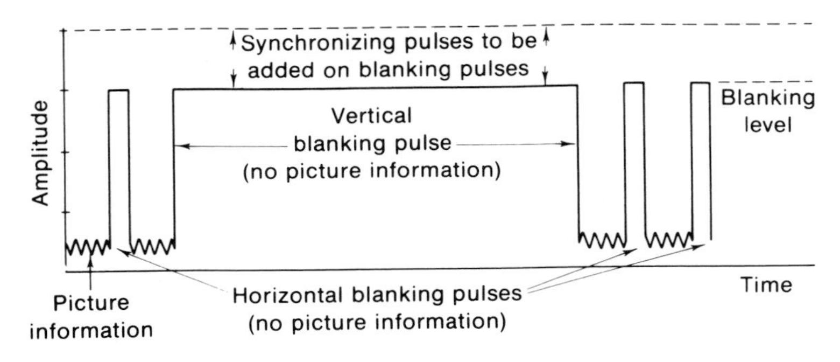

Fig. 7-4 *H* and *V* blanking pulses in video signal. Sync pulses are not shown.

7-2 IRE SCALE OF VIDEO SIGNAL AMPLITUDES

On oscilloscope monitors, the video signal amplitude usually is checked with negative sync polarity to fit the IRE scale shown in Fig. 7-5. IRE stands for Institute of Radio Engineers, now called the Institute of Electrical and Electronic Engineers (IEEE). The total IRE scale includes 140 units, with 100 up and 40 down from zero. The peak-to-peak composite video signal includes 140 IRE units.

SYNC PULSE AMPLITUDE Of the 140 total IRE units, 40 (or approximately 29 percent) are for sync. All the sync pulses have the same amplitude, which is 29 percent of that of the peak-to-peak video signal.

BLACK SETUP Note that the black peaks of camera signal variations are offset from the black blanking level by 7.5 IRE units, which is approximately 5 percent of the total. The purpose is to make sure that color subcarrier signals near black in the camera signal do not interfere with the sync amplitudes.

CAMERA SIGNAL AMPLITUDES Peak white goes to approximately 100 IRE units. Black setup, though, is 7.5 units to offset black in the picture from the blanking level. Subtracting the black setup from peak white, the result is $100 - 7.5 = 92.5$ IRE units for the camera signal variations. This amount is 66 percent of the total 140 IRE units.

Test Point Questions 7-2

Answers at End of Chapter

In the IRE scale for composite video signal, list the number of IRE units used for:

a. Sync
b. Black setup
c. The camera signal

7-3 HORIZONTAL BLANKING TIME

Details of the horizontal blanking period are illustrated in Fig. 7-6. The interval marked H is the time needed to scan one complete line, including trace and retrace. Therefore, the time for H is 1/15,750 s, or 63.5 μs.

The horizontal blanking pulse is only $0.14H$ to $0.18H$ wide. Let us take an average of 16 percent as a typical value. Thus the horizontal blanking time is

$$0.16 \times 63.5\ \mu s = 10.2\ \mu s \text{ (approx.)}$$

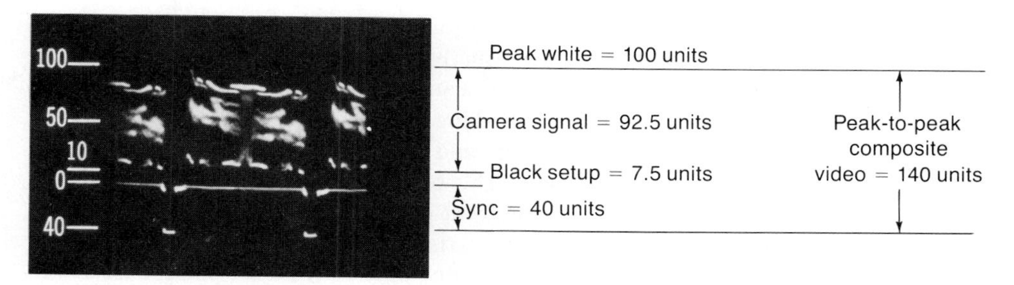

Fig. 7-5 Oscilloscope photograph of two lines of composite video signal with IRE scale of amplitudes. Note scale of 140 IRE units at left.

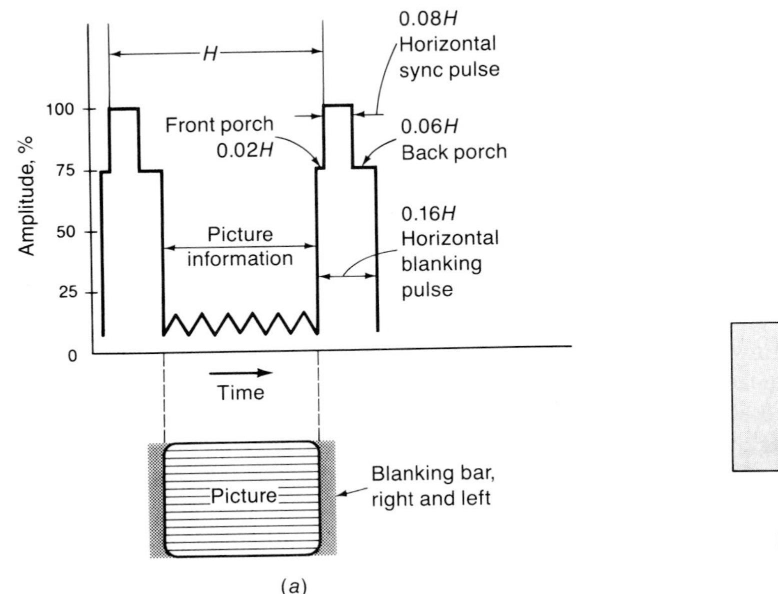

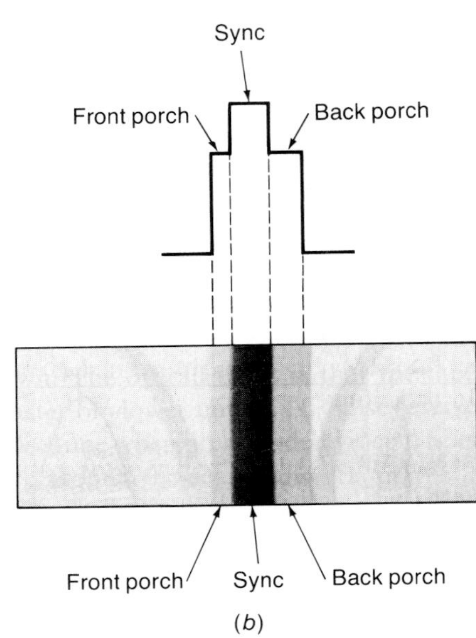

Fig. 7-6 (*a*) Details of horizontal blanking and sync pulses. *H* time is 1/15,750 s = 63.5 μs. In picture below the signal, black edges show blanking. (*b*) *H* blanking moved into picture to show effect on screen. Brightness is higher than normal.

Now we subtract this value from the *H* time of 63.5 μs;

$$63.5\ \mu s - 10.2\ \mu s = 53.3\ \mu s$$

Then 53.3 μs is the time needed for visible scanning, without blanking in each horizontal line. For *H* blanking 10.2 μs is needed to allow time for horizontal retrace.

Superimposed on the *H* blanking pulses are the narrower *H* sync pulses. As noted in Fig. 7-6, each *H* sync pulse is 0.08*H*, or one-half the average width of the blanking pulse. So this sync time is approximately 10 μs/2, or 5 μs.

FRONT PORCH AND BACK PORCH For the remaining half of the blanking time, which is also 5 μs, the signal is at the blanking level. The part just before the sync pulse is called the *front porch*, and the *back porch* follows the sync pulse. The front porch is 0.02*H* wide, and the back porch is 0.06*H* wide. These time periods are 1.27 μs for the front porch and 3.81 μs for the back porch. Note that the back porch is three times longer than the front porch. All these time periods within a horizontal line are summarized in Table 7-1, with the required tolerances.

***H* BLANKING AND *H* SCANNING** The blanking time is slightly longer than typical values of retrace time. As a result, a small part of the trace usually is blanked out at the start and end of every scanning line. The effect of this horizontal blanking is illustrated by the black bars at the left and right sides for the picture in Fig. 7-6*a*. The black at the right edge corresponds to the front porch of horizontal blanking, before retrace starts. Generally, horizontal retrace starts at the leading edge of the sync pulse. Just before retrace (when the scanning beam is completing its trace to the right), the blanking level of the

TABLE 7-1
DETAILS OF HORIZONTAL BLANKING

PERIOD	TIME, μs
Total line (H)	63.5
H blanking	9.5–11.5
H sync pulse	4.75 ± 0.5
Front porch	1.27 (minimum)
Back porch	3.81 (minimum)
Visible line time	52–54

front porch makes the right edge black. With a small part of every line blanked this way, a black bar is formed at the right edge. This black bar at the right can be considered a reproduction of the front-porch part of horizontal blanking.

After the front porch of blanking, horizontal retrace can begin when the sync pulse starts. The flyback is definitely blanked out because the sync level is blacker than black. Although retrace generally starts with the sync pulse, the amount of time needed to complete the flyback depends on the scanning circuits. A typical horizontal flyback time is 7 μs.

The blanking time after the front porch is 8.93 μs, calculated as

$$10.2 - 1.27 = 8.93\ \mu s$$

Now subtract the flyback time of 7 μs for

$$8.93 - 7.00 = 2.93\ \mu s$$

The 2.93 μs is the blanking time that still remains after the retrace to the left edge has been completed.

Although the blanking is still in effect, the sawtooth deflection waveform makes the scanning beam start its trace following flyback. As a result, the first part of trace at the left is blanked. After 2.93 μs of blanked trace time at the left edge, the blanking pulse is removed. Then the video signal reproduces picture information as the scanning beam continues its trace for 53.3 μs of visible trace time. However, the small part of every line blanked at the start of trace forms the black bar at the left edge of the raster. This black edge at the left represents part of every back porch following horizontal sync.

The blanking bars at the sides have no effect on the picture other than to slightly decrease its width, compared with that of the unblanked raster. However, the amplitude of horizontal scanning can be increased to provide the desired picture width.

Figure 7-6*b* shows the effect on the screen of the picture tube for the front porch and back porch during H blanking. The brightness is set higher than normal, in order to make blanking lighter than black. Also, the phase of scanning with respect to blanking must be shifted to put the blanking time into trace time.

SUMMARY OF *H* BLANKING TIME For typical values, the width of each H blanking pulse is 10 μs. The H sync pulse is 5 μs wide, or one-half the blanking time. Just before H sync, the front porch is 1.27 μs. The back porch just after H sync is 3.81 μs. Note that $1.27 + 3.81 = 5\ \mu s$ approximately. Adding this to 5 μs for H sync gives the H blanking time of 10 μs.

Test Point Questions 7-3
Answers at End of Chapter

What are the approximate time periods for the following, in microseconds?

a. Width of H blanking pulse
b. Visible H trace
c. Width of H sync pulse

7-4 VERTICAL BLANKING TIME

The vertical blanking pulses change the video signal amplitude to black so that the scanning beam is blanked out during vertical retraces. The width of the vertical blanking pulse is 0.05 V to

$0.08\,V$, where V is $\frac{1}{60}$ s. If we take 8 percent as maximum, the vertical blanking time is

$$0.08 \times \frac{1}{60}\ \text{s} = 1333\ \mu\text{s}$$

_H_ LINES BLANKED BY _V_ BLANKING The time of 1333 μs is long enough to include many complete horizontal scanning lines. When we divide the 1333-μs vertical blanking time by the 63.5-μs total line period, we get 21. So 21 lines are blanked out in each field, or 42 lines in the frame. The total number of blanked lines in the frame also can be calculated as $0.08 \times 525 = 42$.

The relatively long time blanks not only vertical retrace lines but also a small part of vertical trace at the bottom and top.

SYNC PULSES IN _V_ BLANKING TIME The sync pulses inserted in the composite video signal during the wide vertical blanking pulse are shown in Fig. 7-7. These include equalizing pulses, vertical sync pulses, and some horizontal sync pulses. The signals are shown for the time intervals between the end of one field and the next, to illustrate what happens during vertical blanking time. The two signals shown one above the other are the same except for the half-line displacement between successive fields necessary for odd-line interlaced scanning.

Starting at the left in Fig. 7-7, the last four horizontal scanning lines at the bottom of the raster are shown with the required horizontal blanking and sync pulses. Immediately following the last visible line, the video signal is brought to black by the vertical blanking pulse in preparation for vertical retrace.

The vertical blanking period begins with a group of six equalizing pulses, spaced at half-line intervals.

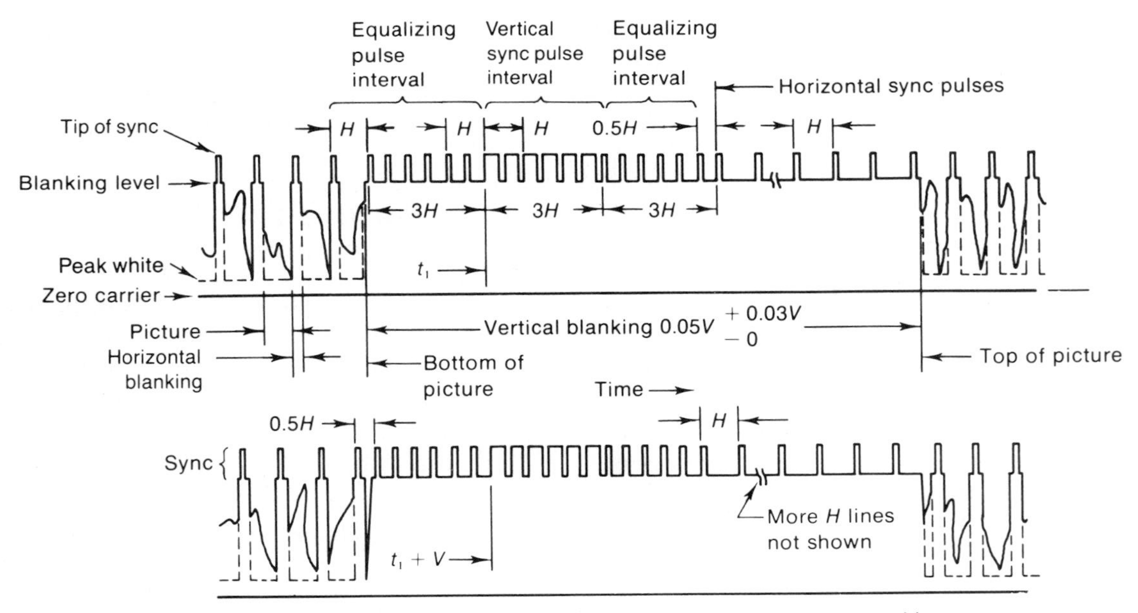

Fig. 7-7 Details of sync and blanking pulses for successive fields in vertical scanning. V time is $\frac{1}{60}$ s = 0.0167 s.

TABLE 7-2
DETAILS OF VERTICAL BLANKING

PERIOD	TIME
Total field (V)	$\frac{1}{60} = 0.0167$ s
V blanking	$0.05V$–$0.08V$, or 0.0008–0.0013 s
Each V sync pulse	27.35 μs
Total of six V sync pulses	$3H = 190.5$ μs
Each E pulse	$0.04H = 2.54$ μs
Each serration	$0.07H = 4.4$ μs
Visible field time	$0.92V$–$0.95V$, or 0.015–0.016 s

Next is the serrated vertical sync pulse that actually produces vertical flyback in the scanning circuits. The serrations also occur at half-line intervals. Therefore, the complete vertical sync pulse is three lines wide.

Following the vertical sync is another group of six equalizing pulses and a train of horizontal pulses.

During the entire vertical blanking period, no picture information is produced, because the signal level is black or blacker than black so that vertical retrace can be blanked out. The details of all the pulses in the vertical blanking interval are summarized in Table 7-2.

Note the position of the first equalizing pulse at the start of vertical blanking in Fig. 7-7. In the signal at the top, the first pulse is a full line away from the previous horizontal sync pulse; in the signal below for the next field, the first pulse is one-half line away. This half-line time difference between even and odd fields continues through all the following pulses, so that the vertical sync pulses for successive fields are timed for odd-line interlaced scanning.

V BLANKING AND V SCANNING The serrated vertical sync pulse forces the vertical deflection circuits to start the flyback. However, the flyback generally does not begin with the start of vertical sync because the sync pulse must build up charge in a capacitor to trigger the scanning circuits. If we assume that vertical flyback starts with the leading edge of the third serration, then the time of one line passes during vertical sync before vertical flyback starts. Also, six equalizing pulses equal to three lines occur before vertical sync. So $3 + 1 = 4$ lines are blanked at the bottom of the picture, just before vertical retrace starts.

How much time is needed for flyback depends on the scanning circuits, but a typical vertical retrace time is five lines. As the scanning beam retraces from bottom to top of the raster, five complete horizontal lines are produced. This vertical retrace can be completed easily within the vertical blanking time.

With 4 lines blanked at the bottom before flyback and 5 lines blanked during flyback, 12 lines remain of the total 21 during vertical blanking. These 12 blanked lines are at the top of the raster at the start of the vertical trace downward.

In summary, 4 lines are blanked at the bottom and 12 lines at the top in each field. In the total frame of two fields, 8 lines are blanked at the bottom and 24 lines at the top. The scanning lines that are produced during vertical trace, but made black by vertical blanking, form black bars at the top and bottom of the picture.

The height of the picture is slightly reduced with blanking, compared with the unblanked raster. However, the height can be corrected easily by increasing the amplitude of the sawtooth waveform for vertical scanning.

SUMMARY OF V BLANKING TIME The vertical blanking pulses repeated at 60 Hz are inserted for every vertical scanning field to blank out V retraces. The V blanking pulse is 1333 μs wide, which is enough time for 21 complete horizontal lines to be scanned in each field.

The serrated V sync pulse also is repeated at 60 Hz to synchronize the vertical scanning for each field. Each *V* sync pulse is six half-lines, or three complete *H* lines, wide. The *V* sync pulse is made much wider than the *H* sync pulses so that they can be separated in the sync circuits at the receiver. Each *V* sync pulse has serrations at half-line intervals in order to maintain the continuity of horizontal synchronization during the *V* sync time.

Just before and after each *V* sync pulse is a group of six equalizing pulses. Given the half-line spacing of the equalizing pulses, each group is three *H* lines long. Half-line spacing maintains the continuity of horizontal synchronization by alternate equalizing pulses during vertical blanking time.

With two pulses in the time of one complete *H* line, the equalizing pulses are repeated at the rate of $2 \times 15{,}750 = 31{,}500$ Hz. The groups of equalizing pulses just before and after *V* sync are used to improve the vertical synchronization for even and odd fields.

The half-line serrations in the vertical sync pulse also have a frequency of 31,500 Hz. Actually, the equalizing pulses and vertical serrations are similar pulses but with opposite polarities.

Test Point Questions 7-4

Answers at End of Chapter

Which pulses in *V* blanking correspond to the following?

a. 3*H* lines wide
b. 21*H* lines wide
c. 31,500 Hz

7-5 PICTURE INFORMATION AND VIDEO SIGNAL AMPLITUDES

The two examples shown in Fig. 7-8 illustrate how the composite video signal corresponds to visual information. In Fig. 7-8*a*, the video signal corresponds to one scanning line for an image with a black vertical bar down the center of a white frame. In Fig. 7-8*b*, the black-and-white values in the picture are reversed from those in Fig. 7-8*a*. These signals are shown with positive sync polarity, but the same idea applies with negative sync polarity.

At the left in Fig.7-8*a*, the camera signal obtained by active scanning of the image is initially at the white level, corresponding to the white background. The scanning beam continues its forward motion across the white background of the frame, and the signal continues at the same white level until it reaches the middle of the picture. When the black bar is scanned, the video signal changes to the black level and remains there while the entire width of the black bar is scanned. Then the signal amplitude changes to the white level, corresponding to the white background, and continues at that level while the forward scanning motion toward the right side of the image is completed.

At the end of the visible trace, the horizontal blanking pulse brings the video signal amplitude to the black level in preparation for horizontal retrace. After retrace, the forward scanning motion begins again at the next horizontal line. Each successive horizontal line in the even and odd fields is scanned this way. As a result, the corresponding composite video signal for the entire picture contains a succession of signals with a waveform identical to that shown in Fig. 7-8*a* for each active horizontal scanning line.

For the image in Fig. 7-8*b* the idea is the same, but the camera signal corresponds to a white vertical bar down the center of a black frame. This signal starts and finishes at the black level and is at the white level in the middle.

These are simple types of images, but the correlation can be extended to an image having any distribution of light and shade. If the pattern contains five vertical black bars against a white background, the composite video signal for each

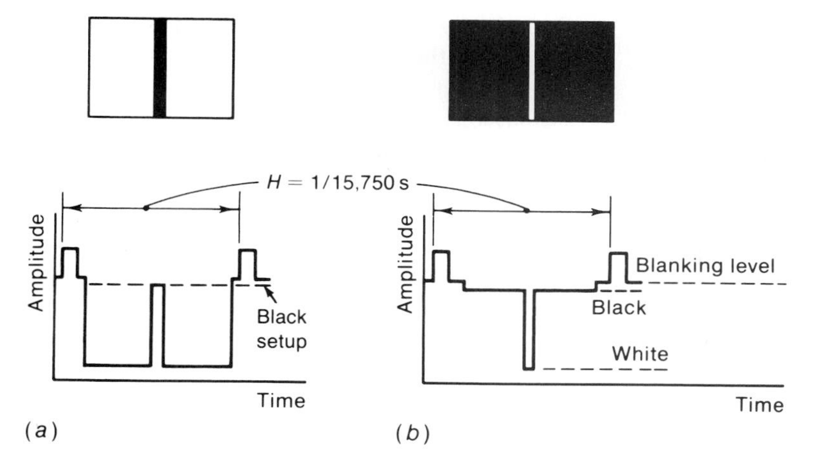

Fig. 7-8 Composite video signal and its picture information. (*a*) Picture with black vertical bar on white background. (*b*) Reverse information with white bar on black background.

horizontal line will include five rapid variations in amplitude from white to black.

As another example, suppose the pattern consists of a horizontal black bar across the center of a white frame. Then most of the horizontal lines will contain white picture information for the entire trace period. The camera signal amplitude will remain at the white level except during the blanking intervals. However, for those horizontal lines that scan the black bar, the camera signal is produced at the black level.

TYPICAL VIDEO SIGNAL VOLTAGES An actual picture consists of elements having different amounts of light and shade with a nonuniform distribution in the horizontal lines and through the vertical fields. When there is motion in the scene, the video signal contains a succession of continuously changing voltages. Within each line, the camera signal amplitude varies for different picture elements. Furthermore, the waveforms of the camera signal for the lines change within the field.

The resulting waveforms are shown by the oscilloscope photographs of a typical video signal in Fig. 7-9. This signal is for the control grid of the picture tube. It has an amplitude of 100 V p-p and negative sync polarity.

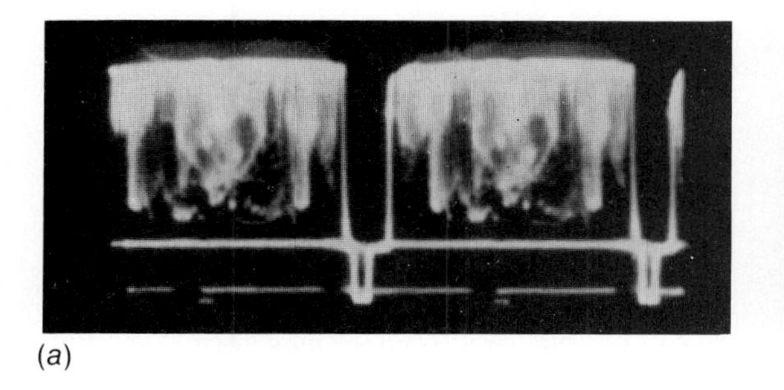

(*a*)

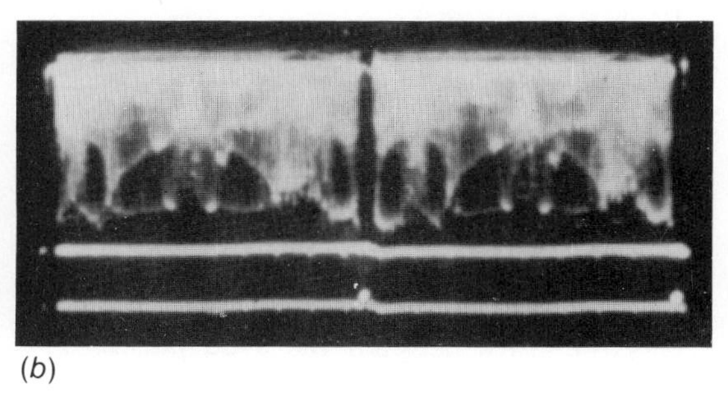

(*b*)

Fig. 7-9 Oscilloscope photographs of composite video signal, shown with sync down for negative polarity. (*a*) Two horizontal lines with picture information between *H* blanking pulses. Oscilloscope internal sweep at 15,750/2 = 7875 Hz. (*b*) Two fields of vertical picture information between *V* blanking pulses. Oscilloscope internal sweep at 60/2 = 30 Hz.

Test Point Questions 7-5

Answers at End of Chapter

Answer True or False.

a. The typical video signal voltage for the picture tube is 1 V p-p.

b. The video signal in Fig. 7-8*a* has more white than that in Fig. 7-8*b*.

7-6 OSCILLOSCOPE WAVEFORMS

When you look at oscilloscope patterns, the camera signal variations are usually hazy as they change with motion in the scene. However, the oscilloscope trace locks in for the *H* blanking and sync pulses at the steady rate of 15,750 Hz or for the *V* pulses at 60 Hz. Preferably, the internal horizontal sweep frequency of the oscilloscope is set at one-half these frequencies, to show a video signal either for two lines, as in Fig. 7-9*a*, or for two fields, as in Fig. 7-9*b*. Then each cycle is shown as wide as possible and with continuity through blanking time.

LINE RATE When the oscilloscope sweep is set at 15,750/2 = 7875 Hz, you see two *H* lines of video signal (Fig. 7-9*a*). When the scene shows a person walking across the room, as an example of horizontal motion, the camera signal variations move across the oscilloscope screen between the *H* pulses.

FIELD RATE When the oscilloscope sweep is 60/2 = 30 Hz, you see two fields of video signal (Fig. 7-9*b*). Any vertical motion in the scene is seen as motion in the camera signal variations across the trace between the sync pulses. The lines extending across the top and bottom of the vertical sync in the oscilloscope pattern are caused by the horizontal sync.

You do not see the equalizing pulses in this pattern because the oscilloscope is locked at the vertical scanning frequency. To see the equalizing pulses and the serrations in the vertical pulses, you must set the internal sweep frequency of the oscilloscope to 31,500 Hz or a submultiple. Usually the horizontal sweep of the oscilloscope must be expanded, too.

OSCILLOSCOPE WAVEFORMS AND PICTURE INFORMATION Refer to Fig. 7-10. The image in Fig. 7-10*a* with horizontal and vertical bars is called a *crosshatch pattern.* This type of image produces similar camera signal variations for both horizontal and vertical scanning. The main application of the crosshatch pattern, though, is to check horizontal and vertical scanning linearity for equal spacing of the bars. The crosshatch pattern is used also when convergence adjustments for color picture tubes are made.

In Fig. 7-10*b,* the oscilloscope waveform shows two *H* lines of camera signal because the internal sweep frequency is 7875 Hz. These variations correspond to the vertical bars in the picture.

In Fig. 7-10*c,* the oscilloscope waveform shows two vertical fields because the internal sweep frequency is 30 Hz. These variations of camera signal correspond to the horizontal bars in the picture.

On most oscilloscopes the 30- and 7875-Hz positions are marked on the internal sweep frequency switch as *V* and *H* for TV. This makes it easy to switch between the video signal for two *H* scanning lines and that for two *V* scanning fields.

Test Point Questions 7-6

Answers at End of Chapter

Refer to the oscilloscope waveforms in Fig. 7-10.

a. Is sync polarity negative or positive?

b. Is the video signal for the vertical bars shown in Fig. 7-10*b* or *c?*

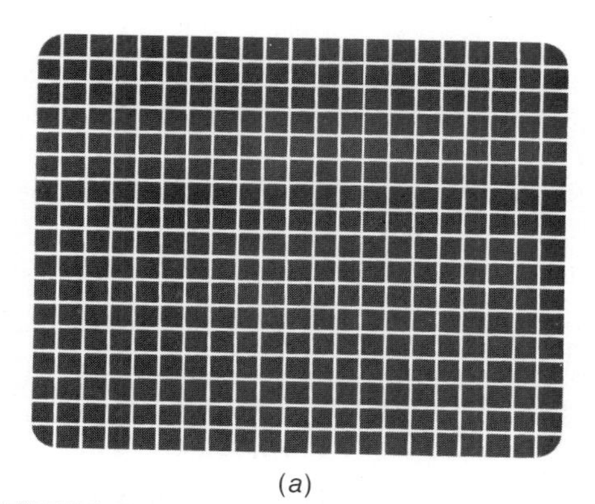

(*a*)

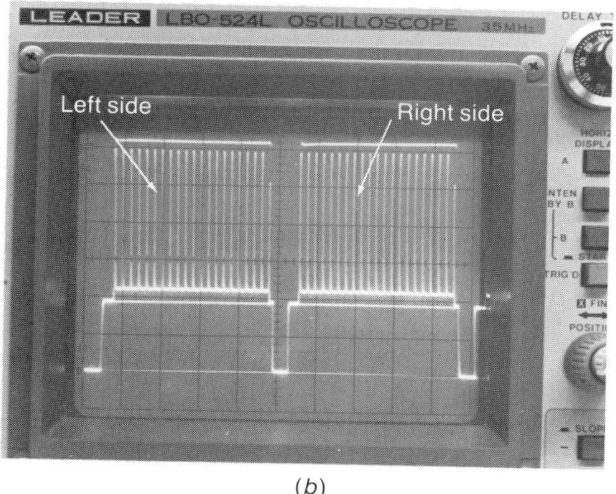

(*b*)

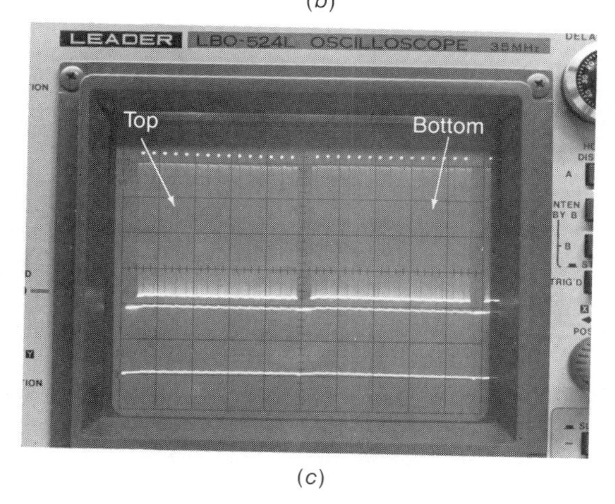

(*c*)

Fig. 7-10 How the video signal waveforms correspond to picture information. (*a*) Crosshatch pattern on screen of picture tube. (*b*) Horizontal picture information with *H* sync pulses. (*c*) Vertical picture information with *V* sync pulses.

7-7 PICTURE INFORMATION AND VIDEO SIGNAL FREQUENCIES

Camera signal frequencies vary from approximately 30 Hz to 4 MHz. Note that 30 Hz at the low end is an audio frequency, and 4 MHz at the high end is actually a radio frequency. This tremendous range of frequencies makes the video signal a wideband signal. It spans a range of approximately 17 octaves.

The camera signal has very rapid changes within a line because the horizontal scanning is fast. Specifically, a 4-MHz signal represents a change in amplitude between two successive picture elements that takes 0.25 μs in horizontal scanning. Note that the 4-MHz limit is only a legal restriction determined by the 6-MHz channel of television broadcast stations.

In vertical scanning, the camera signal variations have much lower frequencies because of the slower scanning speed. A 30-Hz signal represents a change in amplitude between two successive fields repeated at the rate of 60 Hz. Frequencies lower than 30 Hz can be considered as a change in dc level.

VIDEO FREQUENCIES ASSOCIATED WITH HORIZONTAL SCANNING In the checkerboard pattern in Fig. 7-11, the square-wave signal at the top represents the camera signal variations of the composite video signal obtained in scanning one horizontal line. It is desired to find the frequency of this square wave. The frequency of the camera signal variations is very important in determining whether the television system can transmit and reproduce the corresponding picture information.

To determine the frequency of any signal variation, the time for one complete cycle must be known. A *cycle* includes the time from one point on the signal waveform to the next succeeding point that has the same magnitude and direction. Then the frequency is the reciprocal of the period. For example, the period for scanning one hori-

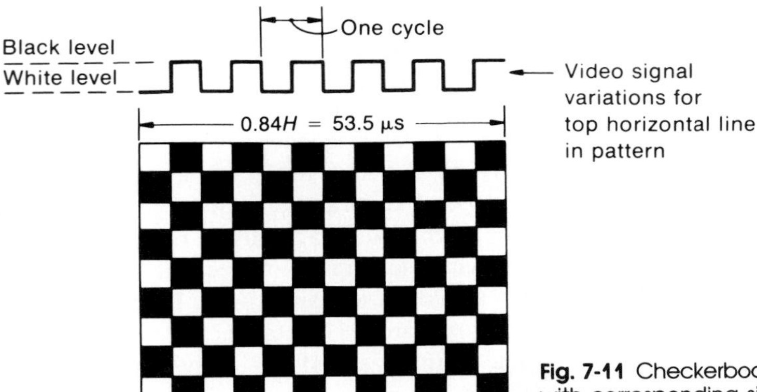

Fig. 7-11 Checkerboard pattern of 12 black and white squares with corresponding signal variations.

zontal line is 1/15,750 s, and so the line-scanning frequency is 15,750 Hz. The camera signal variations within one horizontal line, however, necessarily have a shorter period and a higher frequency.

Note that one complete cycle of camera signal in Fig. 7-11 includes the information in two adjacent picture elements, one white and the other black. Only after scanning the second square does the camera signal have the same magnitude and direction as at the start of the first square. So, to find the frequency of the camera signal variations, we must find out how long it takes to scan two adjacent squares. The time is the period for one cycle of the resultant camera signal.

Now we can calculate the period of one complete cycle of the square-wave camera signal variations in Fig. 7-11. The period for horizontal line scanning is 1/15,750, or 63.5 μs, including trace and retrace. Given a horizontal blanking time of 10.2 μs, the time remaining for visible trace is 53.3 μs. This is the time needed to scan all the picture elements in a line.

The 12 squares in one line are scanned in 53.3 μs. Less time T is needed to scan two squares—$\frac{2}{12}$, or $\frac{1}{6}$, of 53.3 μs:

$$T = \tfrac{1}{6} \times 53.3\ \mu\text{s} = 8.8\ \mu\text{s}$$

The period for one complete cycle of the square-wave signal is T, and the frequency $f = 1/T$. So

$$f = \frac{1}{T} = \frac{1}{8.8\ \mu\text{s}} = 0.11\ \text{MHz}$$

In Fig. 7-11, the frequency of the square-wave camera signal variations shown at the top of the checkerboard pattern is 0.11 MHz.

TYPICAL PICTURE INFORMATION When a typical picture is scanned, the scattered areas of light and shade do not produce a symmetric square-wave signal. However, the differences of light and shade correspond to changes in the camera signal amplitude. The frequency of the resultant camera signal variations always depends on the time needed to scan adjacent areas with different light values.

When large objects with a constant white, gray, or black level are scanned, the corresponding camera signal variations have low frequencies. The reason is the comparatively long time between changes in amplitude.

Smaller areas of light and shade in the image are scanned at higher video frequencies. The highest signal frequencies correspond to variations between very small picture elements in a horizontal line, especially the vertical edge between a white area and a black area.

VIDEO FREQUENCIES ASSOCIATED WITH VERTICAL SCANNING At the opposite extreme, signal variations that correspond to picture elements adjacent in the vertical direction have low frequencies because the vertical scanning rate is comparatively slow. Variations between one line and the next correspond to a frequency of approximately 10 kHz. Slower changes over larger distances in vertical scanning occur at lower frequencies. The very low frequency of 30 Hz corresponds to a variation in light level between two successive fields.

VIDEO FREQUENCIES AND PICTURE INFORMATION Figure 7-12 shows how the size of the picture information relates to the video frequencies. The main body of the image in Fig. 7-12*a* is shown in Fig. 7-12*b* with only the large areas of white and black. These video frequencies extend up to 100 kHz. However, the detail with sharp edges and outlines is filled in by the high video frequencies from 0.1 to 4 MHz shown in Fig. 7-12*c*. Note that the canopy of the building is reproduced in Fig. 7-12*b*, but its stripes and the small lettering need the high-frequency reproduction in Fig. 7-12*c*.

One practical and interesting application is that it is much easier to get a sharp picture in a closeup view of the image than with a long-shot view. An example is a closeup showing only a person's face. Even individual hairs in the eyebrow are not too small relative to the picture width. Then this picture information does not require too high a frequency, and so the reproduction can be sharp and clear. In a long-shot view, very small details of the scene are too small to be reproduced.

In color television also, closeup views and the background look good because of the relatively low video frequencies of the picture information, compared with those of a long-shot view. Specifically, color information is included in the television picture only for video frequencies up to approximately 0.5 MHz, in most receivers.

Test Point Questions 7-7

Answers at End of Chapter

Would you associate the following frequencies with *V* or *H* resolution?

a. 2 kHz
b. 0.5 MHz
c. 3.2 MHz

7-8 MAXIMUM NUMBER OF PICTURE ELEMENTS

If we consider a checkerboard pattern such as Fig. 7-11 with many more squares, the maximum number of picture elements can be calculated by letting each square be one element. Then the total number of elements in the area equals the maximum details in a line horizontally, multiplied by the details in a vertical row. However, horizontal detail and vertical detail must be considered separately in a television picture because of the scanning process. For horizontal detail, the problem lies in determining how many elements correspond to the high-frequency limit of the 4-MHz video signal. The vertical detail involves the question of how many elements can be resolved by the scanning lines.

MAXIMUM HORIZONTAL DETAIL Proceeding in the same manner as in the previous section, we can find the number of elements corresponding to 4 MHz, to show the maximum number of picture elements in a horizontal line and the size of the smallest possible horizontal detail. The period of one complete cycle for a 4-MHz signal variation is $1/(4 \times 10^6)$ s $= 0.25\ \mu$s. This is the time needed to scan two adjacent picture ele-

(a)

(b)

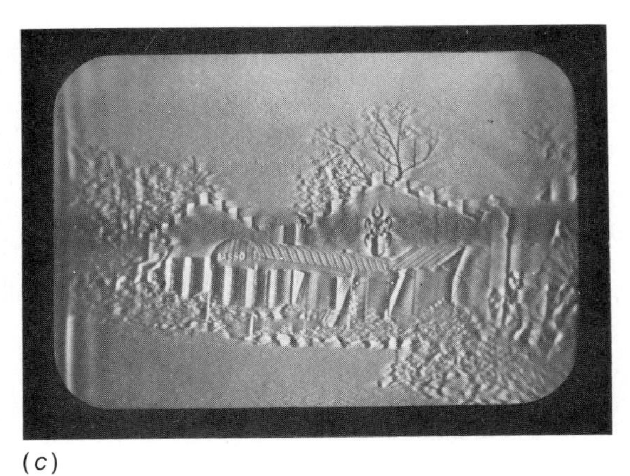
(c)

Fig. 7-12 Effect of video frequencies on picture reproductions. (*a*) Normal picture. (*b*) Only large areas in picture reproduced with low video frequencies up to 0.1 MHz. (*c*) Only edges and outlines reproduced with high video frequencies between 0.1 and 4 MHz.

ments. Since two elements can be scanned in 0.25 μs, eight elements can be scanned in 1 μs. Finally, 8 × 53.3 = 426 picture elements can be scanned during the entire active line period of 53.3 μs. If there were 426 squares in the horizontal direction in the checkerboard pattern in Fig. 7-11, then, the resultant camera signal variations would produce a 4-MHz signal.

UTILIZATION RATIO AND VERTICAL DETAIL

Each scanning line can represent at best only one detail in the vertical direction. However, a scanning line may represent no vertical detail at all by missing a vertical detail completely. Also, two lines may straddle one picture element. The problem in establishing the useful vertical detail, then, is determining how many picture elements can be reproduced by a given number of scanning lines.

The number of scanning lines useful in representing the vertical detail divided by the total number of visible scanning lines is the *utilization ratio.* Theoretical calculations and experimental tests show that the utilization ratio ranges from 0.6 to 0.8 for different images with typical picture content. We can use 0.7 as an average.

Now the maximum possible number of vertical elements can be determined. The number of visible lines is 525 minus those scanned during vertical blanking. With a vertical blanking time of

8 percent, the number of lines blanked out for the entire frame is 0.06 × 525, or approximately 42 lines. Some of these lines occur during vertical retrace, and others are scanned at the top or bottom of the frame, but all are blanked out. Thus 525 − 42 = 483 visible lines remain. With a utilization ratio of 0.7, the number of lines useful in showing vertical detail is

$$483 \times 0.7 = 338$$

This value represents the number of effective scanning lines.

Therefore, the maximum number of vertical details that can be reproduced with 483 visible scanning lines is about 338, with the exact value depending on the utilization ratio.

TOTAL NUMBER OF PICTURE ELEMENTS On the basis of the previous calculations, the maximum number of picture elements possible for the entire image is 426 × 338, or about 144,000. This number is independent of the picture size.

A single frame of 35-mm motion-picture film has about 500,000 picture elements. The smaller 16-mm frame contains one-fourth as many, or about 125,000. So the televised reproduction can have about the same amount of detail as seen in 16-mm motion pictures.

Test Point Questions 7-8

Answers at End of Chapter

Give the maximum number of picture details for

a. Each horizontal line

b. Total picture area

7-9 DC COMPONENT OF THE VIDEO SIGNAL

In addition to continuous amplitude variations for individual picture elements, the average value of the video signal must correspond to the average brightness in the scene. Otherwise, the receiver could not follow changes in brightness. As an example of the importance of the brightness level, the ac camera signal for a gray picture element on a black background is the same as the signal for white on a gray background, assuming there is no average-brightness information to indicate the change in background.

The *average level* of a signal is the arithmetic mean of all the instantaneous values measured from the zero axis. In Fig. 7-13*a*, the average level is higher than in Fig. 7-13*b* because the camera signal variations have higher amplitudes. Now, it is important to remember that the average value of any signal variation for a complete cycle is its dc component. Therefore, the dc component in Fig. 7-13*a* is closer to the black level than that in Fig. 7-13*b*. Although it is illustrated here for one scanning line (for convenience), the required dc component of the video signal is its average value for complete frames, since the background information of the frame indicates the brightness of the scene.

When the average value, or dc component, of the video signal is close to the black level, as in Fig. 7-13*a*, the average brightness is dark. The same ac signal variations in Fig. 7-13*b* have a lighter background because the dc axis is farther from the black level.

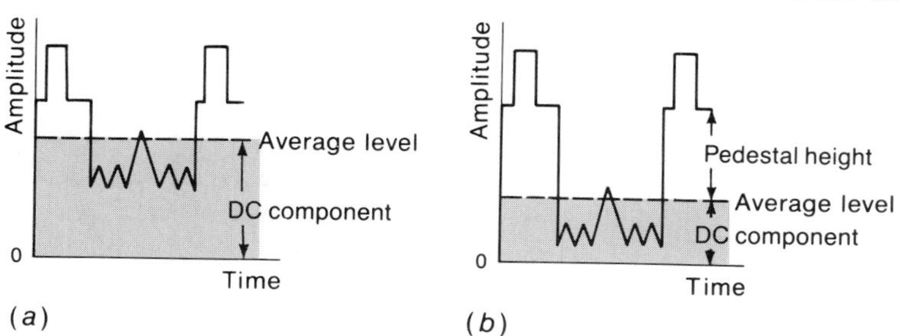

Fig. 7-13 Video signals with same ac variations but different average brightness levels. Only one line of a complete frame is illustrated. (*a*) Dark scene with average value close to black level. (*b*) Light scene with average value further from black level.

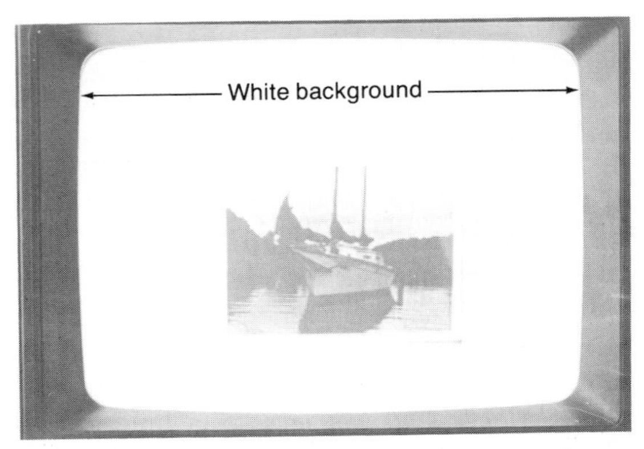

Fig. 7-14 Effect of incorrect brightness without the required dc component. Picture information is too dark because of white background.

The distance between the average axis and the blanking level is called the *pedestal height* of the video signal, as shown in Fig. 7-13*b*. The signal for a light scene has a greater pedestal height than that for a dark scene.

Note that an incorrect dc level results in the wrong brightness. This effect is illustrated in Fig. 7-14. Without the dc component, the picture information here is too dark. This picture requires more pedestal height because of the white background. The transmitted signal has the correct average dc level, but it can be lost by capacitive coupling in the video amplifier.

In monochrome, the wrong dc component causes only incorrect brightness. In color television, though, the dc component is necessary in order to reproduce the correct colors.

Test Point Questions 7-9

Answers at End of Chapter

a. Is the average dc level close to the blanking level for a dark or a light scene?

b. Does the picture tube reproduce black with maximum or zero beam current?

7-10 GAMMA AND CONTRAST IN THE PICTURE

Gamma is a numerical factor used in television and film reproduction to indicate how light values are expanded or compressed. Refer to Fig. 7-15. The exponent of the equations for the curves shown is called gamma (γ). The numerical value of gamma is equal to the slope of the straight-line part of the curve where it rises most sharply. A curve with gamma less than 1 is bowed downward, as in Fig. 7-15*a,* with the greatest slope occurring at the start and the relatively flat part occurring at the end. When gamma is greater than 1, the curve is bowed upward, as in Fig. 7-15*b,* and the slope at the start is comparatively flat whereas at the end it is sharp. With a gamma of 1, the result is a straight line, as in Fig. 7-15*c,* and the slope is constant.

A gamma of 1 implies a linear characteristic—none of the light values are exaggerated. When gamma is greater than 1 for the white parts of the image, the reproduced picture looks "contrasty" because the increases in the white level are expanded by the sharp slope, emphasizing the white parts of the picture. Commercial motion pictures shown in a darkened theater have this high-contrast appearance. Gamma values less than 1 for the white parts of the image compress the changes in white levels to make the picture appear softer, with the gradations in gray level more evident.

Any component in the television system can be assigned a value of gamma to describe the shape of its response curve and contrast characteristics. As a typical example, picture tubes have the control-characteristic curve illustrated in Fig. 7-15*b*. The video signal voltage is always at the control grid of the picture tube with the polarity required to make the signal variations for the white parts of the picture fall on that part of the response curve with the steep slope. As a

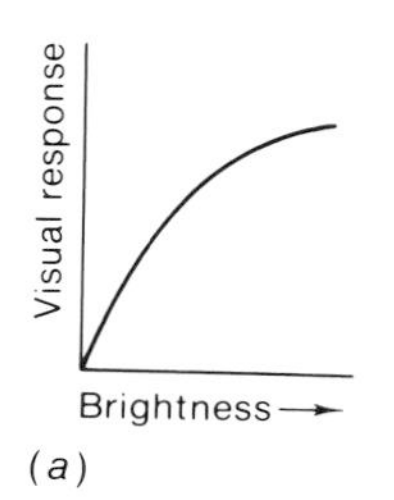

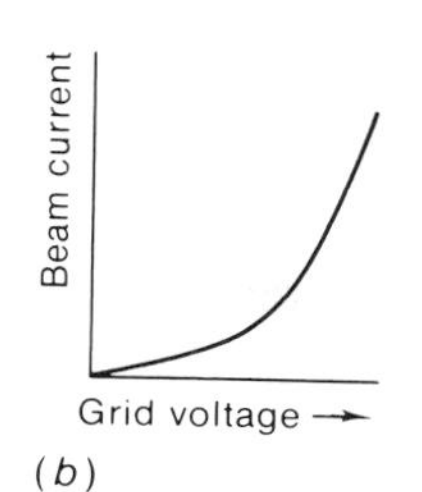

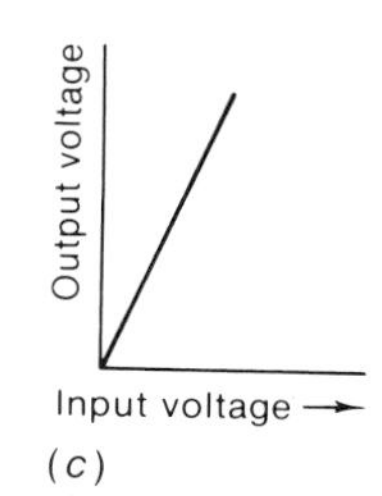

Fig. 7-15 Gamma characteristics. (*a*) Visual response of the eye; gamma is less than 1. (*b*) Control-grid characteristic of picture tube; gamma equals 2.2. (*c*) Linear characteristic of an amplifier; gamma equals 1.

result, a variation in video signal amplitude at the white level produces a greater change in beam current and screen brightness than it would at a darker level. Picture tubes emphasize the white parts of the picture, therefore, with typical gamma values of 2.2 to 3.5. Commercial film also has a gamma greater than 1, with an average value being 1.5.

Amplifiers using linear operation (see Fig. 7-15*c*) have a gamma very nearly unity. The straight-line response shows that the output signal voltage is proportional to the input signal voltage—no signal level is emphasized. If desired, however, an amplifier can be made to operate over the curved portion of its transfer-characteristic curve by shifting the operating bias. The nonlinear amplifier can be used as a gamma-control stage. A gamma value of 0.4545 compensates for 2.22 to provide an overall gamma of 1.

Test Point Questions 7-10

Answers at End of Chapter

a. Does gamma affect the contrast or brightness?

b. Do picture tubes have a gamma greater or less than 1?

7-11 COLOR INFORMATION IN THE VIDEO SIGNAL

For color television, the composite video includes the 3.58-MHz chrominance signal. As a comparison, Fig. 7-16 shows a video signal with and without color. The polarity is shown with sync and with black in the down position while white is in the up position. The relative amplitudes in Fig. 7-16*a* drop from white for the first bar at the left to the gray level and then close to black level. These levels correspond to the relative brightness, or luminance, values for the monochrome information.

In Fig. 7-16*b*, to the video signal is added the 3.58-MHz chrominance signal for the color information in the yellow, green, and blue bars. The specific colors in the *C* signal are not evident because the relative phase angles are not shown. The main point here is that the difference between monochrome and color television is the 3.58-MHz chrominance signal. More details about the 3.58-MHz *C* signal are explained in Chap. 8, "Color Television Circuits and Signals."

Note that the luminance levels in Fig. 7-16*a* are the same as the average levels for the signal variations in Fig. 7-16*b*. This means that without the *C* signal, the color bars in Fig. 7-16*b* would be reproduced in monochrome as the white and gray bars in Fig. 7-16*a*.

Note also that the color signal in Fig. 7-16*a* has a color sync burst on the back porch of horizontal sync. This burst consists of 8 to 11 cycles of the 3.58-MHz color subcarrier signal. Its purpose is to synchronize the 3.58-MHz color oscillator in the receiver. The burst and *C* signal are both 3.58 MHz, but the burst has no picture information, since it is present only during blanking time.

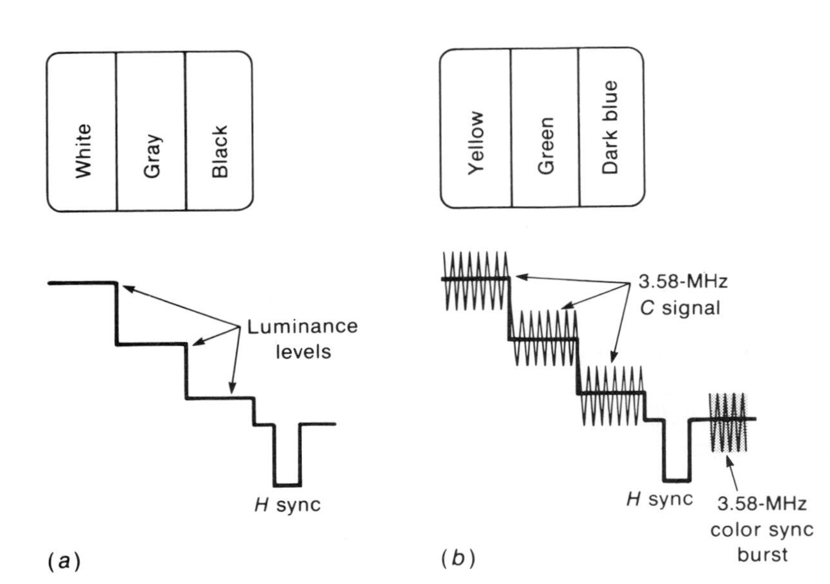

Fig. 7-16 Video signal with and without color. (*a*) Monochrome signal alone, for white, gray, and black picture information. (*b*) Combined with 3.58-MHz chrominance signal for color information.

Test Point Questions 7-11

Answers at End of Chapter

Answer True or False.

a. Color information in the video signal is in the 3.58-MHz *C* signal.

b. Different colors can have lighter or darker luminance values.

SUMMARY

1. The composite video signal includes the camera signal with the picture information, sync pulses, and blanking pulses.
2. The IRE scale for video signal amplitudes includes 140 units p-p. See Fig. 7-5. Sync takes 40 IRE units, with 92.5 units for the camera signal. The black setup is 7.5 units from the blanking level.
3. Horizontal blanking pulses at 15,750 Hz blank out retrace for each *H* line by making the video signal go to the black blanking level. The average width of the *H* blanking pulses is $0.16H$, or 10 μs.
4. Horizontal sync pulses at 15,750 Hz time the scanning for each *H* line. The sync pulses are superimposed on the blanking or pedestal level of the *H* blanking pulses. The width of the *H* sync pulses is approximately 5 μs, or one-half the *H* blanking time. The front porch is the blanking time just before the *H* sync pulse; the back porch is the blanking time just after the pulse.

5. Vertical blanking pulses at 60 Hz blank out the scanning during vertical retrace. Much longer than H blanking, a typical value for V blanking is $0.08V$. This period equals the time needed for 21 lines to be blanked in each field.
6. Vertical sync pulses at 60 Hz time the scanning for each V field. These sync pulses are superimposed on the blanking or pedestal level of the V blanking pulses. The width of the V sync pulse is the time needed to scan $3H$ lines with serrations at half-line intervals.
7. Just before and after the V sync pulses is a group of equalizing pulses. With half-line spacing, the frequency of the equalizing pulses is 31,500 Hz.
8. The high video frequencies in the camera signal variations correspond to small horizontal details. For a 4-MHz video signal, the number of horizontal details in a line is 426.
9. The average utilization ratio of 0.7 means that 70 percent of the visible scanning lines are useful in resolving details in the vertical direction.
10. The dc component of any signal is its average-value axis. In the video signal, the dc component indicates the brightness of the background for signal variations.
11. Gamma is a number that indicates how contrast is expanded or compressed. Picture tubes have a gamma of 2.2, which emphasizes the signal voltages for white.
12. For color television, the composite video signal includes the 3.58-MHz chroma signal, with color sync burst, as shown in Fig. 7-16.

SELF-EXAMINATION

Answers at Back of Book

Answer True or False.

1. The three components of the composite video signal are the camera signal, blanking pulses, and sync pulses, assuming no color.
2. Sync pulses transmitted during vertical blanking time include equalizing pulses, the serrated vertical sync pulse, and horizontal sync pulses.
3. During the front-porch time before a horizontal sync pulse, the scanning beam is at the left edge of the raster.
4. Sync amplitudes take 40 IRE units.
5. Black-and-white variations in the camera signal take 140 IRE units.
6. The visible trace time for one horizontal line is approximately 10 μs.
7. When the vertical blanking pulse starts, the scanning beam is at the top of the raster.
8. The equalizing pulses and serrations in the vertical sync pulse are spaced at half-line intervals.

9. The horizontal blanking pulses can produce vertical black bars at the sides of the raster.
10. The vertical sync pulse for one field starts a half-line away from its timing in the previous field.
11. Camera signal variations between successive horizontal blanking pulses correspond to information from left to right in the picture.
12. In the picture, the left half is white and the right half is black. The corresponding signal frequency for scanning one line is approximately 19 kHz.
13. In the picture, the top half is white and the bottom half is black. The corresponding signal frequency for scanning vertically, then, must be slightly greater than 200 Hz.
14. The high video signal frequencies correspond to greater horizontal detail in the picture.
15. Picture tubes have a gamma greater than 1, causing white to be emphasized, which increases contrast in the reproduced picture.
16. The average brightness of the reproduced picture depends on the dc bias of the picture tube.
17. The chrominance signal and sync burst shown in Fig. 7-16 have the same frequency—3.58 MHz.
18. A television frame contains about the same amount of detail as 35-mm film.

ESSAY QUESTIONS

1. For the following pictures, draw the composite video signal of two consecutive lines in scanning **(a)** an all-white frame, **(b)** two vertical white bars and two black bars equally spaced, **(c)** 10 pairs of vertical bars. Why does this signal have a higher frequency compared with **(b)**.
2. Why are the synchronizing pulses inserted during blanking time?
3. What is the function of the horizontal blanking pulses? Of the vertical blanking pulses?
4. Trace the motion of the scanning beam from the beginning to the end of vertical blanking.
5. Define black setup, gamma, and the utilization ratio.
6. Explain how the blanking level is made black in the reproduced picture.
7. List three types of sync pulses in V blanking time.
8. In the following pairs, which takes longer? **(a)** V blanking or V sync, **(b)** H blanking or H sync, **(c)** V or H blanking.
9. Explain briefly the IRE scale of video signal amplitudes.
10. Give an example of the dc component in any signal waveform.

PROBLEMS

Answers to Odd-Numbered Problems at Back of Book

1. In the checkerboard pattern of Fig. 7-11, if there are 300 squares in a line, what is the frequency of the corresponding signal variations? Use 53.3 μs for the visible trace time.
2. With a utilization ratio of 0.7, what is the maximum number of vertical details for a vertical blanking time of 0.08 V?
3. Assume a facsimile reproduction with specifications of 200 lines per frame, progressive scanning, and 5 frames per second. Calculate the **(a)** time to scan one line, including trace and retrace; (b) visible trace time for one line with 4 percent blanking; **(c)** video frequency corresponding to 100 total black-and-white elements in a line.
4. Calculate the width of each horizontal detail on a screen 20 in. wide for a video signal frequency of 0.5 MHz.
5. Refer to the Worldwide Television Standards in App. D. Calculate the time to scan one line, including trace and retrace for the systems in **(a)** the United States, **(b)** western Europe.

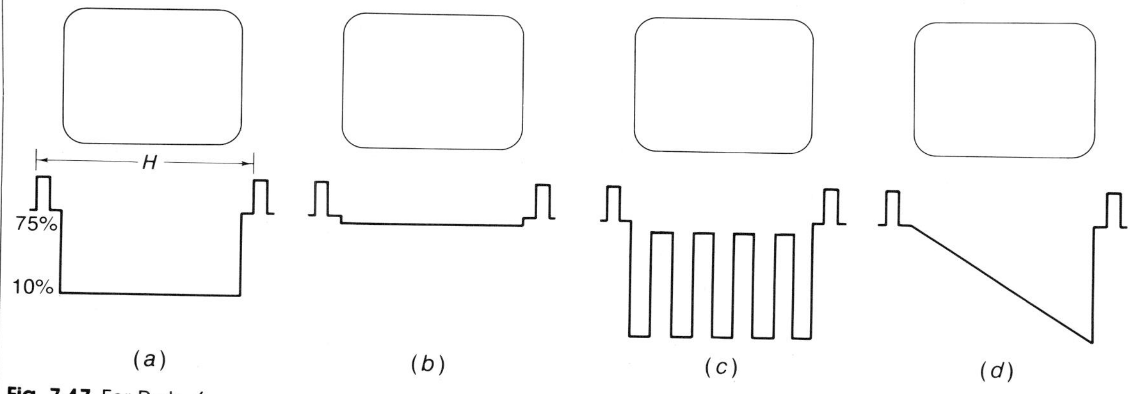

Fig. 7-17 For Prob. 6.

6. Show the pictures that correspond to the video signals in Fig. 7-17. Assume that all the lines of the video signal are the same as the one shown.

SPECIAL QUESTIONS

1. How could a television system have more than 426 horizontal details?
2. How would it be possible to make the number of vertical details much greater?
3. Why does a television picture 4 ft × 3 ft have the same amount of detail as the picture on a 19-in. screen?

ANSWERS TO TEST POINT QUESTIONS

7-1 **a.** Camera signal, *H* sync, and *H* blanking
b. Figure 7-3

7-2 **a.** 40
b. 7.5
c. 92.5

7-3 **a.** 10.2
b. 53.5
c. 5

7-4 **a.** *V* sync
b. *V* blanking
c. Equalizing

7-5 **a.** F
b. T

7-6 **a.** Negative
b. Figure 7-10*b*

7-7 **a.** *V*
b. *H*
c. *H*

7-8 **a.** 426
b. 144,000

7-9 **a.** Dark
b. Zero

7-10 **a.** Contrast
b. Greater

7-11 **a.** T
b. T

8

COLOR TELEVISION CIRCUITS AND SIGNALS

A color picture is actually a monochrome picture but with colors added for the main parts of the scene. The required color information is in the 3.58-MHz chrominance (*C*) signal. To illustrate this idea of the color being in a separate signal, you can turn down the color control to eliminate the color signal, and the result is a black-and-white picture. The monochrome picture is produced by the luminance (*Y*) signal. With both the *C* signal and the *Y* signal, the picture is reproduced in natural color.

Practically all colors can be produced as combinations of red, green, and blue—the primary colors. Other colors, including white, are mixtures of red, green, and blue. A typical picture reproduced on the screen of a tricolor picture tube is shown in color plate I. (All color plates can be found in this chapter.) More details are explained in the following sections:

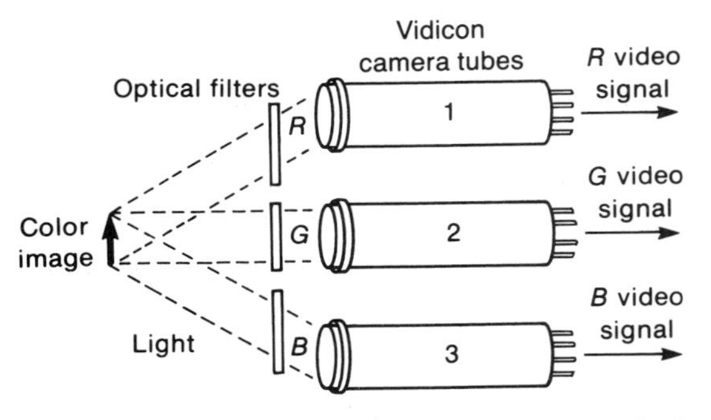

Fig. 8-1 Three vidicon camera tubes producing *R, G,* and *B* video signals for the red, green, and blue colors in the picture.

8-1
RED, GREEN, AND BLUE VIDEO SIGNALS

The color television system begins and ends with red, green, and blue for the color information in the scene. The camera supplies these color video signals from light of different colors. The picture tube converts the red, green, and blue video signals back to light, with the colors corresponding to the original image at the camera tube. In television, the voltages in the color video signal correspond to the colors.

COLOR VIDEO VOLTAGES Refer to Fig. 8-1, where three separate vidicon camera tubes are used for red, green, and blue. These colors in the scene are separated for the camera tubes by optical color filters. As a result, the output from camera tube 1 is a red (*R*) video signal that contains information for only the red parts of the scene. Similarly, tubes 2 and 3 produce green (*G*) and blue (*B*) video signals.

In Fig. 8-2, the picture tube has three electron guns for the red, green, and blue phosphor dots on the screen. Each gun has the usual function of producing a beam of electrons, but the beam excites only one color. The reason is that the shadow mask has tiny holes aligned with the dot trios. When the beams converge at the proper angles, the electrons pass through the mask and excite the color dots.

The red gun produces a red raster and picture on the screen; the green gun and blue gun do

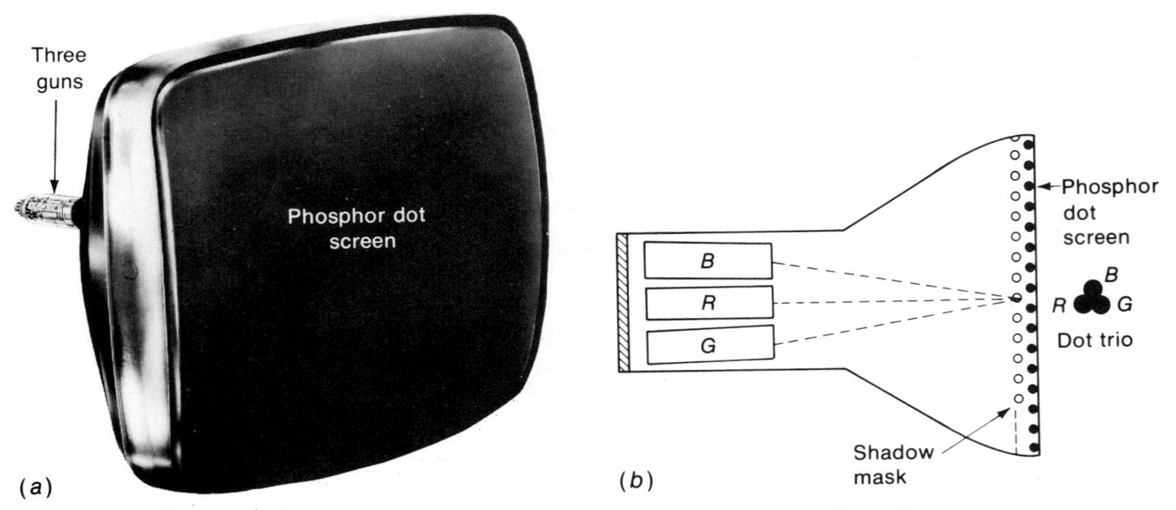

Fig. 8-2 (*a*) Photograph of three-gun tricolor picture tube. (*b*) Internal construction with three electron guns, shadow mask, and dot trios of red, green, and blue phosphors.

the same for their colors. If only one gun is working, you see just one color.

With all three guns operating, the screen reproduces red, green, and blue and their color mixtures. In fact, the white raster is actually a combination of red, green, and blue. Color dots are shown here, but the screen can have vertical stripes of red, green, and blue phosphors.

ENCODING AND DECODING In closed-circuit television, the red, green, and blue video signals are the only information needed to reproduce the picture. For broadcasting, however, these color signals are not compatible with the monochrome television system for black-and-white receivers.

The *R, G,* and *B* video signals are not compatible for black-and-white receivers because each one contains only part of the picture information. They are all needed, but too much bandwidth would have to be used for three separate signals.

Therefore, the color video signals are encoded by combining them in specific proportions, to provide the same video information in a different form. The result of the encoding is the formation of two separate signals—the *C,* or chrominance, or chroma, signal for color and the *Y,* or luminance, or brightness, signal for black-and-white information.

At the receiver, the color picture tube still needs *R, G,* and *B* video signals, corresponding to the color phosphors on the screen. However, the *C* signal is decoded by demodulation. Then this detected output is combined with the luminance signal to recover the original red, green, and blue video signals for the color picture tube. More details of the *R, G,* and *B* video signals are illustrated in Figs. 8-3 to 8-5.

DIFFERENT *R, G,* AND *B* AMPLITUDES In Fig. 8-3, the separate *R, G,* and *B* video signals are shown for a horizontal line scanned across the image with vertical red, green, and blue bars.

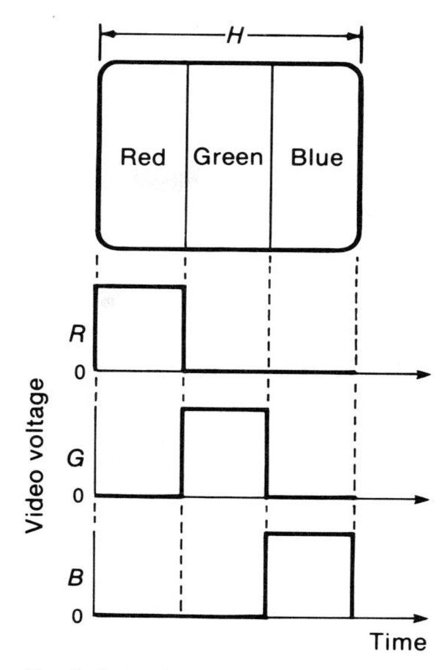

Fig. 8-3 *R, G,* and *B* color video signals for red, green, and blue color bars. These bars have different hues. *H* indicates one horizontal scanning line for width of picture.

Each bar represents picture information of that particular color. The *R* signal voltage is at its full amplitude while the red bar is scanned. However, there is no *R* video signal for the green or blue information. Similarly, the *G* video voltage is produced only when green picture information is scanned, and the *B* video voltage indicates only blue information.

DIFFERENT AMPLITUDES OF THE SAME COLOR See Fig. 8-4. Here the red, pink, and pale pink bars have decreasing values of color intensity. Therefore, the corresponding video voltages have decreasing amplitudes. We can say, then, that *R, G,* or *B* video voltage indicates information of that color, with the relative amplitude depending on the color intensity.

Note that, along with the decreasing amplitudes of *R* signal, the *B* and *G* video signals have increasing amplitudes for pink compared with full red. The *B* and *G* video signals with

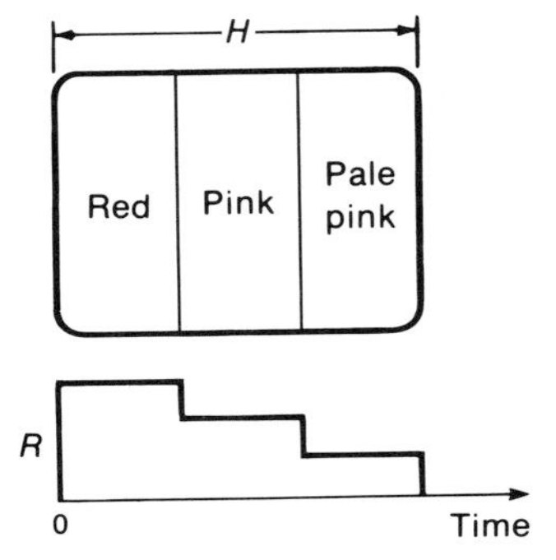

Fig. 8-4 Decreasing amplitudes of R color video signal for red, pink, and pale pink color bars, indicating weaker colors with less color saturation.

R provide the white, which decreases the saturation from red to pink.

COLOR VIDEO FREQUENCIES In Fig. 8-5, all the color bars are red, but the bars just become narrower. This is just a case of less scanning time across smaller details of picture information. The result is higher video frequencies. For either chrominance or luminance information, the high-frequency components of the video signal determine the amount of horizontal detail that can be reproduced in the picture.

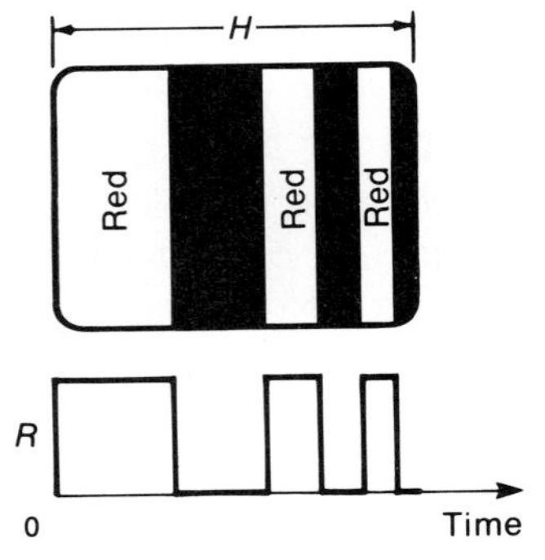

Fig. 8-5 An example of increasing frequencies of color video signal for color bars with less width, indicating smaller details of information.

Test Point Questions 8-1

Answers at End of Chapter

a. What are the phosphor colors for a tricolor picture tube?
b. What is the R video signal amplitude for the green bar in Fig. 8-3?
c. Which color bar in Fig. 8-4 produces the highest R video signal amplitude?
d. Does the R video signal in Fig. 8-5 have different amplitudes or different frequencies?

8-2 COLOR ADDITION

Almost any color can be produced by adding red, green, and blue in different proportions. The additive effect is obtained by superimposing the individual colors. In a tricolor picture tube, the red, green, and blue information on the screen is integrated by the eye to provide the color mixtures in the actual scene. The persistence of the image provides the effect of color mixing.

ADDITIVE COLOR MIXTURES The idea of adding colors is shown in color plate VII. The three circles in red, green, and blue overlap partially. Where the circles are superimposed, the color shown is the mixture produced by adding the primary colors. At the center, all three color circles overlap, resulting in white.

Where only green and blue add, the result is a greenish blue mixture called *cyan.* Some people might consider this color just blue or perhaps turquoise. However, *cyan* is the name to remember for this green-blue mixture.

When only red and blue are added, the bluish red color is called *magenta.* This color is similar to violet or purple, but magenta has more red.

Yellow is an additive color mixture with approximately equal parts of red and green. More red and less green produce orange.

Similarly, practically all natural colors can be produced as mixtures of red, green, and blue, including the so-called neutral colors, such as white and gray.

PRIMARY COLORS The primary colors are combined to form different mixtures. The only requirement is that no primary can be recreated by mixing the other primaries. Red, green, and blue are the primary colors used in television because they produce a wide range of color mixtures when they are added together. Therefore, red, green, and blue are additive primaries.

COMPLEMENTARY COLORS The color that produces white light when it is added to a primary is called its *complement.* For instance, yellow, when added to blue, produces white light. Therefore, yellow is the complement of the blue primary.

The fact that yellow plus blue equals white follows because yellow is a mixture of red and green. Therefore, the combination of yellow and blue actually includes all three primaries.

Similarly, magenta is the complement of green, and cyan is the complement of red. Sometimes the complementary colors cyan, magenta, and yellow are referred to as *minus red, minus green,* and *minus blue,* respectively, because each can be produced as white light minus the corresponding primary.

A primary and its complement can be considered to be opposite colors. The reason is that the complement of any primary contains the other two primaries. This idea is illustrated by the color circle in Fig. 8-6, where the dashed lines connect each primary and its opposite complementary color.

The hue of the complementary colors can be seen in color plate VII. Cyan is a greenish blue,

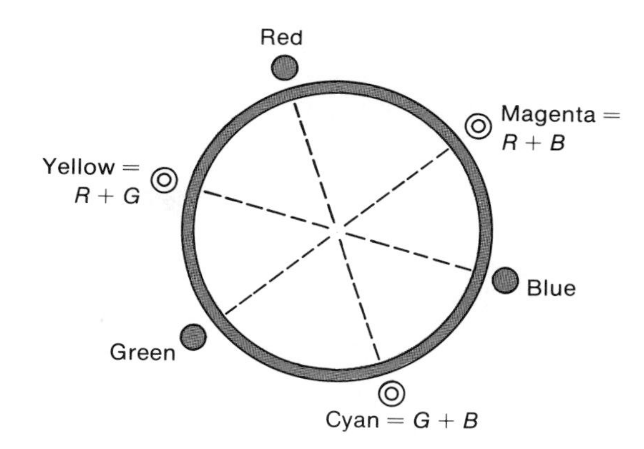

Fig. 8-6 Color wheel showing primary colors red, green, and blue with their opposite, or complementary, colors cyan, magenta, and yellow.

and magenta is a purplish red. When considered as primary colors in a subtractive system, these colors are often labeled simply blue, red, and yellow. However, this blue is really cyan with green and blue; the red is magenta, combining blue and red; the yellow combines green and red.

A *subtractive system* is used in color photography. In this method, mixtures are obtained by subtracting individual primary colors from white light by means of color filters. Thus cyan, magenta, and yellow are the subtractive primary colors used to filter out red, green, and blue, respectively.

In summary, the additive primaries for color television and their complementary colors are:

PRIMARY COLOR	COMPLEMENTARY COLOR
Red	Cyan
Green	Magenta
Blue	Yellow

Furthermore, the components of the complementary colors are

Cyan = blue + green
Magenta = red + blue
Yellow = red + green

ADDING COLOR VOLTAGES What you see on the screen is the superimposed combination of red, green, and blue. This effect is most obvious when you look at a raster alone, without any picture. If the blue gun is cut off by adjusting either the bias or the screen-grid voltage, then the electron beams of the red and green guns can produce a yellow raster. If there is more red and less green, you see the raster color become orange.

Similarly, the blue and green guns operating without the red gun produce cyan; or the red and blue guns alone produce magenta. With all three guns operating to reproduce red, green, and blue in the correct proportions, the raster is white.

All three guns are cut off to reproduce black, which is just the absence of light. Black is the same in color or monochrome.

COMPLEMENTARY VOLTAGE POLARITIES Another important feature of color video voltages is the fact that opposite polarities correspond to complementary colors. To illustrate this idea, assume that the blue video voltage has the polarity that increases the beam current of the blue gun. More blue video voltage produces more beam current from the blue gun, to reproduce more blue in the raster and picture. Although all three guns are operating, in this example we are looking only at the effect of blue. Note now that the opposite polarity of the blue video voltage decreases the beam current. Then less beam current from the blue gun reduces the amount of blue on the screen. The same effect is achieved by increasing the red and green, which is a yellow combination. Furthermore, yellow is the complement of blue. The result, then, is that reversing the polarity of a color video voltage causes a change to its complementary color.

Test Point Questions 8-2

Answers at End of Chapter

a. What color, when added to yellow, will produce white?
b. What color is the complement of blue?
c. Green, when added to blue, produces what color?

8-3 DEFINITIONS OF COLOR TELEVISION TERMS

Any color has three characteristics to specify the visual information: its hue, or tint, which is what we generally call the color; its saturation; and its luminance. Saturation indicates how concentrated, vivid, or intense the color is. Luminance indicates the brightness, or what shade of gray the color would be in a black-and-white picture. We define these qualities of colors and other important terms now in order to analyze the special features of color television.

WHITE Actually, white light can be considered as a mixture of the red, green, and blue in the proper proportions. A glass prism produces the colors of the rainbow from white light. For the opposite effect, red, green, and blue can be added to produce white.

The reference white for television is specified as a color temperature of 6500 K. This is a bluish white, like daylight. The symbol K indicates degrees Kelvin on the absolute temperature scale. In the Kelvin scale, 0 K corresponds to −273°C.

When a color camera is set up, it is aimed at a card specified as reference white. Then the camera is adjusted so that all *R, G,* and *B* video outputs are equal.

HUE The color itself is its hue, or tint. Green leaves have a green hue; a red apple has a red hue. The color of any object is distinguished primarily by its hue. Different hues result when different wavelengths of the light produce the visual sensation in the eye.

SATURATION Saturated colors are vivid, intense, deep, or strong. Pale or weak colors have little saturation. The saturation indicates how little the color is diluted by white. For example, vivid red is fully saturated. When the red is diluted by white, the result is pink, which is really a desaturated red. Note that a fully saturated color has no white.

CHROMINANCE This term is used to combine both hue and saturation. In color television, the 3.58-MHz color signal, specifically, is the chrominance signal. In short, the chrominance includes all the color information, without the brightness. The chrominance and brightness together specify the picture information completely. Chrominance is also called *chroma.*

We can reserve the term *chrominance,* or *chroma,* for the 3.58-MHz modulated subcarrier signal. This C signal contains the hue and saturation for all the colors. Its frequency is 3.58 MHz. However, before modulation and after demodulation, the color information is in the red, green, and blue color video signals. The range of these modulation frequencies, or the baseband for color, can be considered practically as 0 to 0.5 MHz.

Let us summarize these important differences in the frequency ranges:

C signal: Includes side frequencies above and below the 3.58-MHz modulated subcarrier, mainly 3.08 to 4.08 MHz.

R, G, and B video signals: Include baseband frequencies of 0 to 0.5 MHz.

$R - Y$, $B - Y$, and $G - Y$ video signals: Also include the baseband frequencies of 0 to 0.5 MHz. However, these symbols are color mixtures because each has the color components of the $-Y$ signal.

LUMINANCE The luminance indicates the amount of light intensity, which is perceived by the eye as brightness. In a black-and-white picture, the lighter parts have more luminance than the dark areas.

Different colors also have shades of luminance, however, since some colors appear brighter than others. This idea is illustrated by the relative luminosity curve in color plate VIII*b.* The curve shows that the green hues between cyan and orange have maximum brightness.

The luminance really indicates how the color will look in a black-and-white reproduction. Consider a scene being either photographed on black-and-white film or televised in monochrome. The picture includes a colorful costume with a dark red skirt, yellow blouse, and a light blue hat. For the same illumination, these different hues will have different brightness values and so will be reproduced in different shades of monochrome.

As shown by the graph in color plate VIII for relative brightness values of different hues, dark red has low brightness, yellow has high brightness, and blue has medium brightness. Therefore, the monochrome picture reproduction will show a white blouse (for yellow) with a black shirt (for dark red) and a gray hat (for light blue). The relative brightness variations for different hues make it possible to reproduce scenes that are naturally in color as similar pictures in black and white.

In color television, the luminance information is in the luminance, or Y, signal. This abbreviation should not be confused with yellow, because the luminance signal contains only the brightness variations for all the information in the picture.

The Y signal components are 30 percent red,

59 percent green, and 11 percent blue. These percentages approximate the brightness sensation of human vision for different colors. As a result, a monochrome picture produced by the *Y* signal looks correct in shades of gray and white.

COMPATIBILITY Color television is compatible with black-and-white television because essentially the same scanning standards are used, and the luminance signal enables a monochrome receiver to reproduce in black and white a picture televised in color. In addition, color television receivers can use a monochrome signal to reproduce the picture in black and white. Color television broadcasting uses the same 6-MHz broadcast channels as in monochrome transmission. Also, the same picture carrier frequency is used.

SUBCARRIER The subcarrier signal modulates another carrier wave of higher frequency. In color television, the color information modulates the 3.58-MHz color subcarrier signal, which modulates the main picture carrier signal in the standard broadcast channel.

MULTIPLEXING The technique of using one carrier wave for two separate signals is called *multiplexing.* In color television, the 3.58-MHz *C* signal is multiplexed with the *Y* signal as both modulate the main picture carrier wave. Another example of multiplexing is stereo broadcasting in the commercial FM broadcast band, to transmit left and right audio signals on one RF carrier.

Test Point Questions 8-3

Answers at End of Chapter

a. Is red the hue or luminance of a color?
b. Is pink different from red in hue or in saturation?
c. Does red have high or low luminance?

8-4 ENCODING THE PICTURE INFORMATION

Now we can consider in greater detail how the chrominance signal is produced for transmission to the receiver. First, the *R, G,* and *B* video voltages provide the picture information. Then these primary signals are encoded to form separate chrominance and luminance signals.

PRIMARY COLOR VIDEO SIGNALS The camera receives red, green, and blue light corresponding to the color information in the scene, to produce the primary color video signals in Fig. 8-7. These waveforms illustrate the voltages obtained in scanning one horizontal line across the color bars. The red camera tube produces full output for red, but no output for green or blue. Similarly, the green and blue camera tubes have outputs for only their color.

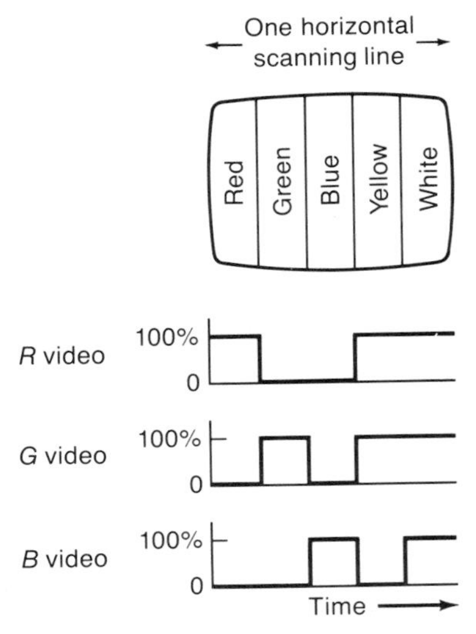

Fig. 8-7 *R, G,* and *B* video signals for color-bar pattern. Included are the primary colors (red, green, and blue) a complementary color (yellow), and white.

Note the values shown for yellow, as an example of a complementary color. Since yellow includes red and green, the video voltage is produced for both these primary colors, as the red and green camera tubes have light input through their color filters. However, there is no blue in yellow, which explains why the blue video voltage is zero for the yellow bar.

The last bar at the right is white, as an example of all three primaries. All three camera tubes have light input, and there are color video signals for red, green, and blue.

The red, green, and blue video voltages are combined to encode the primary color voltages as brightness and chrominance signals for transmission to the receiver. This process is illustrated by the block diagram in Fig. 8-8.

MATRIX SECTION A matrix circuit forms new output voltages from the signal input. The matrix at the transmitter combines the *R, G,* and *B* voltages in specific proportions to form three video signals that are better for broadcasting. One signal contains the brightness information. The other two signals contain the color.

The two color signals out of the matrix must be color mixtures, meaning that they contain *R, G,* and *B.* Two mixtures can have all the original color information of the three primaries. The two color mixtures plus the *Y* luminance correspond to the actual picture information in the *R, G,* and *B* video signals.

Important examples of pairs of two color mixtures to encode the *RGB* color information are

I and *Q* video

or

$R - Y$ and $B - Y$ video

They are useful because $R - Y$ and $B - Y$ have hue phase angles that are 90° apart, as do the *I* and *Q* video signals. In fact, *Q* stands for quadrature phase with respect to the *I* signal. The 90° phase difference is a good way to distinguish between two separate signals.

The *I* and *Q* signals are specified by the FCC for modulation at the transmitter. However, the $R - Y$ and $B - Y$ signals are easier to use in most video circuits. They contain green also, in the *Y* component. The $-Y$ is the luminance signal in negative polarity. Actually, *I* or *Q* can be converted to $R - Y$ or $B - Y$, respectively, or vice versa, as necessary in the encoding or decoding.

For the encoding in Fig. 8-8*a,* the three signals out of the matrix are as follows:

1. *Luminance, or Y, signal.* This combination of *R, G,* and *B* contains the brightness variations, corresponding to a monochrome video signal. The *Y* signal is formed by taking 30 percent of the *R* video, 59 percent of the *G* video, and 11 percent of the *B* video.
2. *A color mixture designated the I signal.* The positive polarity of the *I* signal is orange; the negative polarity is cyan. These colors are chosen as best for the *I* signal in showing small details of color.
3. *A color mixture designated the Q signal.* The positive polarity of the *Q* signal is purple; the negative polarity is yellow-green.

The negative signs for subtracting *R, G,* or *B* signals indicate that the video voltages are added in negative polarity.

REASONS FOR THE *I* AND *Q* SIGNALS Here the letter *Q* is for quadrature, since the *Q* signal modulates the 3.58-MHz color subcarrier signal 90° out of phase with the *I* signal modulation.

The quadrature phase is used to help identify two different color video signals. At the receiver, one phase is detected for one signal while another detector at 90° phase provides the quadrature signal. Since only two color video signals are used for modulation, they can be in quadrature phase.

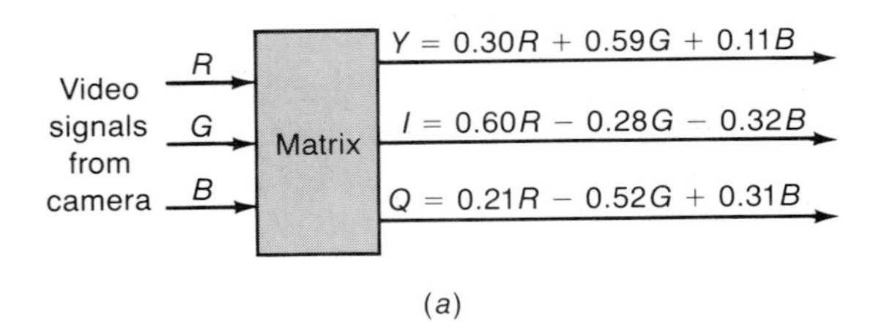

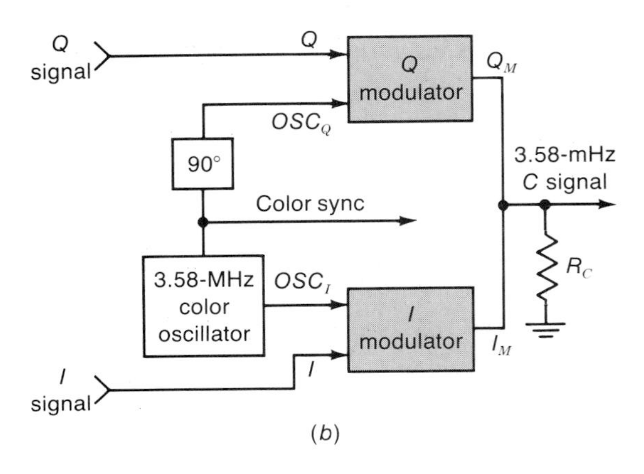

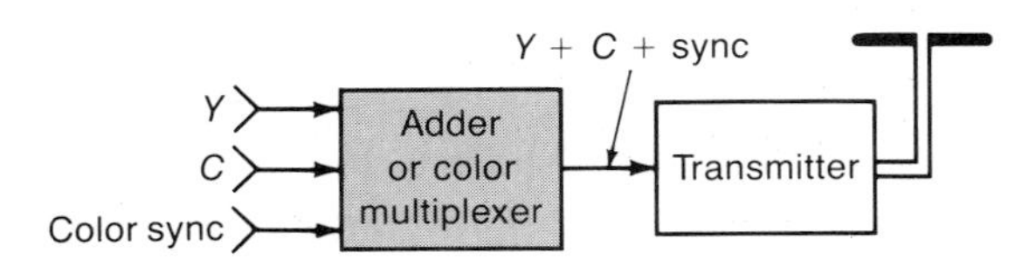

Fig. 8-8 Functions for encoding the color and monochrome picture information for television broadcasting. (*a*) Matrixing to produce *Y*, *I*, and *Q* video signals. (*b*) Chrominance modulation with *I* and *Q* to produce *C* signal. (*c*) Multiplexing of *Y* and *C* signals.

However, the two color video signals used must contain all the *R*, *G*, and *B* color information. Therefore, color mixtures are used. The *I* signal contains the colors between orange and cyan, which are mixtures of the primary colors red, green, and blue. Also, the *Q* signal, with purple and yellow-green, contains *R*, *G*, and *B* mixtures. The two *I* and *Q* signals together contain the color information in the three primary *R*, *G*, and *B* signals.

More bandwidth is used for the *I* signal—1.3 MHz, compared with 0.5 MHz for the *Q* signal. The purpose of this extra bandwidth in the *I* signal is to allow more color detail.

It has been determined experimentally that the orange and cyan of the *I* signal are best for color resolution in very small details. This is the reason why the *I* color mixture is specified as $I = 0.60R - 0.28G - 0.32B$. Automatically, then, the *Q* signal colors are magenta and yellow-green because this color axis is 90° off the *I* color axis.

DISADVANTAGES OF THE *I* AND *Q* SIGNALS The extra bandwidth of the *I* signal is a problem at the receiver. In the 3.58-MHz chrominance modulation, the upper side frequencies can interfere with the 4.5-MHz sound signal. Also, the lower side frequencies of the *I* signal can extend into the frequency range of the *Y* video signal for luminance. Extra filtering would be required to reduce the interference. As a result, receivers seldom use the added bandwidth of the *I* signal. The circuits are much simpler when all the color video signals have the same 0.5-MHz bandwidth. In large-screen projection receivers, though, the extra color resolution of the *I* signal may be used.

Without the extra bandwidth of the *I* signal, the color information in the modulated *C* signal can be detected at different phase angles for different hues. Quadrature phase is generally used, however, to detect two separate color video signals. Examples of the phase angle for different hues are shown later in Fig. 8-16. As a specific example, receivers often use $R - Y$ and $B - Y$ demodulators. These two color mixture signals are also in quadrature with each other, but with phase angles a little different from those of the *I* and *Q* signals. Actually, the receiver can detect the hue information of the modulated *C* signal in different ways as long as the final result is red, green, and blue at the color picture tube.

Test Point Questions 8-4

Answers at End of Chapter

Answer True or False for 8-8*a*.

a. The input to the matrix includes *R, G,* and *B* video signals.
b. The output of the matrix includes the *Y* luminance signal and two color-mixture signals.
c. The *Y* signal has 100 percent *G* video.

8-5 CHROMINANCE MODULATION

The *I* and *Q* signals are transmitted as the modulation sidebands of a 3.58-MHz subcarrier signal, which in turn modulates the main picture carrier wave. As an example, the picture carrier at 67.25 MHz for channel 4 is modulated by the 3.58-MHz video-frequency color subcarrier signal. In the 66- to 72-MHz transmission channel, the chrominance signal is at 67.25 + 3.58 = 70.83 MHz as an RF side frequency of the modulated picture carrier signal.

The value of 3.58 MHz is chosen as a high video frequency to separate the chrominance signal from the lower video frequencies in the luminance signal. Also, the high frequency results in low visibility of any chroma interference in the luminance signal. At the opposite end, the *C* signal frequency cannot be too close to 4.5 MHz, to prevent interference with the sound signal.

Note that the color subcarrier signal has the video frequency of 3.58 MHz for all stations. In terms of the RF picture carrier signal, the 3.58-MHz *C* signal is just another case of video modulation.

Refer to Fig. 8-8*b*. The output from the 3.58-MHz color subcarrier oscillator is coupled to the *I* and *Q* modulators. They also have *I* and *Q* video signal input from the matrix. Each circuit produces amplitude modulation of the 3.58-MHz subcarrier signal. Note the separate inputs for *I* and *Q*, but the common output combines the *I* and *Q* modulation. This combined output is the 3.58-MHz modulated chrominance (*C*), or chroma, signal.

The 3.58-MHz oscillator input to the *Q* modulator is shifted by 90°. Modulating the subcarrier signal in two different phases keeps the *I* and *Q* signals separate from each other. The 90° angle provides maximum separation in phase between two signals.

Note the following labels for the different signals into and out of the modulators to produce the *C* signal in Fig. 8-8*b:*

I = *I* video signal without modulation
OSC_I = in-phase oscillator output at 3.58 MHz
I_M = *I* amplitude modulation on 3.58-MHz subcarrier signal

Q = *Q* video signal without modulation
OSC_Q = quadrature oscillator output shifted by 90°
Q_M = *Q* amplitude modulation on 3.58-MHz subcarrier signal

SUPPRESSING THE SUBCARRIER SIGNAL Using only the modulation sidebands, without the carrier signal itself, is called *suppressed-carrier transmission.* The purpose of suppressing the subcarrier signal is to reduce the interference at 3.58 MHz, which can produce a fine-dot pattern on the screen.

COLOR SYNC BURST With suppressed-carrier transmission, the receiver must have a 3.58-MHz oscillator circuit that generates the subcarrier signal, in order to detect the chrominance signal. Furthermore, a sample of the 3.58-MHz subcarrier signal is transmitted with the *C* signal as a phase reference for the color oscillator at the receiver. In color television, phase angle is hue.

The color synchronization for correct hues in the picture is accomplished by a burst of 8 to 11 cycles of the 3.58-MHz subcarrier signal on the back porch of each horizontal blanking pulse. This color sync burst controls the frequency and phase of the 3.58-MHz oscillator at the receiver. The color sync burst is a sample of the 3.58-MHz subcarrier signal for the receiver.

TOTAL COLORPLEXED VIDEO SIGNAL The C signal with the color information and the Y luminance signal are both coupled to the adder section, or colorplexer. This stage combines the Y signal with the 3.58-MHz C signal to form the total colorplexed video signal. See Fig. 8-8*c*.

This signal is transmitted to the receiver by amplitude modulation of the picture carrier wave in the station's assigned 6-MHz channel. The modulation is a composite color video signal, including deflection sync and blanking pulses.

The oscilloscope waveshape for the colorplexed video signal is shown in Fig. 8-9. This waveform shows how the signal includes all the information needed for the picture. The shaded areas are the 3.58-MHz C signal, corresponding to color bars. The peak-to-peak (p-p) amplitude of the C signal depends on the saturation, or color intensity. The phase angles of the C signal for different hues cannot be seen because individual cycles are not shown.

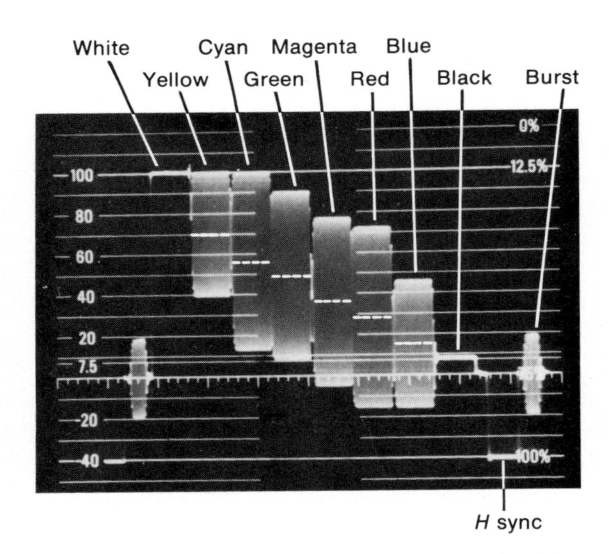

Fig. 8-9 Oscillogram of colorplexed composite video for color-bar pattern. Included are C signal, color sync burst, Y signal, and H deflection sync. The white dotted lines across bars of 3.58-MHz signal indicate luminance level of Y signal.

LUMINANCE LEVEL In addition to the p-p amplitudes for the color bars, note that the average level is different for each bar. Specifically, the distance from the blanking level to the average level of the C signal is a measure of how dark or light the information is. These changing luminance levels are the variations in the Y luminance signal. If the 3.58-MHz C signal were filtered out, the luminance levels would still remain to indicate the relative brightness values. In Fig. 8-9, the average luminance levels form a staircase of voltages from white at the left to black at the right.

HUE AND SATURATION IN THE *C* SIGNAL The two-phase modulation of the 3.58-MHz color subcarrier signal has the effect of concentrating all the color information into one chrominance signal. Consider the example of a strong I signal, with a small Q signal. The resultant C signal has a phase angle close to the orange hue of the I signal. For the opposite case, with a strong Q signal and a small I signal, the modulated C signal has a phase angle close to the purple hue of the Q signal.

With equal amplitudes of the I and Q modulating voltages, the phase of the C signal is between the I and Q phase angles, corresponding to a hue between orange and purple. The result, then, is that the instantaneous phase angle of the 3.58-MHz modulated C signal indicates the hue of the color information.

Furthermore, the amplitude variations of the modulated C signal indicate the strength or intensity of the color information. This variation corresponds to how saturated the color is. As a result:

Hue is in the phase angle of the C signal.

Saturation is the amplitude of the C signal.

Test Point Questions 8-5

Answers at End of Chapter

Refer to Fig. 8-8.

a. Name the three outputs of the matrix.
b. List the two inputs to the I modulator.
c. What is the phase angle for Q modulation?
d. Which stage has inputs of $Y + C$ signals?
e. Which resistor has I and Q modulation?

8-6 DECODING THE PICTURE INFORMATION

Starting with the receiving antenna, the modulated picture carrier signal of the selected channel is amplified in the RF and intermediate-frequency (IF) stages. Then this AM picture signal is rectified in the video detector. The video detector output is the total colorplexed video signal, including the Y and C components. After the video detector, the video circuits divide into two paths, as shown in Fig. 8-10. One path is for the Y luminance signal, and the other is for the 3.58-MHz C signal.

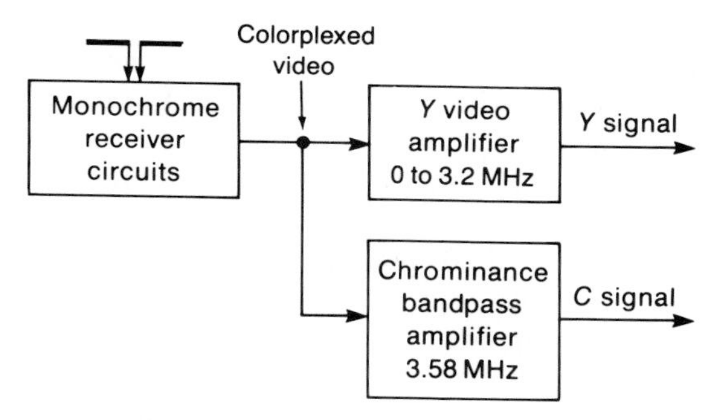

Fig. 8-10 Separating Y luminance signal and 3.58-MHz chrominance signal at output of video detector in the receiver.

SEPARATING THE *C* SIGNAL The output of the Y video amplifier in Fig. 8-10 is luminance signal without the 3.58-MHz color signal. The reason is that the amplifier response is limited to frequencies below 3.2 MHz, approximately. Since the C signal is at 3.58 MHz, it is not amplified in the Y video amplifier.

Note, though, that some color receivers have comb filters to improve the resolution for the Y signal. The *comb filter* spearates the chroma signal but leaves intact the Y components in the 3.58-MHz band. As a result, the full 4-MHz bandwidth of the Y signal can be used for maximum luminance resolution.

The output of the chrominance bandpass amplifier is the C signal. The reason is that this stage is tuned to 3.58 MHz, with a bandpass of ±0.5 MHz usually. Generally this stage is called the *color amplifier,* or *chroma amplifier,* because it supplies the amplified 3.58-MHz C signal for the color. It is also called a *bandpass amplifier* (BPA).

In all color television receivers, the chroma amplifier is tuned to 3.58 MHz for any channel, either VHF or UHF. We can consider 3.58 MHz as the color intermediate frequency, at a fixed value for the video section of the receiver.

The amplified 3.58-MHz C signal includes the chrominance modulation and color sync for the color section of the receiver. The color sync controls the phase of the 3.58-MHz color oscillator for the correct hues. This stage regenerates the 3.58-MHz color subcarrier signal, which is suppressed in transmission.

The original color information is contained in the variations of the 3.58-MHz modulated chroma signal. However, the signal must be demodulated to recover the color video signals.

SYNCHRONOUS DEMODULATION *Synchronous demodulation* is only another term for detection. When a modulated signal is transmitted without its carrier or subcarrier wave, the origi-

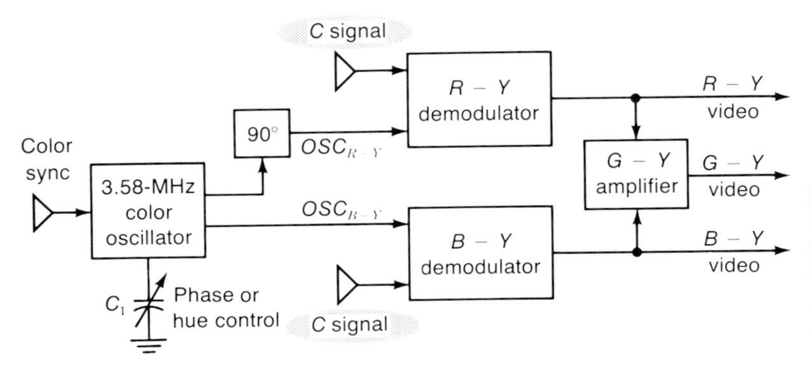

Fig. 8-11 Detecting modulated 3.58-MHz *C* signal with two synchronous demodulators 90° out of phase to recover *R* − *Y* and *B* − *Y* quadrature color video signals. These two voltages are combined to obtain *G* − *Y* signal.

nal carrier wave must be reinserted at the receiver to detect the modulation. Not only is the carrier regenerated, but also its phase must be synchronized with the phase of the carrier in the original modulation. *Synchronous demodulation* refers to the process of detecting a modulated signal when the carrier signal is suppressed.

As shown in Fig. 8-11, the 3.58-MHz color oscillator supplies the subcarrier signal, which is coupled to the demodulators for the *C* signal. Each demodulator has both *C* signal and oscillator input. In demodulation, the *C* signal beats with the regenerated 3.58-MHz subcarrier to provide color video signal for the detected output. Each demodulator is a synchronous detector.

Note that this type of detector has maximum output for the phase of the modulated signal that is the same as the oscillator input. The circuit is a synchronous demodulator because it detects the modulation information that is synchronous with the reinserted carrier. Furthermore, there is practically no output for the signal in quadrature with the phase of the reinserted oscillator voltage. For this reason, two synchronous demodulators are needed to detect two different color video signals.

B − Y AND R − Y DEMODULATORS Many receivers decode the 3.58-MHz chroma signal into *B* − *Y* and *R* − *Y* video signals, instead of *I* and *Q*. The bandwidth of the chroma bandpass amplifier is generally limited to 3.58 ± 0.5 MHz. Then the extra bandwidth of the *I* signal is not used anyway.

The *B* − *Y* video is a color mixture that is close to blue. The phase angle for the hue of *B* − *Y* is exactly 180° opposite to the phase of the color sync burst. As a result, it is relatively simple to lock in the 3.58-MHz color oscillator at the phase of *B* − *Y*.

The *R* − *Y* video signal is a color mixture close to red. The phase angle for the hue of *R* − *Y* is exactly 90° from the phase of *B* − *Y*. These phase angles for different hues are explained in detail later with the illustration in Fig. 8-16.

Furthermore, *B* − *Y* video and *R* − *Y* video can be combined to supply *G* − *Y* video, since the *Y* signal has green in it. The *B* − *Y*, *R* − *Y*, and *G* − *Y* video are called the *color-difference signals*. The bandwidth for all these color video signals is 0 to 0.5 MHz.

In Fig. 8-11, the demodulators produce *B* − *Y* and *R* − *Y* video. Note that the oscillator phase is shifted 90° for the *R* − *Y* demodulator. The two color mixtures are combined in the *G* − *Y* amplifier. Then the three color video signals for *B* − *Y*, *R* − *Y*, and *G* − *Y*, with enough amplification, can be coupled to the tricolor picture tube.

The labels for the different signals in Fig. 8-11 can be summarized as follows:

$C =$ modulated chroma signal; frequency is 3.58 ± 0.5 MHz

$OSC_{B-Y} =$ 3.58-MHz oscillator output in $B - Y$ phase

$OSC_{R-Y} =$ 3.58-MHz oscillator output in quadrature phase

$B - Y =$ color video signal; frequency is 0 to 0.5 MHz

$R - Y =$ color video signal; frequency is 0 to 0.5 MHz

$G - Y =$ color video signal; frequency is 0 to 0.5 MHz

Note that the oscillator and chroma circuits operate at 3.58 MHz, but the detected color video signals are not at 3.58 MHz.

PICTURE TUBE AS A MIXER When the decoding at the receiver provides $R - Y$, $B - Y$, and $G - Y$ video, they can be converted to R, G, and B signals by adding $-Y$ video. The algebraic addition for red, for example, is

$$(R - Y) + Y = R \text{ video}$$

The same idea applies for B and G video signals.

In older receivers with vacuum-tube amplifiers, the common method uses $R - Y$, $B - Y$, and $G - Y$ video to the three control grids and the $-Y$ signal to the three cathodes. The result is still R, G, and B video signals for the picture tube, because the $-Y$ component cancels. For example, for red

$$(R - Y) - (-Y) = R - Y + Y = R$$

The $-Y$ signal is subtracted because it is at the cathode.

In Fig. 8-12, the R, G, and B video signals are applied to the three cathodes of the three-gun tricolor picture tube. Positive sync polarity is required, so that the blanking voltage can cut off the beam current. Remember that positive cathode voltage corresponds to negative voltage at the control grid. In either case, the difference in potential from grid to cathode becomes more negative for black in the picture.

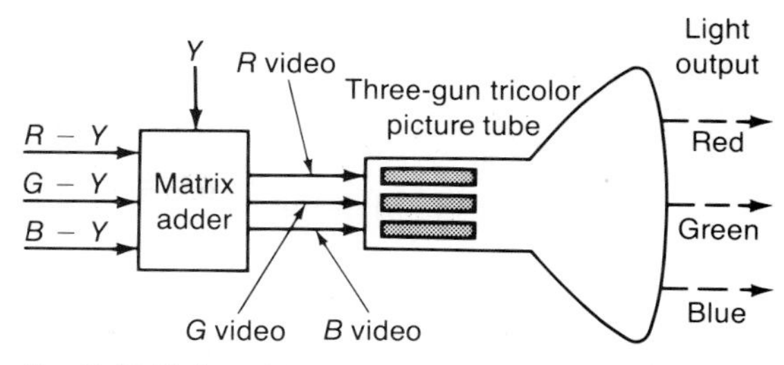

Fig. 8-12 Picture tube as a mixer for red, green, and blue.

With transistorized video circuits, the video drive signals generally are applied to the picture tube cathodes, instead of to the control grids. The reason is that the negative grid is the electrode most likely to have internal arcing from high voltage inside the picture tube.

Either way, the picture tube has R, G, and B video for the three electron guns. Each gun excites only its color on the screen. What you see is the original red, green, and blue color information with their color mixtures in the picture. The sequence of color signals from the transmitter to the receiver is summarized by Table 8-1.

Test Point Questions 8-6

Answers at End of Chapter

a. In Fig. 8-10, what is the center frequency of the chroma bandpass amplifier?

b. In Fig. 8-11, name the two inputs to the $R - Y$ demodulator.

c. What is the phase angle between $B - Y$ and $R - Y$?

d. In Fig. 8-12, list the three video signals for the picture tube.

8-7 *Y* SIGNAL FOR LUMINANCE

Now we can consider in greater detail the luminance signal, which contains the brightness varia-

TABLE 8-1
SEQUENCE OF COLOR SIGNALS

TRANSMITTER ENCODING	RECEIVER DECODING*
1. *R, G,* and *B* video from camera.	1. Antenna signal is RF picture carrier modulated by colorplexed *T* signal.
2. *Y, I,* and *Q* video from matrix.	2. Modulated picture carrier is rectified in video detector.
3. *I* and *Q* modulate 3.58-MHz chrominance signal.	3. Synchronous demodulators for 3.58-MHz *C* signal provide $B - Y$ and $R - Y$ video, which are combined for $G - Y$.
4. Colorplexed *T* signal with *Y* and 3.58-MHz *C* signals.	4. $B - Y$, $R - Y$, and $G - Y$ video added to *Y* video produce *R, G,* and *B* video.
5. Antenna signal is RF picture carrier modulated by colorplexed *T* signal.	5. Red, green, and blue, with their color mixtures, on screen of picture tube.

* For receivers using $B - Y$ and $R - Y$ demodulators. Note that *T* is total colorplexed video signal with *C* and *Y*.

tions of the picture information. The *Y* signal is formed by adding the primary red, green, and blue video signals in the proportions

$$Y = 0.30R + 0.59G + 0.11B \qquad \textbf{(8-1)}$$

These percentages correspond to the relative brightness of the three primary colors. As shown in color plate VIII, the human eye sees green as the brightest color. Therefore, a scene reproduced in black and white by the *Y* signal looks the same as when it is televised in monochrome.

VOLTAGE VALUES FOR THE *Y* SIGNAL Figure 8-13 illustrates how the *Y* signal voltage (Fig. 8-13*d*) is formed from the specified proportions of *R, G,* and *B* voltages for the color-bar pattern. Note that the bars include the primary colors *R, G,* and *G,* their complementary mixtures of two primaries, and white for all three primaries.

The *Y* signal has its maximum relative amplitude of 1.0, or 100 percent for white, because it includes *R, G,* and *B.* This value for white is calculated as

$$Y = 0.30 + 0.59 + 0.11 = 1.00$$

As another example, the cyan color bar in-

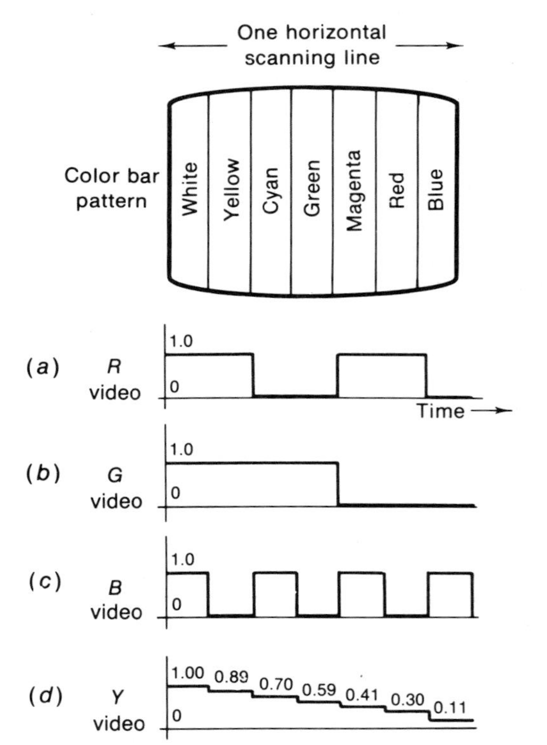

Fig. 8-13 Waveforms of *R, G,* and *B* video signals combined to form the *Y* signal, for the color-bar pattern shown at the top.

Plate I Normal color picture.

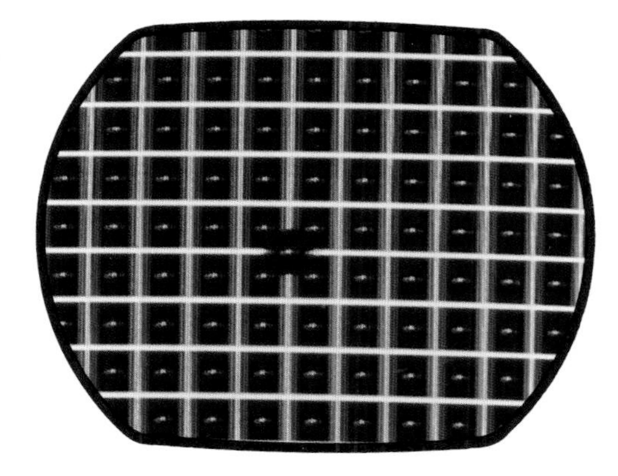

Plate II Color fringing caused by poor convergence, shown with crosshatch pattern.

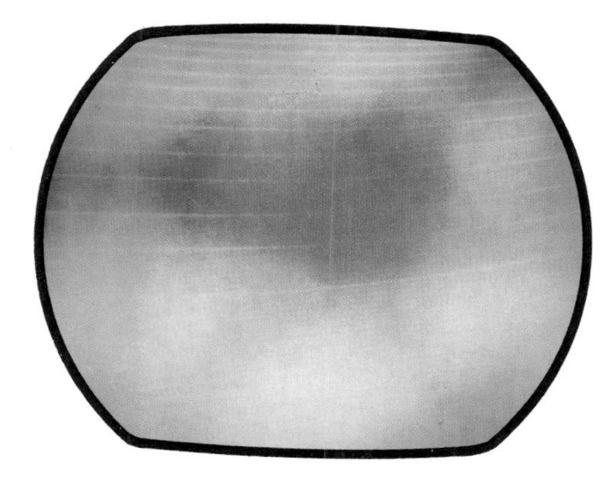

Plate III Red ball on screen for purity adjustment with delta guns.

Plate IV Green bar on screen for purity adjustment with in-line guns.

Plate V Color snow, or confetti.

Plate VI No color sync, shown for EIA bar pattern.

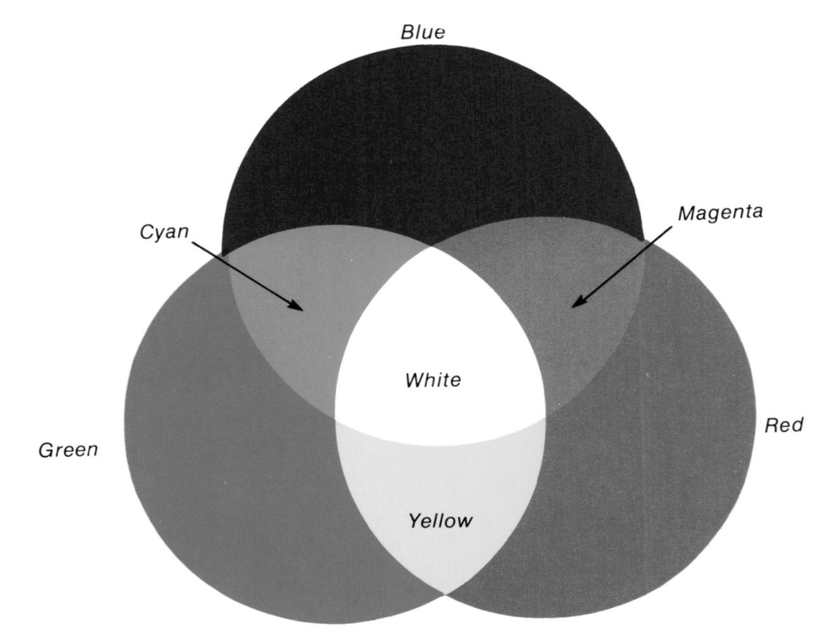

Plate VII Addition of colors.

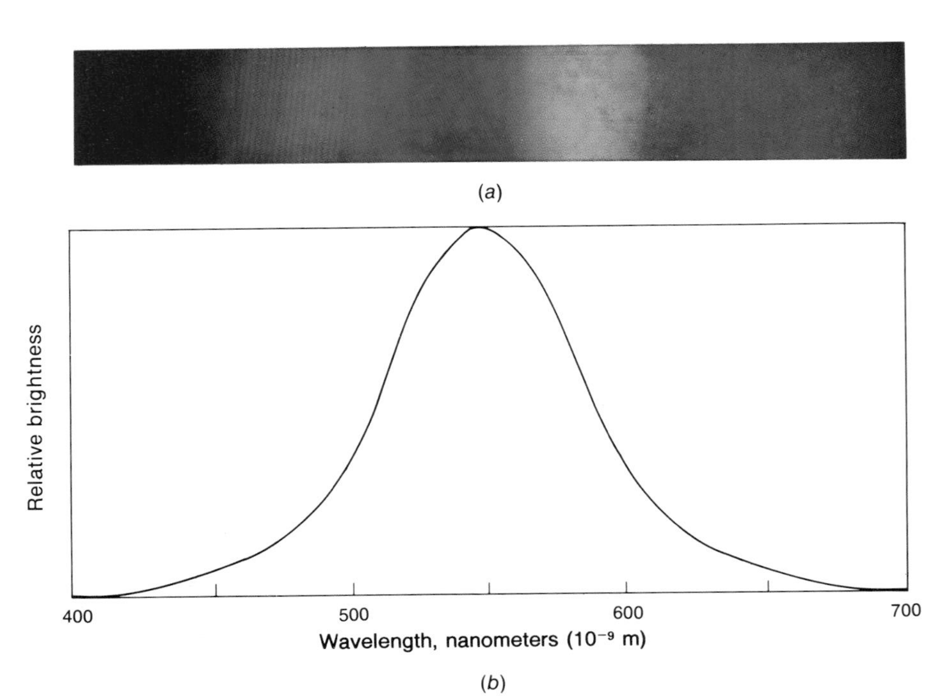

Plate VIII Relative brightness or luminance response of eye to different colors. (*a*) Hues of different wavelengths. (*b*) Relative luminance values.

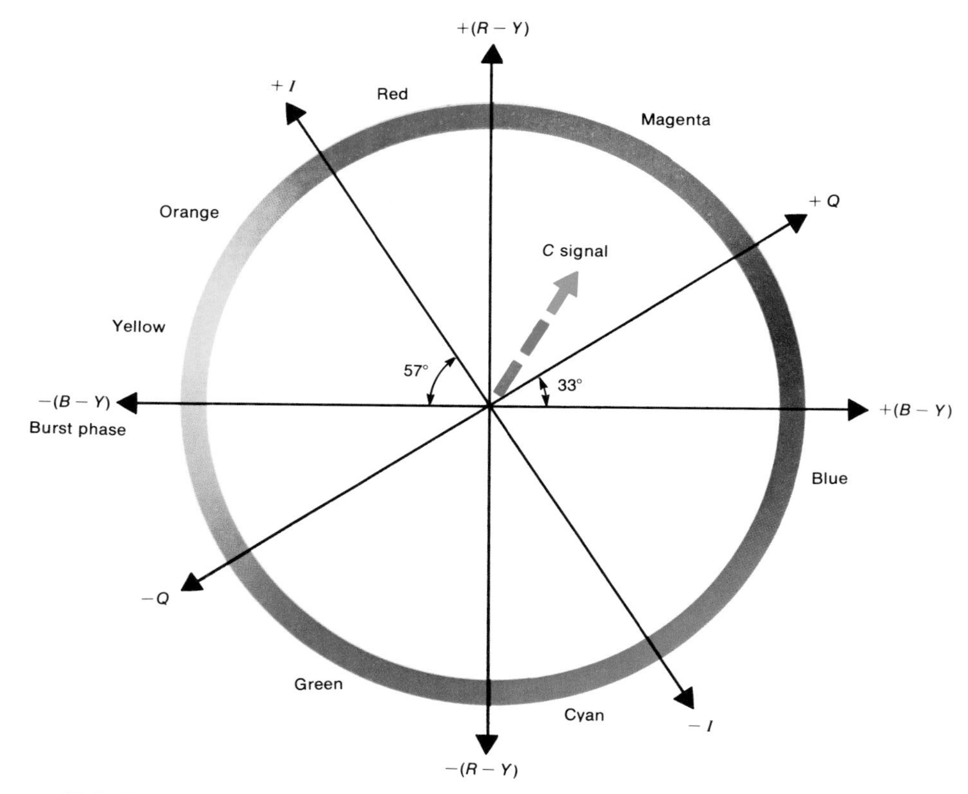

Plate IX Color circle showing hues for different phase angles of chrominance signal.

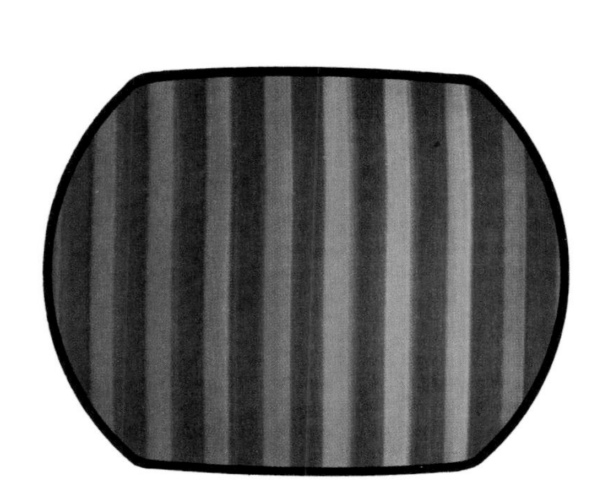

Plate X Color bar pattern corresponding to hue phase angles in Plate XI.

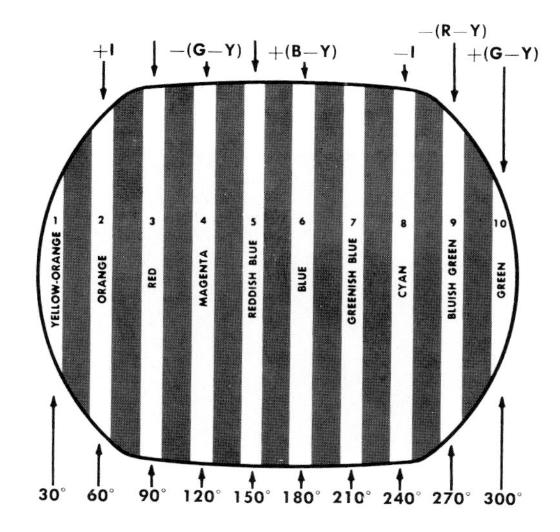

Plate XI Phase angles for color bars in Plate X. Values are clockwise from burst phase.

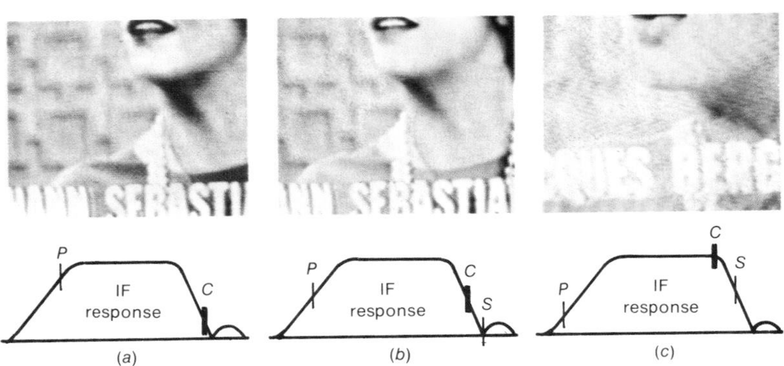

Plate XII Effect of fine tuning control on 920-kHz beat interference in picture. (*a*) No color and no beat. (*b*) Correct tuning with color and no beat. (*c*) Color but with beat pattern.

Plate XIII Silvery effect in highlights of picture because of low emission, illustrated for red gun alone.

Plate XV NTSC color bars. Oscilloscope waveshape in Plate XVI.

Plate XIV Dichroic mirrors inside color camera.

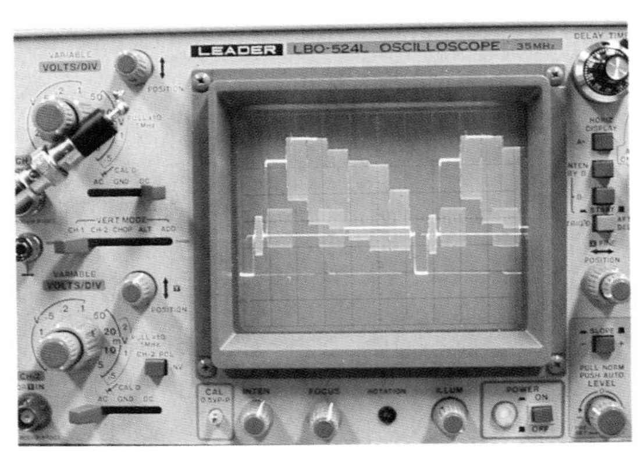

Plate XVI Oscilloscope waveshape at *H* rate for NTSC color bars in Plate XV.

cludes G and B but not R. So the Y value for cyan is calculated as

$$Y = 0 + 0.59 + 0.11 = 0.70$$

All the voltage values of the Y signal can be calculated in this way. The resulting voltages are the relative luminance values for each of the color bars.

If the Y signal alone were used to reproduce this pattern, it would appear as monochrome bars shading from white at the left to gray in the center and approaching black at the right. These light values correspond to the staircase of Y video voltages in Fig. 8-13*d*, for the decreasing relative brightness of these color bars. The colors are picked for this sequence of a descending staircase of luminance values.

BANDWIDTH OF *Y* SIGNAL This signal is transmitted with the full video-frequency bandwidth of 0 to 4 MHz, just as in monochrome broadcasting. However, most receivers cut off the response for video frequencies at 3.2 MHz, approximately. The purpose is to minimize interference with the 3.58-MHz C signal. In monochrome receivers, generally the IF bandwidth is limited to 3 MHz.

MATRIX FOR THE *Y* SIGNAL A matrix has the function of adding several input voltages in the desired proportions to form new combinations of output voltage. One example of forming the Y signal is illustrated in Fig. 8-14. This circuit consists of three voltage dividers with a common resistor R_4. Each divider proportions the R, G, or B input signal in accordance with the resistance of R_1, R_2, or R_3, compared with R_4. The result is the Y signal across R_4 as the common load resistor for the R, G, and B video voltages. Similarly, different resistance values can be used for separate voltage dividers to proportion the R, G, or B voltages in the percentages necessary to form I and Q signals at the transmitter.

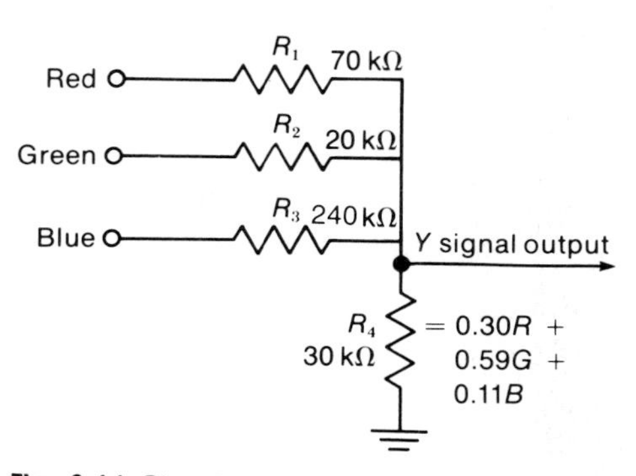

Fig. 8-14 Circuit for resistive voltage divider used as matrix to form Y signal.

Test Point Questions 8-7

Answers at End of Chapter

In Fig. 8-13, what is the value of the Y voltage for the following bars?

a. White
b. Red
c. Green
d. Blue
e. Yellow

8-8 TYPES OF COLOR VIDEO SIGNALS

The main types of color video signals must include the primary colors, as the system starts with R, G, and B voltages for the camera tube and finishes with R, G, and B at the picture tube. However, color mixtures are used for encoding and decoding. The reason is that two color-mixture signals can have all the color information of the three primary colors, allowing the third signal to be Y signal for luminance.

***I* SIGNAL** This color video voltage is produced in the transmitter matrix as the following combination of red, green, and blue:

$$I = 0.60R - 0.28G - 0.32B \qquad \textbf{(8-2)}$$

The minus sign indicates the addition of video voltage of negative polarity. For instance, $-0.32B$ means 32 percent of the total blue video signal but inverted from the polarity that reproduces blue.

With $+I$ polarity, the signal includes red and minus blue, or yellow. They add to produce orange.

For the $-I$ signal, the polarity is reversed for all the primary components. Thus the combination includes green and blue for cyan, with minus red, which is cyan.

As a result, opposite polarities of the I video signal represent the complementary colors orange and cyan, approximately. These hues are in color plate IX, which shows the main color video voltages.

Note that the negative components of $-0.28G$ and $-0.32B$ total -0.60, which equals the positive value of $0.60R$. These values are chosen to make the amplitude of the I video signal become zero for white.

Q SIGNAL The primary color voltages are combined in the transmitter matrix in the following proportions for the Q signal:

$$Q = 0.21R - 0.52G + 0.31B \qquad \textbf{(8-3)}$$

With $+Q$ polarity, this signal includes minus green, or magenta, with red and blue. They combine to form purple hues.

For the $-Q$ signal, this polarity includes mainly green with minus blue, or yellow. The combination is yellow-green.

As a result, opposite polarities of the Q signal represent the complementary colors purple and yellow-green. See color plate IX.

Note that the positive components of $0.21R$ and $0.31B$ total 0.52, to equal the negative component of $-0.52G$. These values are chosen to make the amplitude of the Q signal zero for white.

Both the I and Q signals are zero for white, since there is no chrominance information in white. The luminance information for shades of white is contained in the Y signal.

B − Y SIGNAL The hue of this signal is mainly blue, but it is a color mixture because of the $-Y$ component. When we combine 100 percent blue with the primary components of the Y signal, we get

$$\begin{aligned} B - Y &= 1.00B - (0.30R + 0.59B + 0.11B) \\ &= -0.30R - 0.59G + 0.89B \qquad \textbf{(8-4)} \end{aligned}$$

Note that $-R$ and $-G$, when combined, equal the complement of yellow, which is blue. However, a little more minus green shifts the hue toward magenta, resulting in a purplish blue.

When the $B - Y$ signal is combined with the Y signal in the picture tube, it reproduces the blue information. The effect is $B - Y + Y = B$.

R − Y SIGNAL The hue of $R - Y$ is a purplish red. Combining red with the primary components of the Y signal results in

$$\begin{aligned} R - Y &= 1.00R - (0.30R + 0.59G + 0.11B) \\ &= 0.70R - 0.59G - 0.11B \qquad \textbf{(8-5)} \end{aligned}$$

The minus green is magenta, which is combined with red to produce a purple-red for positive polarity of the $R - Y$ signal. The opposite polarity of the $R - Y$ signal has the hue of cyan-blue.

When the $R - Y$ signal is combined with the Y signal in the picture tube, it reproduces the red information. The effect is $R - Y + Y = R$.

G − Y SIGNAL Combining the $-Y$ signal and 100 percent G results in

$$\begin{aligned} G - Y &= 1.00G - (0.30R + 0.59G + 0.11B) \\ &= -0.30R + 0.41G - 0.11B \qquad \textbf{(8-6)} \end{aligned}$$

The hue of the $G - Y$ signal is a bluish green. The opposite polarity is a purplish red. When the $G - Y$ signal is added to the Y signal in the color picture tube, the green information is reproduced. The effect is $G - Y + Y = G$.

In the receiver, $G - Y$ video is obtained by combining $R - Y$ and $B - Y$ in the following proportions:

$$G - Y = -0.51(R - Y) - 0.19(B - Y) \quad \textbf{(8-7)}$$

This combination is formed in the $G - Y$ amplifier stage.

SUMMARY OF COLOR VIDEO SIGNALS The color-mixture voltages are all related since each is a combination of *R, G,* and *B.* As additional examples, the *I* and *Q* signals can be specified in terms of the color-difference signals as follows:

$$I = -0.27(B - Y) + 0.74(R - Y) \quad \textbf{(8-8)}$$
$$Q = 0.41(B - Y) + 0.48(R - Y) \quad \textbf{(8-9)}$$

All these video signals are color mixtures. They combine *R, G,* and *B* so that two mixtures can contain all the color information of the three primaries.

Note the difference between these color video voltages, without modulation, and the 3.58-MHz modulated *C* signal. There is only one *C* signal, always at 3.58 MHz. This signal is encoded with the chrominance information as hue and saturation, corresponding to the phase and amplitude of the modulation on the 3.58-MHz color subcarrier signal.

However, the different color video signals exist before modulation of the 3.58-MHz color subcarrier signal at the transmitter and after demodulation at the receiver. The color video signals and their main features are summarized in Table 8-2. The colors listed are for positive signal voltage. The opposite polarity for each signal has the opposite hue. You can see these hues in the color circle diagram in color plate IX. The bandwidth is 0.5 MHz for all except the *I* signal.

RELATIVE GAIN VALUES The amplitudes of the color video signals are modified in transmission to prevent modulation past the maximum white and black levels. For instance, yellow with high luminance can overmodulate white; blue with low luminance can overmodulate black. As a result, the receiver must compensate with the following proportions of gain:

$$B - Y \text{ gain} = \frac{1}{49} = 2.04\%$$

$$R - Y \text{ gain} = \frac{1}{87.7} = 1.14\%$$

$$G - Y \text{ gain} = \frac{1}{142.3} = 0.70\%$$

For example, the receiver gain for the $B - Y$ signal is almost double the gain for the $R - Y$ signal. The reason is that, in modulation at the transmitter, the $B - Y$ component is reduced to 49 percent of its normal level.

TABLE 8-2
TYPES OF COLOR VIDEO SIGNALS

NAME	HUE	BANDWIDTH, MHz	NOTES
$B - Y$	Blue	0–0.5	Opposite phase from color sync
$R - Y$	Red	0–0.5	In quadrature with $B - Y$
$G - Y$	Green	0–0.5	Combines $B - Y$ and $R - Y$
I	Orange	0–1.3	Maximum color bandwidth
Q	Purple	0–0.5	In quadrature with I

Test Point Questions 8-8

Answers at End of Chapter

Answer True or False.

a. The hue of the $B - Y$ video signal is mainly blue.

b. The $R - Y$ phase is in quadrature with $B - Y$.

c. The $B - Y$ and $R - Y$ video signals can be combined to form $G - Y$.

d. The $B - Y$ phase is in quadrature with the color sync burst.

8-9 COLOR SYNC BURST

Figure 8-15*a* shows the details of the 3.58-MHz color sync burst transmitted as part of the total composite video signal. The color burst synchronizes the phase of the 3.58-MHz color oscillator in the receiver. Then the 3.58-MHz color subcarrier signal is reinserted in the synchronous demodulators to detect the chrominance signal.

The phase of the reinserted oscillator voltage determines the hues in the detector output. Therefore, the color sync is necessary to establish the correct hues for the demodulators. Then the color automatic frequency control (AFC) can hold the hue values steady. Without color synchronization, the picture has drifting color bars. The effect of no color sync is shown in color plate VI.

The burst is 8 to 11 cycles of the 3.58-MHz subcarrier, transmitted on the back porch of each horizontal blanking pulse. The peak value of the burst is one-half the sync pulse amplitude. Peak-to-peak burst equals the amplitude of sync. However, the average value of the burst coincides with the blanking level. This value corresponds to zero for deflection sync. As a result, the color burst does not interfere with synchronization of the deflection oscillators.

The burst and C signal are both 3.58 MHz. However, the burst is on during blanking time only, when there is no picture information. The C signal is on during visible trace time for the color information in the picture. This comparison is illustrated in Fig. 8-15*b*. The oscilloscope photograph of the video signal in Fig. 8-9 also shows the color sync burst on the back porch of H sync.

The presence or absence of the burst determines how a color receiver recognizes whether a program is in color or monochrome.

Test Point Questions 8-9

Answers at End of Chapter

a. What is the frequency of individual cycles in the color sync burst?

b. What is the repetition rate for the complete group of color sync bursts?

8-10 HUE PHASE ANGLES

Figure 8-16 illustrates how the hues of the modulated C signal are determined by its varying phase angle with respect to the constant phase angle of the color sync burst. Note that the hue of the color sync burst corresponds to yellow-green. When the picture information of this hue is being scanned at the transmitter, the phase angle of the chrominance signal is made the same as the phase of the color sync burst. For other hues, the C signal has different phase angles. How much the phase angle differs from the sync burst phase determines how the hue differs from yellow-green.

In Fig. 8-16*a*, the phase angle of the C signal indicates the hue of purple-red between the angles for blue and red. This phase angle results from equal amounts of I and Q modulation in this example.

You can see all the hues and their phase angles

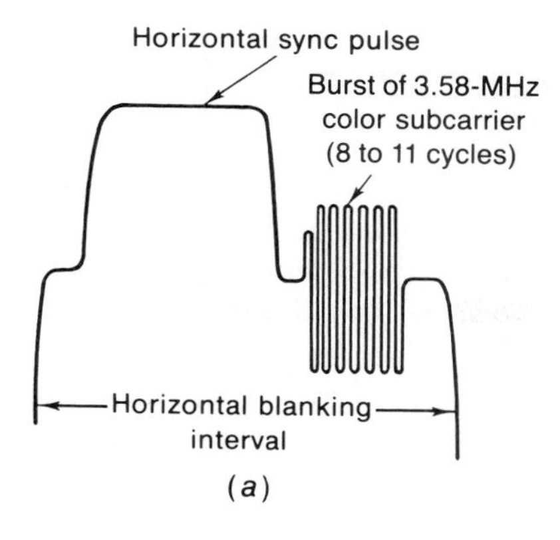

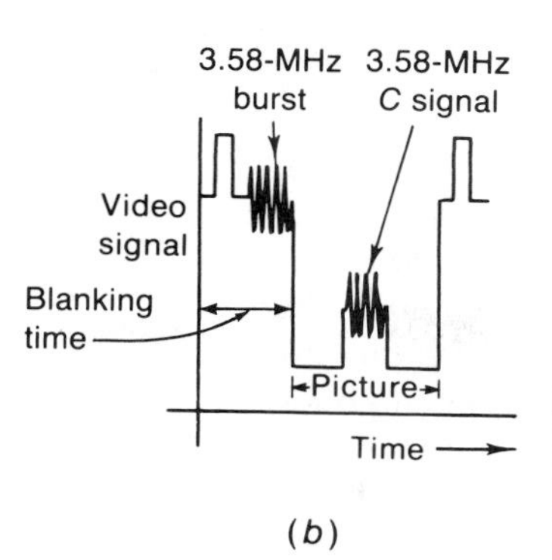

Fig. 8-15 (*a*) Color sync burst on back porch of each *H* sync pulse. (*b*) Comparison of burst and *C* signal, both 3.58 MHz but at different times.

in color plate IX. Opposite hues 180° apart are on a straight line called a *color axis.*

Note that hue phase angles are indicated in different ways. The standard measure for angles is counted counterclockwise as the positive direction from zero, as in Fig. 8-16*a*. Then $B - Y$ is at 0°, and the color sync burst is at 180°.

However, since burst phase is the reference, often the hue phase angles are counted clockwise from the burst. Then the $B - Y$ phase is at 180°.

For the receiver demodulation axes in Fig. 8-16*b*, the angles are indicated by how much they are off the horizontal and vertical axes. This

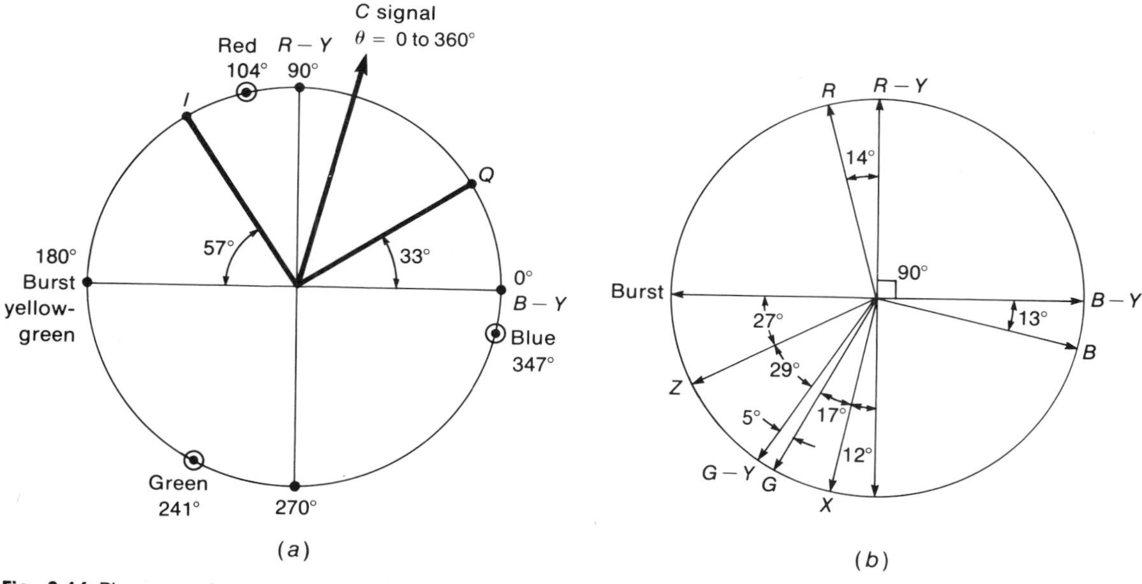

Fig. 8-16 Phase angles of different hues. Relative amplitudes not shown to scale. (*a*) *I* and *Q* phase angles compared with other hues. (*b*) Color axes often used for synchronous demodulation in receiver.

method shows the angular difference between different color axes.

I AND Q AXES These color video signals are used to modulate the 3.58-MHz subcarrier for broadcasting. As shown in Fig. 8-16*a*, the I axis is 57° off the phase of the color sync burst. The Q axis is in quadrature. These angles put the phase of $B - Y$ exactly opposite the burst phase.

$B - Y$ AND $R - Y$ AXES The receiver can recover these hues in demodulating the C signal by reinserting the 3.58-MHz color subcarrier signal at these phase angles. As shown in Fig. 8-16*b*, the $B - Y$ phase is 180° from the burst phase, and the $R - Y$ phase is in quadrature.

Two synchronous demodulators are needed to detect hues on the $R - Y$ and $B - Y$ axes. Then the $R - Y$ and $B - Y$ color video signals are added to form $G - Y$. Or a $G - Y$ demodulator can be used. Counting clockwise from the burst, the phase angles are 90° for $R - Y$, 180° for $B - Y$, and 304° for $G - Y$.

X AND Z AXES As shown in Fig. 8-16*b*, the X axis is close to $-(R - Y)$; the Z axis is close to $-(B - Y)$, or the burst phase. Counting clockwise from the burst, the X axis is at 282° and the Z axis at 333°. They are approximately 51° apart. The X and Z axes can be used in the receiver demodulators even though they are not in quadrature. The advantage is that $R - Y$, $G - Y$, and $B - Y$ can be formed in three amplifier stages that are balanced, to reduce the possibility of color drift.

Test Point Questions 8-10

Answers at End of Chapter

a. What is the hue of the color sync burst?
b. What is the phase difference between the color sync burst and the $B - Y$ video?
c. What is the phase angle of the $R - Y$ video?

8-11 COLORPLEXED COMPOSITE VIDEO SIGNAL

Formation of the total video signal combining luminance and chrominance is illustrated in Fig. 8-17 in successive steps. Starting with the primary colors, the R, G, and B video voltages in Fig. 8-17*a*, *b*, and *c* are shown for the time of scanning one horizontal line across the color bars. The colors are fully saturated, without any white. Thus the relative voltage value for R, G, and B is 100 percent, or 1.0. Also, the saturated complementary colors yellow, cyan, and magenta have only two primary colors, since there is no white to add the third primary.

AMPLITUDES OF THE Y SIGNAL The luminance signal in Fig. 8-17*d* shows the brightness component for each bar. The relative values for Y are calculated by Eq. 8-1. For example, for magenta, combining red and blue without green,

$$Y = 0.30R + 0 + 0.11B$$
$$= 0.41$$

AMPLITUDES OF THE I AND Q SIGNALS The I and Q waveforms in Fig. 8-17*e* and *f* have the relative voltages indicated according to their proportions of primary colors. These values are calculated by Eqs. 8-2 and 8-3. For example, for yellow with red and green but no blue,

$$I = 0.60R - 0.28G - 0.00B = 0.32$$
$$Q = 0.21R - 0.52G + 0.00B = -0.31$$

Note that the I and Q voltages can have positive or negative polarity because their components include positive and negative primary colors.

PHASOR ADDITION FOR THE C SIGNAL The waveform in Fig. 8-17*g* shows the 3.58-MHz color subcarrier signal modulated by the I and Q signals in quadrature. The two-phase amplitude modulation results in varying amplitudes and phase angles for the C signal. The phase

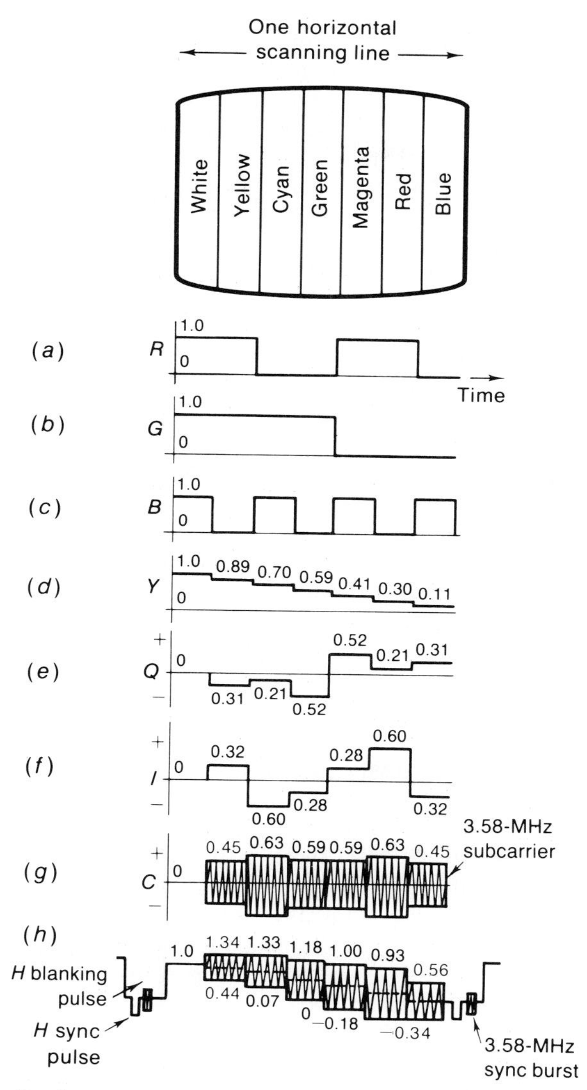

Fig. 8-17 Construction of colorplexed composite video signal from Y, I, and Q voltages. The waveform in (h) at bottom shows total multiplexed T signal combining Y and C signals.

angles cannot be shown, but the varying amplitudes can be calculated. The method of phasor[1] addition for the I and Q signals in quadrature is the same as combining two ac voltages 90° out of phase in series ac circuits, written as

$$C = \sqrt{I^2 + Q^2}$$

For example, for yellow with values of 0.32 for I and −0.31 for Q,

$$\begin{aligned} C &= \sqrt{0.32^2 + (-0.31)^2} \\ &= \sqrt{0.1024 + 0.0961} \\ &= \sqrt{0.1985} \\ &= 0.45 \end{aligned}$$

This method can be used to calculate all the C values for the color bars in Fig. 8-17, by phasor addition of the I and Q amplitudes.

There is no polarity for the C signal because it is a carrier wave with both positive and negative half-cycles. Note that the peak amplitude of 0.45 for the blue or yellow C signal means that it varies 0.45 unit above and below the zero axis of this modulated ac waveform. Yellow and blue have the same amplitude but opposite phase angles because they are complementary colors.

PHASE ANGLE OF THE *C* SIGNAL If we want to know the phase angle θ for the hue, the tangent of this angle equals Q/I. For example, for red with $Q = 0.21$ and $I = 0.60$, we have $\tan\theta = 0.21/0.60 = 0.35$. Thus $\theta = 19°$. This angle is 19° from I, toward Q.

ADDING THE *Y* AND *C* SIGNALS For the total video signal waveform in Fig. 8-17h, the Y amplitudes for luminance are combined with the C signal. The result is that the C signal variations are shifted to the axis of the Y luminance level.

For example, blue has the level of 0.11 in the Y signal and the peak amplitude of 0.45 in the C signal. When we combine these Y and C signals, the result in the colorplexed video signal for blue is that the positive peak goes up to $0.45 + 0.11 = 0.56$. The negative peak goes down to $-0.45 + 0.11 = -0.34$. These maximum and minimum C values are still ±0.45, but around

[1] Components with different angles in time are phasors; vectors have different angles in space.

the average axis of 0.11 for the Y signal, instead of zero.

The same idea applies to all the color bars shown. You can see how the combined signals correspond to the color bars in color plate X.

It is important to realize that the Y signal for luminance information is inserted as the average level of the C signal variations for color information. If the C signal is removed from the colorplexed signal in Fig. 8-17*h*, the result will be the same staircase of Y signal variations shown in Fig. 8-17*d*. In monochrome receivers, therefore, 3.58 MHz is filtered out to remove the color information, but the Y signal remains to provide the luminance variations.

Test Point Questions 8-11

Answers at End of Chapter

In Fig. 8-17 calculate the values for the yellow and blue bars in the

a. Y signal
b. Q signal
c. C signal

8-12 DESATURATED COLORS WITH WHITE

The relative voltage values shown in Fig. 8-17 are for vivid colors that are 100 percent saturated. In this case, there is no primary color video for hues not included in the color. For example, saturated R has zero B and G video voltage; saturated yellow (red-green) has zero B video voltage. This follows from the fact that with zero light input to a given color camera there is no signal output.

In natural scenes, however, most colors are not 100 percent saturated. Thus any color diluted by white light has all three primaries. The following example illustrates how to take into account the amount of desaturation for weaker colors. Assume 80 percent saturation for yellow. Now this color has two components: 80 percent saturated yellow and 20 percent white. The calculations for R, G, and B video signals are as follows:

80% yellow (red-green) produces	$0.80R$	$0.80G$	$0.00B$
20% white (red-green-blue) produces	$0.20R$	$0.20G$	$0.20B$
Total camera output:	$1.00R$	$1.00G$	$0.20B$

These percentages of primary color video voltages can be used to calculate the relative amplitudes of the Y signal and color video signals for 80 percent saturated yellow. For example, this desaturated yellow has the Y value of 0.912. The Q value is −0.248, and I equals 0.256. Compare these with the values of 0.89, −0.31, and 0.32 shown in Fig. 8-17 for 100 percent saturated yellow. Note that the addition of white to desaturate a color increases the luminance value and decreases the chrominance value, compared with 100 percent saturation.

Test Point Questions 8-12

Answers at End of Chapter

Compared with 100 percent saturation, does a desaturated color have

a. More or less luminance for the Y signal?
b. More or less chrominance for the C signal?

8-13 COLOR RESOLUTION AND BANDWIDTH

The Y signal is transmitted with the full video-frequency bandwidth of 4 MHz for maximum horizontal detail in monochrome. However, this bandwidth is not necessary for the color video signals, because for very small details the eye can perceive only the brightness, rather than the color. Therefore, the color information can be transmitted with a restricted bandwidth much

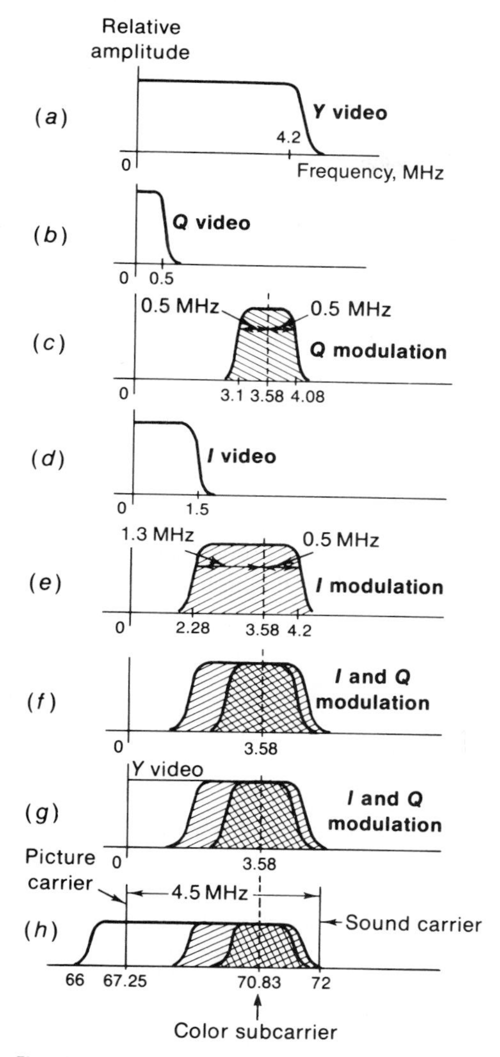

Fig. 8-18 Bandwidths for *Y* signal and color signals. Graph in (*h*) at bottom is for colorplexed composite video signal modulating channel 4 picture carrier at 67.25 MHz.

less than 4 MHz. This feature allows the narrowband chrominance signal to be multiplexed with the wideband luminance signal in the standard 6-MHz broadcast channel. All the color video signals have a bandwidth of 0 to 0.5 MHz, except the *I* signal, which has a bandwidth of 0 to 1.3 MHz. These values are shown in the third column of Table 8-2 on page 181.

The *I* signal for orange and cyan has more bandwidth because smaller details can be resolved for these colors. However, the *I* bandwidth of 0 to 1.3 MHz must be considered in two parts. Frequencies of 0 to 0.5 MHz in the *I* signal are transmitted with double sidebands, using both the upper and lower side frequencies produced by modulation. However, for frequencies between 0.5 and 1.3 MHz, only the lower sidebands are transmitted. This method of vestigial sideband transmission on the 3.58-MHz color subcarrier is used to provide maximum bandwidth for the *I* signal without extending into the frequencies of the sound carrier signal 4.5 MHz from the picture carrier signal. The bandwidths for the *Y, I,* and *Q* signals are illustrated by the graphs in Fig. 8-18.

The extra bandwidth of the *I* signal is generally not used in color receivers. The reason is that the color circuits are much simpler when all the color video signals have the same 0.5-MHz bandwidth, which is the practical baseband for color.

As a result, we can consider the video frequencies of 0 to 0.5 MHz as the practical bandwidth for the color video signal. How the picture information is reproduced can be illustrated by the pattern in Fig. 8-19. The squares and bars are drawn to scale for a screen width of 20 in. The purpose is to show what sizes of picture information can be reproduced with video frequencies up to 0.5 MHz.

The video frequency of 0.5 MHz is one-eighth of 4 MHz. This value of 4 MHz represents 400 horizontal details approximately. Therefore 0.5 MHz can represent one-eighth of 400 horizontal details. So

$$\tfrac{1}{8} \times 400 = 50 \text{ details}$$

Each of the 50 horizontal details corresponds to one-fiftieth of the screen width. On a 20-in. screen, then, the width of each detail is

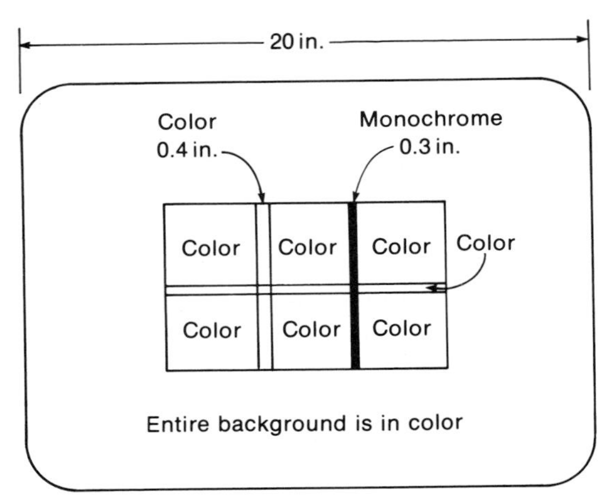

Fig. 8-19 Width of color areas in picture with color video bandwidth up to 0.5 MHz. Distances marked for horizontal width of 20 in. [508 mm] for screen of picture tube.

$$\frac{1}{50} \times 20 \text{ in.} = \frac{20 \text{ in.}}{50} = 0.4 \text{ in.}$$

All horizontal details more than 0.4 in. wide correspond to a video frequency less than 0.5 MHz, which can be reproduced in color. Any details less than 0.4 in. wide correspond to video frequencies higher than 0.5 MHz. This information is not in the color video baseband and will not be in color.

All the squares shown in Fig. 8-19 are in color because their width is greater than 0.4 in. The height of the squares is no problem because vertical scanning produces lower video frequencies.

The vertical bar at the left in Fig. 8-19 is in color because it is 0.4 in. wide. Wider bars will be in color, too. The entire background is in color, because these large areas represent low video frequencies. Also, all horizontal bars are in color.

The thin vertical bar at the right is not in color because its width is less than 0.4 in. This video information is higher than 0.5 MHz.

The vertical edges between the pattern at the center and the background also are in monochrome. These narrow horizontal details correspond to high video frequencies.

In summary, then, almost all the picture is reproduced in color, except for thin vertical lines and edge details less than 0.4 in. wide. This information corresponds to video frequencies above 0.5 MHz.

An actual scene with typical picture information really looks as if it were all in color. The horizontal details in monochrome could not be perceived in color anyway because they are too small. Effectively, people and objects in the scene are outlined in monochrome, but they are filled in with color.

Sometimes, when the camera view moves in for a closeup, you can see small details in color, because their relative width becomes larger compared with the screen size. For the opposite case, when the camera view changes to a long shot, details that were in color become too small, and so you see them in monochrome.

Test Point Questions 8-13

Answers at End of Chapter

a. What are the practical baseband frequencies for the color video signal?

b. Which is easier to show in color, small details or large areas of picture information?

8-14 COLOR SUBCARRIER FREQUENCY

This value must be a high video frequency, between 2 and 4 MHz approximately. If the color subcarrier signal frequency is too low, it can produce excessive interference with the luminance signal. At the opposite extreme, the chrominance signal can interfere with the sound signal. The choice of approximately 3.58 MHz for the color subcarrier signal is a compromise that allows

0.5-MHz sidebands for chrominance information below and above the subcarrier signal frequency. Also, there is room for the extra 0.8 MHz of lower sideband frequencies of the I signal. Most important for compatibility, 3.58 MHz is a high enough video frequency to have little response in monochrome receivers. These sets use the luminance signal alone, and the 3.58-MHz chrominance signal has practically no effect.

The exact frequency of the color subcarrier signal is based on the following additional factors:

1. The transmitted picture carrier and sound carrier frequencies cannot be changed, in order to preserve the 4.5-MHz beat for intercarrier sound receivers.
2. There will be an interfering beat frequency of approximately 0.92 MHz, or 920 kHz, between the color subcarrier frequencies near 3.58 MHz and the intercarrier sound signal at 4.5 MHz.
3. There will be interfering beat frequencies between the chrominance signal and the higher video frequencies of the luminance signal.

To minimize these interference effects, the color subcarrier frequency is made exactly 3.579545 MHz. This frequency is determined by harmonic relations for the color subcarrier signal, the horizontal line-scanning frequency, and the 4.5-MHz intercarrier beat.

HORIZONTAL SCANNING FREQUENCY Specifically, the sound carrier frequency of 4.5 MHz is made to be the 286th harmonic of the horizontal line frequency. Therefore

$$f_H = \frac{4.5 \text{ MHz}}{286} = 15{,}734.27 \text{ Hz}$$

where f_H is the horizontal line-scanning frequency for color television broadcasting. Note that 286 is the even number that will make f_H closest to the value of 15,750 Hz used for horizontal scanning in monochrome television. The slight difference has practically no effect on horizontal scanning and sync in the receiver because of the horizontal AFC circuit.

VERTICAL SCANNING FREQUENCY The vertical scanning frequency also is changed slightly since there must be 262.5 lines per field. Then the vertical field-scanning frequency is

$$f_V = \frac{15{,}734.27 \text{ Hz}}{262.5} = 59.94 \text{ Hz}$$

The slight difference of 0.06 Hz below 60 Hz has practically no effect on vertical scanning and sync in the receiver. An oscillator that can be triggered by 60-Hz pulses also can be synchronized by 59.94-Hz pulses. Note that when the scanning frequencies are shifted slightly for color television, the transmitted sync is changed also to the new frequencies for f_V and f_H. Anyway, practically all programs are broadcast with the color TV system, including old black-and-white movies.

COLOR FREQUENCY With the horizontal line-scanning frequency chosen, now the color subcarrier can be determined. This value is made to be the 455th harmonic of $f_H/2$:

$$C = 455 \times \frac{15{,}734.27 \text{ Hz}}{2} = 3.579545 \text{ MHz}$$

To obtain this exact frequency, the color oscillator is crystal-controlled. A typical quartz crystal unit is shown in Fig. 8-20. The multiple of 455 is chosen as an odd number that makes C close to 3.58 MHz.

FREQUENCY INTERLACE Because of the odd-line interlaced scanning pattern, picture information for video frequencies that are odd multiples of $f_H/2$ tends to cancel in the effect on the screen of the picture tube. The cancellation results because these frequencies have opposite voltage polarities for the picture information on even and odd scanning lines. You can see the canceling

Fig. 8-20 Crystal for color oscillator. Frequency is exactly 3579.545 kHz = 3.579545 MHz.

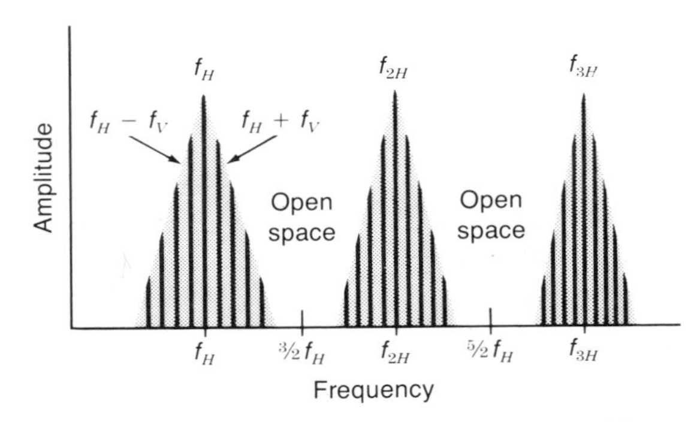

Fig. 8-21 Clusters of frequencies in video signal for a static scene without motion. f_H is horizontal line scanning frequency; f_V is vertical scanning frequency. Open spaces in the spectrum can be used for interleaving video frequencies, or frequency interlace.

effect by coupling a signal generator output voltage at 2 to 4 MHz to the video amplifier to produce a diagonal-bar interference pattern on the picture tube screen. By adjusting the generator frequency carefully and watching the screen pattern closely, at certain frequencies the interference pattern will disappear. These frequencies are odd multiples of one-half the horizontal line-scanning frequency.

This technique of interlacing odd and even harmonic components of two different signals to minimize interference between them is called *frequency interlace.* As a result, the chrominance signal can be transmitted in the same 6-MHz channel as the luminance and sound signals with practically no interference.

The reason why the frequency components of the Y and C video signals can be interlaced is illustrated in Fig. 8-21. Note the clusters of frequencies around f_H, which is the frequency repeated for every horizontal scanning line. Each cluster has pairs of frequencies, with one above and the other below f_H by the vertical scanning frequency of approximately 60 Hz. For a scene with little motion, there are about 20 pairs. The bandwidth used around f_H, then, is about $\pm 20 \times 60$ Hz $= \pm 1200$ Hz. These clusters of signal frequencies are for the Y signal.

Note the open spaces between the clusters of Y signal frequencies. The spaces are at odd multiples of one-half the horizontal line-scanning frequency, such as $3/2 H$ or $5/2 H$ shown in the figure. Remember that the color subcarrier frequency of 3.579545 MHz is made to be an odd multiple of $H/2$. Therefore, the signal frequencies for the modulated 3.58-MHz chroma signal fall in the spaces between the clusters of Y video signal frequencies. As a result, the Y and C signal frequencies are interleaved, or interlaced, for minimum interference between them.

Test Point Questions 8-14

Answers at End of Chapter

a. What is the exact horizontal line-scanning frequency for color television?

b. What is the exact vertical field-scanning frequency for color television?

c. What is the exact color subcarrier frequency?

d. Which frequency is made exactly an odd multiple of $H/2$—the Y, C, or sound signal?

8-15
COLOR TELEVISION SYSTEMS

The standards described here are those of the National Television System Committee (NTSC). This group, formed by the Electronic Industries Association, also prepared the standards for monochrome television in the United States. The FCC approved the monochrome standards in 1941. The NTSC color television system was adopted in 1954.

Historically, color television broadcasting began experimentally in about 1949 with two competing systems by RCA and CBS. The CBS system used a mechanical color wheel with red, green, and blue filters in sequential fields. This method used scanning frequencies that were not compatible with monochrome broadcasting. The RCA system used compatible scanning standards. The CBS system was adopted for a short time in 1951 but was used very little. Then the NTSC prepared new standards based on the RCA system. After field trials, the NTSC color television system was adopted by the FCC. The NTSC color television system is standard in the United States, Canada, Japan, and many countries in the western hemisphere.

In Europe, the main color television systems are phase alternation by line (PAL) and SECAM.[2] The PAL system is similar to the NTSC system, but for each successive line one component of the chrominance signal is reversed in polarity. The purpose is to average any errors in hue phase. This system is used in Germany and many European countries. SECAM is a French system with a sequential technique and memory storage. In this method, two chrominance signals are transmitted, one at a time, for successive lines.

Note that other countries may have scanning standards and a channel width different from those of the United States. Also, the color subcarrier frequency of 3.58 MHz in the NTSC system is essentially for a 6-MHz broadcast channel. Standards for principal television systems of the world are listed in App. D.

Test Point Questions 8-15

Answers at End of Chapter

Answer True or False.

a. The NTSC and SECAM color television systems are the same.

b. The PAL system alternates the phase of the color signal in successive lines.

---

[2] For more details on PAL and SECAM, see C. R. G. Reed, *Principles of Colour Television Systems*, Isaac Pitman and Sons Ltd., London, 1969.

SUMMARY

The following definitions summarize the main features of color television.

***B* − *Y* signal** Color mixture is close to blue. Phase is 180° opposite to color sync burst. Bandwidth is 0 to 0.5 MHz.

Burst Color sync. Is 8 to 11 cycles of 3.58-MHz color subcarrier transmitted on back porch of every horizontal pulse. Needed to synchronize phase of 3.58-MHz oscillator in receiver for correct hues in *C* signal. The hue of color sync phase is yellow-green.

Chrominance signal Also called the *chroma,* or *C, signal.* Is 3.58-MHz color subcarrier with quadrature modulation by I and Q color video signals. Amplitude of C signal is saturation; phase angle is hue.

Colorplexer Also called the *multiplexer.* Combines C signal and Y luminance signal. Result is total colorplexed composite video signal transmitted to receiver as amplitude modulation of picture carrier.

Compatibility Ability of monochrome receiver to use Y signal for picture in black and white. Also allows color receiver to reproduce monochrome picture. Compatibility results from transmission of Y signal for luminance and use of practically the same scanning standards for color and monochrome.

Complementary color Opposite hue and phase angle from its primary color. Cyan, magenta, and yellow are complements of red, green, and blue, respectively.

Decoding Converting hue and saturation in the C signal to R, G, and B primary color video signals for the tricolor picture tube.

Encoding Converting the R, G, and B primary color video signals to hue and saturation in the C signal.

Frequency interlace Placing of harmonic frequencies of C signal midway between harmonics of horizontal scanning frequency f_H. Accomplished by making color subcarrier frequency exactly 3.579545 MHz. This frequency is an odd multiple of $H/2$.

$G - Y$ signal Color mixture close to green. Bandwidth is 0 to 0.5 MHz. Usually formed by combining $B - Y$ and $R - Y$ video signals.

Hue Also called *tint.* Wavelength of light for the color. The varying phase angles in the 3.58-MHz C signal indicate the different hues in the picture information.

I signal Color video signal transmitted as amplitude modulation of the 3.58-MHz C signal. Hue axis is orange and cyan. This is the only color video signal with bandwidth of 0 to 1.3 MHz.

Luminance Also brightness, for either color or monochrome information. Luminance information is in the Y signal.

Matrix Combines signals in specific proportions. Transmitter matrix forms Y, I, and Q video signals in the output for R, G, and B input. At the receiver, the three-gun picture tube is often the matrix for input of $R - Y$, $B - Y$, $G - Y$, and Y signals to produce red, green, and blue light from the screen.

Monochrome In black and white. Just luminance or brightness without color. The Y signal is a monochrome signal.

Multiplexing Combining of two signals on one carrier.

NTSC National Television System Committee. The name for the standard color television system adopted by the FCC for use in the United States.

Primary colors Red, green, and blue. Opposite voltage polarities are the complementary colors cyan, magenta, and yellow.

***Q* signal** Color video signal that modulates 3.58-MHz *C* signal in quadrature with *I* signal. Hues are green and magenta. Bandwidth is 0 to 0.5 MHz.

***R* − *Y* signal** Color mixture close to red. Phase is in quadrature with *B* − *Y*. Bandwidth is 0 to 0.5 MHz.

Saturation Intensity of color. Full saturation means no dilution by white. Different saturation values are varying peak-to-peak amplitudes in the 3.58-MHz modulated *C* signal.

Subcarrier A carrier that modulates another carrier wave of higher frequency. In color television the 3.58-MHz color subcarrier modulates the RF picture carrier wave in the standard broadcast channel.

Suppressed subcarrier Transmission of the modulation sidebands without the subcarrier itself. Requires reinsertion of the subcarrier at the receiver for detecting the modulation.

Synchronous demodulator Detector circuit for a specific phase of the modulated signal. Is necessary with a suppressed-carrier signal.

SELF-EXAMINATION

Answers at Back of Book

Choose (a), (b), (c), or (d).

1. Brightness variations of the picture information are in which signal? (a) *I*, (b) *Q*, (c) *Y*, (d) *R* − *Y*.
2. The hue 180° out of phase with red is (a) cyan, (b) yellow, (c) green, (d) blue.
3. Greater p-p amplitude of the 3.58-MHz chrominance signal indicates more (a) white, (b) yellow, (c), hue, (d) saturation.
4. The interfering beat frequency of 920 kHz is between the 3.58-MHz color subcarrier and the (a) 4.5-MHz intercarrier sound, (b) picture carrier, (c) lower adjacent sound (d) upper adjacent picture.
5. The hue of color sync phase is (a) red, (b) cyan, (c) blue, (d) yellow-green.
6. Which signal has color information for 1.3-MHz bandwidth? (a) *I*, (b) *Y*, (c) *R* − *Y*, (d) *B* − *Y*.
7. Which of the following is false? (a) The *I* video hues are orange or cyan. (b) The transmitter matrix output includes *Y*, *I*, and *Q* video. (c) A three-gun picture tube can serve as a matrix. (d) A fully saturated color is mostly white.

8. The color with the most luminance is (a) red, (b) yellow, (c) green, (d) blue.
9. What is the hue of a color 90° leading sync burst phase? (a) Yellow, (b) cyan, (c) blue, (d) orange.
10. The average voltage value of the 3.58-MHz modulated chrominance signal is (a) zero for most colors, (b) close to black for yellow, (c) the brightness of the color, (d) the saturation of the color.
11. The second IF value for color in receivers, for any station, is (a) 0.5 MHz, (b) 1.3 MHz, (c) 3.58 MHz, (d) 4.5 MHz.
12. If the 3.58-MHz C amplifier in the receiver does not operate, the result will be (a) no color, (b) no red, (c) too much blue, (d) too much yellow.

ESSAY QUESTIONS

1. What is meant by color addition? List the three additive primary colors.
2. What color corresponds to white light minus red? White minus blue? White minus green?
3. Why are the primary color video voltages converted to Y and C signals for broadcasting?
4. Define hue, saturation, luminance, and chrominance.
5. What is the video-frequency bandwidth of the Y signal?
6. What parts of the picture are reproduced in black and white by the Y signal? What parts are reproduced in full color as mixtures of red, green, and blue?
7. What hues correspond to the following? $+I$, $-I$, $+Q$, $-Q$, $R - Y$, $-(R - Y)$, $B - Y$, and color sync burst.
8. How is the 3.58-MHz modulated chrominance signal transmitted to the receiver? Why is the 3.58-MHz signal called a subcarrier?
9. Describe the color sync burst signal and give its purpose.
10. How does the colorplexed video signal indicate hue, saturation, and luminance of the picture information?
11. Why is the chrominance signal transmitted with the subcarrier suppressed?
12. Why is the color subcarrier frequency made exactly 3.579545 MHz?
13. **(a)** Explain how color sync burst and H deflection sync differ in amplitude and frequency. **(b)** Explain the difference in timing between the 3.58-MHz color sync burst and 3.58-MHz chrominance signal.
14. A scene displays a wide yellow vertical bar against a black background. How will this picture appear in a monochrome reproduction?
15. What is the effect of the chrominance signal in a monochrome receiver with video-frequency response up to 3.2 MHz?

PROBLEMS

Answers to Odd-Numbered Problems at Back of Book

1. Show the calculations for Y luminance values of blue, red, green, yellow, and white.
2. Prove that if $G - Y$ is $-0.51(R - Y) - 0.19(B - Y)$, then this equals $-0.30R + 0.41G - 0.11B$, by substituting the R, G, and B values for Y.
3. **(a)** Calculate the value of C voltage when $I = 0.4$ and $Q = 0.3$. **(b)** What is the approximate hue of this color?
4. A symmetric voltage varies between the peak of 0.79 V and minimum of 0.11 V. Calculate the **(a)** peak-to-peak value and **(b)** average level.

SPECIAL QUESTIONS

1. Name two applications of color video signals other than television broadcasting.
2. In a comparison of monochrome and color television receivers, what sections are essentially the same and which sections are different?

ANSWERS TO TEST POINT QUESTIONS

8-1 **a.** Red, green, and blue
b. Zero
c. Red
d. Frequencies

8-2 **a.** Blue
b. Yellow
c. Cyan

8-3 **a.** Hue
b. Saturation
c. Low

8-4 **a.** T
b. T
c. F

8-5 **a.** Y, I, and Q
b. I and OSC_I
c. 90°
d. Multiplexer
e. R_C

8-6 **a.** 3.58 MHz
b. C and OSC_{R-Y}
c. 90°
d. R, G, and B

8-7 **a.** 1.00
b. 0.30
c. 0.59
d. 0.11
e. 0.89

8-8 **a.** T
b. T
c. T
d. F

8-9 **a.** 3.58 MHz
b. 15,750 Hz (approx.)

8-10 **a.** Yellow-green
b. 180°
c. 90°

8-11 **a.** 0.89 and 0.11
b. −0.31 and +0.31
c. 0.45 and 0.45

8-12 **a.** More
b. Less

8-13 **a.** 0 to 0.5 MHz
b. Large areas

8-14 **a.** 15,734.27 Hz
b. 59.94 Hz
c. 3.579545 MHz
d. C signal

8-15 **a.** F
b. T

9

VIDEO TEST SIGNALS

Since the beginning of television broadcasting, specialized test patterns and test signals have been developed to standardize TV operations for the best performance. An important example is the EIA test pattern shown in Fig. 9-1. This standard pattern provides a reference for checking resolution, scanning linearity, interlacing, and additional characteristics of the reproduced picture.

Some tests are used to check the camera and monitor during setup. An important requirement is to match different cameras used for the same program. Other tests are in constant use to check the performance of long-distance links for broadcast stations in a TV network. The testing is for monochrome and color, especially the amplitude and phase of the 3.58-MHz chroma signal. Finally, some test signals are broadcast during the vertical blanking interval. In this case, they are available at the receiver. The main methods of testing are discussed in the following sections:

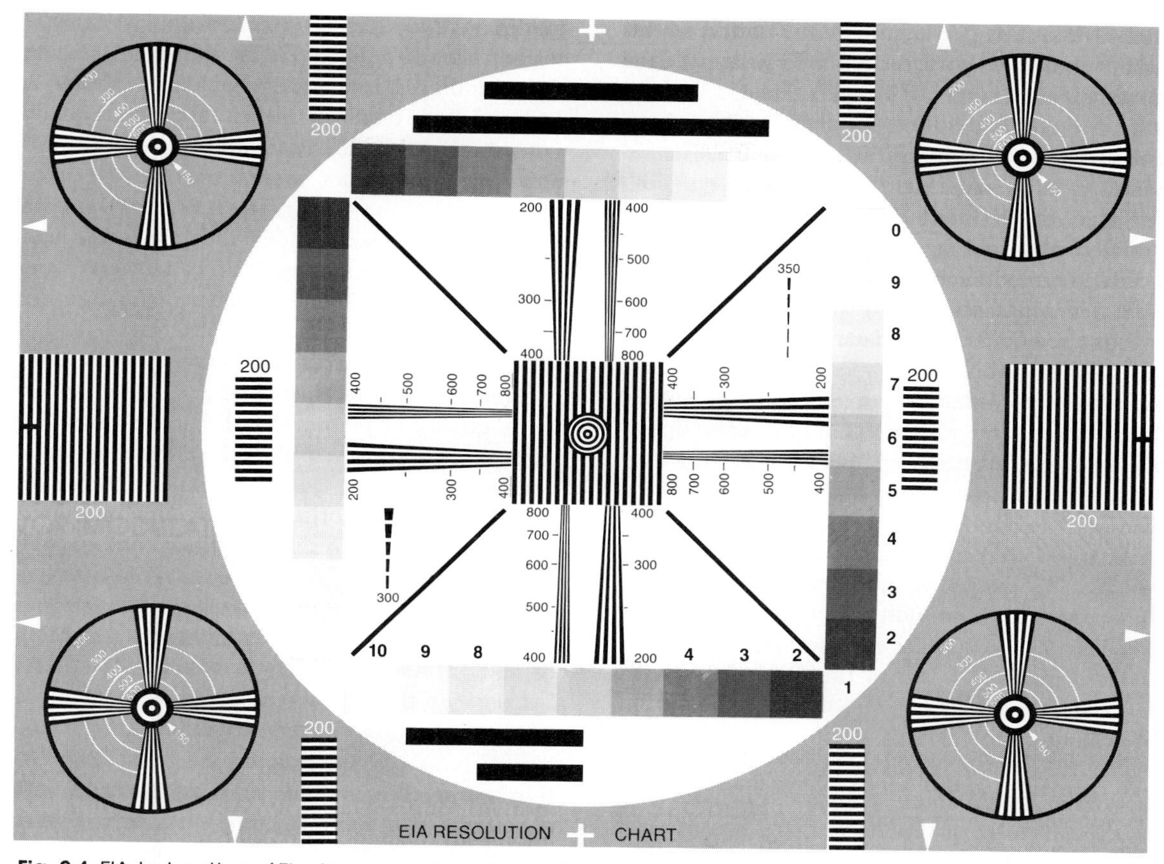

Fig. 9-1 EIA test pattern. (*Electronic Industries Association*)

9-1 EIA TEST PATTERN

The standard test chart in Fig. 9-1 was developed by the Electronic Industries Association (EIA). The chart appears quite busy because there are many separate parts in the pattern. However, each has its own function.

FRAMING First, the camera must be aimed at the chart and adjusted so that the chart just fills the active screen area. The six white arrowheads around the edges of the chart aid in perfect framing. There are two arrowheads across the top and at each side. The framing adjustments require an underscanned monitor, to see the edges of the raster.

CENTERING The white crosses at the top and bottom indicate a vertical axis down the middle for horizontal centering. Also, the black dashes at the sides indicate a horizontal axis across the center. Unless the test pattern is framed and centered precisely, the numbers on the chart that indicate resolution are meaningless.

DEFLECTION LINEARITY An approximate but obvious indicator, for both the camera and the monitor, is provided by the large, white circular area. Errors in linearity are easily seen if the circle appears elliptical or egg-shaped. In television, the simple shape of a circle is hard to reproduce because it requires linear scanning. The basic form of a square is also a test of scanning linearity.

For a more precise check, the horizontal and vertical linearity are checked separately. Consider horizontal scanning first. Note three squares across the middle of the pattern—one at the center and one at the left and right sides. These squares each contain an equal number of vertical lines for the same width. When horizontal linearity is perfect, all three squares have equal width. Otherwise, a square could be squeezed or expanded to a rectangle.

To check vertical linearity, the pattern has six narrow rectangles, in two rows top to bottom. Note that the two middle rectangles are at the exact vertical center of the picture. The size of the rectangles is a test of the vertical linearity. They should all have the same height from top to bottom of the pattern.

The 200 mark indicated at these rectangles is for resolution, not linearity. Also, the four small test patterns at the corners are used to check resolution and geometric distortion. These corner patterns are used to check the camera's performance.

ASPECT RATIO Note the square formed by the four bars of gray-scale chips placed just inside the central white disk. Each bar has 10 numbered steps of gray scale. When the aspect ratio is correct, at 4:3, this border of the gray-scale chips is a perfect square.

CONTRAST RANGE The 10 numbered steps of gray-scale chips have reflectances that range from a maximum for peak white to about one-thirtieth of that value. When the video signal processing is linear, it should be possible to distinguish 10 distinct shades from white through gray to black.

INTERLACING The diagonal bars at 45° in the white disk are used to check the interlacing of the scanning lines in the raster. When the even and odd lines of the scanning raster are equally spaced, the diagonal lines appear smooth and unbroken. With poor interlacing, however, the scanning lines become paired. When two lines are too close to each other, the space to the next pair is too big. As a result, the diagonal lines become jagged and have a stair-step appearance.

RESOLUTION Lines of different thickness and spacing are used to check the resolution, which is the quality of picture detail. Vertical lines are used to check the horizontal resolution, while horizontal lines are used for vertical resolution.

Note that the horizontal detail is measured in the number of resolution lines that occupy three-fourths of the picture width. That distance is equal to the height of the picture. The purpose is to have equal numbers correspond to the same resolution, horizontally or vertically.

Consider the three squares of vertical lines, labeled 200, across the center of the pattern. One square is at the left, one at the right, and the third at the center. The label of 200 indicates this many lines of resolution. With this spacing and thickness, 200 lines would occupy three-fourths of the picture width. When the individual lines can be seen on the screen, the horizontal resolution equals 200 lines.

Note the six rectangles of short horizontal marks, also marked 200, in two vertical columns. The individual marks in each rectangle are spaced to equal 200 lines for the total picture height. Therefore, they represent 200-line vertical resolution.

Spacing for the concentric circles at the center of the pattern represents 300-line resolution, horizontal and vertical. At the four corners of the pattern, the concentric circles are spaced for 150-line resolution.

The test pattern also has wedges to check the resolution up to 800 lines, as described next in

Sec. 9-2. In addition, how the test pattern can be used to check streaking and ringing is explained in Secs. 9-3 and 9-4.

Test Point Questions 9-1
Answers at End of Chapter

a. In the test pattern, is the H resolution measured by horizontal or vertical lines?
b. How many horizontal details can be resolved with 300-line resolution?
c. How many gray-scale steps are in the EIA test pattern?
d. Do smooth, unbroken diagonal lines show good interlacing or a correct aspect ratio?

9-2 RESOLUTION WEDGES IN THE TEST PATTERN

In Fig. 9-1, there are four pairs of wedges with converging lines for increasing resolution numbers. An obvious use is to check linearity. The top and bottom wedges should have the same length for good vertical linearity. Also, the side wedges must be equal for good horizontal linearity. However, the main use of the wedges is to check resolution.

HORIZONTAL RESOLUTION This value is marked on the top and bottom wedges. From the widest part of the wedge marked 200, the lines converge to 400-line resolution where the wedge meets the square at the center. The spacing for the adjacent wedge continues the resolution from 400 to 800. The resolution can be checked visually by noting the point on the wedge where the individual lines can no longer be seen but appear to blur together. This would occur at about 250-line resolution for a typical color receiver.

An approximate conversion from lines of horizontal resolution to megahertz of video signal bandwidth can be made by dividing the lines by 80. The answer is in megahertz for the video frequency. As an example, 250 lines converts to

$$\frac{250 \text{ lines}}{80} = 3.125 \text{ MHz}$$

This value for the highest video frequency is typical for most color receivers because a trap in the luminance video amplifier filters out 3.58 MHz to minimize the interference from the color signal.

The conversion factor of 80 is derived as follows. With N lines of resolution, $N/2$ is the number of complete cycles for signal variations across black in each line of the wedge and the white space between lines. The visible trace takes 53.3 μs for horizontal scanning, but only three-quarters of the time applies because the resolution values are given in terms of picture height, which is three-fourths of the width. This time is 53.3 μs $\times$ 0.75 = 40 μs approximately. So $N/2$ cycles of the video signal are produced in 40 μs. For one cycle, $T = 40\ \mu\text{s}/(N/2)$. Taking the reciprocal for the frequency yields

$$\begin{aligned} f &= \frac{1}{40 \times 10^{-6} \text{ s}} \left(\frac{N}{2}\right) \\ &= \frac{N}{80} \times 10^{6} \text{ Hz} \\ &= \frac{N}{80} \text{ MHz} \end{aligned}$$

VERTICAL RESOLUTION The vertical resolution is marked on the side wedges. A typical value for receivers is 330-line resolution. Good vertical resolution is mainly a question of the beam spot size, its focusing, and the interlacing of the scanning lines.

CORNER RESOLUTION Similar wedges are used in the four corners of the test pattern to measure the resolution there. The corners usually have less resolution than at the center, especially for wide-angle picture tubes. Resolution values that are specified for camera tubes are usually given for the centers and the corners.

Test Point Questions 9-2

Answers at End of Chapter

a. Is horizontal resolution indicated by the lines in the vertical or horizontal wedges?
b. How many actual horizontal details correspond to the resolution of 210 lines?
c. What video frequency corresponds to 240 lines of horizontal resolution?

9-3 TESTS FOR STREAKING OR SMEAR IN THE PICTURE

Streaking is mainly a problem of phase distortion for middle and low video frequencies, from about 100 kHz down. The streaking, or smearing, shows as a continuation of a wide bar of picture information after a sharp change to the opposite color. As examples, a wide black bar can show streaks to the right into a white area. Or white can be smeared into black areas. An example of streaking in the picture is shown in Fig. 9-2.

Fig. 9-2 Smear in the picture.

The cause of streaking is phase distortion for video signal frequencies of 10 to 100 kHz. In the video signal, phase distortion can be seen as a tilt in the square wave of the picture information. Phase distortion in an amplifier means that the phase-angle shift is not proportional to the frequency.

BARS IN THE TEST PATTERN TO CHECK STREAKING In the EIA test pattern of Fig. 9-1, note the two wide, black bars at the top of the large white disk and the two bars at the bottom. The frequency at which the phase distortion and smearing can be checked is related to the width of these bars. For example, the phase distortion at 100 kHz shows as streaking of the shortest bar, at the bottom of the white disk. The longest bar, which is second from the top, can indicate streaking for 30 kHz. This bar is about $3\frac{1}{3}$ times wider than the shortest bar for a frequency 0.3 times lower, compared with the shortest bar. The intermediate values are 50 kHz for the top bar and 60 kHz for the bar second from the bottom.

Test Point Questions 9-3

Answers at End of Chapter

Answer True or False.

a. Phase distortion in the video signal causes excessive snow.
b. Figure 9-2 shows smear in the picture.

9-4 TESTS FOR RINGING IN THE PICTURE

Frequency distortion in the form of too much relative gain for some high video frequencies results in ringing or overshoot. Typically, the excessive gain is in the frequency range of 2 to 4 MHz. The amplifier is just short of being an oscillator circuit, but it can be shock-excited into several cycles of oscillations by an abrupt transient variation in the video signal. Ringing can be seen in the test pattern as an increase in contrast at some point in the vertical wedges. Divide the number of resolution lines by 80 to get the frequency at which the ringing occurs. An example of ringing in the picture is shown in Fig. 9-3.

In addition, a number of abrupt horizontal scanning transitions are provided by vertical black dashes in the white disk of the EIA pattern. In Fig. 9-1, there are two groups of these dashes, one in the upper right quadrant and the other at the lower left. The thickness of each vertical dash represents a single line for horizontal resolution that ranges from 100 to 300 and 350 to 550. A thinner line corresponds to higher resolution. In the lower left quadrant, the 300 at the bottom of the group of five dashes is for the bottom dash. Then the dashes get thicker, progressing to 100-line resolution for the widest dash at the top of the group.

In the upper right quadrant, the 350 at the top of the group of five dashes is for the top dash. Then the dashes get thinner, progressing to 550-line resolution for the thinnest dash at the bottom of the group.

Ringing in the picture shows as greater contrast, with multiple lines trailing to the right for each of the ringing cycles. Since each individual dash represents a particular frequency, the ringing condition appears worst where the burst of energy matches the frequency at which ringing occurs in the video amplifier circuit. Once again, convert the line-resolution number in the test pattern to its video frequency by dividing by 80.

Fig. 9-3 Ringing in the window signal. Note the multiple outlines.

For example, suppose that the ringing occurs at the marker for 300-line resolution. The corresponding video frequency is $300/80 = 3.75$ MHz. This value is the frequency at which the video amplifier circuit is ringing.

Actually, a small amount of ringing may be permissible, for it improves the contrast for high-frequency details at the vertical edges of the objects in the scene. When it produces trailing outlines, however, the excessive ringing is objectionable. Generally the ringing is caused by stray resonance effects in the video amplifier circuit.

Test Point Questions 9-4

Answers at End of Chapter

a. Is excessive ringing in the picture shown by Fig. 9-2 or 9-3?

b. Can excessive gain at 3.75 MHz cause smear or ringing?

9-5 MONOSCOPE SIGNALS

A monoscope is a special camera tube with a fixed image of a test pattern printed on the target plate. The test patterns that were broadcast during the daytime in the very early days of television were produced by monoscopes.

The monoscope pattern is similar in many respects to the EIA test pattern. Included are circles for checking linearity, resolution wedges marked in lines or frequency (or both), and shades of gray in concentric circles at the center. The broadcast station call letters were usually on the pattern. Today, you may still see a monoscope test pattern on some channels, for a short time in the very early hours of the morning at the start or end of the broadcast day. A monoscope pattern can provide a good check of the receiver operation.

Monoscope signals are not produced by a camera pointed at a test chart. Instead, a special camera tube similar to a vidicon is used. The target plate is engraved photographically with conduction and insulation paths in the form of white and black areas of the pattern. The monoscope requires precision deflection sync and linearity so that the pattern can be used to adjust monitors and receivers.

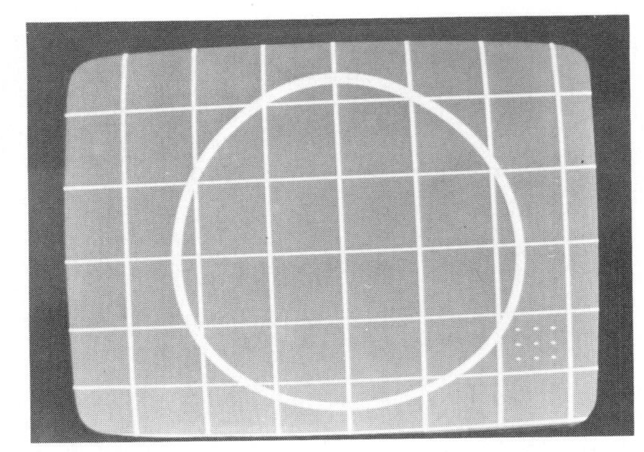

Fig. 9-4 Vertical nonlinearity in crosshatch pattern. Picture stretched at top and crowded at bottom. Dots identify lower right corner.

Test Point Questions 9-5

Answers at End of Chapter

Answer True or False.

a. The monoscope is a type of picture tube.

b. A fixed image is engraved on the target plate of the monoscope.

9-6 BALL CHART FOR CHECKING CAMERA LINEARITY

An independent reference is needed to check the deflection linearity. To illustrate, suppose that the monitor shows an egg-shaped test pattern. The poor linearity can be in either the camera or the monitor. If the monitor deflection is adjusted for a circle but the nonlinearity is in the camera, the linearity problem will show up as soon as another signal source is used.

However, the monitor can be checked independently by using electronic test signals for linearity. Specifically, a crosshatch signal generator is used. The crosshatch is a pattern of equally spaced vertical and horizontal white lines on a black background. This pattern is used also to check convergence for color picture tubes, as described in Chap. 5.

The crosshatch pattern is an independent reference for linearity because the equal-line spacing is produced by signals at precise multiples of the *H* and *V* scanning frequencies. An example is the studio color-bar generator, which also produces a crosshatch pattern. There are 17 vertical bars and 14 horizontal bars from oscillators operating at 315 kHz and 900 Hz, respectively.

The 315-kHz oscillator actually produces 20 vertical bars, because 315 kHz is 20 times the *H* scan rate of 15,750 kHz. However, three bars occur during *H* blanking time, which leaves $20 - 3 = 17$ vertical bars that are visible.

Also, the 900-Hz oscillator actually produces 15 horizontal bars, since $900/60 = 15$. However, one bar occurs during the *V* blanking time, leaving 14 visible horizontal bars. Examples of horizontal and vertical nonlinearity on a crosshatch pattern are shown in Figs. 9-4 and 9-5.

To make use of this precise bar spacing for an independent check of deflection linearity, the ball chart shown in Fig. 9-6 is used with the crosshatch pattern. The camera is aimed and focused on the chart, and the arrowheads at the edges frame the chart precisely on the active picture area. Then a special-effects generator (SEG) is used to superimpose the crosshatch pattern

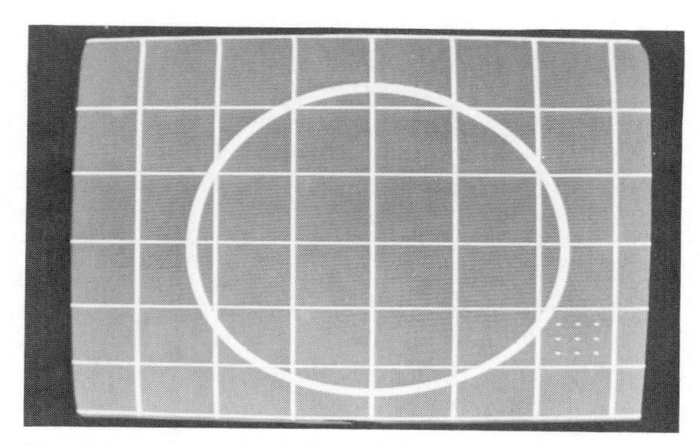

Fig. 9-5 Horizontal nonlinearity in crosshatch pattern. Circle appears egg-shaped.

from a studio color-bar generator over the camera picture of the ball chart. Centering adjustments on the generator permit the crosshatch pattern to be shifted up, down, or sideways to place the crosshatch bar intersections over the white centers of the balls at the center of the ball pattern.

The superimposed picture is observed on a monitor. If the camera linearity is perfect, the crosshatch intersections cross the center of the white balls at every point on the screen, for 0 percent error. Poor linearity or improper scan size causes the intersections to miss the centers of the balls. When the intersections cross within the inner radius of the white balls, the deflection linearity error is less than 1 percent of the picture height. Within the radius of the black outer balls, the linearity error is less than 2 percent. These values indicate the linear scanning precision required for broadcast cameras, for errors greater than 2 percent cannot be tolerated. Note that this method of using the ball chart with a crosshatch signal makes the test of deflection linearity in the camera totally independent of the monitor used for observation.

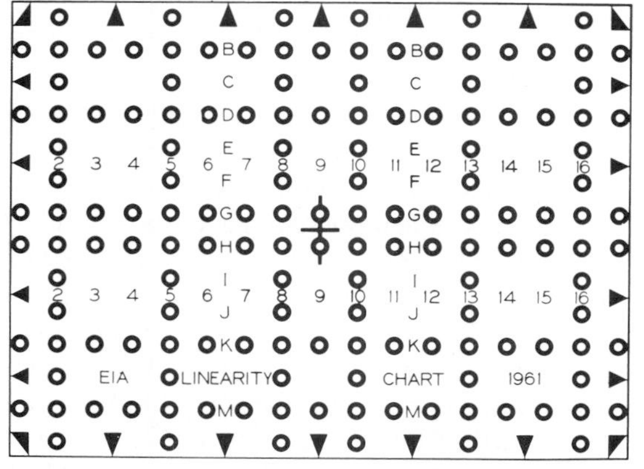

Fig. 9-6 Ball chart used to check deflection linearity in cameras. (*EIA*)

Test Point Questions 9-6

Answers at End of Chapter

a. Is the ball chart used with a crosshatch pattern or with color bars?

b. Is the ball chart test for the camera or the monitor?

c. Is the maximum permissible nonlinearity for broadcast cameras 0.1, 2, or 20 percent?

9-7
EIA STANDARD COLOR-BAR SIGNAL

In general, a color-bar generator produces precise, repeatable signals for vertical color bars that can be used for testing and adjustment procedures. The signals are encoded on the 3.58-MHz color subcarrier frequency. Specifically, the EIA has developed a color-bar signal that corresponds to the pattern shown in Fig. 9-7. It conforms to EIA standard RS-189A. There are many features that facilitate tests for correct color and luminance.

The top three-fourths of the height in Fig. 9-7 includes seven vertical bars of equal width. First at the left is white, and the bars continue in yellow, cyan, green, magenta, red, and blue across the width of the picture. This sequence is chosen because the luminance values then form

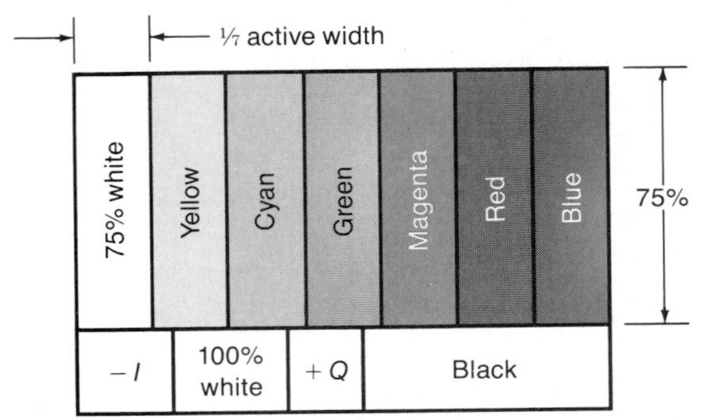

Fig. 9-7 Picture format of EIA standard color-bar signal. The shaded areas indicate color. (*Leader Instrument Corp.*)

a descending staircase of Y signal. Of the colors, yellow has the highest luminance value of 89 percent, which is equal to $0.59G + 0.30R$. At the opposite extreme, blue has the lowest luminance of 11 percent.

The lower quarter of the picture height contains a short, white bar, with 100 percent luminance to straddle the yellow and cyan bars. As a result, it is convenient to check these luminance values against white. In addition, color signals for $-I$ and $+Q$ are placed to the left and right of the white bar.

100 AND 75 PERCENT COLOR BARS The early generators produced color bars that were fully saturated at 100 percent. This value means that the R, G, and B signals into the encoder are at the 100 percent level for peak white, or 100 IRE units. However, this method places an unnecessary burden on the transmission equipment because of the peak excursions on the modulated 3.58-MHz chroma signal. For the yellow bar, as an example, the maximum level is 33 percent above peak white, owing to high luminance. Also, the low luminance of the blue bar results in signal amplitudes 33 percent below black setup. These extreme values make demands on linearity in the signal processing that will not be necessary in practical cases, since 100 percent saturated colors never occur in actual camera signals.

Therefore, the standard color-bar signal has been reduced to what is now called *75 percent color bars*. This percentage does *not* mean 75 percent saturation. It simply means that the amplitudes of the R, G, and B signals into the encoder are at 75 IRE units, instead of 100. The resulting color bars are still fully saturated. For a 75 percent red bar, for example, there is still no green or blue that would exist with some white.

***Y* VALUES FOR STANDARD COLOR BARS** Figure 9-8 shows the oscilloscope waveform of the video signal for the EIA standard color bars at the H line rate. The amplitude scale at the left is in IRE units. The shaded areas in the waveform indicate color. Note the color sync burst with an amplitude of ± 20 IRE units.

The values marked on the steps, such as +77 for white and +28 for red, are the Y luminance levels for each of the bars. For the white bar at the left, its Y value of 0.77 is calculated as follows. First, subtracting 7.5 IRE units of setup from 100 yields 92.5 units of signal variation. Then taking 75 percent of 92.5 units gives $0.75 \times 92.5 = 69.375$ units. Finally, putting back the 7.5 units of setup yields $69.375 + 7.5 = 76.875$, which is rounded off to 77 units.

As another example, we can calculate the Y value of the red bar. We take 30 percent of the 69.375 units for the white bar, which equals 20.813 units. Then we put back the 7.5 units for setup. The sum is $20.813 + 7.5 = 28.313$. This value is rounded off to 28 IRE units for the Y level of the 75 percent red bar. The same procedure can be used to calculate Y values for all the color bars. Note that the Y values here differ a little from those calculated in Chap. 8 because the EIA bars are 75 percent and black setup is used.

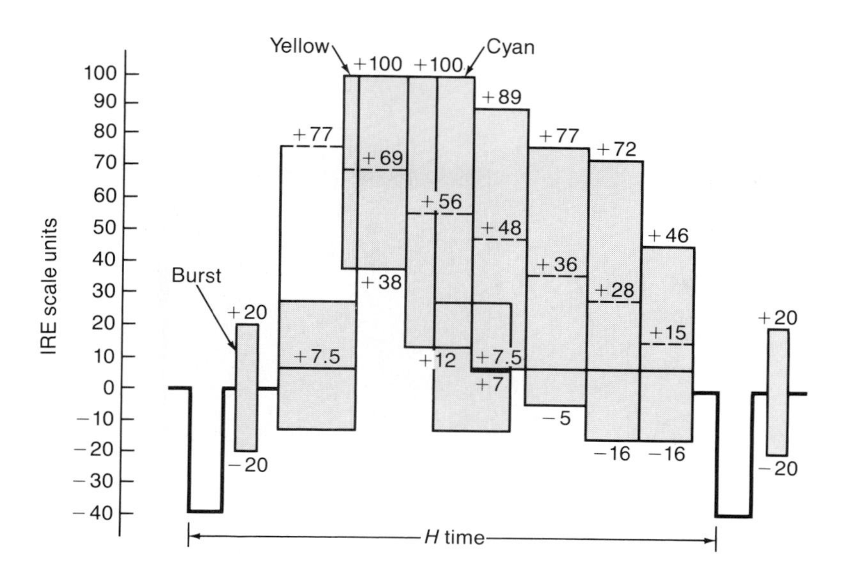

Fig. 9-8 Waveform of standard 75 percent color bars. (*EIA*)

C VALUES OF STANDARD COLOR BARS The peak chroma values of the 3.58-MHz modulated subcarrier signal are shown also in Fig. 9-8, if we take into account the 7.5 IRE units of setup. Thus the values of the C signal for yellow are ±31 units around the Y axis of 69. The peak is at $69 + 31 = 100$ units. Note that the peak of 100 IRE units also is reached for the cyan bar.

The fact that the peak is 100 IRE units for the yellow and cyan bars provides a useful check of relative amplitudes. Note that the 100 percent white bar straddles the yellow and cyan bars (see Fig. 9-7). Now look at the oscilloscope waveform in Fig. 9-9. It shows that the chroma peaks of yellow and cyan, at the left, just touch the 100 level of the white bar. This observation means that the chroma saturation is correct. Such factors as cable loss have not reduced the relative amplitude of the 3.58-MHz chroma signal.

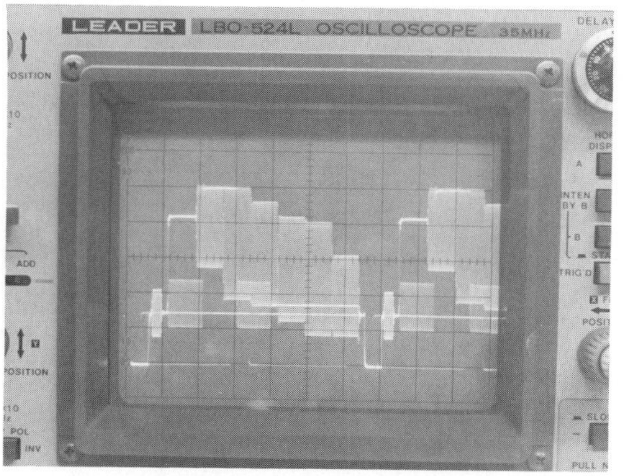

Fig. 9-9 Correct chroma level is indicated when positive subcarrier peaks of yellow and cyan bars reach the 100 percent level of white.

VECTOR DISPLAY Figure 9-10 shows the vectors for the chroma values of the 75 percent color bars, plotted in polar coordinates to show both amplitude and phase. Amplitude here is the peak-to-peak swing in the chroma signal. The amplitudes are measured radially from the center with circles indicating 20 to 100 IRE units. The angles are measured counterclockwise from the horizontal $B - Y$ axis at 0°. The $R - Y$ axis is perpendicular at 90°. The burst is at 180°, opposite $B - Y$.

As examples of reading the vector values, yel-

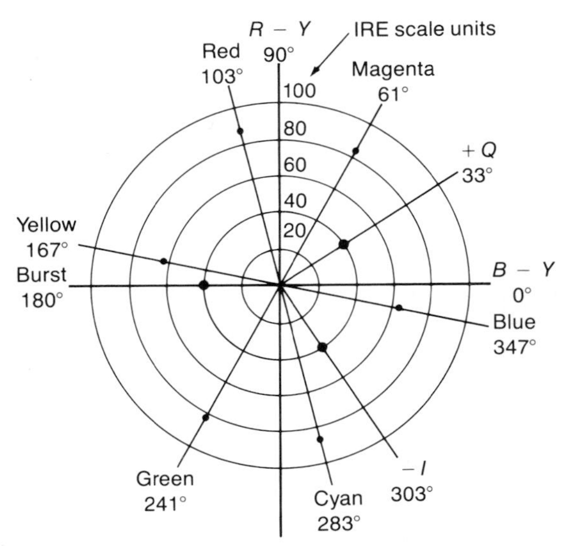

Fig. 9-10 Vector drawing to show relative amplitude and phase angles for all colors in the 75 percent color-bar signal. (*EIA*)

low has an amplitude of 62 IRE units with the phase angle of 167°. The complementary color, blue, has the same amplitude of 62 units but an opposite phase angle of 347°. Note that 347° − 167° = 180°. Additional examples are 40 units at 33° for the $+Q$ signal, with the −I signal also 40 units at 303°. Note that $+Q$ and $-I$ are perpendicular, since $-I$ is 57° from 0° and 57° + 33° = 90°.

VECTORSCOPE A vectorscope is an oscilloscope that can show on the screen the same indication as the vector pattern in Fig. 9-10. The oscilloscope uses X and Y deflection, without internal horizontal sweep. For the X axis, the $B - Y$ signal is applied for horizontal deflection and the $R - Y$ signal is used for vertical deflection. A precision chroma decoder is used to supply the $B - Y$ and $R - Y$ signal inputs.

Figure 9-11 shows the vectorscope display. The bright dots indicate the tips of the vectors. They are bright because the beam stays at one spot for the duration of each bar in the color-bar pattern. The curved lines connecting the dots show the rapid changes in phase and amplitude at the intersections between the bars.

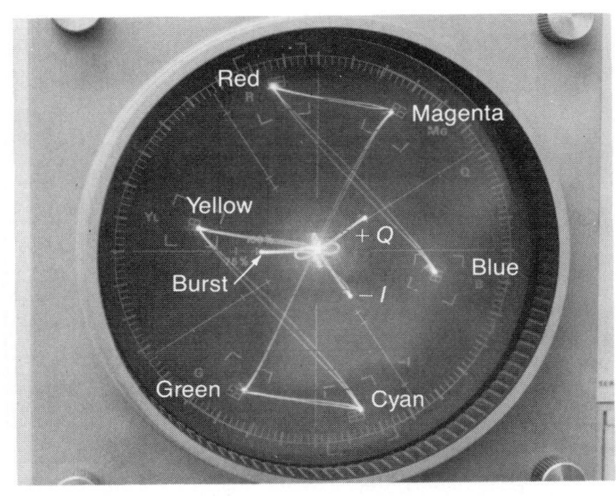

Fig. 9-11 Vectorscope display on oscilloscope screen for precise checks of color amplitudes and phase angles.

The screen of the vectorscope is calibrated in IRE units and phase angle. The small squares indicate a tolerance of ±2.5 IRE units and ±2.5° in phase angle. The larger sector-shaped borders that surround each square indicate a tolerance of ±20 IRE units and ±10° in phase. Target marks are shown also for burst and the I and Q signals. A vectorscope can be set up to lock in the decoder on the burst signal of one source while displaying the bars of another source. This technique allows different color sources to be matched in phase.

Test Point Questions 9-7

Answers at End of Chapter

a. What is the Y luminance value in IRE units for the yellow bar in Fig. 9-7?

b. What is the peak-to-peak value of the C signal in IRE units for the yellow bar in Fig. 9-8?

c. Which peak C value matches 100 percent white in amplitude, cyan or blue?

d. In Fig. 9-10, what is the phase angle for red?

9-8 WINDOW SIGNAL

This electronically generated test signal is shown in Fig. 9-12. It consists of a 100 percent white rectangle that occupies one-half the picture width and one-half the height on a black background. The window provides 100 percent peak white which makes signal-level adjustments easy. Also, the window signal has a carefully controlled rise-time for the vertical edges, with harmonics that stay within the 4.2-MHz video passband. For this reason, the window signal is useful in testing transient conditions such as overshoot, ringing, streaking, and smear.

Figure 9-13 illustrates the effect of horizontal streaking in the window signal. The square-wave video signal is shown in Fig. 9-13*a,* with the picture in Fig. 9-13*b.* A leading phase shift at low video frequencies causes a tilt at the leading edge of the square wave. The signal is actually integrated as capacitive voltage in an *RC* circuit. This form of transient distortion on a square wave is called *sag, droop,* or *tilt* in the flat part of the waveform. It is measured in percentage of tilt. For example, when the leading edge is at 100 IRE units but the top part of the square wave drops to 80, the tilt is 20 units out of 100, or 20 percent. The amount of tilt in transmission links is usually held within 1 or 2 percent.

Fig. 9-12 How the window signal looks on the TV screen.

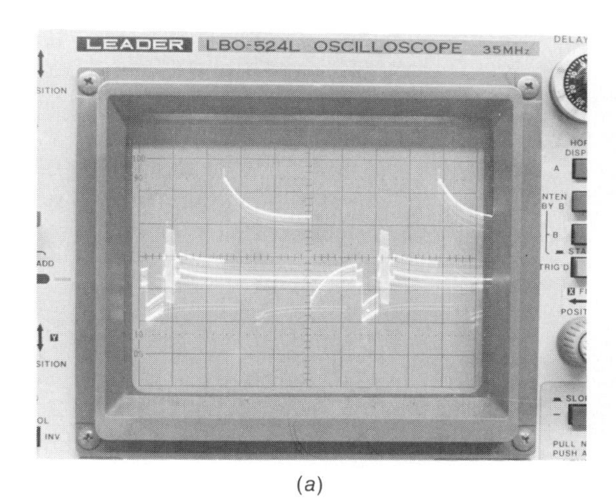

(*a*)

(*b*)

Fig. 9-13 Phase distortion and resultant streaking for window signal. (*a*) Tilt in waveform of video signal. (*b*) Streaks in picture.

Note that the waveform in Fig. 9-13*a* is brighter at the leading edge at the left and a little darker for the trailing edge at the right. Also, the black following the window is blacker owing to the waveform distortion. This effect is what causes the streaking in the picture. The photograph in Fig. 9-13*b* is taken from the picture tube screen by using the video signal in Fig. 9-13*a*. The brightness has been raised to show the effects in the black regions. Note the broad streak that flows out to the right of the window. The effects are seen continued on the next lines. As a result, the streaking continues on subsequent lines and appears as a streak starting at the left edge of the image.

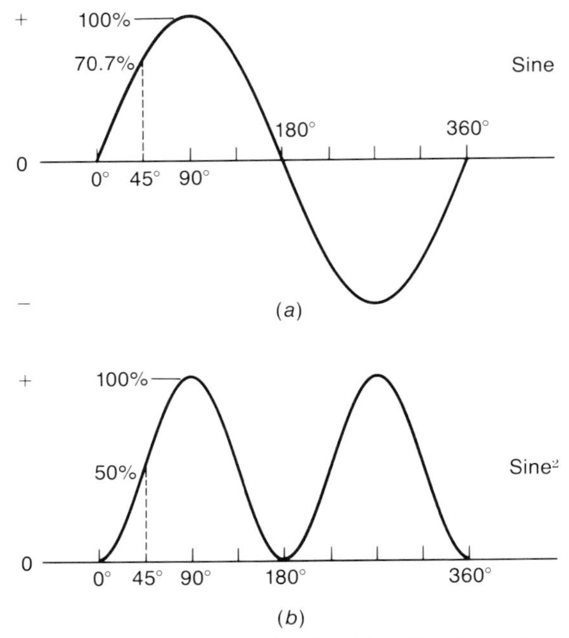

Fig. 9-14 (*a*) Sine wave. (*b*) Squaring the sine values produces the sine-squared waveform. Note that negative values, when squared, become positive.

Test Point Questions 9-8

Answers at End of Chapter

a. How many IRE units is the white window signal?

b. How many microseconds is the width of the window signal?

c. Do the effects for the window signal in Fig. 9-13 illustrate high-frequency ringing or low-frequency streaking?

9-9 SINE-SQUARED TEST SIGNALS

Figure 9-14 illustrates what is meant by a sine-squared wave. The basic sine waveform is shown in Fig. 9-14*a*. When the sine values are squared, the result is the waveform in Fig. 9-14*b*. Note that the negative half-cycle in Fig. 9-14*a* becomes positive in Fig. 9-14*b*, since the square of a negative number is positive. The waveform has a wider top and less slope at the rising and falling edges, compared with a sine or cosine curve. The sine-squared pulse is used for checking the high-frequency response of video equipment.

The specific form of the sine-squared test signal is shown in Fig. 9-15. Often this signal accompanies the window signal. Then it appears as a single vertical white line of the same height as the window and usually to the left. An oscilloscope set to display one horizontal line of the video signal shows the sine-squared test signal to be the single pulse in Fig. 9-15. Its positive peak is at the white level of 100 IRE units with the negative peak at the zero level of blanking.

HALF-AMPLITUDE DURATION Pulse techniques are used in all types of electronic systems to check the response in terms of risetime, overshoot, ringing, and phase delay. However, the practically perfect square high-frequency pulses produced by a conventional pulse generator will show ringing and other effects outside the passband of a typical video signal. To relate these effects to actual picture distortion, a pulse is needed that has a frequency spectrum within the normal 4.2-MHz video passband. What is of interest in the TV system is what happens to the signal-frequency components inside, not outside, the normal passband. The sine-squared signal is very useful because the band of frequencies it contains, for the fundamental and all its harmonics, is determined by a single factor called the *half-amplitude duration* (HAD). See Fig. 9-15. As the name says, the HAD is the time between the two points when the pulse is at half its peak amplitude. In Fig. 9-15, the HAD is 0.125 μs.

T SINE-SQUARED PULSE Here T is 0.125 μs. This time is the HAD of a T pulse. The value 0.125 μs is chosen because it is the time for a single picture element. It corresponds to a 4-MHz video signal for 426 picture elements in the unblanked horizontal scanning time of 53.3 μs. Note that two adjacent pixels provide a complete cycle of video signal.

The pulse in Fig. 9-15 is a T sine-squared pulse with HAD = 0.125 μs. Actually it is derived from a 4-MHz cosine wave, with an added dc component that shifts the negative peaks to the zero blanking level.

A T sine-squared pulse has a frequency response that is down to 50 percent at 4 MHz, with practically no energy beyond 8 MHz. This pulse is used to evaluate wideband video systems.

$2T$ SINE-SQUARED PULSE This pulse has an HAD of 0.250 μs, corresponding to two picture elements. Its harmonic content drops to one-half at 2 MHz and is practically zero beyond 4 MHz.

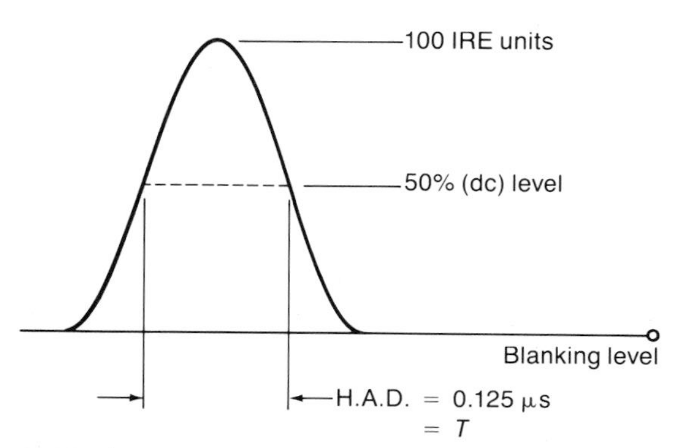

Fig. 9-15 T sine-squared pulse. A T of 0.125 μs corresponds to the time of one picture element.

The $2T$ pulse is ideal for evaluating 4-MHz video systems because it closely resembles the content of a typical camera signal.

USING THE SINE-SQUARED PULSE An amplifier with no amplitude, frequency, or phase distortion within the 4-MHz band passes the $2T$ pulse intact, and it appears as shown by the dotted line in Fig. 9-16*a*. Its peak amplitude should be at 100 IRE units, or just equal to the flat part of the white window signal. Remember that the sine-squared pulses are used in conjunction with the window signal, as a white vertical line to the left of the window.

Frequency distortion caused by incorrect relative values of high-order harmonics causes the distortion shown by the solid pulse in Fig. 9-16*a*. The pulse has less width, but it is still symmetric. It is narrower because of a change in relative amplitudes for certain harmonic fre-

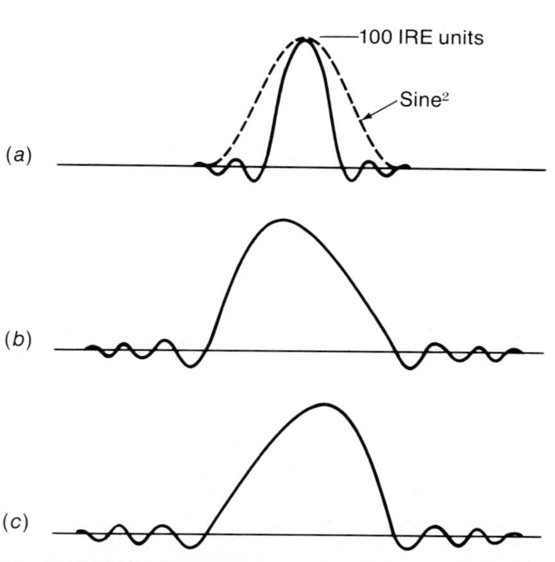

Fig. 9-16 Using the sine-squared pulse to check frequency and phase distortion. (*a*) Less pulse width but same symmetry shows frequency distortion but no phase distortion. (*b*) Tilt shows leading phase shift. (*c*) Opposite tilt shows lagging phase shift.

quencies. When there is phase distortion, it causes tilt, or lack of symmetry, as shown in Fig. 9-16*b* and *c*.

The small lobes that precede and follow the pulse are called *overshoots* when they are positive and *undershoots* when they are negative. The overshoots and undershoots produce multiple outlines in the picture.

K GRATICULE To evaluate the sine-squared pulse quantitatively, a special graticule is used on the studio waveform monitor (Fig. 9-17). This graticule, called the *K factor*, marks the acceptable boundaries for the pulse and its minor lobes. The limits were developed by expert observers who assigned values for picture degradation caused by artificially generated echo signals. Multiple outlines look like ghosts in the picture, but only for vertical edges.

On the *K* graticule in Fig. 9-17, the solid line represents a *K* factor of 4 percent; the dashed line is 2 percent. When the reproduced pulse falls within the boundaries of the dashed lines, the *K* factor is 2 percent. This value means that there is practically no visible picture degradation. The *K* graticule can be used with either *T* or 2*T* sine-squared pulses by changing the horizontal time base of the waveform monitor.

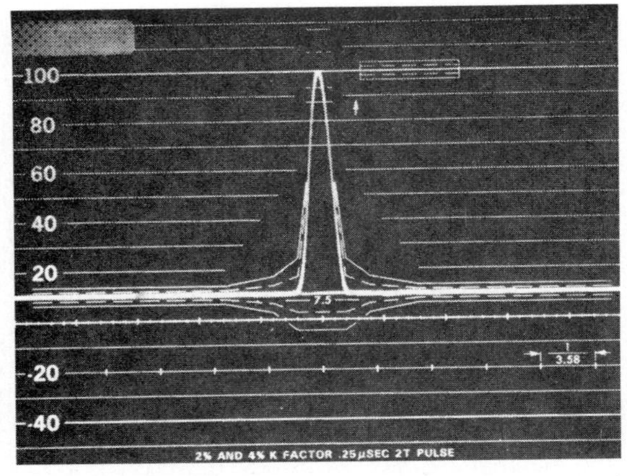

Fig. 9-17 The *K* factor graticule shows acceptable limits of distortion on the sine-squared pulse. (*Tektronix*)

MODULATED 20*T* AND 12.5*T* PULSES The *T* and 2*T* pulses were developed for monochrome systems. For color signals, distortion for the sidebands of the 3.58-MHz subcarrier is of greater concern. For these reasons, wider pulses at 20*T* and 12.5*T* were developed. These pulses are modulated on the 3.58-MHz color subcarrier.

For the 12.5*T* pulse with HAD = 1.56 μs, this time corresponds to the video frequency of approximately 640 kHz. This relatively low frequency is just above the range of color video signals such as $R - Y$, $B - Y$, and $G - Y$.

Furthermore, the 3.58-MHz modulation makes it possible to judge changes in the relative luminance-to-chrominance amplitudes, as well as relative phase changes in the chroma signal. The effects of high and low chroma are shown in Fig. 9-18*b* and *c*. Note the lower amplitudes in Fig. 9-18*c*. The effect of leading and lagging chroma phase is shown in Fig. 9-18*d* and *e*, respectively. These two examples show tilt in the waveforms.

Test Point Questions 9-9

Answers at End of Chapter

a. Does a *T* sine-squared pulse have an HAD of one or two picture elements?

b. A 2*T* sine-squared pulse has an HAD of how many microseconds?

c. A 2*T* sine-squared pulse has no high-frequency components above how many megahertz?

d. A modulated 12.5*T* pulse has a peak amplitude higher than the flat part of the window signal. Is the gain for 3.58 MHz too high or too low?

9-10 STAIR-STEP TEST SIGNALS

The sine-squared test signals are designed to evaluate frequency and phase distortion. A stair-step signal, though, is used to evaluate the amplitude

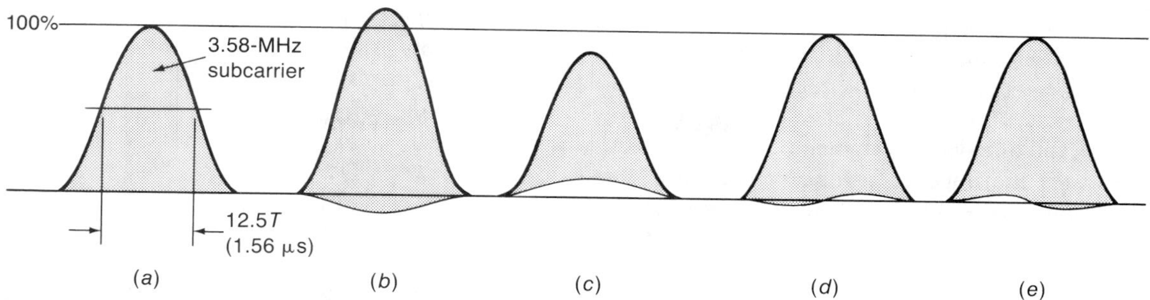

Fig. 9-18 Use of the modulated 12.5T sine-squared pulse to evaluate relative amplitude and phase of chroma. (*a*) 12.5T modulated sine-squared pulse. (*b*) Chroma high. (*c*) Chroma low. (*d*) Chroma θ leading. (*e*) Chroma θ lagging.

distortion, or nonlinearity in the system. The stair step of voltage is generated electronically. It consists of a series of vertical bars in the picture that start at either the blanking or the setup level and get brighter in equal increments from left to right. There may be a few steps or as many as 10.

Figure 9-19*a* shows a standardized stair step consisting of six steps with equal risers between setup at 7.5 IRE units and peak white at 100 units. There are six steps and five risers. Each riser, then, steps up 92.5/5 = 18.5 IRE units. When the amplification is linear, all the risers remain equal. Compression at the higher steps indicates less gain for white amplitudes. This nonlinear amplitude distortion may be caused by incorrect bias in an amplifier. Also, not enough frequency deviation in an FM microwave link may show up as a shortening of the top riser. These transmitters generally use FM for the picture carrier signal, which is converted to the standard AM picture signal for broadcasting.

DIFFERENTIATED STAIR STEP Waveform monitors at the studio are equipped with a special high-pass filter that can be switched in to differ-

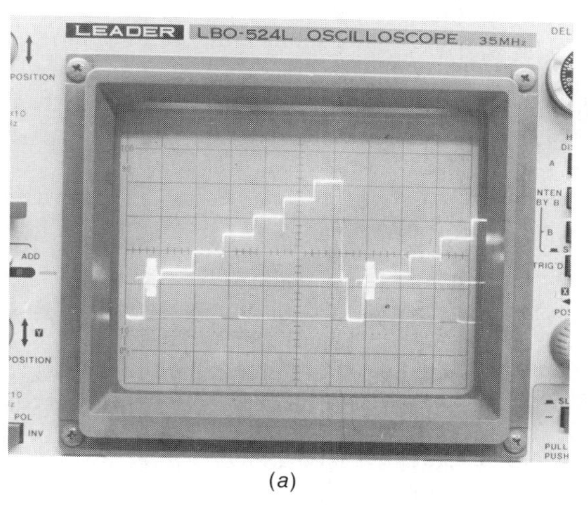

(*a*)

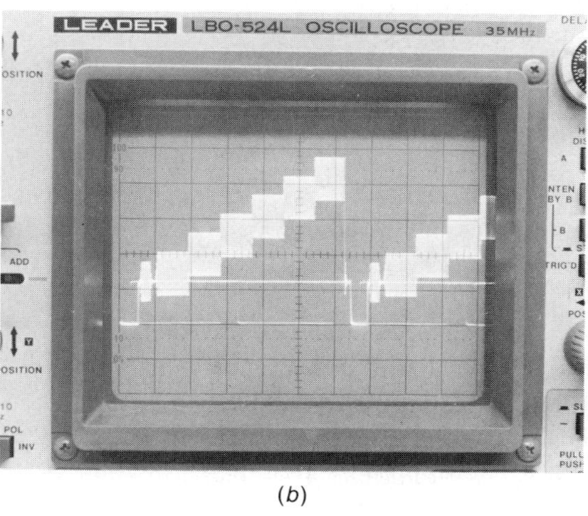

(*b*)

Fig. 9-19 (*a*) Stair-step signal. (*b*) Modulated stair-step signal.

entiate the stair-step signal. Differentiation emphasizes a change in level. The result in the waveform is five spikes at the leading edge of each riser. When the amplifier gain is uniform, all the spikes have the same amplitude. In effect, the risers are lined up at one voltage level for their spikes to allow easy comparison on the oscilloscope screen.

MODULATED STAIR STEP This signal adds a sample of the 3.58-MHz color subcarrier signal at a fixed phase, usually $-(B-Y)$ or burst phase, with the fixed amplitude of 40 IRE units p-p. See Fig. 9-19*b*. The modulated stair step is useful in showing the effects of amplitude nonlinearity for a color signal. For example, compressed whites act to compress the chroma signal at its highest luminance (Y) levels. Then fully saturated yellow and cyan appear to lose saturation in color.

To see the effects of nonlinearity on the modulated stair step, a switch selector on the waveform monitor places a 3.58-MHz bandpass filter in series with the oscilloscope input. The filter removes all the Y signal information, and only the chroma signal remains. When amplification is linear, the p-p amplitudes of the 3.58-MHz subcarrier signal remain equal at 40 IRE units, and they all show up with the same amplitude on the oscilloscope waveform.

DIFFERENTIAL GAIN This factor is used to specify the amount of nonlinearity as a percentage. The differential gain is

$$D_g = \left(1 - \frac{x}{y}\right)100 \qquad \textbf{(9-1)}$$

where x is the smallest amplitude in the modulated steps and y is the amplitude of the uniform steps. The amplitudes are p-p values of the 3.58-MHz burst in each step of the modulated waveform. For example, when all bursts but the top step are 40 IRE units and the top-step burst is 35 IRE units, the differential gain is

$$\begin{aligned} D_g &= \left(1 - \frac{35}{40}\right)100 \\ &= (1 - 0.875)100 \\ &= (0.125)(100) = 12.5\% \end{aligned}$$

The smaller the value of D_g, the better the linearity. Well-designed equipment usually has differential gain ratings below 4 percent, approximately.

DIFFERENTIAL PHASE Although it is not an obvious fact, the amount of phase shift in an amplifier can shift with a change in the dc operating point. For example, the emitter-junction capacitance tends to increase as the forward bias is raised for a transistor amplifier. As a result of the shift in operating point, the phase-angle response may be changed. In color television, the resulting phase distortion can cause a change in hue between dark and bright parts of the picture.

The modulated stair-step signal, with its constant phase of subcarrier bursts on all the steps, is used to evaluate differential phase, expressed in degrees. With a vectorscope, this signal can indicate the spread in phase angle at each of the steps. Naturally, the smaller the number for the phase-angle shift, the better the response. In well-designed equipment, the specification is less than 4° for the differential phase distortion.

Test Point Questions 9-10

Answers at End of Chapter

a. In Fig. 9-19*a*, the luminance value of the darkest step is at how many IRE units?

b. What is the p-p value for a 3.58-MHz signal on each step of the modulated stair-step signal in IRE units?

c. In Formula 9-1, x is 39 and y is 40. Calculate the differential gain.

9-11 TEST SIGNALS IN THE VERTICAL BLANKING INTERVAL

In the early days of television, tests of network transmission links were done at night, after normal broadcasting was finished. Now, though, there is almost no time to tie up busy transmission links for test purposes. Therefore, any unused time in the standard TV signal has been explored as a place to insert test signals. A relatively long time that can be used is within the vertical blanking period.

The vertical blanking time includes 21 complete horizontal lines in each field. The first nine of these lines are used for the following:

3*H* lines for the leading equalizing pulses

3*H* lines for the vertical sync pulse

3*H* lines for the trailing equalizing pulses

These pulses are needed for vertical synchronizing information. However, $21 - 9 = 12$ horizontal lines that still remain within the vertical blanking time of 21 lines. These 12 lines can be used for test signals inserted between the *H* blanking pulses that remain in the vertical blanking time. The *H* sync and color burst within the *H* blanking time are not disturbed.

Specific lines have specific uses for test purposes. To use this information, special oscilloscopes or waveform monitors include gating circuits to display the desired lines in the vertical blanking interval that have test signals.

To indicate specific lines, they are numbered. The usual method counts line 1 from the leading equalizing pulses to line 21 at the end of vertical blanking. An illustration of the pulses in the vertical blanking interval is shown in Fig. 7-7.

In the first and odd fields, line 1 includes the first two equalizing pulses. These pulses and the serrations in the vertical sync pulse are repeated at half-line intervals. There are three lines for the six equalizing pulses before the *V* sync. Then the serrated vertical sync pulse takes three more lines. The six equalizing pulses that follow the *V* sync also take three lines. After these nine lines, the count is lines 10, 11, 12, 13, 14, 15, 16, 17, 18, 19, 20, and 21 to the end of vertical blanking.

In the second and odd fields, line 1 is the first full line, not a half-line. Here, line 1 starts from the second equalizing pulse. Then the line count continues as in the odd fields.

Test Point Questions 9-11

Answers at End of Chapter

a. How many *H* lines wide is the vertical sync pulse?

b. What is the count for the *H* line just after all the equalizing pulses?

9-12 VERTICAL INTERVAL TEST SIGNAL (VITS)

Figure 9-20 shows the vertical interval test signal (VITS) recommended by the Network Transmission Committee of the EIA. The signal uses lines 17 and 18 in vertical blanking of both TV fields. Line 17 is used mainly for a *multiburst* signal, which contains video frequencies of 0.5 to 4.2 MHz. Line 18 has a sine-squared test signal in odd fields and modulated stair step in even fields.

ODD FIELDS Refer to Fig. 9-20*a* for line 17 in odd fields. The test signal starts with a white step or flag at 100 IRE units for an amplitude reference. It is followed by a series of bursts of unmodulated carrier wave (cw) signal at different video frequencies. Each burst rides on a center axis that permits the p-p sine wave to vary between the black setup level and peak white. The burst frequencies are at 0.5, 1.5, 2.0, 3.0, 3.6, and 4.2 MHz from left to right. Their relative amplitudes when you check on a TV screen or oscilloscope indicates the approximate frequency

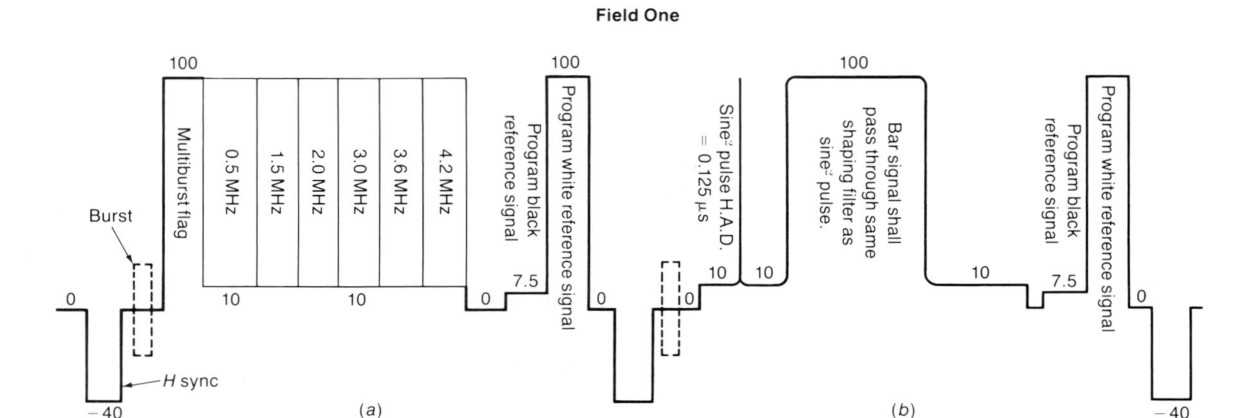

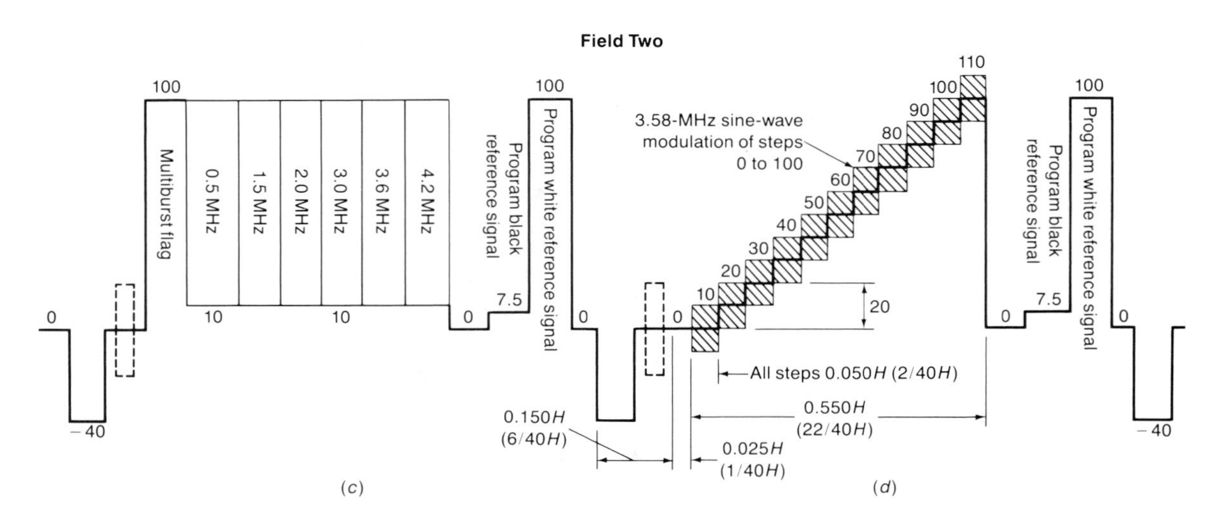

Fig. 9-20 VITS recommended by the Network Transmission Committee. (*a*) Line 17 in odd fields (multiburst). (*b*) Line 18 in odd fields (sine-squared pulse and bar). (*c*) Line 17 in even fields (multiburst). (*d*) Line 18 in even fields (modulated stair-step pulse). (*EIA*)

response through the video passband. The remainder of line 17 contains a reference white bar with 7.5 percent black setup.

Refer to Fig. 9-20*b* for line 18 in odd fields. This line contains a sine-squared test pulse followed by a "bar" signal. The bar corresponds to a window signal for only one line. The end of line 18 also has a 100 percent white bar for amplitude calibration and reference, as in line 17.

These are successive lines in an odd field. The signal in Fig. 9-20*a* is followed by the signal in Fig. 9-20*b*.

EVEN FIELDS Now consider line 17 in even fields, as shown in Fig. 9-20*c*. It also has the multiburst test signal, like line 17 in odd fields. However, line 18 for odd fields, shown in Fig. 9-20*d*, contains the modulated stair-step signal. There are 10 steps, each with a p-p amplitude of 20 IRE units.

OBSERVING THE VITS On most TV receivers the VITS can be seen by rotating the vertical hold control carefully to make the picture roll downward slowly. Then the resulting VITS patterns are observed in the lines close to the bottom of the blanking bar. See Fig. 9-21. Turn up the brightness if necessary.

Checking the VITS with an oscilloscope requires an oscilloscope that can be locked to the beginning of a field. Then the VITS can be seen by using a short time base of 150 μs/cm or less. A sweep magnifier or delayed sweep is needed to expand the two *H* lines enough for a good observation. A waveform monitor has a calibrated time-base generator that permits lines 17 to 21 to be viewed just by selection on a front panel switch.

Test Point Questions 9-12

Answers at End of Chapter

a. Which two lines in *V* blanking are used for VITS?

b. What line is used for the multiburst test signal?

c. What is the highest test frequency in the multiburst?

9-13 VERTICAL INTERVAL REFERENCE SIGNAL (VIRS)

These tests are used to evaluate performance of the transmission system, for chroma and luminance. In addition, the vertical interval reference signal (VIRS) can be used in the signal processing

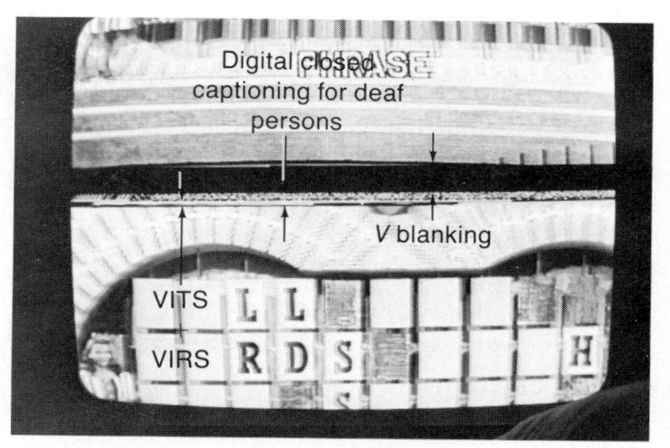

Fig. 9-21 How the VITS and VIRS in vertical blanking interval appear on screen of TV receiver.

circuits. The signal is shown in Fig. 9-22. It is transmitted on line 19 of the vertical blanking interval, in even and odd fields.

One thing that can go wrong is the phase of the color burst. At the output of the camera, color burst is the key to correct phase and hue for the line of signal that follows the burst. With many stages of signal processing on a long, complicated network link, however, the color burst may be removed, reshaped, and put back into the composite signal by equipment called a *processing amplifier.* After a number of these operations, the final burst phase may be in error, compared with the information on the active scan line. The VIRS provides a sample of the correct burst phase. As a result, an automatic phase control circuit can compare the signal with reference burst and reset the phase if needed. The amplitude of the reference burst is sensed also to correct the subcarrier amplitude as necessary.

Refer to Fig. 9-22 for details of the VIRS. The reference values include the following:

1. A chroma bar of 3.58 MHz. The p-p amplitude is 40 IRE units on an axis of 70 units. The time intervals marked at the bottom of the figure indicate that the width of the chroma reference bar is 24 μs.
2. Luminance reference level of 50 IRE units. This level is on for 12 μs.

3. Black setup reference level of 7.5 IRE units, which is also on for 12 μs.

The entire time interval for the VIRS is 62 μs plus 1.3 μs for the front porch of *H* sync, on line 19 of the vertical blanking.

The VIRS is not used to diagnose distortion. Its function is to establish the correct values of chroma amplitude and phase, with the luminance and black setup levels, as the signal left the origination point.

Since it is part of the transmitted signal, the VIRS is available at the receiver. Circuits have been developed to set the color phase for hue or tint and the chroma level automatically, using VIRS as the reference. However, manual adjustments are provided also, to satisfy individual preferences in color. These receivers are considered to have automatic VIRS control.

However, there is a problem with VIRS control in receivers used with video cassette recorders. These home-type machines require two lines of sequential chroma signal to function properly. With VIRS on a single line, the chroma is reproduced at one-half amplitude on the tape. A receiver using automatic VIRS will detect the lower amplitude as a chroma error and increase the gain, to produce an oversaturated color picture. Another problem is that pulses for the video-head switching in the recorder may interfere with the VIRS processing circuits in the receiver when the tape is played back. The details of video cassette recorders are explained in Chap. 10.

Test Point Questions 9-13

Answers at End of Chapter

a. Name two test signals transmitted in the vertical blanking interval.

b. Is VIRS transmitted on line 17, 18, or 19?

c. Which test signal has the reference values for the chroma phase and amplitude?

9-14 COMMUNICATIONS SIGNALS IN THE VERTICAL BLANKING INTERVAL

Of the 21 lines in *V* blanking, the first 9 are used for *V* sync and equalizing pulses and lines 17, 18, and 19 are for VITS and VIRS. Therefore,

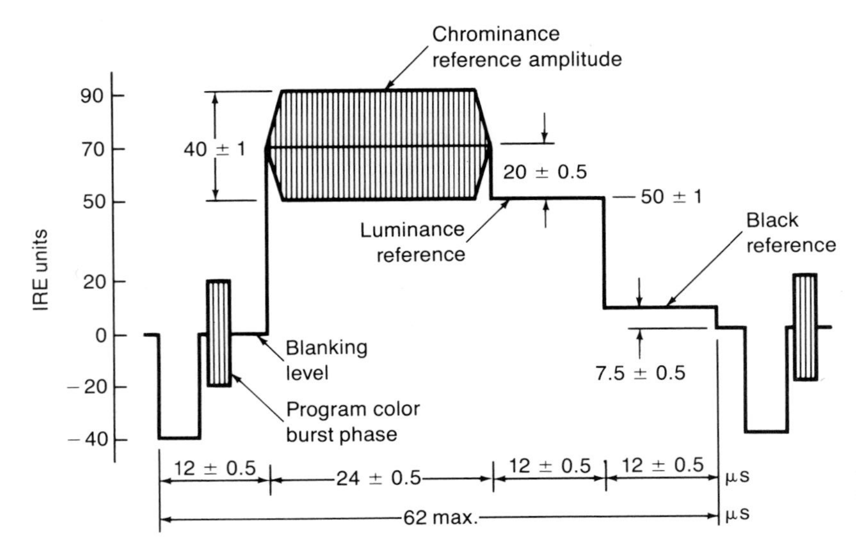

Fig. 9-22 Details of the VIRS, transmitted on line 19 during vertical blanking interval of even and odd fields.

lines 10, 11, 12, 13, 14, 15, and 16 are free for other uses. These lines have become extremely useful for special communications systems.

SMPTE CODE Program originators use three lines per field, such as 12, 13, and 14, to store data in the form of a digital code. The agreed code has been set up by the Society of Motion Pictures and Television Engineers (SMPTE). This SMPTE time code is used to identify the program material, time of day, frame number, and other production information. The time-coded videotapes are used in computer editing to form complete programs from separate production "cuts." Note that the code signals exist on the original videotapes but must be removed prior to broadcasting in order to meet FCC requirements.

VISUAL CAPTIONS A recent addition to an approved vertical interval signal is digital encoding for signals that superimpose captions for the hearing-impaired on the TV picture. A special decoder at the receiver gates out the lines used to carry data for the captions. Then the data are processed to form alphanumerical symbols, which include numbers and letters.

TELETEXT AND VIDEOTEXT Another system similar to captions is the transmission of a much larger quantity of data words to permit reproduction of full pages of alphanumerical characters in text form. Graphics with simple pictures or graphs can be included.

The time available in the vertical blanking interval can be used for text data. This method requires a decoder at the receiver to gate out the specific lines and process the digital signal. Systems of this type are being used now in Europe, Japan, and Canada. In the United States, work is progressing on specifying standards for such a system.

When the data are distributed in the form of video signals, the system is considered *videotext*. The method of using the TV broadcast signal, or cable signal, is called *teletext*. A videotext unit is shown in Fig. 1-23.

Test Point Questions 9-14

Answers at End of Chapter

Answer True or False.

a. The SMPTE code uses lines 4, 5, and 6 in the *V* blanking time.

b. Visual captions for the TV picture can be encoded in the *V* blanking time.

c. Teletext data use *H* blanking time in all horizontal lines.

SUMMARY

1. The test pattern in Fig. 9-1 includes black-and-white converging lines to check the picture quality of detail, or resolution. The vertical wedges indicate horizontal resolution, as the beam scans across individual lines. The ability to resolve lines on the side wedges indicates vertical resolution.
2. The side wedges also show poor interlacing by a moiré effect on the diagonal lines.
3. Horizontal resolution is measured for the details in three-fourths of the width, corresponding to the height. Typical horizontal resolution in television receivers is 250 lines, corresponding to 3.125-MHz video-frequency response.

4. The test pattern in Fig. 9-1 has 10 equal steps of gray scale between black and white.
5. Streaking or smear in the picture is caused by phase distortion for video frequencies of about 100 kHz and lower. See Fig. 9-2.
6. Ringing in the picture means multiple outlines of edges to the right. See Fig. 9-3. The cause is excessive gain at high frequencies, about 2 to 4 MHz and above, which puts the amplifier on the brink of oscillations.
7. A monoscope is a special camera tube with a test pattern printed on the image plate.
8. The ball chart in Fig. 9-6 is used with a separate crosshatch generator to check camera linearity, independent of the monitor.
9. The EIA standard color-bar signal (Fig. 9-7) includes *R, G, B* bars and their complementary colors and white, to check the chrominance and luminance values. The colors have 75 percent amplitude, in terms of IRE units, but they are fully saturated.
10. The window signal in Fig. 9-12 consists of a 100 percent white rectangle, one-half the picture height and width, on a black background. This pattern is useful for checking streaking and ringing.
11. Sine-squared pulses are used for checking response at high video frequencies. The HAD is the half-amplitude duration of the pulse. The T pulse has an HAD of 0.125 μs, the time for 1 pixel, with 0.250 μs for a $2T$ pulse. The $20T$ and $12.5T$ pulses are longer, to check the frequency response for color video signals up to 640 kHz.
12. The stair-step signal in Fig. 9-19*a* is used to check amplitude distortion in the luminance signal. The modulated stair-step signal in Fig. 9-19*b* is used to check the amplitude nonlinearity for a 3.58-MHz chroma signal.
13. VITS, the vertical interval test signal, is shown in Fig. 9-20. It uses lines 17 and 18 in vertical blanking time of even and odd fields for test signals to check their frequency response and amplitude distortion.
14. VIRS, the vertical interval reference signal, is shown in Fig. 19-22. It is transmitted on line 19 of the vertical blanking period, in even and odd fields. The VIRS is used to evaluate the performance of the transmission system, for chroma and luminance.
15. Teletext is a system of transmitting communications signals in the vertical blanking interval, by either broadcasting or cable television.

SELF-EXAMINATION

Answers at Back of Book

Answer True or False.

1. The highest video frequencies correspond to horizontal detail.
2. The lowest video frequencies tend to produce ringing.

3. The ability to resolve individual lines in the top and bottom wedges of the test pattern indicates horizontal resolution.
4. A horizontal resolution of 300 lines corresponds to 400 pixels of picture information.
5. The ability to resolve individual lines in the side wedges of the test pattern indicates vertical resolution.
6. Diagonal lines in the picture information provide a good test of interlacing.
7. The test pattern in Fig. 9-1 has 30 equal steps of gray-scale values between black and white.
8. Horizontal resolution of 240 lines corresponds to a video-frequency response of 24 MHz.
9. Streaking and smear in the picture are caused by phase distortion for video frequencies in the range of 10 to 100 kHz.
10. Ringing in the picture is produced by oscillations at high video frequencies.
11. A monoscope is a special type of color picture tube.
12. The ball chart is used to check camera linearity.
13. A crosshatch pattern has equally spaced horizontal and vertical bars.
14. The EIA color-bar pattern has *R, G, B,* and their complementary colors at an amplitude of 75 IRE units.
15. A vectorscope shows phase angles for different hues.
16. The window signal is used to check the chroma saturation.
17. The HAD of a $2T$ sine-squared test pulse is 0.25 μs.
18. The stair-step signal is used to check the amplitude distortion for the Y signal.
19. A modulated stair-step signal includes the 3.58-MHz chroma signal.
20. The VITS and VIRS are test signals transmitted during the vertical blanking interval.
21. The vertical blanking interval has six lines that are not used for vertical synchronization.
22. The multiburst test signal in the VITS is a check for high video-frequency response.
23. Teletext is a system for transmitting communications signals during the vertical blanking interval.
24. A videotext system can use public telephone lines for distribution of communications signals and data.

ESSAY QUESTIONS

1. Name at least five uses for the EIA test pattern in Fig. 9-1.
2. Why is horizontal-line resolution measured in terms of the picture height?
3. List typical values of horizontal and vertical resolution for a color TV receiver.

4. Compare the causes and effects for streaking and ringing in the picture.
5. What is the effect of phase distortion on a square-wave signal?
6. What is meant by ringing in an *LC* circuit?
7. Why does ringing produce multiple outlines in the picture?
8. What is a monoscope?
9. List two uses for a crosshatch pattern.
10. How is the EIA ball chart used?
11. Name three characteristics of the EIA standard color-bar pattern that is illustrated in Fig. 9-7.
12. What are the complementary colors of red, green, and blue, for the EIA standard color-bar pattern?
13. What is the function of a vectorscope?
14. Name one use of the window signal.
15. List the uses for the stair-step test signal and modulated stair-step signal.
16. Define differential gain.
17. Define the HAD of a sine-squared test signal.
18. Why is a sine-squared test signal better than square-wave pulses?
19. Define the following sine-squared test signals: T, $2T$, $12.5T$, and $20T$.
20. What is the purpose of a K graticule?
21. How many lines in the vertical blanking interval are reserved for vertical synchronization, with equalizing pulses?
22. List the specific test signals in VITS.
23. Describe the VIRS test signal.
24. What is meant by *teletext* and *videotext?*

PROBLEMS

Answers to Odd-Numbered Problems at Back of Book

1. Calculate the video-frequency response corresponding to the horizontal resolution of **(a)** 200 lines, **(b)** 320 lines.
2. What horizontal resolution corresponds to the frequency of **(a)** 2.5 MHz, **(b)** 4 MHz?
3. What is the horizontal scanning time for the following number of pixels? **(a)** 1, **(b)** 2, **(c)** 12.5, **(d)** 20.
4. Calculate the L needed with capacitance at 20 pF and a resonant frequency of 2.4 MHz.
5. Use Formula 9-1 to calculate the differential gain with $x = 30$ IRE units and $y = 40$ IRE units.
6. Calculate the video signal frequency for each scanning line across the window signal in Fig. 9-12.

SPECIAL QUESTIONS

1. How is the EIA standard color-bar pattern different from the color bars produced by a conventional gated-rainbow color-bar generator?
2. Have you ever seen the VITS on the screen of a television receiver? How did it look?
3. Describe any test pattern you may have seen broadcast by a television station.
4. Why are good resolution and linearity more important for the television camera than for a TV receiver?

ANSWERS TO TEST POINT QUESTIONS

9-1 **a.** Vertical
b. 400
c. 10
d. Good interlacing

9-2 **a.** Vertical
b. 280
c. 3 MHz

9-3 **a.** F
b. T

9-4 **a.** Figure 9-3
b. Ringing

9-5 **a.** F
b. T

9-6 **a.** Crosshatch
b. Camera
c. 2 percent

9-7 **a.** 69 units
b. ±31 or 62 units
c. Cyan
d. 103°

9-8 **a.** 100
b. 26.65 μs
c. Streaking

9-9 **a.** One
b. 0.25 μs
c. 4 MHz
d. High

9-10 **a.** 7.5
b. 40
c. 2.5 percent

9-11 **a.** Three
b. Line 10

9-12 **a.** 17 and 18
b. 17
c. 4.2 MHz

9-13 **a.** VITS and VIRS
b. 19
c. VIRS

9-14 **a.** F
b. T
c. F

10

VIDEO TAPE RECORDERS AND DISK PLAYERS

Video recording has become one of the most important applications of television. Video signals are recorded on magnetic tape, as in audio tape recorders, or on plastic disks, as in phonograph records. Video tape recording (VTR) is popular because you can easily make your own recordings of picture and sound for a program and play them back through the TV receiver. The consumer type of video disk, however, is for playback only.

The tape recording can be done reel to reel, for broadcast equipment, or with cassettes. Most common is the video cassette recorder (VCR) for consumer equipment because there is no manual threading of the tape (Fig. 10-1). The cassette can either record or play back in the forward direction; then it is rewound to the start, as audio tape cassettes are. However, there is no turnover of the video cassette. The playing time is typically 2, 4, 6, or 8 hours (h).

For VCR equipment, two different systems are common. One is the Betamax format used by Sony. The other is the video home system (VHS) format used by most other manufacturers. The two systems are similar but not compatible. Both use ½-in. tape. More details are explained in the following sections:

10-1 VIDEO RECORDING REQUIREMENTS

As with audio recording, in video recording the signal information is stored on the tape or disk, but video recording has additional problems. First, the video signal is a wideband signal, which means that the ratio of the highest to the lowest frequency is very large. For video frequencies of 30 Hz to 4 MHz, the signal-frequency range is approximately 17 octaves. Remember that each octave includes a doubling of the frequency range. And this frequency range still does not include the dc component of the video signal, which indicates average brightness. No recording system could handle such a tremendous range in signal frequencies. The maximum range is about 10 to 13 octaves.

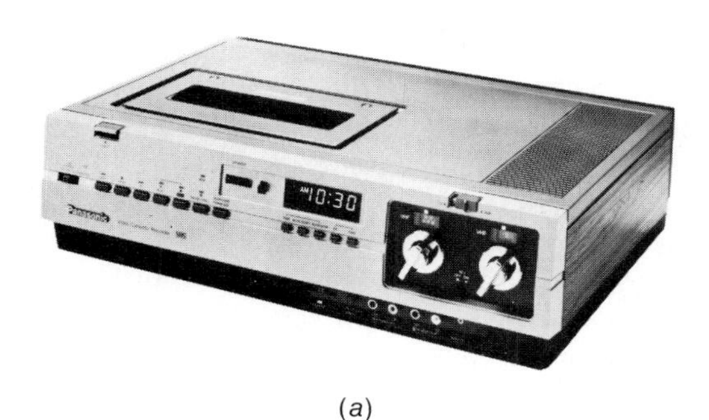

(*a*)

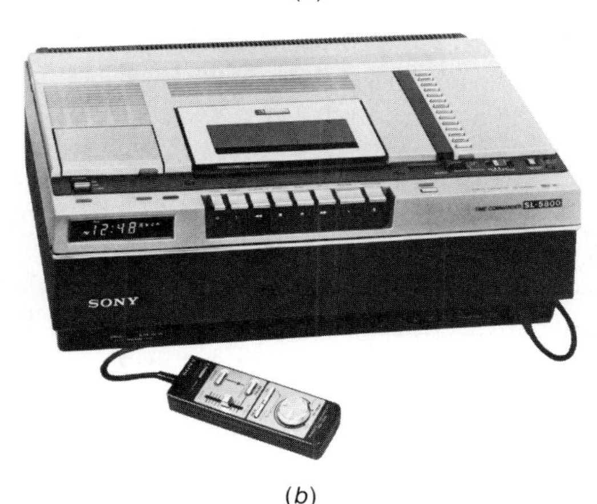

(*b*)

(*c*)

Fig. 10-1 Video cassette recorders. (*a*) Panasonic VCR using VHS format. (*b*) Sony VCR using Betamax format. (*c*) Video cassette for ½-in. tape (bottom view). Lid at front is held open to expose tape. Size is 7⅜ × 4¼ in. [187.3 × 108 mm].

FM RECORDING However, the bandwidth problem is solved by making the video modulate a higher-frequency carrier signal for the recording signal. As a typical example, 3.5 MHz can be used for the modulated carrier wave. It is modulated by the *Y* luminance signal, not the chroma signal. Generally, the luminance bandwidth is limited to approximately 2.5 MHz. In the modulated carrier signal, then, the sidebands extend from 1 to 6 MHz. These values equal 3.5 ± 2.5 MHz. The frequency range of 6:1 is less than 3 octaves, or 8:1, which is practical for recording. Frequency modulation is used. Note that this modulation technique eliminates the need for the separate ac bias required in audio recording.

ROTATING HEADS How can such high frequencies—in the megahertz range—be used for recording? This problem is solved by rotating the heads in a video tape recorder. Instead of having the tape travel very fast for high frequencies, the recording head rotates at high velocity. The tape actually moves quite slowly. However, the relative speed between the head gap and the tape, called the *writing speed,* limits the highest frequency for recording.

SLANT TRACKS The playing time should be long, so that television programs can be recorded in multiples of 1 h without too much tape being required. This feature is provided by using *helical-scan,* or *slant-track,* recording.

The tape is made to cross the head gap at an angle, instead of parallel to it. Then the magnetic recording is made on diagonal paths across the tape. On each diagonal track, or "swipe," there is a corresponding video signal for a vertical scanning field. Two swipes make a television frame. Figure 10-2 illustrates the diagonal tracks for the video signal on the tape. The audio signal is recorded straight across the top edge of the tape. Along the bottom edge the control track provides timing reference signals for playback.

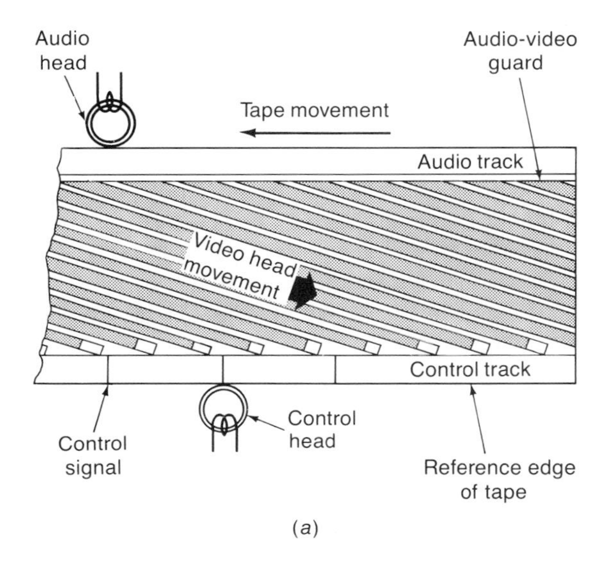

(*a*)

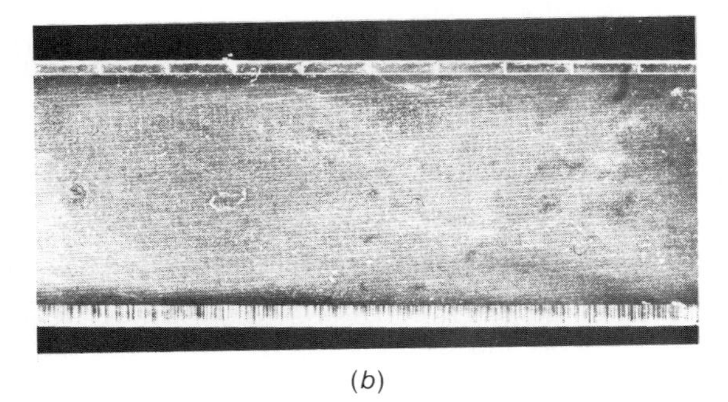

(*b*)

Fig. 10-2 EIAJ standard for ½-in. tape in video recorders. (*a*) Slant tracks for video signal, with audio and control tracks at edges of tape. (*b*) Photograph of actual magnetic recording on tape. Note small angle of slant tracks. (*From* Videocassette Recorders *by G. P. McGinty, McGraw-Hill Book Company, New York, 1979*)

SERVOCONTROLS The video recording technique requires precise control. The motors have servocontrols to monitor tape travel and head speed. Keep in mind that the exact V and H scanning frequencies in color television are 59.94 and 15,734.26 Hz, respectively.

Humidity is a problem because moisture increases the friction on the tape. Some VCR machines have an automatic shutoff when the humidity is too high.

VCR CONNECTIONS TO THE TV RECEIVER The antenna signal for the receiver is routed first into the VCR and then out. The VCR has its own RF tuner and IF section. In the VCR, the RF picture and associated sound signals are converted to baseband video and audio for recording. The TV receiver can be either on or off.

For playback, the VCR has a modulator that puts out the video and audio signals on the RF carrier frequency for channel 3 or 4. A manual switch on the VCR modulator is set for whichever channel is not being used for broadcasting. Therefore, the TV receiver is set to channel 3 or 4 for the VCR playback.

More details of the VCR connections are shown in Fig. 10-3. All the input and output jacks are for 75-Ω coaxial cable. Only the VHF operation is shown here, but duplicate signal paths are provided for the UHF channels.

Consider, first, the case of antenna signal for the VHF channels, without cable television. The antenna input is connected to the VHF input jack on the VCR. With 300-Ω twin-lead cable, a balun is used to convert to the 75-Ω coaxial jack. The two-way splitter in the VCR provides parallel paths for signals traveling to the VHF

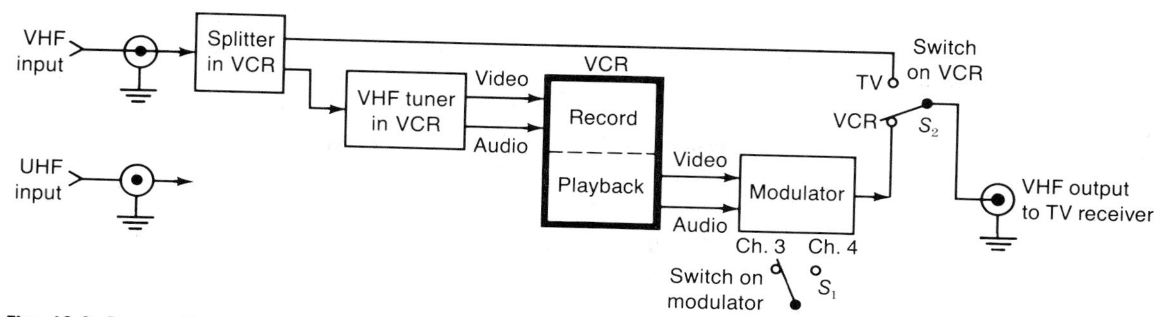

Fig. 10-3 Connections for video cassette recorder and TV receiver. The VCR tuner and splitter are duplicated for UHF channels.

tuner in the TV receiver and the VHF tuner in the VCR. For recording, the VCR tuner and IF section supply baseband video and audio signals to be recorded on the tape.

On playback, the video and audio signals from the tape go to the modulator in the VCR. The modulator supplies the RF picture and sound carrier signals for the TV receiver on channel 3 or 4. The modulator switch S_1, which is part of the modulator, can be set for either channel. Also, the VCR switch S_2 on the recorder is set to the VCR position for playback. Switch S_2 on the front panel of the VCR is like an A–B switch; it enables one to choose either the playback signal or the antenna input signal. From S_2, the playback signal goes to the output jack, which is connected by a cable to the antenna input terminals of the TV receiver. A balun may be needed here also.

You can record any channel selected by the VCR tuner. The receiver can be off or on the same channel to monitor the recording, or you can watch one channel while recording a program on another channel. For playback, though, the receiver must be on channel 3 or 4, with S_2 in the VCR position.

In the case of cable TV, which has a separate converter box for the receiver, different methods of hookup are possible. If you connect the VCR in the signal path after the cable converter, you can record any of the cable channels. The channel selected by the cable converter goes to the VCR. Then the VCR tuner must be set to channel 3 or 4, according to the cable converter output. With this method, the VCR output goes to the receiver antenna terminals. One disadvantage, though, is that you cannot watch a program on a channel other than the channel being recorded.

Another method is to connect the VCR in the signal path before the cable converter. The cable input line goes to the VCR input jack for VHF, and the VCR output goes to the converter input. In this case, you record one of the channels selected by the VCR tuner. However, you can record one program while watching a program on another channel.

Test Point Questions 10-1
Answers at End of Chapter

Answer True or False.

a. The range of 30 to 240 Hz is 3 octaves.
b. Frequency modulation cannot be used for video signals.
c. In video recording, both the tape and the head gap are in motion.
d. The VCR and TV receiver must be operating on the same channel in order to record.

10-2 TAPE RECORDING AND PLAYBACK

Refer to Fig. 10-4 to review the basics of tape recording. The recording head is an electromagnet. It has a core of high permeability, on which is wound a coil for the signal current. To record, the signal current is fed into the coil to magnetize the tape. On playback, the moving tape induces a weak signal in the coil. The head coil has many turns of fine wire.

Its core is made with a ferrite material that has a very high magnetic permeability. The complete head measures about ⅛ × 1/16 in. [3.2 × 1.6 mm] for any one dimension.

The gap is a very thin layer of silicon dioxide, which is glass. Its magnetic reluctance is high, which means that its permeability is low.

Magnetic lines of force can go through the magnetic tape much more easily than through the gap. A typical gap width for video recorders is only 0.3 to 0.6 μm (1 μm = 10^{-6} m). Note that 0.6 μm equals 24 millionths of an inch.

The tape itself is an acetate ribbon coated with fine particles of a magnetic material such as cobalt-doped ferric oxide (Fe_2O_3) or chromium dioxide (CrO_2). Chromium tape requires a stronger magnetizing field.

The nonmagnetic gap of the head bears against the tape surface, perpendicular to the direction of tape travel. Because of its high reluctance,

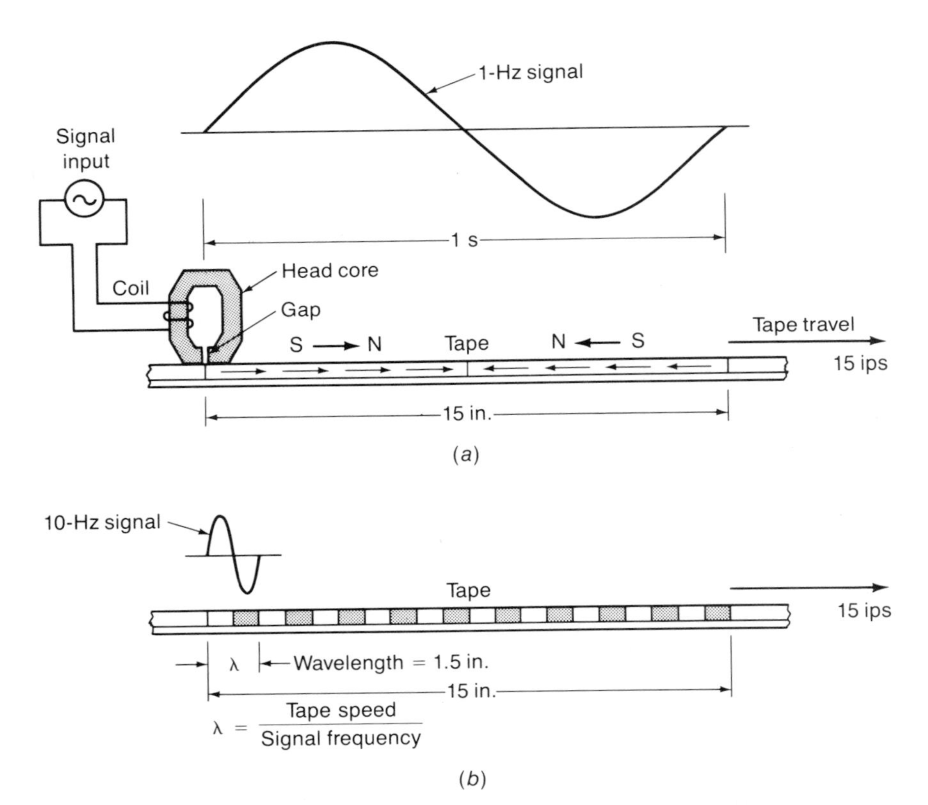

Fig. 10-4 Wavelength λ that can be recorded depends on tape speed and signal frequency. (*a*) Tape travel past head gap. (*b*) Recorded signal on magnetic tape illustrated for 10-Hz frequency.

the gap causes the magnetic lines of force produced by the head to be diverted into the tape surface. In this way, the tape is magnetized with the signal variations. The process is called *magnetic induction.* The magnetization is retained on the tape, to store the signal information.

RECORDED WAVELENGTH The direction of the magnetic field induced in the tape is either in line with or opposite to the tape travel. This effect is illustrated by opposite arrows on the tape in Fig. 10-4*a*. The opposite directions correspond to opposite polarities of the magnetizing signal shown at the top of the illustration. The signal frequency used here is 1 Hz. A complete cycle of recording current, then, takes 1 s.

Assume that the tape moves at the speed of 15 inches per second (ips). Then a full cycle of the magnetization pattern on the tape, with opposite polarities, will be produced on 15 in. of tape. This pattern is illustrated by arrows to the right for one-half the tape distance and arrows to the left for the other half.

The result for this 1-Hz frequency is that 15 in. of tape travels past the head gap in the time of one cycle for the signal. This distance in the long dimension of the tape occupied by one complete magnetization cycle is called the *recorded wavelength* λ. In this example, λ = 15 in.

As the signal frequency increases, the recorded wavelength becomes shorter. In Fig. 10-4*b*, the signal frequency is raised to 10 Hz. Now only 1.5 in. of tape travels past the head gap in the time of one cycle, with the same 15-ips tape speed. With λ = 1.5 in., the result is 10 wavelengths on the tape, as indicated by the shaded areas.

The recorded wavelength also becomes longer with a higher tape speed. Then more tape can move across the gap in one cycle of signal. To calculate the recorded wavelength,

$$\lambda = \frac{s \text{ (speed of tape)}}{f \text{ (frequency of signal)}} \qquad \textbf{(10-1)}$$

With f in hertz and s in length per second, λ has the same units as the tape speed. For the example in Fig. 10-4*b*,

$$\lambda = \frac{s}{f} = \frac{15 \text{ ips}}{10 \text{ Hz}} = 1.5 \text{ in.}$$

Another example can be taken for audio cassette recorders with a tape speed of 1.875 ips. For a top recording frequency of 12,000 Hz, the minimum recorded wavelength is

$$\begin{aligned} \lambda &= \frac{s}{f} = \frac{1.875 \text{ ips}}{12{,}000 \text{ Hz}} \\ &= 0.000156 \text{ in.} \\ &= 0.156 \times 10^{-3} \text{ in.} \\ &= 0.156 \text{ mil} \end{aligned}$$

The smallest value of λ is important because it limits the high-frequency response. A wavelength shorter than the width of the gap cannot be played back. Practically speaking, the shortest recorded λ should be about twice the width of the head gap.

PLAYBACK FREQUENCY RESPONSE When recorded signals on the tape are played back, the output voltage from the head increases with higher frequencies. The reason is that the voltage induced in the coil winding varies with the rate of change of flux. Higher frequencies produce a faster rate of change. This effect is an application of Faraday's law of induced voltage. The characteristics for induced voltage apply to playback but not to the recording.

If a tape recording were made with signal frequencies that vary from 0 Hz, for direct current, to some high frequency, then the voltage output from the head would vary as shown by the graph in Fig. 10-5. The output is 0 V at 0 Hz because there is no flux change for a steady direct current. The effect corresponds to the reason why a transformer cannot couple a dc voltage. With higher frequencies, the output voltage rises steadily, in direct proportion to the frequency. The output level from the head is in millivolts. When the

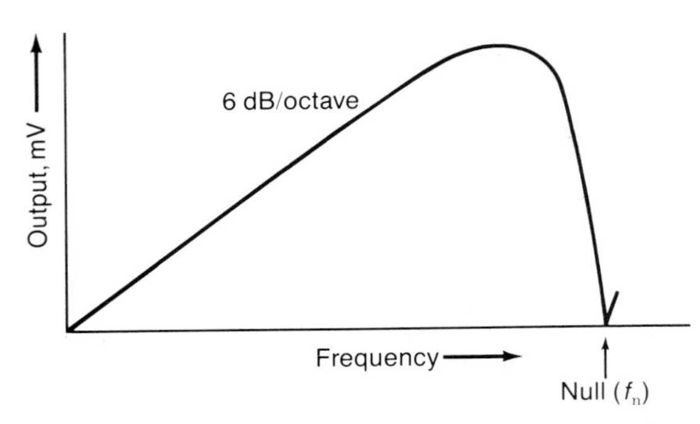

Fig. 10-5 Plot of output signal voltage from head versus signal frequency for tape playback.

frequency is multiplied by a factor of 2, the output voltage doubles. Remember that a frequency range of 2:1 is 1 octave. Also, double the voltage equals 6 dB. Therefore, the curve rises with a slope of 6 dB per octave.

HEAD GAP AND RECORDED WAVELENGTH However, the frequency response curve does not rise indefinitely. It peaks at a maximum output voltage and then drops into a deep *null.* The null for practically zero output occurs at the frequency at which the recorded wavelength just equals the width of the head gap. For this frequency, the gap straddles a full wavelength of signal on the tape. Two areas of equal and opposite magnetic polarity result. The magnetic effects cancel, resulting in the output null.

The ratio of the head gap to the recorded wavelength puts a ceiling on the high-frequency response in the tape recording. Two methods can be used to solve the problem. One is to make the thickness of the head gap extremely small. The other is to increase the relative speed between the head and the tape. Instead of speeding up the tape, though, the head is rotated. The relative velocity of the head gap is called the *writing speed.*

The gap size has been reduced steadily by new techniques in the manufacture of heads. Semiconductor methods of fabrication are used to grow molecular-thin layers of an inert material such as silicon dioxide.

WRITING SPEED To increase the writing speed, the video head is made to rotate past sections of tape at a very high velocity. A common writing speed with this rotating-head technique is 7 m/s. Keep in mind that the tape is moving only a few centimeters per second.

The highest signal frequency can be determined now in terms of the writing speed and recorded wavelength. The calculations are made according to Formula 10–1, but the writing speed, instead of the tape speed, is used for s. Also, the formula can be inverted to find the signal frequency:

$$f = \frac{s \text{ (writing speed)}}{\lambda \text{ (recorded wavelength)}} \qquad \textbf{(10-2)}$$

When the recorded wavelength equals a gap width of 0.6 μm and the writing speed is 7.2 m/s,

$$f_n = \frac{7.2 \text{ m/s}}{0.6 \times 10^{-6} \text{ m}}$$

$$= \frac{7.2}{0.6} \times 10^6 \text{ Hz}$$

$$= 12 \text{ MHz}$$

This 12-MHz frequency is labeled f_n because it would be at the null point of the response curve in Fig. 10-5. The peak of the playback curve occurs at about $0.5f_n$, since the graph is drawn for a logarithmic scale on the horizontal axis. For $0.5f_n$, the frequency equals 6 MHz. Therefore, the fast writing speed produced by the rotating head allows enough bandwidth to record video signals in the megahertz range.

Note, though, that other factors affect the high-frequency response. As usual, eddy currents and hysteresis in the magnetic core produce high-frequency losses. Another problem in recording high frequencies is a self-erasure effect in the magnetic domains on the tape.

Test Point Questions 10-2

Answers at End of Chapter

a. Which is nonmagnetic, the head core, the gap, or the tape?

b. Is the high-frequency response improved with a thicker or a thinner head gap?

c. How many octaves does a range of 4:1 in frequencies equal?

10-3 VCR MODULATION FOR THE LUMINANCE SIGNAL

The luminance video signal with black-and-white information is converted to a frequency-modulated signal for the recording current. As illustrated in Fig. 10-6*a,* the FM circuit uses a voltage-controlled oscillator (VCO). The video signal voltage makes the oscillator frequency vary to produce FM signal output. The results are shown in the graph of frequencies in Fig. 10-6*b.*

Consider the frequencies shown for the Betamax system. The tip of sync in the video signal is clamped at the voltage level that produces 3.5 MHz in the oscillator output. The peak white video voltage causes the oscillator frequency to rise to 4.8 MHz. The total frequency swing is 4.8 − 3.5 = 1.3 MHz.

For the VHS system, the tip of sync produces 3.4 MHz. The peak white causes the frequency to rise to 4.4 MHz. This frequency swing is 4.4 − 3.4 = 1.0 MHz. The principle of using the FM recording signal is essentially the same in the Betamax and VHS systems, but the frequencies are a little different.

Modulation is necessary in order to reduce the frequency range in octaves for recording the luminance signal. The range of highest to lowest frequencies is reduced from about seventeen octaves in the video signal to less than 3 octaves in the modulated signal for recording.

Although amplitude modulation could be used, FM has been selected for the recorded signal. The reason is that an FM system can be made insensitive to amplitude variations in the

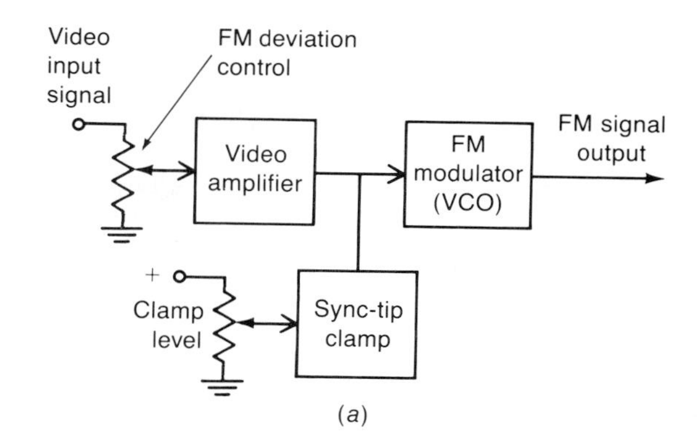

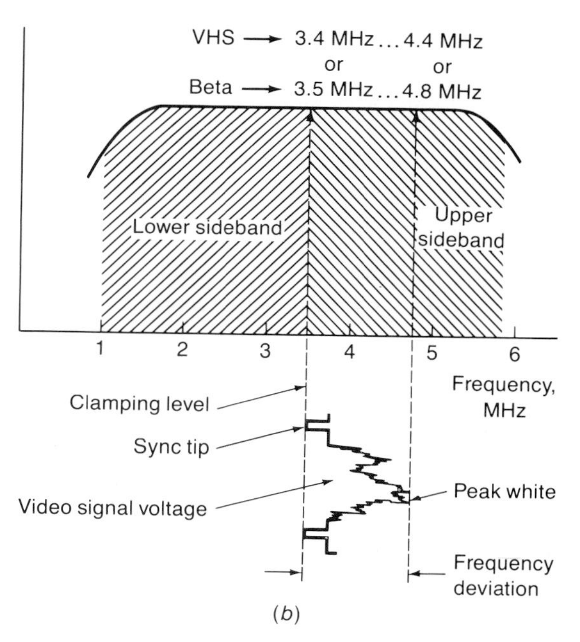

Fig. 10-6 FM system for recording the luminance signal. (*a*) Circuit for frequency modulation. (*b*) Frequency deviation in FM signal produced by video modulation.

playback signal. The VCR machine itself inserts undesired amplitude modulation of the signal when playing back a recorded track that is not exactly the same as the path of the playback head on the tape. This effect makes the output level of the playback signal vary. However, amplitude changes can be eliminated from the FM playback signal.

Another advantage of FM is that saturation recording can be used. Since amplitude distortion does not change the FM signal, it is possible to drive the magnetic tape fully into saturation, in both directions for both signal polarities. In fact, the recorded FM signal is practically a square wave. The saturation recording allows the strongest possible playback signal.

Test Point Questions 10-3

Answers at End of Chapter

Answer True or False.

a. The frequency range of the recorded FM signal is about 10 octaves.

b. For video recording FM is better than AM.

c. In the VHS and Betamax systems, the luminance signal is modulated for recording.

10-4 COLOR-UNDER SYSTEM FOR THE CHROMA SIGNAL

The color-under system is used in VCR machines to correct a problem called the *time-base error,* which has a drastic effect on color. The time-base errors are caused by mechanical factors that produce variations in the writing speed for the head on the tape. One cause is longitudinal vibration in the tape itself, which results from the friction created where the tape rubs against the stationary guides. This effect causes stretching and bunching of the recorded signal. Then the time-base references for recording and playback are not exactly the same.

The time-base error causes small changes in timing for the deflection sync. In the reproduced picture, the effect shows small bands, or "wiggles," in vertical bars. However, the greatest effect of the time-base error is on the color. Alterations in the frequency and phase of the chroma subcarrier signal translate to a loss of color sync and phase errors that cause color bands in the picture.

DOWN CONVERSION OF THE FREQUENCY FOR RECORDING The solution to the time-base error problem has been found in the color-under technique for the 3.58-MHz chroma signal. These frequencies are beat down to lower frequencies for recording. Then they are shifted up to their original frequencies in the playback. Note that the color-under system is used for home-type VCR machines but is not required in studio equipment.

The arrangement for down conversion of the chroma frequencies is illustrated in Fig. 10-7. In the mixer stage, the heterodyning, or beat, effect is similar to the action in a superheterodyne receiver. The signals into the mixer are the sidebands of the 3.58-MHz chroma signal and the cw output from a local oscillator. Consider the cw oscillator frequency at 4.21 MHz for the VHS system. The frequency difference corresponding to 3.58 MHz is equal to 629 kHz approximately. In addition, the chroma sideband frequencies ±0.5 MHz around the subcarrier signal become sidebands ±500 kHz around the lower subcarrier frequency of 629 kHz. As a result, the frequency band for the chroma signal out of the mixer as a down converter is 129 to 1129 kHz. The mixer output circuit has a filter to pass only these lower chroma frequencies for recording. This downshifted chroma signal is applied to the record heads in parallel with the high-frequency FM luminance signal to record both luminance and chrominance signals on the tape.

The downshifted chroma signal, now at a new lower frequency, is recorded like an audio signal

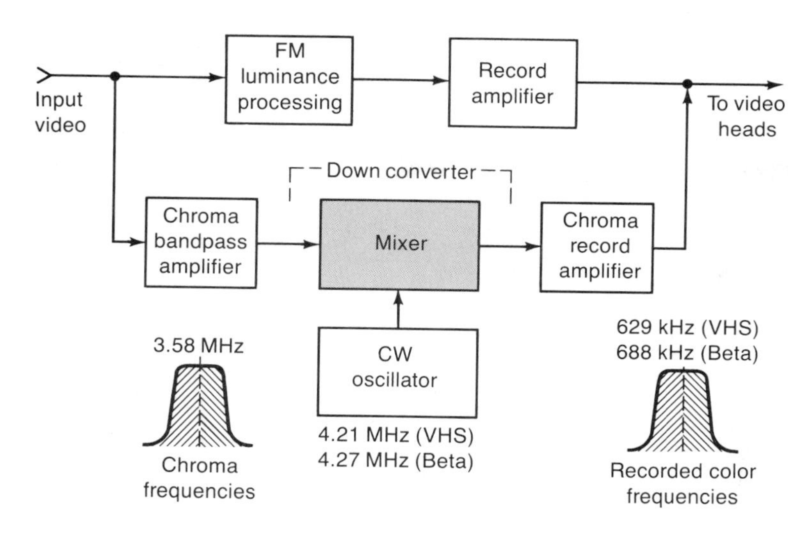

Fig. 10-7 Circuits for color-under processing. The 3.58-MHz chroma signal is converted to lower frequencies for recording.

in an audio tape recorder. There is no modulation. In fact, the recorded FM luminance signal serves as the ac recording bias for the chroma signal, to minimize the amplitude distortion on the tape. The FM signal has a higher frequency and a constant level, as required for ac bias.

The same principle applies in the Betamax system but with slightly different frequencies. There 688 kHz corresponds to the 3.58-MHz color subcarrier. The range of color frequencies is in the band of ±500 kHz, from 188 to 1188 kHz.

It is interesting to note that the color-under system makes the chroma frequencies lower than in the FM luminance signal. For normal colorplexed video, the frequency of the 3.58-MHz chroma signal is higher than most luminance signal frequencies.

UP CONVERSION OF THE PLAYBACK SIGNAL The heterodyne process is reversed in playback, as shown in Fig. 10-8, to raise the color-under signal to 3.58 MHz. These circuits are at the bottom of the illustration. At the top, the luminance signal is processed with FM detection to recover the original luminance video signal. Finally, the luminance and chroma signals are combined in an adder stage to provide the desired colorplexed video signal output.

Consider values for the VHS system with 629 kHz as the color-under frequency corresponding to 3.58 MHz. The playback signal from the video heads is at 629 kHz for color. This signal is separated by a low-pass filter into the cw regenerator. The cw signal from the oscillator again is at 4.21 MHz. As a result, the color-under signal is raised to its former 3.58-MHz center frequency for the chroma signal. The chroma sideband frequencies are also raised.

CANCELLATION OF THE TIME-BASE ERROR The frequency conversion down and up is only part of the process in avoiding the time-base error. The key to the problem lies in the method used to regenerate the cw signal. In playback, the cw signal is developed as a multiple of the horizontal sync frequency taken from the tape. This cw signal has all the jitter components in the playback signal. When the cw signal is heterodyned with the playback signal, the two frequencies change up or down by the same

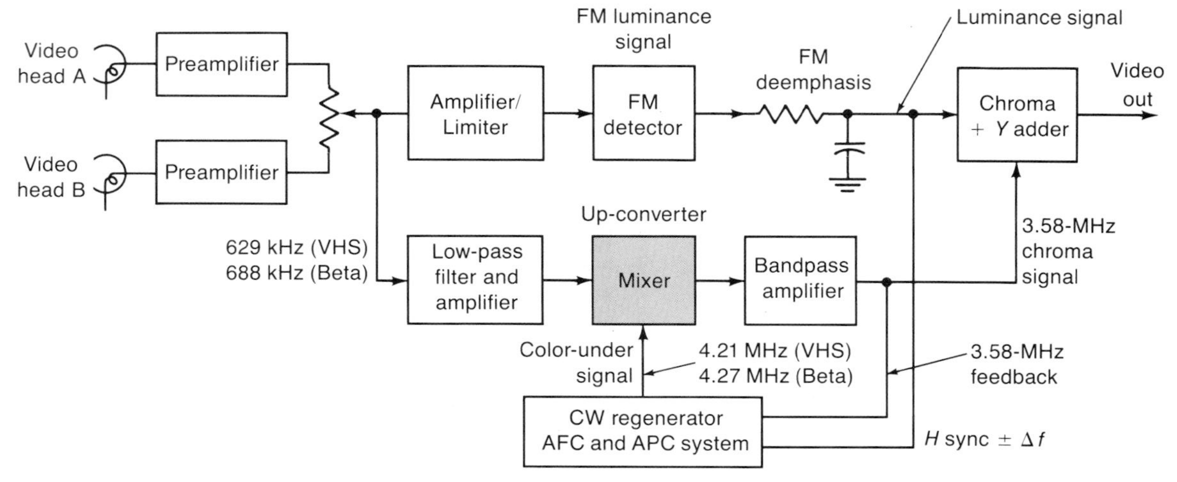

Fig. 10-8 Circuits for up conversion of chroma signal in playback, in color-under system for recording.

amount. The frequency difference, therefore, is not affected by small changes in frequency or phase in the playback signal.

The system is not perfect because it is still subject to errors in burst gating and other factors in regeneration of the cw signal. However, the method does provide good picture quality for the consumer type of VCR.

COMBINED COLOR AND LUMINANCE SIGNALS The combined frequencies for the color-under signal and the FM luminance signal are shown in Fig. 10-9, which summarizes the VCR system for recording. The total bandwidth is 1 to 6 MHz, approximately, to include sidebands of the frequency-modulated luminance signal. On the low-frequency side, a filter is used to provide

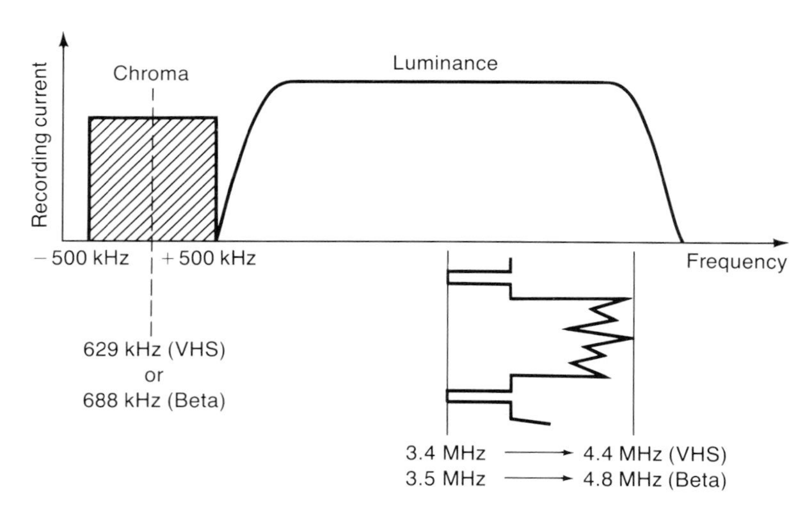

Fig. 10-9 Frequencies used in VCR for color-under signal and FM luminance signal.

a slot in the spectrum for the color-under frequencies.

The color-under signal is recorded directly on the tape, without modulation, along with the FM luminance signal. In addition, the luminance signal provides high-frequency ac bias for recording the color signal.

The lowest frequencies for recording are in the color-under signal, at about 129 or 188 kHz. These frequencies create no problem with rotating heads. The highest frequencies are 5 to 6 MHz in the FM luminance signal. These frequencies determine the writing speed required for the rotating head gap.

Test Point Questions 10-4

Answers at End of Chapter

a. Which is recorded as an FM signal, the luminance or the chroma signal?

b. Is 700 kHz a color-under or a luminance frequency?

c. In the VHS system, to what color-under frequency does 3.58 MHz correspond?

d. What is the highest frequency to be played back in a typical VCR?

10-5 ROTARY HEAD-DRUM ASSEMBLY

The basic arrangement for helical scanning of the tape is shown in Fig. 10-10. The tape is pulled around a cylindrical assembly called the *head drum,* or *scanner.* At the top, the rotating drum has two video heads on opposite sides. However, the lower section of the drum is stationary. In this part a guide band, which is a machined shoulder, guides the tape downward as the tape flows around the drum. The tape is in contact with the drum for a little more than 180°.

Where the tape enters and exits the drum, stationary guide posts are carefully positioned and tilted to start the tape moving down as it enters

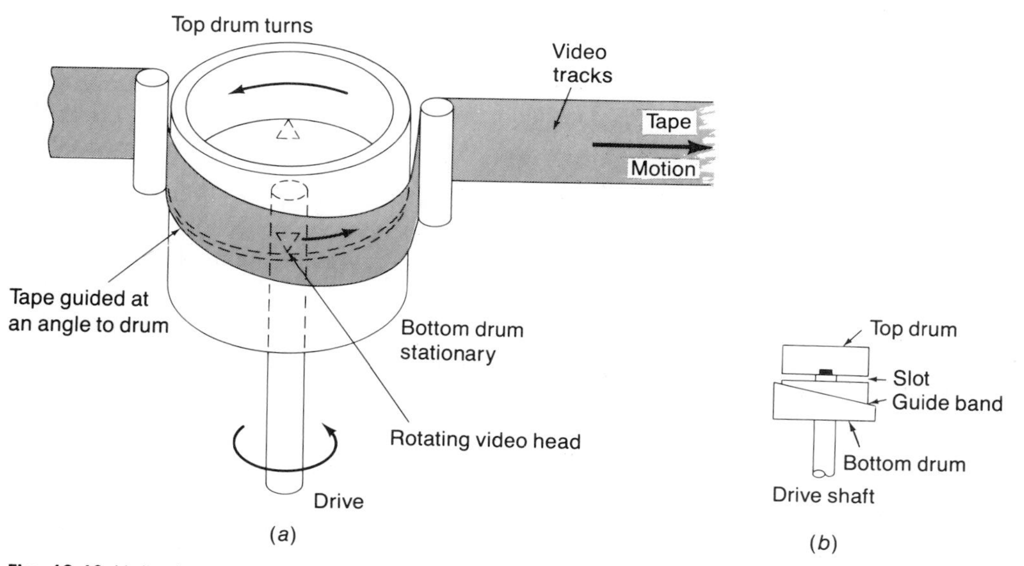

Fig. 10-10 Helical-scan system. (*a*) Tape against the rotating head. (*b*) Details of drum assembly.

the drum area and to straighten the tape as it leaves. These are the entrance and exit guides.

The upper part of the drum assembly rotates counterclockwise, as shown in Fig. 10-10. It carries the two video recording heads, mounted on the lower surface of the rotating part of the drum. The recording heads are precisely 180° apart, opposite each other on the same diameter of the drum. They protrude slightly to press into the tape surface.

SLANT TRACKS Since the tape is angled downward as it flows around the drum, each video head crosses the width of the tape at a shallow angle. Each pass, or swipe, starts near the lower edge of the tape and finishes near the upper edge. Since the recording path is in the shape of a helix, this system is called *helical-scan,* or *slant-track, recording.* The slant tracks on the tape are shown in Fig. 10-2.

ONE TV FIELD PER HEAD PASS Most helical-scan machines record one complete vertical scanning field in the time taken for each pass of a video head. Each head is in contact with the tape for one-half revolution. Thus two fields for a complete television frame are recorded in one complete rotation of the drum assembly.

The heads alternate in recording sequential fields. Since a one-half turn takes approximately $\frac{1}{60}$ s for one field, a full turn takes $\frac{1}{30}$ s. The rotational speed, then, is 30 revolutions per second (rps), or $30 \times 60 = 1800$ rpm for the head-drum scanner.

OVERLAP IN RECORDING The signal to be recorded is applied to both heads. In some cases, the recording signal is simply applied to the two heads in parallel. The actual recording is produced by the head that is in contact with the tape. On the next half-turn, the other head records the next field. However, the tape wraps around the scanner for a little more than 180°. As a result, there is a short period when both heads are in contact with the tape. Both heads, then, record the same information. This overlap is at the start of the pass for one head and the end of the pass for the other head. The overlap period of double recording lasts about +3 and −3 horizontal lines, shown as $3H$ in Fig. 10-11.

HEAD SWITCHING IN PLAYBACK When the tape is played back, the signals from the two heads are separated electrically, with each driving its low-noise preamplifier. Because of the recorded overlap, duplicate playback signals are produced at the same time for $6H$ lines. However, the preamplifiers are switched on and off by a 30-Hz square wave. The 30-Hz gating signal is developed by a magnetic pulse generator coupled to the rotating drum.

The 30-Hz signal turns on the preamplifier for the head that is in contact with the tape and turns off the other preamplifier. However, the switching, or gating, point is chosen so that it falls in the center of the overlap period. When the output signals from the switched preamplifiers are added, the result is a uniform envelope of playback signal with no gaps.

The switching point must be the same for each TV field. This means that particular parts of the video signal for each field must occur at the same point of each recorded track. The scanner servosystem does just that. It separates the vertical sync from the video signal to be recorded and synchronizes the scanner with the sync signal. Specifically, the vertical sync is recorded 9 or 10 horizontal lines following the start of each head pass. Remember that the head switch occurs in the middle of the overlap, which is about 3 lines after the start of the pass. Therefore, the switching occurs about 6 lines (9 − 3) before the point where the vertical sync is recorded on the tape. The 9 lines include $3H$ for the equalizing pulses. For example, the specification of the Betamax system is $6.5H$ ahead of V sync, as shown in Fig. 10-11.

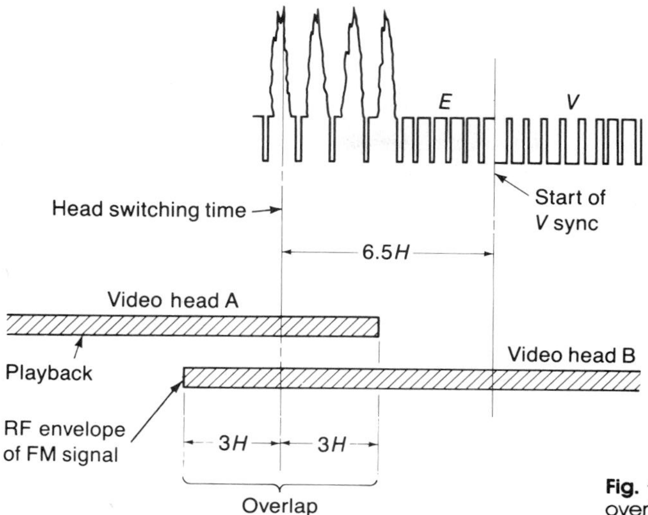

Fig. 10-11 Video head switching in playback, showing overlap of $3H + 3H$ lines.

The head-switching signal is actually in the picture area, approximately three lines before the vertical blanking bar at the bottom. You can see the switching effect as jitter to the left or right, when the raster does not fill the bottom of the screen. The decision to place the head-switching point in the actual picture area, rather than within the vertical blanking (where it would be invisible), is based on the practical aspect of compensating for a major timing error in the tape travel called *skew error.* This error is common to all helical-scan machines because of the switching between fields.

SKEW ERROR There is a difference in back tension on the tape between the time that the recording was made and when it is played back. The actual length of the recorded pass increases by a microscopic amount of tape when the hold-back tension is too tight or decreases when the tape is too loose. The problem is not that the tape stretches, but that the air layer trapped between the tape and the scanner surface is squeezed out more or less, depending on the tape tension. As a result, *H* lines of signal are bunched too close together or spread too far apart. The effect shows up abruptly at the head-switching point, as illustrated in Fig. 10-12. At this point, the skew error of several microseconds can affect the horizontal synchronization in the picture. The skew error is minimized by careful adjustment of the hold-back tension at the entrance side of the scanner assembly.

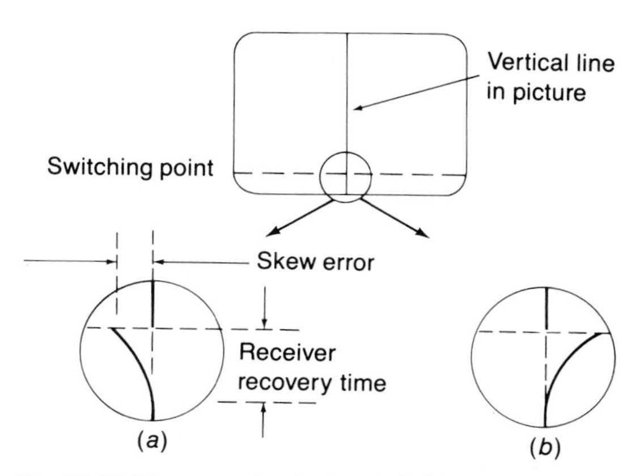

Fig. 10-12 Skew error in playback. (*a*) Playback tension greater than recording tension. (*b*) Playback tension less than recording tension.

Because of skew error, it is difficult for the horizontal deflection system in the TV receiver to stay in sync. Some time is needed for the horizontal AFC system to stabilize. Older receivers take an appreciable part of a field to recover from the abrupt timing error in *H* sync. Receivers made since about 1970 are designed to stabilize very quickly.

By putting the head-switching point ahead of the vertical blanking time, the TV receiver is given the entire *V* blanking period plus three lines to recover from the effects of skew errors. When full recovery is made in the blanking time, the top of the picture is stable. If stabilization of *H* sync takes longer, the top of the picture may shake sideways. This effect is called *flag waving.*

In summary, then, the two heads are switched in sequential fields for playback. The overlap provides 6*H* lines to permit head switching. The head switching occurs 3*H* before *V* blanking to minimize the effect of skew error on horizontal synchronization in the TV receiver.

DRUM DIAMETER Since the rotational speed is fixed at 1800 rpm for one field per pass, the remaining variable in determining the writing speed is the drum diameter. The larger the drum diameter, the higher the writing speed. Actual calculations are based on the exact field rate of 59.84 Hz for color television, not on 60 Hz.

In the Betamax system, typical values are as follows: head-gap width = 0.6 μm; writing speed required = 6.9 m/s for recording up to 5 MHz; diameter of the scanner drum is 74.487 mm.

The VHS head drum is slightly smaller. Also, the head gap of 0.3 μm is thinner. The writing speed is 5.8 m/s for recording up to 5 MHz.

FOUR-HEAD MACHINES Some models of the VCR include another pair of video heads, which makes four in all. The added pair is used in long-play or extended-play operation, where the tape speed is slowed considerably. The VCR is essentially still a two-head machine, because not all the heads are used at the same time. One pair is used for standard play of 2 h. The other pair is for extended play up to 6 h. Four-head machines provide improved performance of special effects, such as slow, pause, fast search, etc.

In VHS recorders, the slower tape speeds for longer playing time are as follows:

33.35 mm/s for 2 h

16.67 mm/s for 4 h

11.12 mm/s for 6 h

ROTARY TRANSFORMERS The signals to be recorded are coupled to the rotating heads by means of a rotary transformer built into the scanner. The transformer primary is part of the lower stationary part of the drum; the rotating upper drum contains the transformer secondary. Ferrite cup-shaped core pieces hold the windings. The low-reluctance path provides good magnetic coupling.

In recording, the signal is connected to the stationary winding, as the primary, with magnetic coupling to the rotating secondary winding. In playback, the rotating winding acts as the primary coupling the signal into the stationary winding which acts as the secondary.

Test Point Questions 10-5

Answers at End of Chapter

a. How many TV fields does a slant track record in one pass?

b. Is the angle of wrap that the tape makes around the scanner head slightly more or less than 180°?

c. Does head switching take place at the top or bottom of the TV picture?

d. Does increasing the drum diameter increase or decrease the writing speed?

10-6 SCANNER SERVOSYSTEMS

Two separate servoloops are used to control the motor that drives the rotating upper-drum assembly with the video heads. One loop is for speed control. The rotation is precisely 29.97 rps for the frame frequency in color television. The other loop controls the phase, or timing. This part of the servosystem makes sure that one of the two video heads, called the *reference head,* crosses the spot on the track where vertical sync is to be recorded at the precise instant it occurs in the video signal.

The required control of speed and timing can be compared to an electric clock. When you plug in the clock, it starts running immediately at the correct speed. But its phase or timing must be set manually by moving the hands until the clock is in phase with local time. So, too, the speed servo runs the scanner at the correct speed for the first requirement. Also, the phase loop acts to speed up or slow down the rotation to achieve the correct relative timing between a specific angular position of the reference video head and the arrival of vertical sync. When the timing condition is correct, the phase-correction loop stops functioning, while the speed servo runs the scanner motor. The phase loop checks on the relative timing once per scanner revolution and applies correction as needed.

SPEED SERVOLOOP Figure 10-13 shows a block diagram of the scanner servosystems. At the top, the circuit loop for speed is fed from a frequency generator that is part of the servomotor for the scanner. The generator produces a voltage at a frequency proportional to the speed of rotation. It is called the *tone generator,* or *tachometer.*

Frequency is converted to a variable dc voltage by the block labeled "F-V converter." The dc voltage is applied to an operational amplifier (op

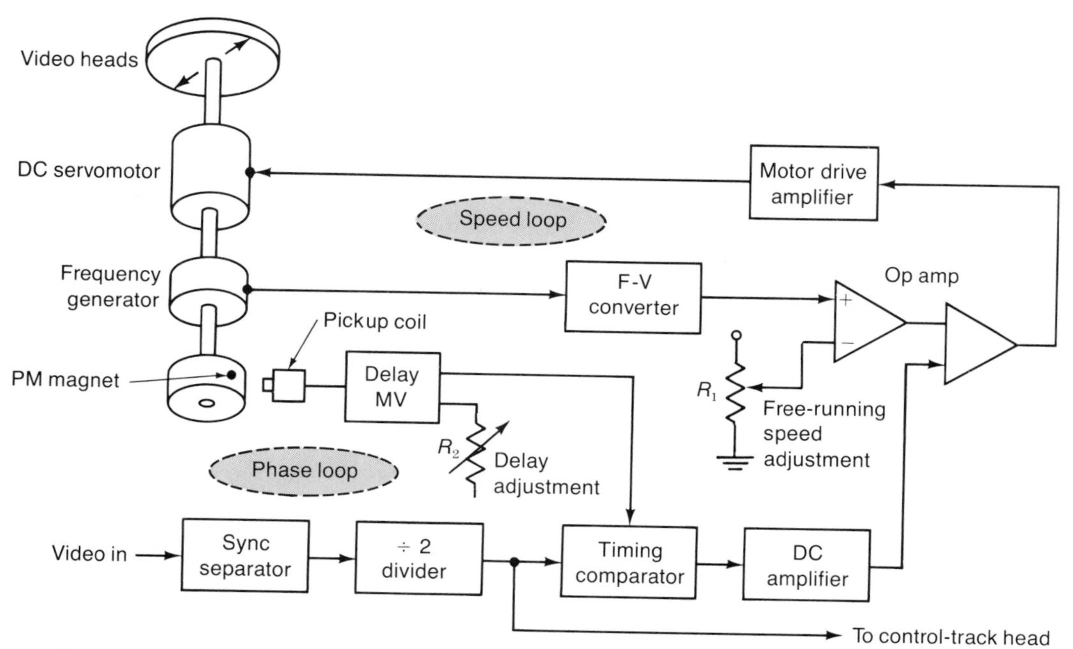

Fig. 10-13 Basic servosystems for speed and phase for scanner in recording mode.

amp), along with an adjustable dc voltage from resistor R_1. This controls the free-running speed adjustment. The speed servomotor is adjusted to make the scanner run at the correct speed when the phase correction is zero.

PHASE SERVOLOOP The circuit loop at the bottom of Fig. 10-13 compares two timing events in the recording mode. One is a 30-Hz pulse coincident in time with every other vertical sync pulse in the signal to be recorded. The other event is a pulse generated by the scanner itself, in the pickup coil shown next to the rotating magnet. This pulse signals when the reference video head is in the correct position, near the start of the pass, to record vertical sync in the processed FM recording signal.

The *V* sync timing reference is obtained from the video signal. It is applied to a sync separator stage, followed by an integrator. This *RC* low-pass filter provides *V* sync without the *H* sync. The *V* sync signal at 60 Hz is divided by 2 for the timing comparator. Actually, the divided frequency equals 29.97 Hz.

The scanner timing pulse is developed by an electromagnetic pulse generator, which is coupled to the scanner spindle. Often, a small permanent magnet is embedded in the motor flywheel, as in Fig. 10-13. As the magnet sweeps past a stationary pickup coil, a pulse of voltage is induced in the coil. Two magnets 180° apart are used in VHS machines. They are poled in opposite directions to produce positive and negative pulses. One of the pulses is used as a positional reference for the phase servoloop. In addition, both pulses are used for the head-switching action described with Fig. 10-11.

Figure 10-14 shows a typical waveform for the pickup coil. The coil position is set so that the pulse is generated slightly sooner than it should be, before the point of *V* sync. Then the delay multivibrator (MV) can be adjusted by R_2 to vary the timing without any mechanical adjustment of the pickup coil itself being needed.

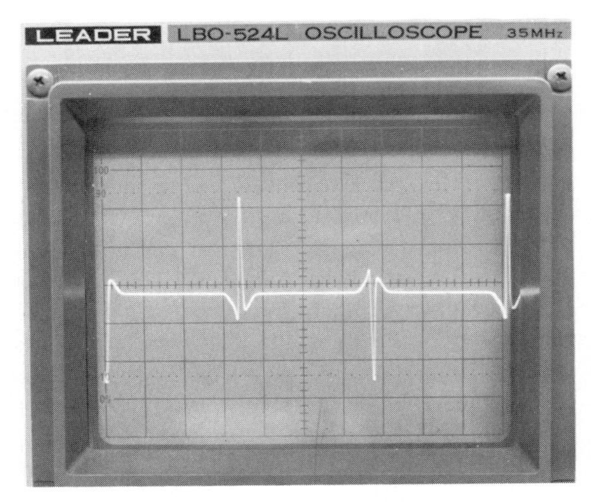

Fig. 10-14 Waveform for scanner pickup coil.

TIMING COMPARATOR The timing comparison between the *V* sync and the pickup coil pulse usually is made by a circuit called a *sample-and-hold gate.* Its function is illustrated in Fig. 10-15. The separated *V* sync pulse triggers a linear voltage-ramp generator. The sawtooth voltage rise is fed to the electronic switch S_1. However, S_1 is turned on only when it has the narrow pulse output of the pulse former, delayed from the pickup coil output. During the brief period that the switch is on, the ramp voltage charges an output capacitor C_1 to whatever ramp voltage is present at the time of sampling. When the switch is open, without a sampling pulse, the capacitor is isolated without any discharge path. Therefore, C_1 holds the sample voltage until the next sampling pulse occurs. The output voltage is essentially a dc value of correction voltage for the scanner motor.

As an example of phase control, assume that the reference video head is late coming into position. Then the pickup coil pulse also is late. The voltage ramp in the timing comparator is sampled later, when it has increased to a higher voltage. As a result, the dc output of the sample-and-hold gate goes higher, and the scanner motor

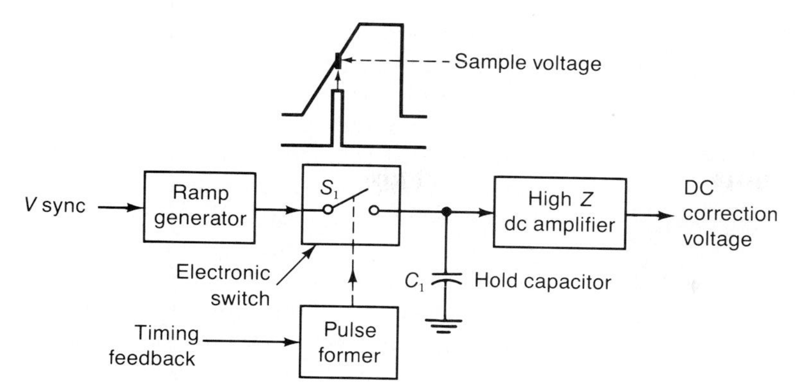

Fig. 10-15 Sample-and-hold gate used as timing comparator for phase servoloop in Fig. 10-13.

is driven harder. The motor speeds up until the phase-timing condition is corrected.

Note that the voltage ramp for sampling is sometimes descending, with negative-going polarity. However, the dc amplifier following the gate can invert the sense of correction to achieve the same effect on the motor speed.

In many cases, the free-running speed control in the speed loop of the scanner motor is adjusted to put the sample pulse in the center of the sampling ramp. The control is the potentiometer R_1 in Fig. 10-13. This method puts the entire system in the center of the correction range for the phase loop. For this reason, the free-running speed control might have a name such as *sample position,* instead of a label for speed.

Test Point Questions 10-6

Answers at End of Chapter

Answer True or False.

a. The timing reference for the scanner servo in recording is the *V* sync divided by 2.

b. A tone generator on the scanner shaft indicates the frequency of rotation.

c. A pickup coil next to a magnet on the scanner shaft indicates the position of the reference video head.

d. A sample-and-hold circuit is used as a timing comparator.

10-7 CONTROL TRACK AND CAPSTAN SERVOSYSTEM

During playback, a new timing reference must be used for the servosystem. This reference must indicate that a prerecorded track is in position around the scanner, and the reference head should be sweeping over the precise point on the tape track where vertical sync has been recorded. The required timing reference is recorded on a separate longitudinal track along the bottom of the tape called the *control track.* The control track is needed for playback because there is an additional requirement that the tape travel at exactly the same speed as in the recording.

The control-track signal is recorded by a stationary head on the exit side of the scanner, at a point before the tape is engaged by a capstan–pinch roller drive system. Figure 10-16 shows a typical assembly. The capstan is a smooth metal cylinder that rotates to move the tape. The pinch roller holds the tape against the capstan so that the tape travels at constant speed.

The stationary head assembly also includes the audio recording head. The audio signal is recorded along the top edge of the tape. The audio is recorded in the conventional way, as with the more familiar audio tape recorders.

The audio track and control track are longitudinal along the top and bottom of the ½-in. tape,

Fig. 10-16 Stationary head stack includes audio and control-track heads.

as shown in Fig. 10-2. Between them are the diagonal stripes of recorded video signal.

CTL PULSE During the recording process, a sample of the 29.97-Hz rectangular wave that was developed from vertical sync is applied to the control-track head (CTL). This pulse is recorded on the control track at the precise instant that the reference video head is recording vertical sync in the FM processed video signal. In playback, the CTL picks up this pulse for the capstan servo. The system is illustrated in Fig. 10-17, with the CTL and capstan motor shown at the top.

CAPSTAN SERVOSYSTEM For the playback, a separate and independent timing reference must be used for both the scanner and capstan servosystem. The independent reference is generally a 29.97-Hz signal developed by digital countdown from a separate crystal oscillator at 3.579545 MHz. The common timing reference is fed to both the scanner and the capstan servosystems.

The regulating action can be visualized in the following steps. First, the scanner locks to the crystal reference, putting the reference video head at the correct angular position for playback of the recorded signal. Also, a phase comparator in the capstan servosystem compares this same 29.97-Hz pulse with the CTL playback pulse. When the phase comparison is correct, the comparator indicates that the prerecorded video track is positioned precisely around the scanner. When the CTL pulse is late, the capstan servosystem acts to speed up the capstan motor and the tape to bring about the correct timing. For a CTL pulse that is too early, the capstan motor is slowed down. The overall effect is that the tape is pulled faster or slower until CTL pulses arrive at the precise time when prerecorded video tracks are in place around the scanner.

The capstan servosystem includes two loops usually. One is for speed and the other is for phase, based on the control-track pulses.

In the recording mode, the capstan servo is just a speed controller. An internal frequency generator that is part of the capstan assembly is used to control the tape speed.

TRACKING FOR PLAYBACK A timing error in the phase comparison of the capstan servo in playback causes the tape to be too early or too late in its path around the scanner. Then the path of the video heads strays off the center of the recorded diagonal tracks and into neighboring tracks. So the playback path is not tracking with the recording path. The result is a weaker playback signal and a smaller signal-to-noise ratio. The reproduced picture becomes snowy.

Fine precision is required in the mechanical guides and shoulders that position the tape on the scanner. Also, the distance along the tape path from the scanner to the control track head is critical. Moving the CTL head closer to the scanner, by even a microscopic amount, causes the CTL pulses to be played back too early.

Errors of this type create interchange problems, in which tapes recorded on one machine cannot be played back with minimum noise on another machine. We assume the machines use

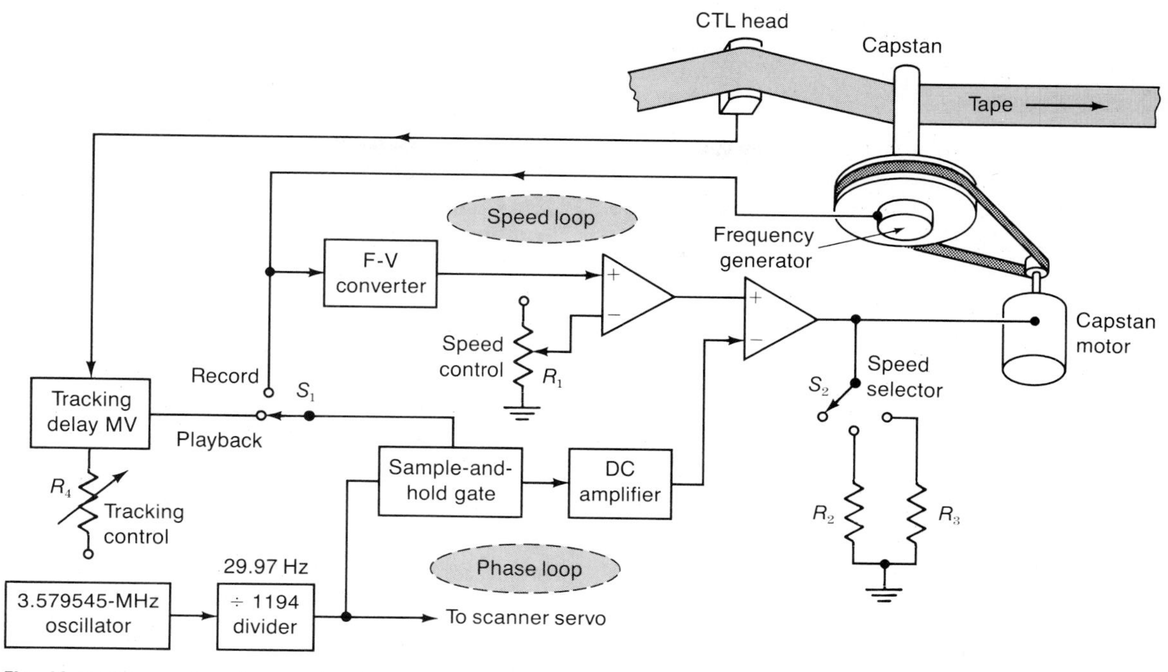

Fig. 10-17 Servosystem for capstan to keep tape moving at uniform speed.

the same format. Cassettes recorded on a Betamax recorder cannot be played back on a VHS machine, or vice versa. Even if both machines have the same format, a VCR machine always plays back its own recordings better than the recording from another machine.

Test tapes offered by the manufacturer have precise prerecorded signals for tracking and CTL position adjustments. An example is shown in Fig. 10-18.

To compensate for minor differences between similar machines, a front-panel tracking control is provided. This control is potentiometer R_4 in Fig. 10-17. The control adjusts the time delay in one of the delay multivibrators. When the control is set at midrange, at a detent or click stop, the total delay is $\frac{1}{30}$ s. Then the delayed pulse actually represents the previous tape pulse. By varying the tracking control, the total delay is made longer or shorter. The effect is exactly the same as actually moving the CTL head closer to or farther from the scanner, which determines the tracking of the recorded signal. The tracking control is adjusted for minimum snow in the reproduced picture. Note that the tracking delay

Fig. 10-18 Alignment cassette is used for adjustments of head switching and tracking.

is disabled during the record mode, so that the CTL pulses are recorded correctly, regardless of the setting of the tracking control.

MULTISPEED OPERATION Most VCR machines offer two or three tape speeds for longer playing time. For example, VHS recorders usually have 2-, 4-, and 6-h play. The corresponding tape speeds are 33.35, 16.67, and 11.12 mm/s, respectively. Therefore, the capstan servosystem has provisions for changing the capstan speed in accordance with a front-panel selector switch for the record mode of operation. In Fig. 10-17, switch S_2 selects the desired speed for the capstan motor.

In playback, speed selection is done automatically to accommodate the repetition rate of the recorded control-track signals. The capstan servosystem selects from the available capstan speeds until the correct rate of CTL pulses is produced.

Test Point Questions 10-7
Answers at End of Chapter

a. Which two recording heads are stationary?
b. Is tape speed controlled by the capstan or the scanner?
c. Does poor tracking of the video heads cause overload distortion or snow in the picture?
d. What is the exact frequency of the CTL pulses?

10-8 ZERO GUARD-BAND SYSTEMS

In early reel-to-reel video tape recorders, the heads were set up to provide a vacant strip of space between the individual slant tracks on the tape. This space, called a *guard band,* isolates one track from the adjacent tracks on both sides. The purpose of the guard band is to prevent interference, called *crosstalk,* between the two recorded channels.

The problem with guard bands is that they waste valuable space on the tape. This space could provide greater information density if it were used for recording the video signal. For this reason, the Betamax and VHS systems have completely eliminated the guard band. Adjacent video tracks are butted against each other, side by side. This method is called a *zero guard-band system.* The big advantage is the longer playing time for a given length of tape.

Elimination of the guard band requires that other methods provide the necessary separation between playback signals from adjacent video tracks. In the Betamax format, one head with its track is labeled A and the other B. For VHS, they are labeled 1 and 2. The methods of isolating tracks include tilting the gaps with opposite angles for opposite heads and using special circuits to cancel crosstalk in the color signal.

HEADS WITH CANTED AZIMUTH ANGLES The term canted means sloping or slanting. An azimuth angle is a perpendicular angle with respect to the horizontal plane. In conventional audio recording, the head angle is not canted. The azimuth angle that the head makes with the long dimension of the tape is 90°. This head angle must be adjusted carefully for proper playback. In audio recorders, for instance, an error in azimuth angle produces a particular symptom. The machine plays back its own recordings correctly, but the high-frequency response suffers when another tape, either prerecorded or from another machine is played. The reason for the drop in high-frequency response is a phase error at short recorded wavelengths. Signals played back at the top of the tape differ slightly from those played back at the bottom of the tape. The resulting phase error can cause high-frequency components of the signal to cancel.

In VCR machines, the idea of azimuth error is put to practical use to cancel crosstalk in the

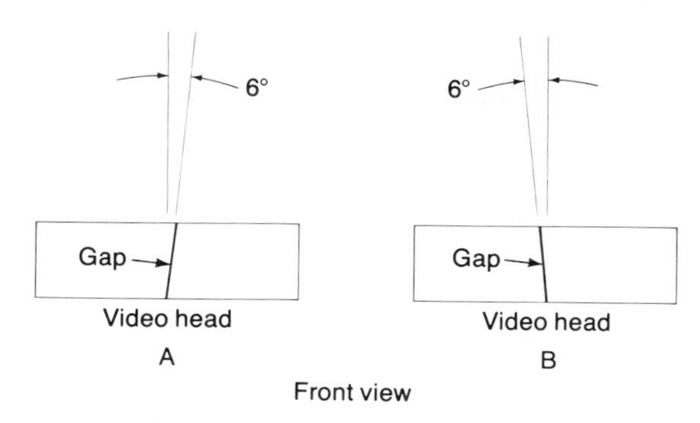

Fig. 10-19 Head gap is canted, or tilted, 6° in opposite directions on two video heads, for zero guard-band system in VHS format. Tilt is 7° in Betamax format.

luminance signal. The gaps are canted 6° from the vertical in opposite directions, as shown in Fig. 10-19 for the VHS system. The angle is 7° in the Betamax system.

The total angle between heads is 12° in VHS and 14° in the Betamax, which is a very large azimuth error. As a result, the A head ignores high-frequency signals recorded on the B tracks and vice versa. The method works well for the FM luminance signal, which is at the high end of the frequency spectrum for recording. These frequencies are in the megahertz range. However, the system creates almost no isolation between tracks for the color-under frequencies used for recording the color signal. These frequencies are around 629 or 688 kHz.

The color crosstalk can be canceled, though, by special filter circuits. The method is based on the frequency interlace characteristics of the 3.58-MHz chroma signal.

COMB FILTERS The heart of the chroma isolation system is a device called the *comb filter,* which passes only specific frequencies in exact multiples. It is actually a delay line with a delay time of one complete *H* scanning line equal to 63.5 μs. A delay this long is difficult to achieve by electronic means. Instead, the input is converted by the filter to an acoustic signal that is propagated through a glass substrate. The speed of propagation equals the speed of sound waves in the glass medium. A long delay time can be produced in a very small unit because of the slow speed of sound compared with the speed of electric waves.

Figure 10-20 shows an actual comb filter with the cover removed. The entire unit is only ½ in. [12.7 mm] square. It contains two sonic transducers at the lower corners. One acts as a

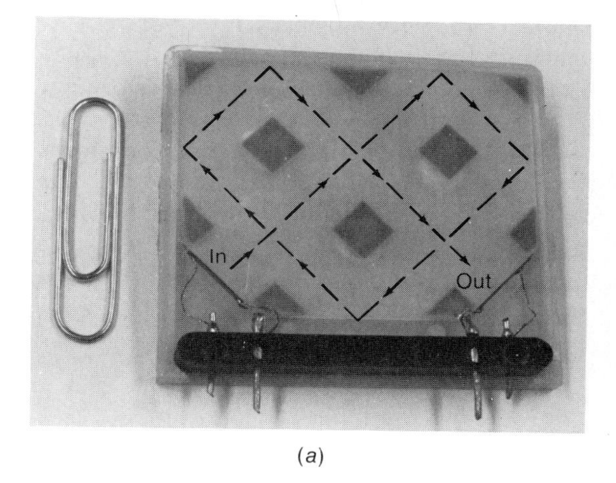

(*a*)

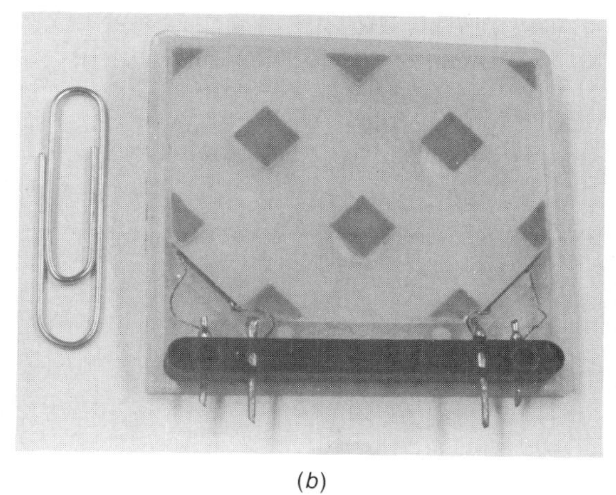

(*b*)

Fig. 10-20 Construction of comb filter. (*a*) Route of acoustic signal. (*b*) Filter unit with cover removed.

loudspeaker, at the input, to produce supersonic waves. The other picks up the delayed sonic signal and, serving as a microphone, converts the acoustic wave to an electric signal. Note that the sonic signal frequencies are much higher than the range of human hearing, but they are still sound waves.

The method of using a comb filter is illustrated in Fig. 10-21. In Fig. 10-21*a,* note the two paths in parallel for the chroma signal input. One path bypasses the filter while the other path has a delay time of 1*H* equal to 63.5 μs. The two signals are combined at point A in the output. At this point the two signals can be either added or subtracted, by reversing the leads at the output pickup transducer.

To see how the system functions, we review some basic aspects of frequency interlace in the chroma signal. This feature is described in Chap. 8, "Color Television Circuits and Signals." Briefly, though, the color subcarrier signal is made 3.579545 MHz, so that it is an odd multiple of one-half the *H* line-scanning frequency. Thus for any one line that ends in a complete cycle of subcarrier, the next line in the same field ends in a half-cycle of subcarrier. The half-cycle offset of subcarrier signal applies to successive lines in either the odd or the even field.

Now consider the comb filter in Fig. 10-21 where the direct and delayed signals are subtracted. The subtraction occurs between the line being scanned and the line immediately before. These two chroma signals are in opposite phase. Subtraction of the opposite phases means addition of the two chroma signals, so they actually double in amplitude. However, the luminance components in the chroma signal are canceled by subtraction.

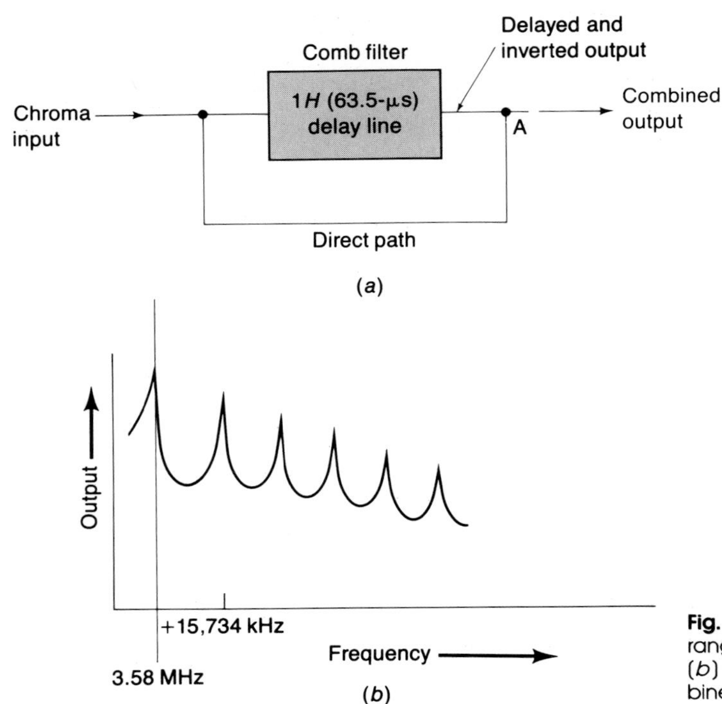

Fig. 10-21 Effect of comb filter. (*a*) Circuit arrangement with two paths for chroma signal. (*b*) Frequency response at point A for combined output.

The doubling of the chroma signal and the cancellation of the luminance signal occur for the frequency components at the H line-scanning rate and all the harmonic frequencies. As a result, the frequency response looks like Fig. 10-21*b*, which is the reason for the name *comb filter*. This response also makes the comb filter desirable for separating the chroma signal from the luminance signal in television receivers.

CANCELLATION OF COLOR CROSSTALK To put the comb filter to use in the VCR, it is placed following the heterodyne-up converter. Then the filtering occurs after the chroma signal has been restored to the correct subcarrier frequency of 3.58 MHz for playback. The crucial part is to have color processing circuits that provide two effects:

1. They keep the desired signals from the A and B heads in their correct line-to-line phase relation of 180°.
2. They make crosstalk signals have the same phase, line to line, so that they can be canceled by the comb filter.

When these phase relations are produced, the desired chroma signal doubles in amplitude, but the crosstalk signals cancel to zero.

Such color processing circuits are used for the recording heads in the VHS and Betamax systems. Both use a comb filter to cancel crosstalk, but the signal-switching circuits are different. The switching is done for both recording and playback to make the crosstalk signals have the in-phase relation that is canceled by the comb filter. As a result, chroma crosstalk from adjacent tracks is canceled.

Test Point Questions 10-8

Answers at End of Chapter

a. In the zero guard-band system, at what angle is each head canted?

b. Does the canted azimuth angle work better for luminance or chroma signals?

c. What is the time delay of the comb filter?

d. Specify the frequency that is the 455th harmonic of $H/2$.

10-9 PATH OF TAPE TRAVEL

The transport system drives the tape past the rotating video scanner and the stationary assembly with the audio and control-track heads. Figure 10-22 shows the path of tape travel after the tape has been threaded or loaded into the VCR machine. Extreme mechanical precision is required, because the transport components support the tape as it moves in the guided path.

When you insert the cassette, its front lid opens to expose the tape to the machine. The threading is done in the machine by withdrawing a loop of tape and fitting it into the proper path. A separate dc motor may be used to automatically pull out the tape for a loop. In some machines, a mechanical link to the capstan motor is used for threading the tape.

The running path of the tape is the same for recording or playback. At the end, the tape is rewound, since there is no turnover of the cartridge. To finish the operation, the tape loop is guided back into the cassette for unthreading. When you push the eject button, the takeup reel is driven to absorb the slack in the shrinking loop. Then the cassette can be removed.

As shown in Fig. 10-22, the cassette has two reels. The tape travels from the supply reel at the left to the takeup reel at the right. Each end of the tape is attached to a reel.

Note the guideposts inside the cassette at the exit and entrance. Let us follow the running path of the tape as it leaves the supply reel. The tape goes partly around a stationary guide pin first, then against a tension pole and another supply guide pole. The tension pole presses against the

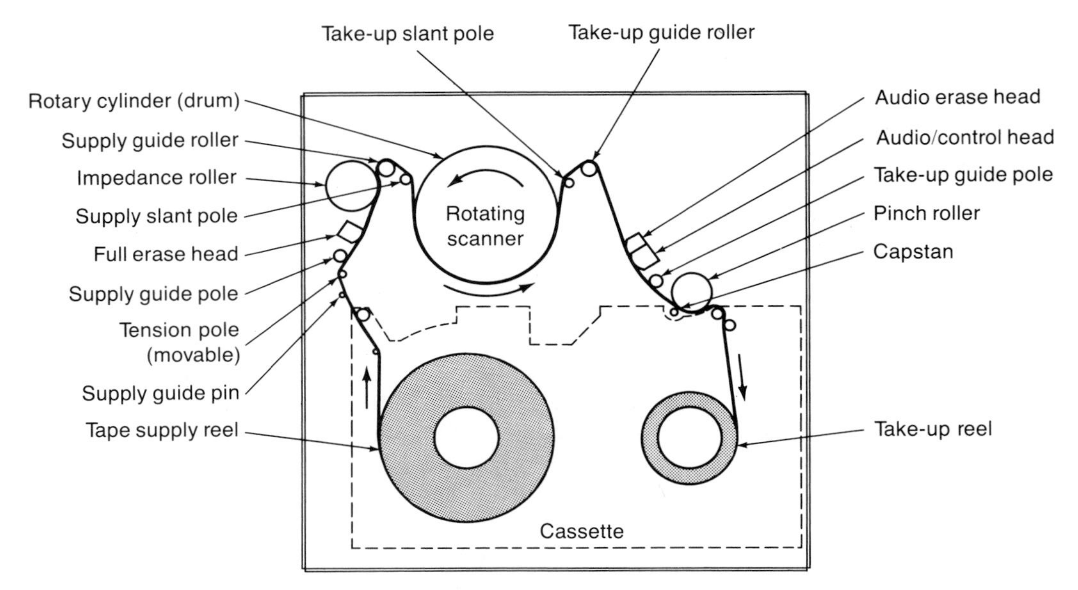

Fig. 10-22 Path of tape from cassette in video tape recorder. (*JVC model HR-7300*)

tape spanned between the two stationary guides. As the tape tension increases, the pole moves to the right slightly, for less tension. Although it is not shown here, the tension pole is mounted on a sensing arm that is part of an electromechanical servosystem. This arm regulates the tape hold-back tension according to how much tape is on the supply reel.

Next along the tape path is a full-track erase head. All previous tape signals are erased before recording. The erase head is energized during the record mode with a 70- to 90-kHz signal from the bias oscillator used for audio recording. This ac bias erases the tape completely before the tape reaches the video scanner. Then the tape can be used over and over to record different programs. However, a small plastic tab at the back of the cassette can be broken off to prevent erasure, if desired, as in audio cassettes.

The impedance roller, next in the tape path, is a large-diameter wheel that turns freely. Its function is to smooth out longitudinal vibrations before the tape reaches the scanner. Then the supply-guide roller alters the tape direction into the slant pole. This pole is the entrance guide for the scanner. The guide is slanted to make the tape flow downward. Tape travels around the front of the scanner. The lower edge of the tape serves as a reference position, bearing against a precision shelf machined into the surface of the lower scanning assembly. Although it is not evident in the drawing, the scanner itself is tilted, so that the tape stays nearly horizontal to the chassis.

The tape emerges from the scanner at the exit guide, labeled as the takeup slant pole. Next, at the takeup-guide roller, the tape changes direction, going back toward the takeup reel in the cassette. Then the tape flows past an assembly of two stationary heads.

The first is the audio erase head, for the audio track only. Its purpose is to allow audio *dubbing* on the tape. The dubbing is new audio material, such as commentary or music, that can be added to a previously recorded video program.

The second stationary head has two parts. At

the top is the audio record-playback head for the sound associated with the picture. At the bottom is the control record-playback head for the control pulses.

Next in the tape path, a takeup guide pole sets the tape position across the stationary heads. The tape is metered out at constant speed by being squeezed between the rotating capstan and the pinch roller. Finally, the tape is accumulated by the mechanically driven takeup reel.

Note that the rotating scanner turns counterclockwise, moving the heads in the same direction as tape travel. This direction actually reduces the writing speed, since the tape is moving in the same direction as the heads. However, the tape speed is extremely slow, which has a negligible effect on the writing speed. A system with both motions in the same direction has been adopted in order to trap air between the scanner and tape surface to form an air bearing which helps protect the tape.

Test Point Questions 10-9
Answers at End of Chapter

Answer True or False.

a. The supply reel of tape in the video cassette is at the left side.
b. The audio track can be erased, but the video tracks cannot.
c. Back tension on the tape is controlled by the tension pole at the left in Fig. 10-22.
d. The audio and control heads rotate in the same direction as the video scanner.

10-10 VIDEO DISK SYSTEMS

A video disk looks like a 12-in. phonograph record. However, much greater packing density is needed for recording the wideband video signal. The range is reduced by FM processing, though, as in video tape recorders.

In the video disk, microscopic pits in the surface store the video and audio information. To recover the signal, there are two basic methods of playback:

1. *Optical.* A laser beam tracks the recorded pits. Variations of light reflected from the disk provide the playback signal. The playback head does not touch the disk.
2. *Capacitive.* A diamond stylus rides on the record to provide capacitance variations for playback. The capacitance is between the metallized disk and a metal electrode attached to the stylus.

The reflective optical system was developed by the North American Philips Co. (NAP) and the Music Corporation of America (MCA). It is sometimes called *Laservision,* and the machine is a video laser player (VLP). In addition, a different optical system that is transmissive instead of reflective has industrial applications.

In the capacitive system, in one method there are very fine grooves in the disk, about 10,000 grooves per inch of radius, which is about 40 times more than on audio records. This type of capacitive electronic disk (CED) with grooves was developed by RCA for its Selectavision player (Fig. 10-23).

Another capacitive system was developed by Japan Victor Company (JVC) to eliminate the grooves in the disk. Its purpose is to increase

Fig. 10-23 Video disk player. (*RCA*)

the density of recorded information. A servocontrol guides the playback stylus on the disk. This method is called the *very high density* (*VHD*) disk system.

Both the RCA and VHD systems are capacitive. However, the RCA disk has grooves and the VHD disk does not.

The reason for having video disk players in competition with VCR machines is that the records can be pressed out easily at a much lower cost than tapes of prerecorded programs. Also video disk players are cheaper than video tape recorders generally. In addition, the disk can have better picture quality than ½-in. magnetic tape and rapid access to any program segment. Another advantage is that a disk player can easily provide freeze-frame operation. This factor may be important for industrial uses, such as retrieving stored information. However, the main disadvantage is that the disks are only for playback in home-type machines, since recording of a video disk requires elaborate equipment.

The playback time of the video disk is typically 1 h each side, or 2 h with turnover. The capacitance disk plays from the outside inward, like phonograph records, but the optical disk plays from the inside outward.

Test Point Questions 10-10

Answers at End of Chapter

Answer True or False.

a. The CED system is based on variations in capacitance.

b. The VHD system requires a laser light beam.

c. Video disk machines generally are used for playback but not for recording.

10-11 OPTICAL DISKS

The optical disk uses light reflected from microscopic pits in the surface that correspond to the video and audio signals. The pits are etched out and then coated with reflective aluminum when the disk is manufactured. In playback, a laser light beam is reflected from the bottom of the disk, to provide signal information corresponding to the pit variations, as illustrated in Fig. 10-24.

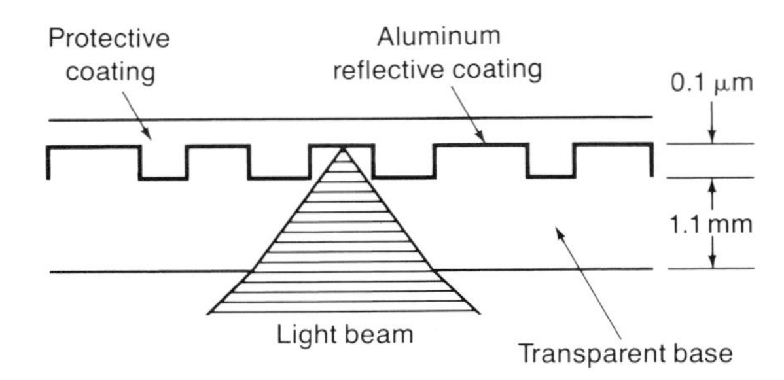

Fig. 10-24 Optical video disk is scanned by laser light beam from the bottom.

LASER LIGHT BEAM The source of light is a helium-neon laser operating at a wavelength of 632×10^{-9} m, in the spectrum of red light. A laser beam is used because it produces light in a very sharp beam, with specific polarization of its electromagnetic field. The laser output is *phasecoherent,* which means that all frequency components are in phase. Because of these features, the laser beam can be controlled much better than ordinary light.

The word *laser* is an abbreviation of *l*ight *a*mplification by *s*timulated *e*mission of *r*adiation. In the laser source, neon atoms are excited to radiate light at just one specific frequency. The power is low, so that the laser is safe.

OPTICAL DISK There are no grooves in the optical disk. Instead, the disk is impressed with microscopic pits on tracks that spiral out from the center hub to the outside edge. Each spiral is only 0.4 μm wide, and they are spaced 1.6 μm from one another. The depth of the pits is controlled very precisely so that it remains constant. The width and spacing of the pits are changed for the signal variations. Then the entire surface is given a metal coating that can reflect light. Finally, a transparent base is applied to provide a protective coating (Fig. 10-24).

The pit depth is made to equal one-quarter wavelength of the red light in the laser beam. Thus the light reflected from the bottom of the pit makes a round trip of one-half wavelength. As a result, light reflected from the pit is 180° out of phase with light from the smooth surface. This system provides two distinct values for the amount of reflected light. As the name indicates, the pits have a lower amplitude.

The disk speed is set to play back a complete frame, or two fields, in one revolution. Thus the disk rotates at 30 rps, or 30 × 60 = 1800 rpm. As an added feature, coded information is recorded in the vertical blanking to permit indexing to a particular frame.

MODULATION TECHNIQUES Just as in VCR machines, the video signal for the disk is frequency-modulated to reduce the octave range. The FM signal is produced before the photoetching process that creates the disk master. Because of the high density of pit packing possible in disks, it is possible to use high frequencies for the FM signal.

Figure 10-25 illustrates the frequency modulation technique. In Fig. 10-25*a*, the FM spectrum is shown for the video modulating signal, including the 3.58-MHz chroma signal. The tip of sync is clamped to the voltage that makes the modulated oscillator operate at 7.6 MHz. Peak white drives the frequency modulator up to 9.3 MHz. The p-p difference in frequencies, then, is 9.3 − 7.6 = 1.7 MHz.

The 3.58-MHz chroma signal is part of the composite video signal applied to the modulator. The color-under processing of VCR machines is not used here. The bandwidth is sufficient in video disk recording, and the cyclical time-base error is corrected by a servo-driven mirror in the playback system.

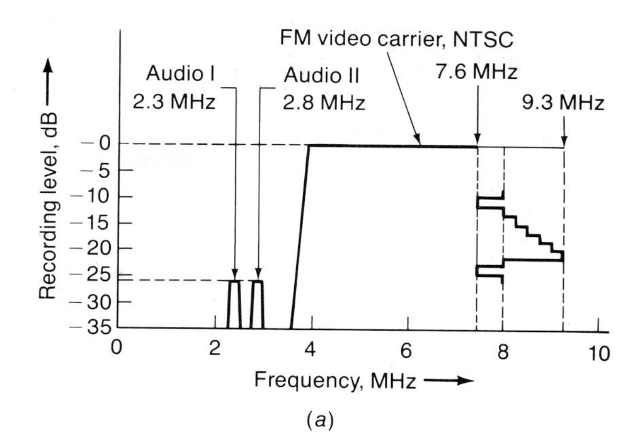

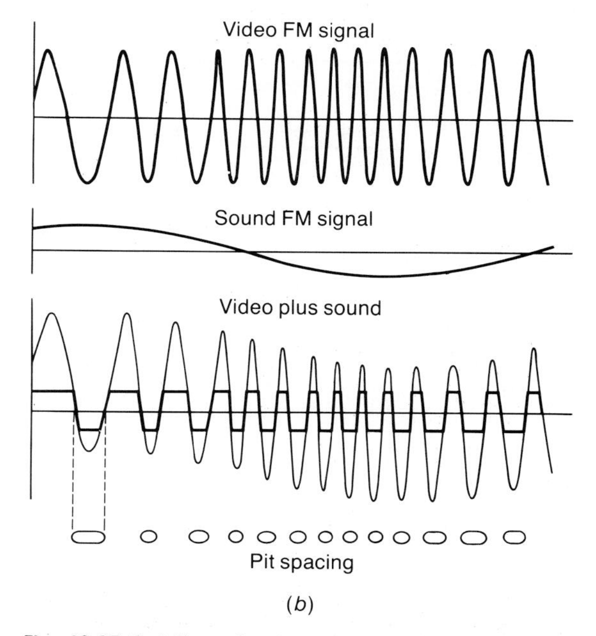

Fig. 10-25 Relation of video and audio signals to pit pattern on disk. (*a*) Spectrum of frequencies in FM signals. (*b*) Recorded signal and pit pattern. (*From Magnavox VH-8000 service manual*).

Note that audio signal is recorded in two FM bands at the lower end of the frequency spectrum in Fig. 10-25*a*. The channel separation is sufficient for two completely separate audio signals. They can be used for stereo sound or for bilingual recordings.

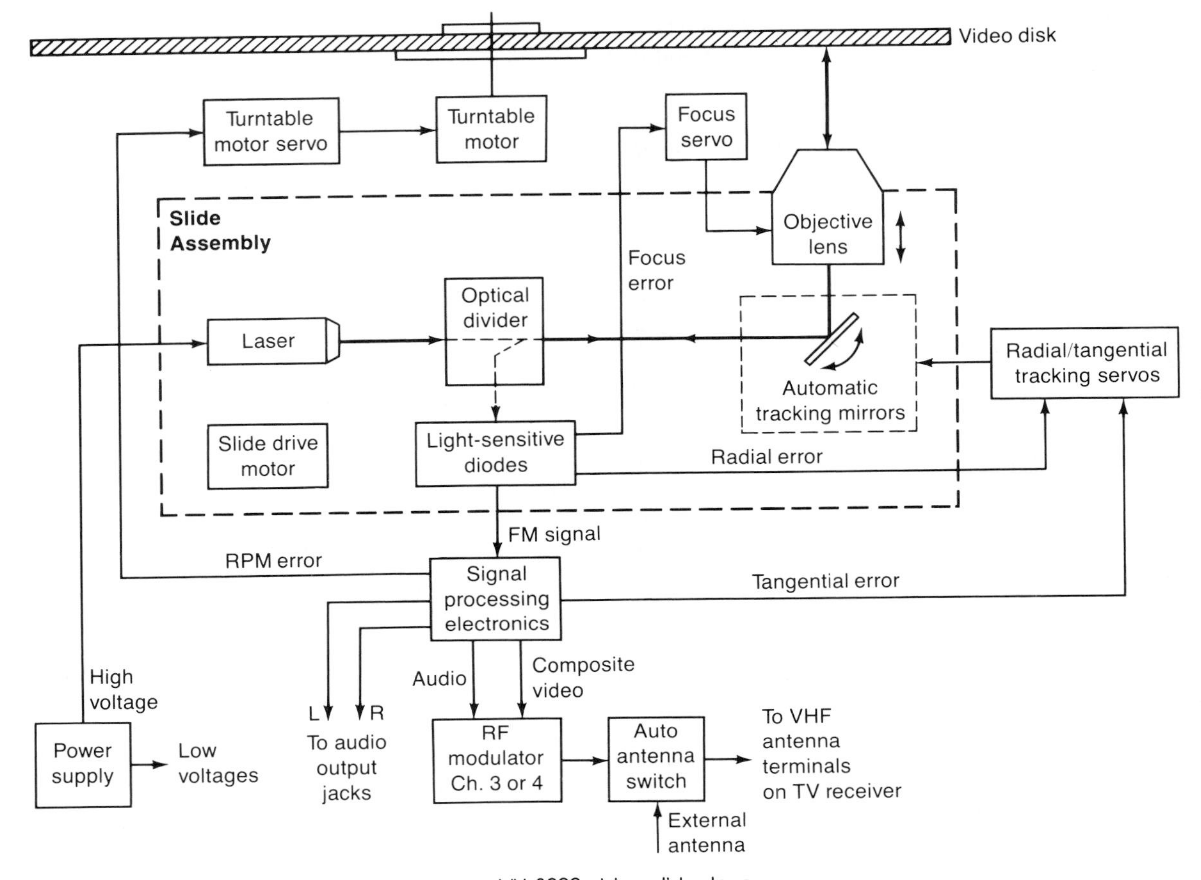

Fig. 10-26 Basic block diagram of Magnavox VH-8000 video disk player.

Figure 10-25*b* shows how the video and audio FM waveforms are combined to record pit variations on the disk. The two waves are added. Then the combined wave is clipped symmetrically. Since it is an FM signal, the amplitude clipping does not change the signal variations. The time duration of each half-cycle in the signal waveform determines the length of each pit.

OPTICAL PLAYBACK SYSTEM Refer to Fig. 10-26 to see how the pit variations on the video disk are converted to signal output. The entire optical system is housed in a slide assembly at the center of the illustration. The assembly traverses the bottom of the disk from the hub outward to the edge. One advantage of moving from the inside outward is that probably it would be easier to play disks of different sizes because the starting position is always the same.

In the slide assembly there is a servo-controlled objective lens. The lens focuses light on the disk and receives the reflected light. The servo that drives this lens keeps the reflected light in focus for the light-sensitive diodes that convert reflected light values to an FM playback signal.

Two servo-actuated tracking mirrors in the

slide assembly detect and correct tracking errors. The mirror for radial tracking tilts to keep the system at the center of the tracks of pits being scanned. Another mirror tilts in a direction tangent to the pit spiral. This mirror corrects for time-base error caused by small changes in rotation and by the effects of an off-center hub on the disk. Variations in chroma burst in the playback signal control the tangential tracking mirror. The system is a form of electromechanical correction for time-base error in the color signal.

In the optical system, the key to separation of the light beams is their direction of polarization. Light output from the laser is polarized vertically. A diffraction grating divides the light beam into three parts, one for reading the disk pits and the other two for tracking correction. Light focused on the disk is made to have circular polarization, in one direction. The reflected light has circular polarization in the opposite direction. This polarization is changed to horizontal for the light-sensitive diodes that produce the output signal.

Finally, the signal processing electronic circuits convert the FM playback signal to video and audio output. Then the baseband signals modulate an RF carrier for channel 3 or channel 4 to feed to the television receiver for playback. This method of interfacing with the receiver is the same as with VCR machines.

Test Point Questions 10-11

Answers at End of Chapter

Answer True or False.

a. A laser source produces coherent light.

b. The recorded pits on an optical video disk vary in depth.

c. The color-under process is necessary in optical video disk recording.

d. In Fig. 10-25*a*, the recorded frequency for the blanking level is 8 MHz.

10-12 CAPACITANCE DISKS

The video disk developed by RCA uses spiral V grooves on which a diamond stylus rides, as shown in Fig. 10-27. Information is recorded by varying the depth of the groove on the disk. At the trailing edge of the stylus is a tiny metal electrode that serves as one plate of a capacitor. The disk itself, made of a conductive material, acts as the other plate. The dielectric is the space between the electrode on the pickup and the groove. The capacitance decreases as the groove becomes deeper. In playback, the changes in capacitance are made to vary the resonant frequency of a high-frequency oscillator to provide the output signal.

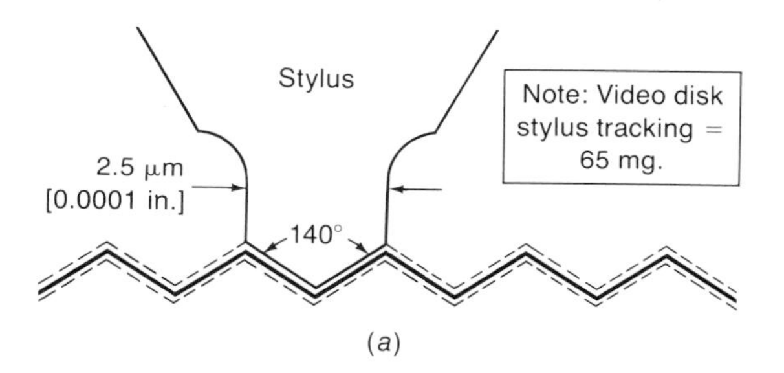

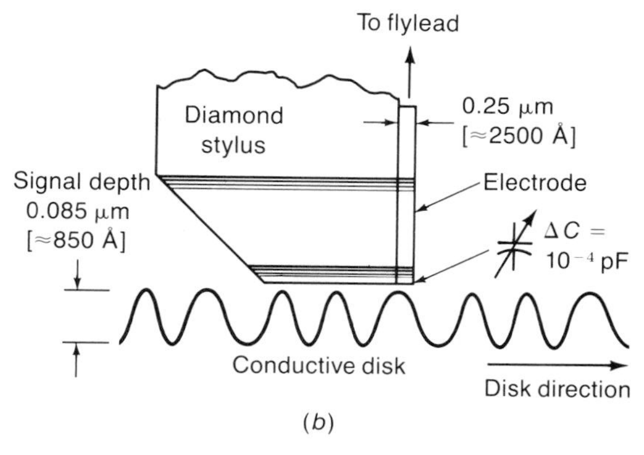

Fig. 10-27 Stylus-groove contact in capacitance disk system. 1 μm = 10^{-6} m. (*a*) Front view. (*b*) Side view. (*RCA*)

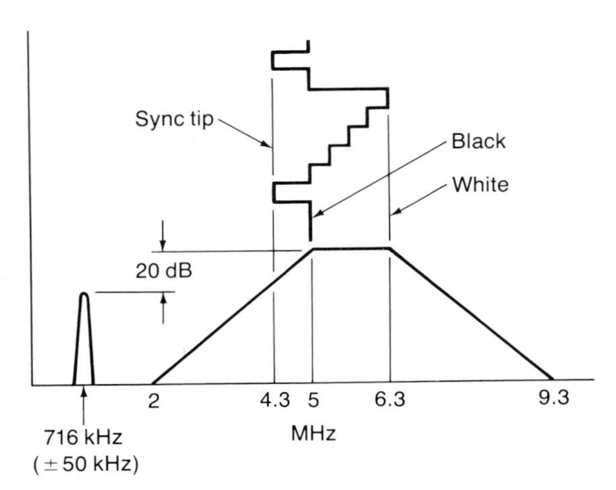

Fig. 10-28 Spectrum of modulation frequencies in CED system.

The capacitance disk must be enclosed in a plastic cover, called a *disk caddy,* for protection. The caddy unlocks when the disk is inserted into the player, so that the disk is left in the player as the caddy is removed.

SPECTRUM OF MODULATION FREQUENCIES

As in the VCR and optical disk systems, frequency modulation is employed to carry the video information. The frequency deviation ranges from 4.3 MHz for tip of sync to 6.3 MHz for maximum white, as shown in Fig. 10-28. In addition, the audio signal is at 716 kHz with a frequency swing of ±50 kHz.

Similar to the color-under system for the VCR, the 3.58-MHz chroma signal is heterodyned down to 1.53 MHz. For the CED, this method is called *buried-subcarrier encoding.*

PLAYBACK SIGNAL The maximum variation in capacitance C with groove depth has the very small value of 10 pF. To make this C effective, it is part of a UHF-tuned circuit that is formed with a resonant section of transmission line. The resonant frequency is 910 MHz with maximum capacitance. As the C decreases, the resonant frequency can increase to 920 MHz.

In addition, output from a UHF oscillator operating at 915 MHz is loosely coupled into the variable tuned circuit. As a result, the oscillator frequency is at the sloping side of the response curve for the resonant line section. The circuit arrangement is illustrated in Fig. 10-29*a,* with the response curve shown in Fig. 10-29*b.*

The resonant frequency of the tuned circuit varies as the stylus capacitance changes. Then the oscillator output at 915 MHz is at different points on the response curve, with higher or

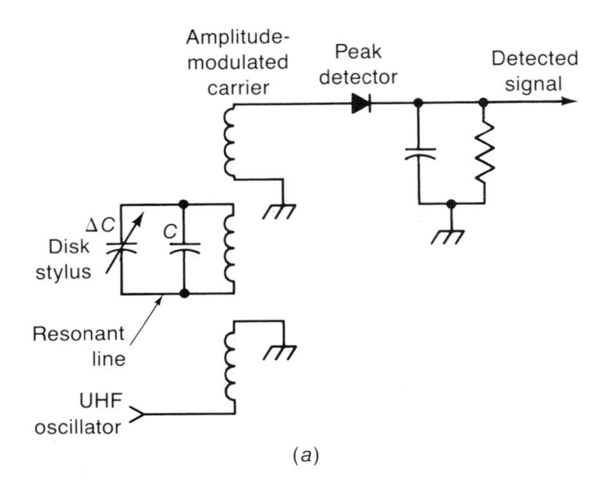

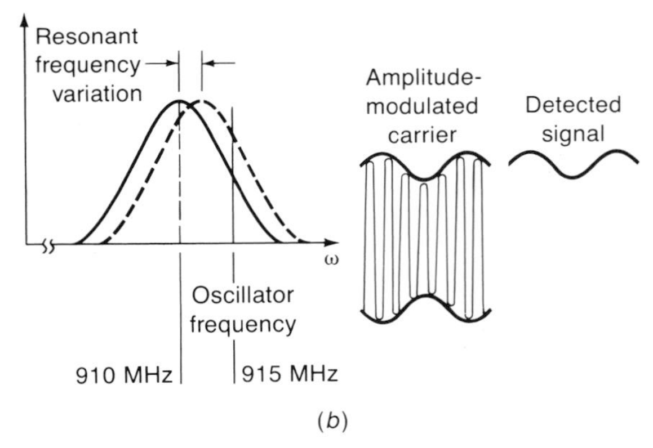

Fig. 10-29 Producing the playback signal from capacitance variations in CED system. (*a*) Circuit arrangement. (*b*) Frequency-response curve showing slope detection of 915-MHz modulated carrier signal.

lower amplitudes. Effectively, the action provides slope detection of an FM signal. In this way, the frequency changes in the recorded signal are converted to amplitude changes. Then a simple diode detector recovers the signal information from the amplitude variations of the envelope on the 915-MHz carrier signal.

CED DISK SPEED The RCA disk stores eight fields on each disk rotation. Thus the rotational speed is $60/8 = 7.5$ rps, or $7.5 \times 60 = 450$ rpm. The disk drive is provided by a multipole hysteresis motor that is locked into 450 rpm by the power-line frequency.

TRACKING The tiny grooves, about 10,000 per inch, do not allow enough lateral pressure alone to guide the stylus. Instead, the pickup is supported by a short arm that is servo-driven to cross the record radially. The motor that drives the arm is servo-controlled by sensor plates on either side of the stylus assembly. The plates have a 260-kHz control signal coupled through the pickup output lead, which is called the *flylead.* As a result of the servocontrol, the stylus stays in the center of the grooves.

GROOVE LOCK As in ordinary phonograph records, a defect in the disk surface can make the stylus stay in one particular groove. To prevent this problem in the CED system, a field identification number is encoded in the vertical blanking of the video signal. This number becomes part of the readout signal in playback. It is compared with a predicted field number that is based on shaft revolutions. Lack of agreement in the numbers activates a "kicker" system which advances the stylus four frames at a time until the field numbers correspond.

VHD SYSTEM A variation of the variable-capacitance disk has been developed by Japan Victor Company (JVC), and it is called the very high density (VHD) system. The disk also has pits of varying depth, but there are no grooves. As

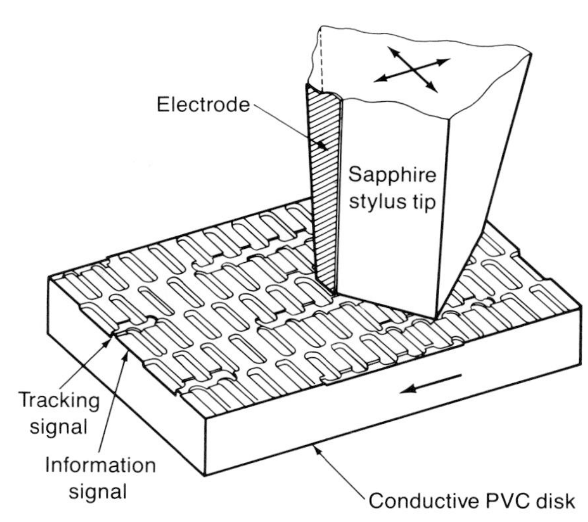

Fig. 10-30 Stylus-disk contact in VHD system. (*JVC*)

a result, more information can be recorded in tracks that are very close, as shown in Fig. 10-30. The diamond stylus is quite wide, straddling several tracks. However, the pickup electrode is narrow enough to pick up signals in each track of recorded information. Tracking signals on both sides are used to guide the stylus.

The audio and video signals are FM-encoded with a 6.6-MHz video carrier frequency. The maximum playing time is 1 h each side. There are two frames, or four fields, per disk revolution. So the disk speed is $60/4 = 15$ rps, or $15 \times 60 = 900$ rpm.

Test Point Questions 10-12

Answers at End of Chapter

Answer True or False.

a. The CED and VHD systems both use capacitance variations for the signal.

b. The deeper the pit in a disk, the greater the capacitance.

c. A color-under system is used in the CED method but not for optical disks.

d. Disk rotation is 60 rpm in the CED system.

SUMMARY

1. Video signals can be recorded on either magnetic tape or plastic disks. Generally the video cassette recorder (VCR) is used for consumer equipment for recording and playback on tape. Disks are used only for playback.
2. For VCR machines, the two formats are Betamax and video home system (VHS). Both use ½-in. tape, but the two systems are not compatible.
3. Typical playing time is 2, 4, 6, or 8 h for video cassettes. The tape travels from the supply reel at the left to the takeup reel at the right.
4. The two types of video disks are optical disks and capacitance disks. In the optical system, a laser beam is reflected from pits in the disk. With the capacitive electronic disk (CED), a stylus reads the pit variations as changes in capacitance.
5. Generally video signals are recorded as the modulation on an FM carrier at a higher frequency, in order to reduce the octave range of frequencies. The carrier also serves as ac bias for the color video recording.
6. VCR machines use helical-scan or slant-track recording, with diagonal tracks of video signal across the tape. A longitudinal track across the top edge is used for the audio signal, and there is a control track across the bottom.
7. The video recording head rotates at high velocity in order to provide a fast writing speed for signal frequencies in the megahertz range.
8. In the VHS and Betamax systems, the luminance information is recorded as an FM signal with a center frequency of 3.4 or 3.5 MHz. These values are shown in Fig. 10-6.
9. In the color-under process used in VHS and Betamax recorders, the 3.58-MHz chroma signal is heterodyned down to a lower frequency of 629 or 688 kHz for recording. The purpose is to shift the color frequencies away from frequencies for the FM luminance signal. In the playback circuits, though, the color-under signal is raised to 3.58 MHz.
10. In VCR machines, the rotating video scanner has two recording heads mounted 180° apart. Each head records or plays back one field for each slant track.
11. Head-switching is necessary, but there is some overlap between fields. Skew error caused by incorrect back tension on the tape, can produce a temporary loss of *H* sync at the bottom of the picture in playback.
12. Servocontrol systems are the features that make video recording practical. Servocontrol is necessary for frequency and phase regulation of the scanner head. Also, the capstan that meters out the tape at constant speed is servo-controlled, and the back tension on the tape is regulated mechanically.
13. The control track along the bottom of the tape has timing pulses for each field. The pulses are recorded and played back by a stationary control-track head. Their function is to make the tape speeds in recording and playback exactly the same.
14. In the zero guard-band system, there is no unused space between the slant tracks for the video signal. To minimize interference between tracks, the

two recording heads are tilted slightly in opposite directions. In addition, electronic circuits are used with a comb filter to cancel chroma crosstalk from adjacent tracks.

SELF-EXAMINATION

Answers at Back of Book

Choose (a), (b), (c), or (d).

1. How many octaves is the frequency range of 1 to 8 MHz? (a) 1, (b) 2, (c) 3, (d) 8.
2. Which system can be used for both recording and playback? (a) CED, (b) VHD, (c) laser disk, (d) VHS.
3. How many TV fields are recorded on one slant track of tape? (a) 1, (b) 2, (c) 4, (d) 60.
4. The video heads rotate at high velocity to increase the (a) tape speed, (b) writing speed, (c) reel rotation, (d) tape tension.
5. A typical frequency for the FM luminance signal in VCR recording is (a) 0.1 MHz, (b) 3.5 MHz, (c) 10 MHz, (d) 680 kHz.
6. Which of the following applies to the color-under technique? (a) Chroma amplitudes are decreased. (b) Chroma frequencies are reduced. (c) Luminance frequencies are decreased. (d) Chroma and luminance frequencies are reduced.
7. What oscillator frequency is needed to heterodyne 629 kHz up to 3.58 MHz? (a) 3 MHz, (b) 4.21 MHz, (c) 6.3 MHz, (d) 10 MHz.
8. A comb filter is used to (a) cancel chroma crosstalk, (b) separate white from black, (c) clip the sync from blanking, (d) separate alternating from direct current.
9. Switching for each field is required for the (a) audio head, (b) control-track head, (c) video heads, (d) erase head.
10. Servocontrol of speed and phase is used for the (a) control head, (b) erase head, (c) audio head, (d) video head scanner.
11. The part that rotates to meter out the tape at constant speed is the (a) control head, (b) erase head, (c) entrance guide, (d) capstan.
12. To make the tape speed the same in playback as in recording, the tape speed is regulated by the (a) audio track, (b) control-track pulses, (c) video slant tracks, (d) erase head.
13. Tilting the video head gaps is necessary with the (a) color-under, (b) zero guard bands, (c) FM luminance signal, (d) long-play tapes.
14. Which system uses a laser light beam for playback? (a) CED, (b) VHD, (c) Betamax, (d) VLP.
15. In the CED system, the disk capacitance varies with the (a) pit depth, (b) disk size, (c) speed of rotation, (d) wavelength of the scanning light.

ESSAY QUESTIONS

1. Explain briefly how a VCR is hooked up with a TV receiver.
2. What is the purpose of using an FM signal for video recording? Why is FM better than AM for this application?
3. What is the purpose of using rotating heads for video recording?
4. Define writing speed. Which moves slower, the tape or the recording head?
5. Give typical values for **(a)** the head gap on a video head and **(b)** the tape speed for 2-h play of a video cassette.
6. What is meant by the null frequency f_n in Fig. 10-5?
7. What is the frequency range of the FM luminance signal for recording in the VHS and Betamax systems?
8. What is the frequency range of the color-under signal for recording chroma information in the VHS and Betamax systems?
9. What are two advantages of the color-under technique?
10. Draw an illustration of the recorded tracks on magnetic tape for video, audio, and control-pulse signals.
11. What is the function of the control track?
12. Describe briefly two erase functions in the VCR.
13. Explain briefly three servocontrol systems in the VCR.
14. List the functions of the rotating and stationary heads in the VCR.
15. Describe the construction and function of the capstan for tape travel in the VCR.
16. Name two features of the video tape cassette.
17. What is meant by skew error in the VCR?
18. Name one advantage and one disadvantage of the zero guard-band system for video recording.
19. What is meant by canted heads for video recording?
20. What is the purpose of a comb filter?
21. What systems are indicated by VHS, VLP, CED, and VHD?
22. What is the unique feature of a laser light beam?
23. Compare the disk systems using light reflection and capacitance variation.
24. Compare the CED and VHD systems for capacitance disks.

PROBLEMS

Answers to Odd-Numbered Problems at Back of Book

1. Using Formula 10-1 for the recorded wavelength, calculate λ in meters for a tape speed of 33.35 mm/s and frequency of 3.5 MHz in video recorders.
2. Calculate λ in inches for a tape speed of 1⅞ ips and a frequency of 10 kHz in audio recorders.

3. What frequency is 10 octaves above 30 Hz?
4. How many octaves are there between 4 and 8 MHz?
5. Using Formula 10-2 for the null frequency f_n in recording, calculate f_n for a writing speed of 24 m/s and recorded wavelength λ of 0.6×10^{-6} m.
6. What value of writing speed is needed with $\lambda = 0.6 \times 10^{-6}$ m and $f_n =$ 12 MHz?
7. Calculate the highest and lowest frequencies for a subcarrier signal at 629 kHz with bandwidth of ±500 kHz.

SPECIAL QUESTIONS

1. Which method do you like better, video tape or disks? Explain why briefly.
2. Name one application of laser light other than the videodisk.
3. How would you hook up a VCR, disk player, and video game to one TV receiver?

ANSWERS TO TEST POINT QUESTIONS

10-1 **a.** T
b. F
c. T
d. F

10-2 **a.** Gap
b. Thinner
c. 2

10-3 **a.** F
b. T
c. T

10-4 **a.** Luminance
b. Color-under
c. 629 kHz
d. 5 to 6 MHz

10-5 **a.** One
b. More
c. Bottom
d. Increases

10-6 **a.** T
b. T
c. T
d. T

10-7 **a.** Control and audio
b. Capstan
c. Snow
d. 29.97 Hz

10-8 **a.** 6 or 7°
b. Luminance
c. $1H$ or 63.5 μs
d. 3.579545 MHz

10-9 **a.** T
b. F
c. T
d. F

10-10 **a.** T
b. F
c. T

10-11 **a.** T
b. F
c. F
d. T

10-12 **a.** T
b. F
c. T
d. F

11

TELEVISION TRANSMISSION

The method of transmitting the amplitude-modulated picture signal is similar to the more familiar system of radio broadcasting. In both cases, the amplitude of an RF carrier wave is made to vary with the modulating voltage. The modulation is the baseband signal. For television, the baseband signal is a composite video signal. Television broadcasting is really like a radio system, but it includes both pictures and sound. The associated sound signal is transmitted by frequency modulation (FM) on a separate carrier wave in the same broadcast channel as the picture signal.

Note that the term *picture signal* is used here to mean the modulated carrier wave. The video signal is the signal for a picture tube. The video signal for television corresponds to the audio signal for a sound system. More details of the AM picture signal and the associated FM sound signal are explained in the following sections:

11-1 NEGATIVE TRANSMISSION

As shown in Fig. 11-1, peak white in the video signal produces the lowest amplitudes in the AM picture signal. This result is accomplished by negative-polarity modulation. The modulating signal is applied in the polarity that reduces the RF carrier amplitude for peak white in the video signal. Tip of sync produces the maximum carrier amplitude, which is the 100 percent level.

Note the following relative amplitudes for the amplitude-modulated RF picture signal in Fig. 11-1:

Tip of sync = 100%
Blanking level = 75%
Black setup = 67.5%
Maximum white = 10 to 15%, or 12.5%

The sync pulses occupy the top 25 percent of the carrier amplitude. The picture information is between 67.5 percent for black and an average of 12.5 percent for peak white. Although the chroma modulation is not shown here, it is multiplexed on the RF picture carrier signal with the luminance values in the same range as black-and-white information.

The carrier signal does not go below 10 percent because there is distortion when the amplitude becomes zero. Furthermore, the intercarrier sound signal in the receiver cannot be produced without the picture carrier signal.

All these relative amplitudes are the same for the top or the bottom of the modulation envelope. The positive and negative half-cycles of the RF carrier are equal, which produces a symmetric envelope of amplitude variations. This factor explains why the modulated signal must be rectified to recover the baseband signal in the modulation envelope.

ADVANTAGES OF NEGATIVE TRANSMISSION

One advantage of negative transmission is that noise pulses in the transmitted RF signal increase the carrier amplitude toward black, instead of white. This effect makes noise streaks in the picture less obvious.

The transmitter uses less power in negative transmission. Since typical pictures are mostly white, the carrier amplitude is low most of the time when the picture information is transmitted.

Perhaps most important is the practical advantage of having the tip of sync as a reference for the carrier strength, independent of picture information. A peak diode detector circuit can easily provide dc voltage that is proportional to the amount of the RF carrier signal. The dc voltage is used for bias in the automatic gain control (AGC) system of the receiver.

IRE AND CARRIER AMPLITUDES In the composite video signal used as the baseband signal for modulation, usually the relative amplitudes are

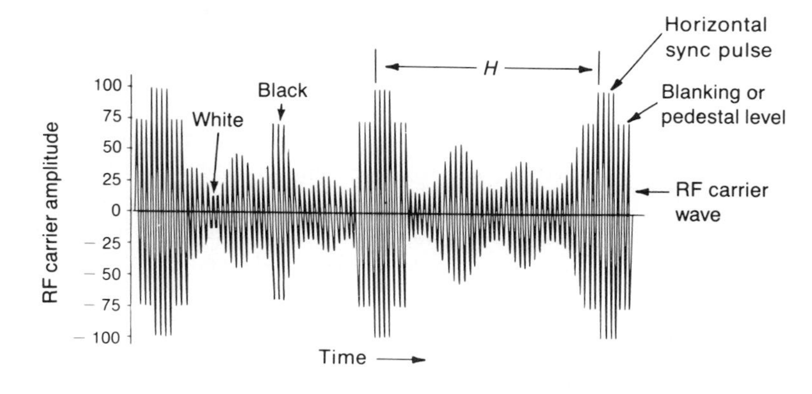

Fig. 11-1 Transmitted picture carrier wave, amplitude-modulated by composite video signal.

TABLE 11-1
COMPARISON OF IRE AND CARRIER AMPLITUDES

LEVEL	LEVELS OF VIDEO, IRE UNITS	RF CARRIER LEVEL, PERCENT
Tip of sync	−40	100
Blanking	0	75
Black setup	10	67.5
Peak white	100	12.5
Not used	120	0

indicated on the IRE scale. As shown in Chap. 7, "Video Signal Analysis," the composite video signal varies from −40 IRE units for the tip of sync to zero for the blanking level to +100 IRE units for peak white. The corresponding amplitudes in Fig. 11-1 are the 100 percent carrier level for the tip of sync, 75 percent for the blanking level, and 12.5 percent for peak white.

More details of the comparison are given in Table 11-1. In summary, the 40 IRE units of sync correspond to the top 25 percent of the carrier amplitude. The 10 IRE units for black setup correspond to 7.5 percent of the carrier signal. The IRE level of 100 becomes 12.5 percent of the carrier amplitude for peak white. Actually, 20 more IRE units, up to 120, correspond to the 12.5 percent of carrier amplitude that is not used for modulation. This percentage of carrier signal is calculated as 20/160 IRE units, which is 0.125, or 12.5 percent.

Test Point Questions 11-1

Answers at End of Chapter

With negative transmission, give the percentages of carrier signal amplitude for the following:

a. Maximum white
b. Blanking
c. Tip of sync

11-2 VESTIGIAL SIDEBAND TRANSMISSION

The AM picture signal is not transmitted as a normal double-sideband signal. Instead, a part of the lower sideband is filtered out before transmission, and a vestige of the sidebands remains. The purpose is to reduce the frequency band needed for the video modulation in the picture signal. Specifically, a 6-MHz television broadcast channel is used instead of 8 MHz, or more, that would be needed for double sidebands with 4-MHz modulation.

AMPLITUDE MODULATION The example in Fig. 11-2 illustrates how an AM signal is produced, in order to analyze the sidebands. This method is high-level modulation in the output circuit of the final RF amplifier. Small numbers are used for the frequencies to simplify the calculations. The RF carrier frequency is taken as 100 kHz. It is modulated by 5000 Hz, as an audio frequency for the baseband modulation. The V^+ for the RF amplifier is assumed to be a 600-V dc supply voltage. The peak value of the sine wave modulating voltage also equals 600 V, in order to have 100 percent modulation.

Note that the audio voltage across the secondary of the modulation transformer T_2 is in series with V^+ for the RF amplifier. Therefore, the effective supply voltage for the RF amplifier varies at the audio rate. As a result, the amplitude of the RF output varies in the same way. Maximum and minimum values are listed in Table 11-2 for one cycle of audio modulation.

The varying amplitudes of the RF carrier wave provide an envelope that corresponds to the audio modulating signal. Note that both the positive and the negative peaks of the RF carrier wave are equal above and below the center axis. They have exactly the same amplitude variations. The envelope is symmetric because any point on the

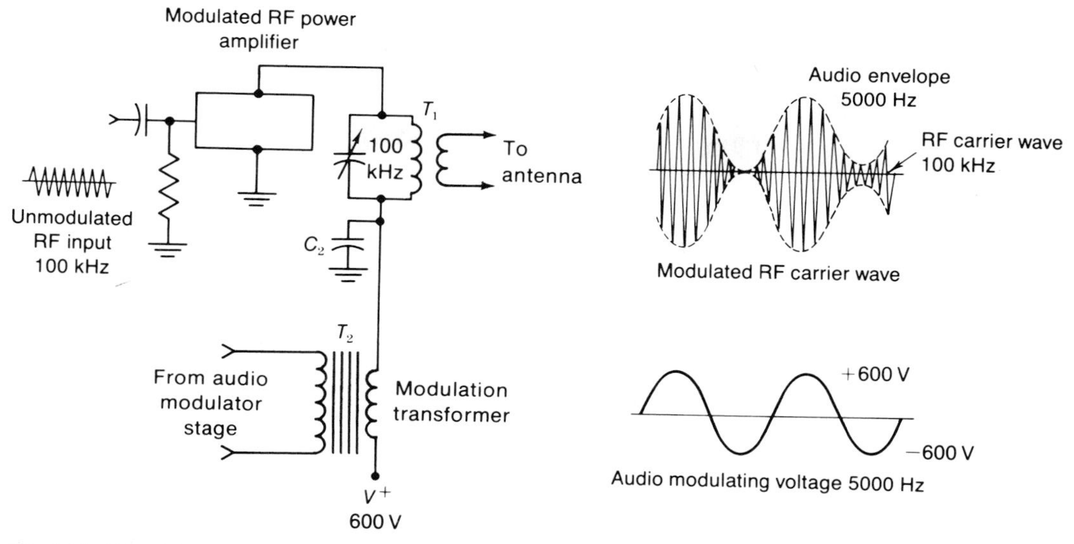

Fig. 11-2 Circuit for amplitude modulation. The 100-kHz RF carrier is amplitude-modulated by the 5000-Hz baseband signal.

audio waveform includes many cycles of the RF carrier signal.

The result of the modulation in this case is that an AM signal using an RF carrier at 100 kHz is produced. Its amplitude varies at the audio rate of 5000 Hz, or 5 kHz. Either the top or the bottom envelope corresponds to the audio modulating signal.

SIDE-CARRIER FREQUENCIES Refer to Fig. 11-3. The AM wave is equal to the sum of the unmodulated RF carrier and two RF side frequencies. Note that the carrier signal and its side frequencies all have a constant level. Also, the amplitude of the side carrier is one-half the unmodulated carrier level, for 100 percent modulation.

Each side frequency differs from the carrier by the audio modulating frequency. The upper side frequency in this example is

$$100 \text{ kHz} + 5 \text{ kHz} = 105 \text{ kHz}$$

TABLE 11-2
MODULATION VALUES FOR FIG. 11-2

AUDIO VOLTAGE	V^+ VOLTAGE	RF AMPLIFIER VOLTAGE	MODULATED RF SIGNAL AMPLITUDE
0	600	600	Carrier level
+600	600	1200	Double carrier level
0	600	600	Carrier level
−600	600	0	Zero
0	600	600	Carrier level

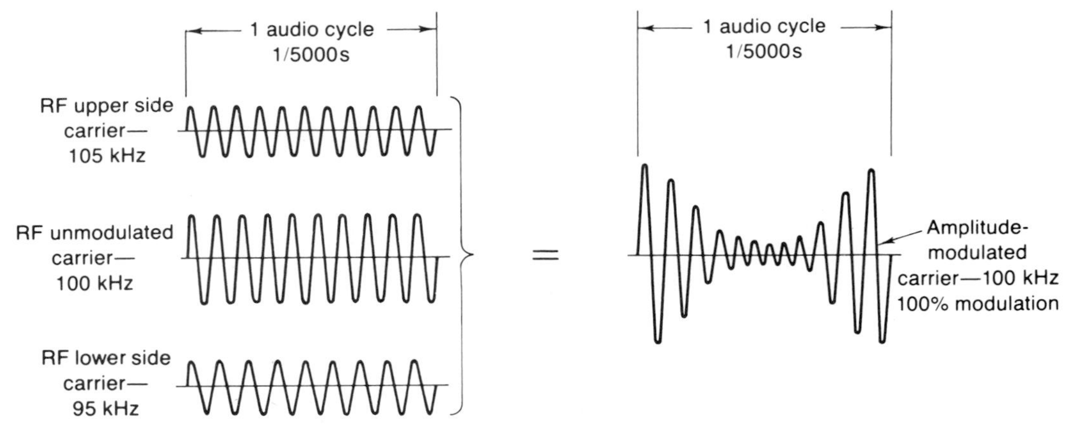

Fig. 11-3 How an AM wave corresponds to unmodulated RF carrier plus two RF side carrier signals produced by modulation. This example is for one modulating frequency.

The lower side frequency is

$$100 \text{ kHz} - 5 \text{ kHz} = 95 \text{ kHz}$$

The process of amplitude modulation automatically produces the upper and lower side frequencies. An AM signal can be considered in terms of either its amplitude variations or its side frequencies. The two concepts are equivalent. Actually, the three waveforms at the left in Fig. 11-3, when added graphically, equal the waveform at the right.

Side frequencies are produced because the modulated RF carrier wave is distorted slightly from a pure sine wave by the amplitude variations. A sharper slope generates higher frequencies. Less slope corresponds to lower frequencies. The new frequency components produced are the side frequencies.

The RF side frequencies should not be confused with the audio envelope in the AM signal. The envelope has a 5000-Hz audio frequency in this example. However, the RF side frequencies are 105 and 95 kHz, close to the carrier signal frequency of 100 kHz.

SIDEBANDS When the carrier is modulated with a signal that has a band of frequency components, each modulating frequency produces a pair of side frequencies. In each pair, one side frequency is higher than the carrier frequency and one is lower. All the upper side frequencies are considered as the *upper sideband,* with all the lower side frequencies being the *lower sideband.* The double sidebands are illustrated in Fig. 11-4, for modulation with a continuous range of audio frequencies from 0 to 5000 Hz.

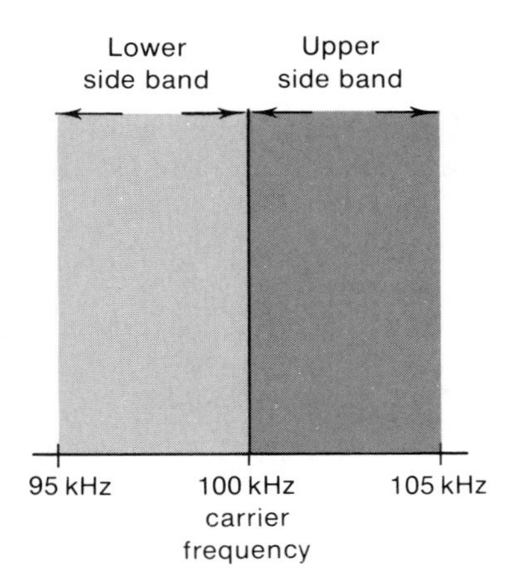

Fig. 11-4 Double sidebands resulting from amplitude modulation of 100-kHz carrier with all modulating frequencies up to 5 kHz.

The sidebands determine the bandwidth needed for an AM signal. In this example, the carrier is at 100 kHz, but the bandwidth of ±5 kHz, or 10 kHz total, is needed to include the modulation. Any AM signal automatically has double sidebands.

The fact that an AM signal has frequency components in the sidebands does not make it like frequency modulation. In FM, the RF carrier frequency varies in step with the *amount* of audio modulating *voltage,* not its frequency. Frequency modulation is explained in greater detail in Sec. 11-5.

SINGLE-SIDEBAND (SSB) TRANSMISSION Figure 11-5, in which just one side frequency is transmitted with the carrier signal, illustrates SSB transmission. Note that the resultant modulated wave has amplitude variations for only 50 percent modulation, instead of the 100 percent modulation produced with both sidebands. In Fig. 11-5, the AM wave varies 50 percent above and below the unmodulated carrier level. Therefore, an SSB signal has one-half the percentage modulation compared with a double-sideband (DSB) signal.

Except for the amount of amplitude modulation, the envelope of the carrier plus one sideband has the same information as double sidebands. Note that the AM envelope in Fig. 11-5 still corresponds to the audio modulating voltage.

Furthermore, the SSB envelope is not cut off at the top or bottom of the AM wave. Note that the radio frequencies for one sideband are filtered out, but the audio envelope is not. To cut off one side of the envelope, rectification of the AM signal would be necessary.

VESTIGIAL SIDEBANDS In this method of broadcasting the AM picture signal, all the upper sideband but only a part, or vestige, of the lower sideband is used. Specifically, the upper sideband has all video modulating frequencies up to 4 MHz. The lower sideband, however, includes video modulating frequencies for only 0 to 0.75 MHz, approximately.

The effects of the unequal modulation are corrected in the receiver by its IF response. The way in which this method conserves bandwidth can be seen from the channel frequencies in Fig. 11-9 on page 267. In short, 4-MHz video modulation can be used in the 6-MHz channel. Note that the picture carrier frequency is not at the center of the channel, to allow for the different sidebands. The vestigial sideband transmission used for the AM picture signal is designated by the FCC as emission type A5C.

Test Point Questions 11-2

Answers at End of Chapter

Answer True or False for vestigial sideband transmission of the AM picture signal.

a. All the upper sideband is transmitted.
b. None of the lower sideband is transmitted.
c. With 0.1-MHz modulation of a 61.25-MHz carrier, the side frequencies are 61.15 and 61.35 MHz.

11-3 TELEVISION BROADCAST CHANNELS

Each station is assigned a 6-MHz channel by the FCC for transmitting its AM picture signal

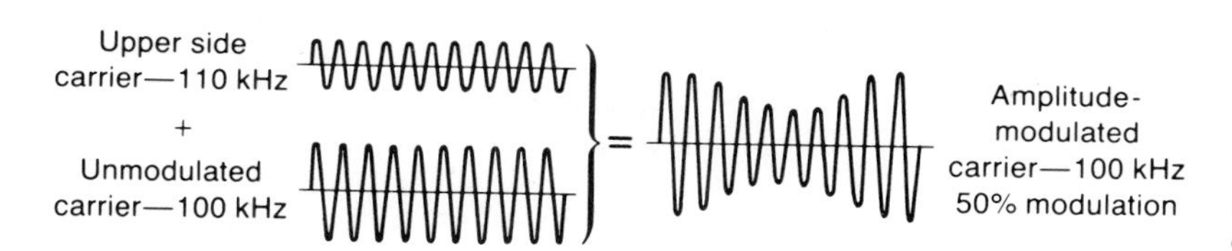

Fig. 11-5 AM wave consisting of unmodulated carrier and only one side carrier.

and FM sound signal. Vestigial sideband transmission is used for the picture signal, to reduce bandwidth. The picture and sound are individual signals on separate carrier waves separated by 4.5 MHz. For color, the 3.58-MHz chroma subcarrier is multiplexed on the picture carrier as a video modulating signal.

ASSIGNED CHANNELS For the modulation process, the picture carrier must have a frequency much higher than the highest video modulating frequency of 4 MHz. Therefore, the television channels are assigned to the VHF and UHF bands. Remember that the VHF band includes 30 to 300 MHz and the UHF band 300 to 3000 MHz. The frequencies for all the VHF and UHF channels are listed in Table 11-3. Usually the channels are considered in the three groups indicated by horizontal lines on the table, because of the big separation in frequencies.

The number of channels in any one locality depends on its population. A small city may have only one channel. New York City has 12 stations, including VHF and UHF channels. Many cities have one or more channels reserved for public television or educational television.

LOWBAND VHF CHANNELS The lowband VHF channels include channels 2, 3, 4, 5, and 6 from 54 to 88 MHz. The band of 44 to 50 MHz used to be channel 1, but now these frequencies are assigned to other radio services because of interference problems. On rotary-switch tuners for the receiver, the channel 1 position is used for changing to UHF operation.

HIGHBAND VHF CHANNELS These channels include 7, 8, 9, 10, 11, 12, and 13 from 174 to 216 MHz in the VHF band. Note the big skip in frequencies from 88 MHz at the top of channel 6 to 174 MHz at the bottom of channel 7. The frequencies of 88 to 174 MHz not used for television channels are reserved for other services, including the 88- to 108-MHz band for commercial FM radio broadcasting.

UHF CHANNELS The UHF channels include channels 14 to 83 with frequencies of 470 to 890 MHz. Some of the upper UHF channels from 70 to 83 may be reserved for special services, such as educational TV broadcasting.

COCHANNEL STATIONS One channel can be used by many broadcast stations, but they must be far enough apart to minimize interference. The required separation is generally 170 to 220 mi [274 to 354 km] for VHF stations and 150 to 205 mi [241 to 330 km] for UHF stations. The transmission distance is less for UHF signals because of the high frequencies. Power output is typically 5 to 50 kW. An example of cochannel stations is the use of channel 4 in both New York and Connecticut.

ADJACENT CHANNELS An adjacent channel must be next in frequency, not just for the channel number. For instance, channels 4 and 5 are not adjacent because of a 4-MHz skip between 72 and 76 MHz. However, channels 2, 3, and 4 are adjacent. This example is illustrated in Fig. 11-6. The highband VHF channels 7 to 13 are all adjacent. Also, all the UHF channels are adjacent because of the continuous 6-MHz bands.

LOWER ADJACENT CHANNEL For the example of channels 2, 3, and 4 in Fig. 11-6, channel 2 is the lower adjacent channel with the receiver tuned to channel 3. When the receiver is tuned to channel 4, channel 3 becomes the lower adjacent channel.

UPPER ADJACENT CHANNEL With the receiver still tuned to channel 3, channel 4 is the upper adjacent channel. However, channel 5 is not adjacent when the receiver is tuned to channel 4.

CHANNEL INTERFERENCE Cochannel stations can interfere with each other in fringe areas be-

TABLE 11-3
TELEVISION CHANNEL ALLOCATIONS

CHANNEL NUMBER	FREQUENCY BAND, MHz	CHANNEL NUMBER	FREQUENCY BAND, MHz
1*	—	42	638–644
2	54–60	43	644–650
3	60–66	44	650–656
4	66–72	45	656–662
5	76–82	46	662–668
6	82–88	47	668–674
7	174–180	48	674–680
8	180–186	49	680–686
9	186–192	50	686–692
10	192–198	51	692–698
11	198–204	52	698–704
12	204–210	53	704–710
13	210–216	54	710–716
14	470–476	55	716–722
15	476–482	56	722–728
16	482–488	57	728–734
17	488–494	58	734–740
18	494–500	59	740–746
19	500–506	60	746–752
20	506–512	61	752–758
21	512–518	62	758–764
22	518–524	63	764–770
23	524–530	64	770–776
24	530–536	65	776–782
25	536–542	66	782–788
26	542–548	67	788–794
27	548–554	68	794–800
28	554–560	69	800–806
29	560–566	70†	806–812
30	566–572	71	812–818
31	572–578	72	818–824
32	578–584	73	824–830
33	584–590	74	830–836
34	590–596	75	836–842
35	596–602	76	842–848
36	602–608	77	848–854
37‡	608–614	78	854–860
38	614–620	79	860–866
39	620–626	80	866–872
40	626–632	81	872–878
41	632–638	82	878–884
		83	884–890

* The 44- to 50-MHz bank was television channel 1 but is now assigned to other services.
† Channels 70 to 83 are also allocated for land mobile radio. For television, these UHF channels are used for special services.
‡ Channel 37 is not available for TV assignment.

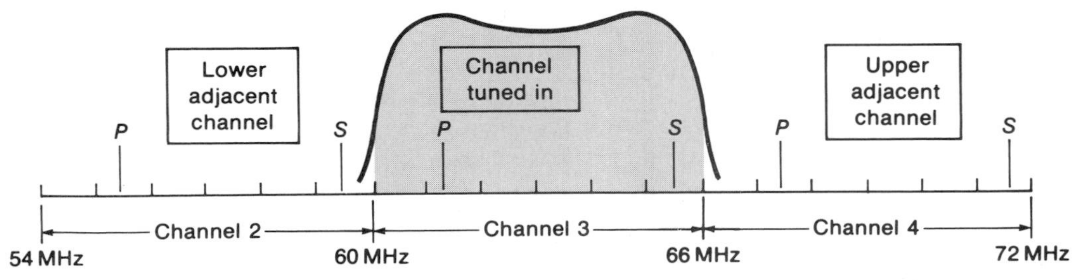

Fig. 11-6 Example of channels 2 and 4 as adjacent channels when receiver is tuned to channel 3.

tween the two transmitters. Usually there is a horizontal-bar pattern, called the *venetian-blind effect,* as shown in Fig. 11-7. The bars result from an audio-frequency beat between the two picture carrier signals, which are slightly offset in frequency.

With interference from an adjacent channel, some of the sidebands from the picture signal can beat with the desired picture carrier. Then picture information of the interfering station is superimposed on the desired picture. You may see an interfering picture moving across the screen. Most obvious is the black vertical bar produced by horizontal blanking, as shown in Fig. 11-8. This bar drifts from side to side because of the slight phase difference between the two signals. This interference is called the *windshield-wiper effect.*

Fig. 11-7 Venetian-blind effect caused by cochannel interference.

The remedy for cochannel interference is the use of a more directional antenna for the receiver. Cochannel stations are usually in different directions. The adjacent-channel selectivity of the receiver is determined by wave traps in the IF section.

Test Point Questions 11-3

Answers at End of Chapter

Answer True or False.

a. The picture and sound signals use separate carriers transmitted in one 6-MHz channel.
b. The UHF television channels are 40 MHz wide.
c. Channels 6 and 7 are most likely to have adjacent-channel interference.

11-4 STANDARD TELEVISION CHANNEL

Figure 11-9*a* illustrates how the picture and sound signals fit into the 6-MHz channel. The picture carrier frequency is not at the center of the channel, because of vestigial sideband transmission. Note the following spacings for the carrier frequencies:

Fig. 11-8 Windshield-wiper effect caused by interference from lower adjacent channel.

1. The picture carrier P is 1.25 MHz above the low end of the channel.
2. The sound carrier S is 4.5 MHz above the picture carrier, or S is 0.25 MHz below the top end of the channel.
3. The color subcarrier C is 3.58 MHz above the picture carrier, as video modulation in the upper sideband.

Specific frequencies for channel 3 are shown in Fig. 11-9*b*. The picture and sound carrier frequencies for all the television channels are listed in App. A.

EXAMPLES OF RF CHANNEL FREQUENCIES See Fig. 11-9*b* for channel 3, which is 60 to 66 MHz. The picture carrier is

$$P = 60 + 1.25 = 61.25 \text{ MHz}$$

The sound carrier is

$$S = 61.25 + 4.5 = 65.75 \text{ MHz}$$

The color subcarrier signal is

$$C = 61.25 + 3.58 = 64.83 \text{ MHz}$$

The sidebands of the FM sound signal are not shown. The FM sound signal requires a bandwidth of only 50 kHz, with a frequency deviation of ±25 kHz for 100 percent modulation.

VESTIGIAL SIDEBANDS OF THE PICTURE SIGNAL With vestigial sideband transmission, all the upper side frequencies up to 65.25 MHz are transmitted for 4-MHz video modulation. The values are 61.25 + 4.0 = 65.25 MHz. Higher

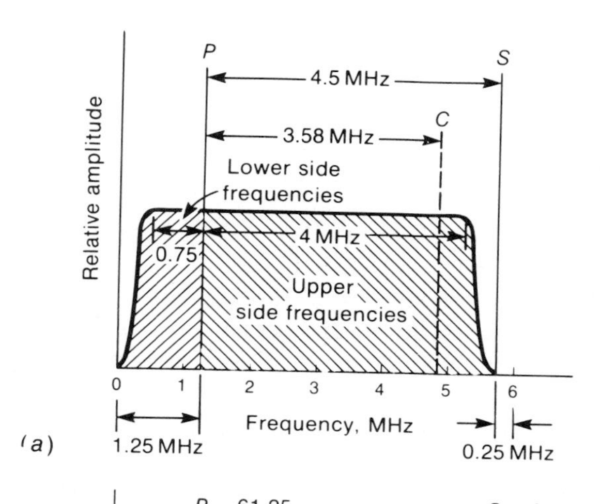

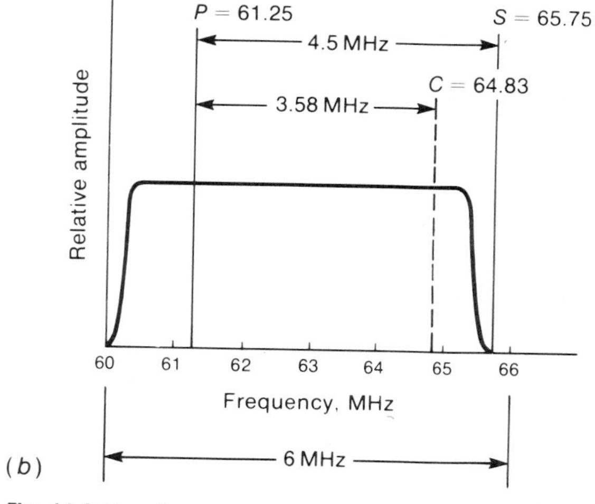

Fig. 11-9 How frequencies are used in standard 6-MHz television broadcast channel. P is picture carrier, S is sound carrier, C is chroma subcarrier. (*a*) Frequency separations, in general, for any channel. (*b*) Specific frequencies for channel 3 at 60 to 66 MHz.

side frequencies can interfere with the sound signal.

However, only that part of the lower sideband down to approximately 60.5 MHz is transmitted. This lower side frequency is for 0.75-MHz video modulation. Side frequencies below 60.5 MHz are at the low end of the channel or outside the channel.

When the video modulating voltage has a frequency of 0.75 MHz, both the upper and lower side frequencies are transmitted. The lower frequency is

$$61.25 - 0.75 = 60.5 \text{ MHz}$$

while the upper frequency is

$$61.25 + 0.75 = 62 \text{ MHz}$$

Both 60.5 and 62 MHz are in the channel. For this case, the AM picture carrier is a normal double-sideband signal. The same is true for any video modulating signal with a frequency less than 0.75 MHz.

However, for video modulation frequencies higher than 0.75 MHz, only the upper side frequencies are transmitted with normal amplitude. Consider 2-MHz video modulation. The upper side frequency is 61.25 + 2.0 = 63.25 MHz, which is in the channel. The lower side frequency is 61.25 − 2.0 = 59.25 MHz, which is outside the channel. In this case, only the upper side frequency is transmitted, as in single-sideband transmission. All the lower side frequencies that are below the channel are filtered out by a vestigial sideband filter at the transmitter.

The result is vestigial sideband transmission for the AM picture signal. In this method double-sideband transmission is used for video modulating frequencies of approximately 0.75 MHz or less. Single-sideband transmission is used for higher video modulating frequencies, from 0.75 up to 4 MHz.

The 3.58-MHz chroma subcarrier frequency is at 64.83 MHz as an upper side frequency of the modulated picture carrier in channel 3. In a receiver tuned to channel 3, the RF circuits must pass 64.83 MHz in order to have the color signal.

ADVANTAGE OF VESTIGIAL SIDEBAND TRANSMISSION With the picture carrier 1.25 MHz from the end of the channel, video modulating frequencies up to 4 MHz can be transmitted in the 6-MHz channel. A video-frequency limit of about 2.5 MHz would be necessary if double-sideband transmission were used with the picture carrier at the center of the channel.

It might seem desirable to place the picture carrier at the lower edge of the channel and use single-sideband transmission completely. However, this method is not practical. The undesirable lower side frequencies are eliminated by a filter, which cannot have ideal cutoff characteristics. The result is phase distortion for the side frequencies close to those of the carrier signal, which causes smear in the picture. Remember that the low video frequencies have the most important luminance information for large areas in the picture.

The compromise of vestigial sideband transmission is practically perfect. Lower side frequencies are removed only when they are far enough from the picture carrier to avoid phase distortion. The picture carrier itself and side frequencies close to the carrier are not attenuated.

COMPENSATING FOR VESTIGIAL SIDEBAND TRANSMISSION The picture signal has distortion in terms of the relative amplitudes for different modulation frequencies. Remember that a signal transmitted with only one sideband represents only 50 percent modulation, compared with double sidebands. In effect, this method is a low-frequency boost for the video modulating signal. However, the boost is corrected by deemphasizing the low video frequencies by the same amount in the IF amplifier of the television receiver.

Specifically, the IF picture carrier frequency at 45.75 MHz has 50 percent relative gain at the edge of the IF response curve. The transmitter RF output and the receiver IF gain complement each other exactly.

Test Point Questions 11-4

Answers at End of Chapter

List the values for the following frequencies in channel 4, which is 66 to 72 MHz.

a. Picture carrier

b. Upper side carrier for 3-MHz video modulation

c. Color subcarrier

d. Sound carrier

11-5 FM SOUND SIGNAL

Frequency modulation is used for the associated sound signal in order to gain the advantages of less noise and interference. The FM sound signal in television is essentially the same as in FM radio broadcasting except that the maximum frequency swing is ±25 kHz, instead of ±75 kHz.

A separate carrier, 4.5 MHz above the picture carrier, is used for the associated sound signal, with both in the standard 6-MHz television channel. The range of audio modulating frequencies is 50 to 15,000 Hz, as in FM radio, to allow reproduction of high-fidelity sound.

FREQUENCY CHANGES IN AN FM SIGNAL The idea of frequency modulation is illustrated in Fig. 11-10. Although the RF oscillator is tuned to 100 kHz, the frequency is changed by varying the capacitance C_V of the varactor diode. How much the oscillator frequency is changed depends on how much C_V changes, as its reverse voltage is varied by the 60-Hz modulating voltage. The rate of frequency changes in the RF output here is 60 Hz. Thus the FM output is an RF signal varying in frequency around 100 kHz, at the same rate as the 60-Hz modulation. A circuit such as this one is sometimes called a *wobbulator,* because the output frequency wobbles around the center value of 100 kHz. Small numbers are used here to simplify the values. Generally the VHF and UHF bands are used for FM signals.

Note that the frequency change of the RF oscillator can be made almost any amount and has no relation to the repetition rate of the frequency swings. For the same 60-Hz repetition rate, the oscillator frequency can change by ±10 kHz, ±20 kHz, or any number, depending on the amount of signal voltage applied to the varactor capacitor diode. Or, one value of frequency swing, such as ±10 kHz, can be produced at a rate faster or slower than 60 Hz by changing

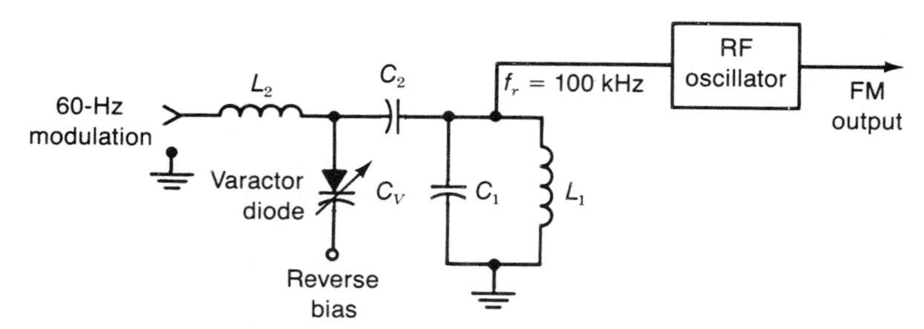

Fig. 11-10 A method of producing frequency modulation. Capacitive diode C_V varies oscillator frequency at rate of 60-Hz modulation. L_2 is an RF choke.

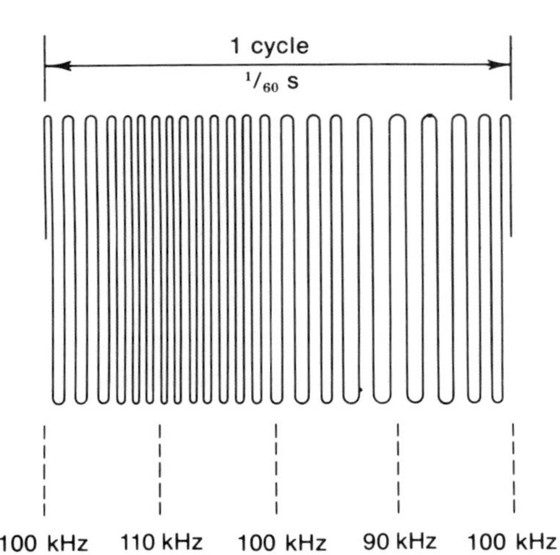

Fig. 11-11 FM output produced by circuit in Fig. 11-10. Amplitude is constant, but instantaneous frequency is continuously changing.

the frequency of the modulating voltage applied to the varactor.

Figure 11-11 illustrates the FM output from the oscillator in Fig. 11-10. The amplitude remains the same at all times, but the frequency is changing continuously. The maximum frequency change of the 100-kHz carrier in this example is ±10 kHz, corresponding to the peak voltage of the 60-Hz modulating signal. Values between zero and the peak voltage have frequency changes less than ±10 kHz. The repetition rate is 60 Hz. In this way, the information of the modulating signal is in the frequency changes of the RF carrier. The characteristics of an FM signal, compared with an AM signal, are summarized in Table 11-4.

CENTER FREQUENCY The frequency of the RF carrier without modulation, or when the modulating voltage is zero, is called the *center frequency.* In Figs. 11-10 and 11-11, the center frequency is 100 kHz. The center frequency is also called the *rest frequency.*

FREQUENCY DEVIATION The change from the center frequency is called the *frequency deviation.* For the example in Fig. 11-11, the frequency deviation is 10 kHz, from 100 kHz to either 110 or 90 kHz. The frequency deviation is generally taken for the maximum value at the peak of the audio modulating voltage.

FREQUENCY SWING When there are equal amounts of change above and below the center frequency, the total frequency swing is twice the deviation frequency. The opposite changes in frequency correspond to opposite polarities of the modulation. For the example of 10-kHz deviation, the frequency swing is ±10 kHz, or a total of 20 kHz.

PERCENTAGE OF MODULATION The ratio of actual frequency swing to the amount defined

TABLE 11-4
COMPARISON OF FM AND AM SIGNALS

FM	AM
Carrier amplitude is constant.	Carrier amplitude varies with modulation.
Carrier frequency varies with modulation.	Carrier frequency is constant.
Modulating-voltage *amplitude* determines RF carrier *frequency.*	Modulating-voltage *amplitude* determines RF carrier *amplitude.*
Modulating frequency is rate of frequency changes in the RF carrier wave.	Modulating frequency is rate of amplitude changes in the RF carrier wave.

by the FCC for 100 percent modulation, expressed as a percentage, is called the *percentage of modulation.* In FM radio, ±75 kHz is 100 percent modulation. For the TV sound signal, ±25 kHz is 100 percent modulation. Less swing is used to conserve space in the television channel.

As an example for the TV sound signal, suppose that the frequency swing is ±15 kHz. Then the percentage of modulation is

$$\frac{15\text{ kHz}}{25\text{ kHz}} = \frac{3}{5} = 0.6, \text{ or } 60\%$$

The same frequency swing of ±15 kHz would be 20 percent modulation for the FM radio broadcast system, since 15/75 = ⅕, or 20 percent.

The percentage of modulation varies with the intensity of the audio voltage. For weak audio, the audio voltage is small and there is little frequency swing, so there is a small percentage of modulation. The audio voltage is greater for louder sound, producing a greater frequency swing and a higher modulation percentage. For the loudest audio signal, the frequency swing should be the amount defined as 100 percent modulation.

MODULATION INDEX This value is calculated as the frequency deviation of the RF carrier divided by the audio modulating frequency:

$$M = \frac{\Delta f}{f_a} \qquad \textbf{(11-1)}$$

For example, assume that a frequency deviation of 10 kHz is produced by 10,000-Hz audio. Then $M = 1$.

The modulation index indicates how many pairs of sidebands are in the FM signal. Unlike AM, frequency modulation can produce multiple pairs of sideband frequencies for values of M greater than 1.

For $M \leq 1$, though, an FM signal has only one pair of sidebands, as in an AM signal.

PHASE MODULATION In this method, the phase angle of the RF carrier is shifted in proportion to the amplitude of the audio modulating voltage. The varying phase corresponds to changes in carrier signal frequency. Therefore, phase modulation (PM) results in an equivalent FM signal, or *indirect FM.* In many cases, the FM transmitter actually uses phase modulation in a crystal-controlled oscillator, for excellent center-frequency stability.

An important characteristic of PM is the fact that the amount of equivalent, or indirect, FM increases with higher audio frequencies. The reason is a faster change in phase angle. However, an audio correction filter is used in the modulation, to provide the same frequency swings as in direct FM.

PREEMPHASIS AND DEEMPHASIS *Preemphasis* refers to the boosting of the high audio frequencies in modulation at the transmitter. The purpose is to increase the signal-to-noise ratio for high audio frequencies, from about 2400 to 15,000 Hz. Generally these values are harmonics of the stronger fundamental frequencies. *Deemphasis* means the attenuation of these frequencies by the same amount that they were boosted. The deemphasis circuit is at the output of the FM detector in the receiver. A low-pass RC filter is used for the deemphasis. The RC time constant is 75 μs, to match the preemphasis.

Although it would seem that no progress is made with equal preemphasis and deemphasis, actually there is a great improvement in the signal-to-noise ratio. The reason is that interfering noise in the transmitted signal is added by PM. The resultant indirect FM increases for higher audio frequencies. When the signal and noise are both reduced by deemphasis, the signal returns to normal while the noise is reduced below nor-

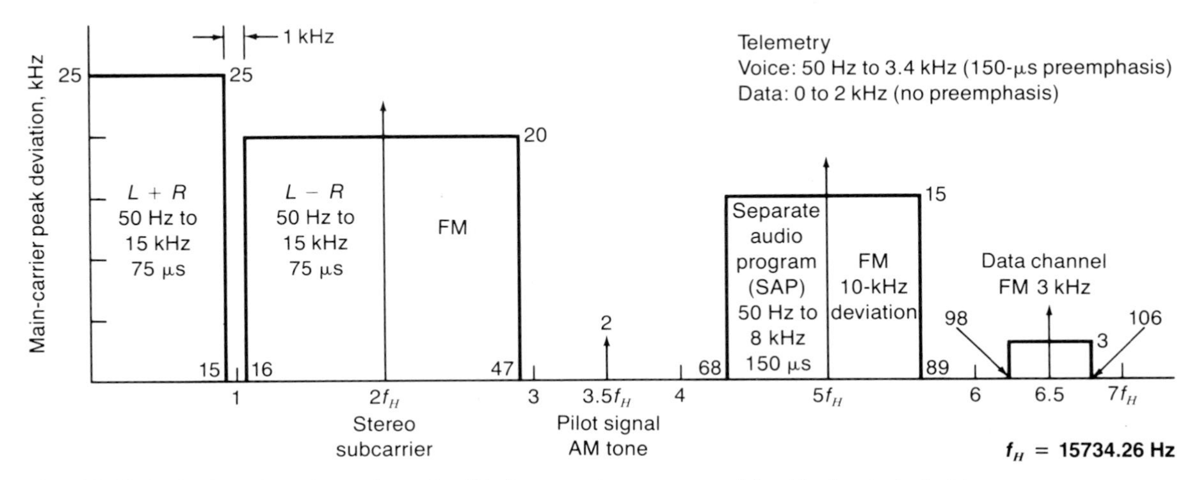

Fig. 11-12 Audio baseband spectrum for TV stereo system proposed by Electronic Industries Association of Japan (EIAJ). Peak deviation of main carrier for FM signal equals 65 kHz. For horizontal line-scanning frequency in color television, f_H = 15,734.26 Hz. (*From Electronics*)

mal. This explains why the preemphasis and deemphasis system is used in FM but not in AM.

STEREOPHONIC SOUND In commercial FM radio, most stations broadcast in stereo. The method encodes the audio in two signals:

Left + right, or $L + R$

Left − right, or $L - R$

The $L + R$ signal corresponds to the original audio, for compatibility in monophonic receivers. The $L - R$ signal is the additional signal needed for enhanced audio with the stereo effect.

For transmission, the $L + R$ signal modulates the main carrier signal. The $L - R$ signal modulates a 38-kHz subcarrier, which is suppressed to minimize interference. A 19-kHz pilot tone is transmitted so that the receiver can regenerate the 38-kHz subcarrier. Then the stereo processing circuits can decode the information to provide the original left and right audio signals for separate stereo channels.

STEREO SOUND FOR TV A similar method can be used for stereo sound in television. Several systems have been proposed, but the main features are illustrated in Fig. 11-12 for the EIAJ method. In this system, the $L - R$ stereo signal modulates a suppressed subcarrier at 31.4 kHz. This frequency is chosen as $2f_H$, where f_H is the horizontal line-scanning frequency of 15,734.20 Hz, or approximately 15.7 kHz. The pilot signal is at $3.5f_H$. Multiples of f_H are used in order to interleave the frequency components of the sound modulation with the video signal frequencies.

In addition, the signals shown at the right in Fig. 11-12 are for channels with separate audio programs (SAP). One possible use is for second-language broadcasts.

Test Point Questions 11-5

Answers at End of Chapter

List the following values for the FM sound signal in television:

a. Maximum frequency deviation

b. Separation of center frequency from the picture carrier signal

c. Percentage of modulation for ±20-kHz swing

11-6 TELEVISION TRANSMISSION STANDARDS

The standards are specified by the FCC. Included are the requirements for signal amplitudes, power output, and tolerance for the carrier frequencies. The waveform in Fig. 11-13*a* shows amplitude values in the AM picture signal. For comparison, frequencies in a standard 6-MHz channel are shown in Fig. 11-13*b*. The purpose here is to emphasize the difference between amplitude characteristics of a standard signal and frequency characteristics of a standard channel.

The AM picture signal is designated as type A5C emission. This transmission means amplitude modulation, with full carrier signal but vestigial sidebands.

The FM sound signal is designated as type *F5* emission. This transmission means frequency modulation with a ±25-kHz maximum swing. In FM radio broadcasting with ±75-kHz maximum swing, the emission is F3.

In Fig. 11-13*a*, the waveform of the AM picture signal shows negative transmission, or negative polarity of modulation. This method reduces the effect of noise pulses in the picture. The tip of sync produces a maximum carrier signal at 100 percent amplitude. The top 25 percent is for sync, with the blanking level at 75 percent. Black setup is 6.25 percent below blanking. Peak white produces the lowest carrier signal amplitude of 12.5 ± 2.5 percent.

The graph of frequencies in Fig. 11-13*b* shows vestigial sideband transmission. This method is used to allow 4-MHz video modulation in the 6-MHz channel. The upper sideband (USB) extends to 4 MHz above the carrier frequency. Then the higher frequencies drop off to practically zero to prevent interference with the sound signal. The lower sideband (LSB) extends flat down to 0.75 MHz below the picture carrier frequency. Then the frequencies drop off to practically zero to prevent interference with the lower adjacent channel.

TRANSMITTER POWER The visual transmitter that produces the AM picture signal generally

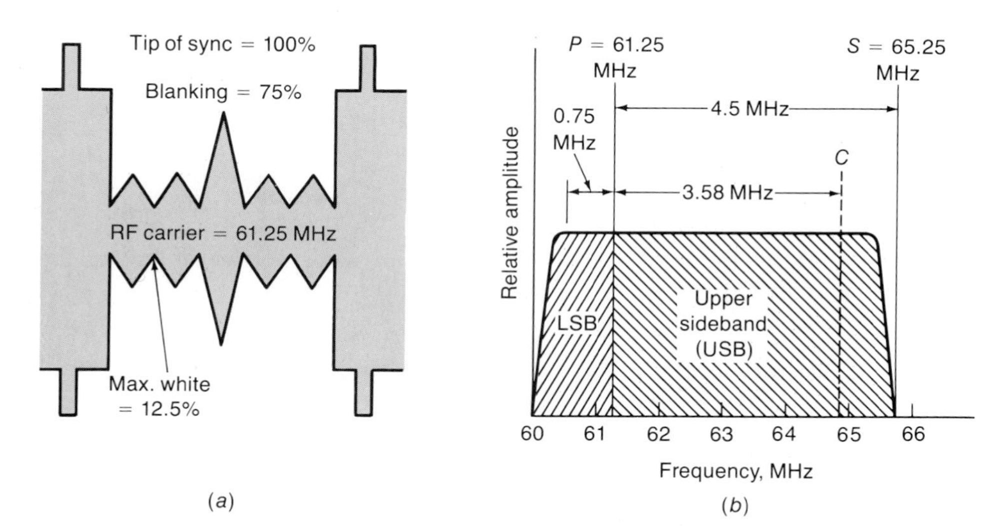

Fig. 11-13 Comparison of amplitude and frequency standards for television transmission channel. The example here is channel 3. (*a*) Amplitude levels for AM picture signal. (*b*) Frequencies in 6-MHz channel.

has a peak power rating of 0.5, 5, 20, or 50 kW. However, the effective radiated power (ERP) is much higher because it includes the antenna gain. The transmitter output of 4.5 kW, as an example that includes 0.5 kW of cable losses, can be multiplied by an antenna gain of 10 to get an ERP of 45 kW. Often the power is specified in units of dBk, which means decibels over 1 kW.

The aural transmitter that produces the FM sound signal can have a power output 0.5 to 1.5 times the picture-signal power. Generally, the sound is transmitted at one-half the power of the picture signal, in order to minimize interference. Usually there is no problem in receiving the sound signal.

FREQUENCY TOLERANCES The tolerance for the picture carrier frequency is ±1000 Hz. The sound carrier frequency must be 4.5 MHz ± 1000 Hz above the picture carrier frequency. These tolerances apply to color transmission. The chroma subcarrier frequency is 3.579545 MHz ± 10 Hz. Keep in mind that a tolerance of 1000 Hz is 1 kHz, or 0.001 MHz. The ratio to 100 MHz is only 0.001 percent.

CARRIER OFFSET FREQUENCY The exact carrier frequencies for different stations on the same channel are offset by +10 kHz or −10 kHz. The purpose is to reduce the effect of interference between cochannel stations. An offset of 10 kHz is chosen as approximately two-thirds the horizontal line-scanning frequency of 15,750 Hz.

TRANSLATOR STATIONS Translator stations convert channel frequencies of one station to another channel for rebroadcasting. The purpose is to minimize interference or to provide TV service for a small area in a 5- to 15-mi [8- to 14-km] range. The power output is 1 to 10 W for VHF channels or up to 100 W for UHF channels.

LOW-POWER TV STATIONS The FCC plans to license about 1000 low-power TV stations, about the same number as major television stations. Many more channel assignments will be possible, then, especially for minority groups and small local areas for special program sources. The transmitter power is 10 to 100 W for VHF channels and up to 1000 W for UHF channels. Except for the power restriction, low-power stations can operate on any of the VHF and UHF channels, except 37 and 70 to 83, which are not available for regular TV broadcasting. However, there must not be interference with full-service stations. Channels that can interfere with one another are as follows:

n = cochannel
$n \pm 1$ = adjacent channel
$n \pm 11$ = local oscillator interference
$n \pm 8$ = IF beat interference
$n \pm 14$ = sound image-frequency interference
$n \pm 15$ = picture image-frequency interference

Note that the power is specified for the transmitter, without taking into account the gain of the antenna and its height. The effective radiated power can be much greater.

Test Point Questions 11-6

Answers at End of Chapter

a. What is the tolerance for the picture carrier frequency?
b. What is the emission-type number for vestigial sideband transmission?
c. What is the frequency offset for cochannel stations?

11-7 LINE-OF-SIGHT TRANSMISSION

In the VHF and UFH bands, radio is propagated mainly by waves close to the surface of the earth, rather than skywaves from the ionized atmosphere. The transmission distance is limited, therefore, to the straight-line path to the horizon. This characteristic is called *line-of-sight transmission.* However, the horizon distance for radio waves is about 15 percent longer because of refraction effects.

The height above the earth is important for transmitting and receiving antennas. For example, the radio horizon distance is about 20 mi [32 km] for an antenna height of 200 ft [61 m] and 50 mi [80 km] for a height of 1000 ft [305 m]. Figure 11-14 shows the transmitting antennas on top of the World Trade Center for all the television stations in New York City. This antenna is approximately 1800 ft [549 m] high, which allows a radio horizon distance of 60 mi [97 km]. Included are antennas for FM radio broadcast stations, which are also in the VHF band.

In line-of-sight transmission, the horizon distance for the receiving antenna is added. For instance, an antenna height of 200 ft [61 m] at the receiver allows a horizon distance of 20 mi [32 km]. Thus 20 mi [32 km] plus 60 mi [97 km] for the transmitting antenna gives a total distance of 80 mi [129 km].

Fig. 11-14 Television transmitting antennas atop the World Trade Center in New York City. Antenna height is approximately 1800 ft [549 m].

REFLECTIONS As the ground wave travels, it encounters buildings, towers, bridges, hills, and other obstructions. When the object is a good conductor and its size is an appreciable part of the radio signal's wavelength, the obstruction will reflect the radio wave. What happens is that the conductor intercepts the radio wave signal, current flows in the obstruction (as in an antenna), and the obstruction reradiates the signal. Reflection of radio waves can occur at any frequency, but it is more of a problem in the VHF and UHF bands because of the higher frequencies.

For television channel frequencies between 54 and 890 MHz, the wavelengths are between 17 and 1 ft [5.2 and 0.3 m]. The shortest wavelength corresponds to the highest frequency. Obstructions of comparable size, or bigger, can reflect the television carrier signals. Even an airplane can cause reflections.

When a reflected signal, in addition to the direct wave, arrives at the receiving antenna, the result is multipath signals. They differ slightly in time. The effect is multiple images in the picture, which are called *ghosts* (Fig. 11-15).

HORIZONTAL HALF-WAVE DIPOLE The basic antenna for transmitters or receivers in the VHF band is the half-wave dipole illustrated in Fig. 11-16. This type is called a *resonant* antenna, which means that a specific length is best for a particular frequency. The overall length of the

Fig. 11-15 Multiple images, or ghosts, in the picture.

half-wave dipole can be calculated as $L = 462/f$, where L is in feet and f is in megahertz. For example, for a frequency of 100 MHz, the length of a half-wave is 4.62 ft [1.4 m]. In Fig. 11-16, each pole would be 2.31 ft [0.7 m] for the overall length of a half-wave. The spacing between the two poles is negligible.

In the VHF band of 30 to 300 MHz, the half-wave is a practical size for the mounting of the antenna conductors. The half-wave dipole is often called a *Hertz antenna.*

ANTENNA POLARIZATION The *direction of polarization* for radio waves is defined as the plane of the electric field, with a perpendicular magnetic field. In practical terms, a horizontal antenna radiates an electromagnetic wave with horizontal polarization. A vertical antenna produces vertical polarization. For maximum signal pickup, the receiving antenna should have the same polarization as the signal. In general, horizontal polarization is often used in the VHF band, because at these frequencies noise created by electrical equipment usually is vertically polarized.

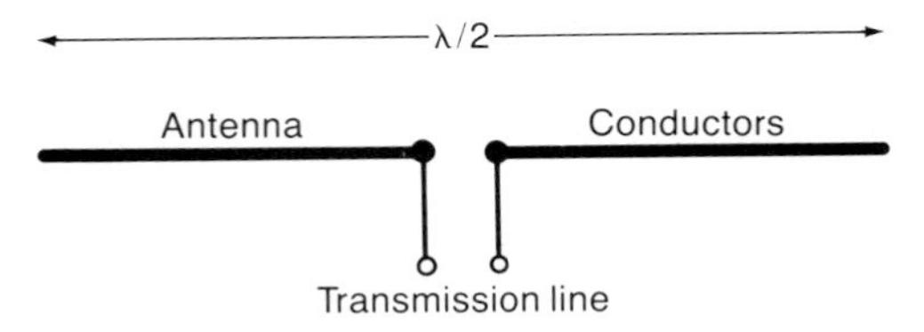

Fig. 11-16 Half-wave dipole antenna.

In the past, the FCC standard for the television transmitter was horizontal polarization. However, it is being changed to *circular polarization,* which is a method that combines horizontal and vertical polarization. The purpose is to improve reception of the signal by indoor antennas. In this method of reception, there really is no specific direction of polarization in the signal. Circular polarization is used also for the transmitted signal in the FM radio broadcast band.

Test Point Questions 11-7

Answers at End of Chapter

Answer True or False.

a. Line-of-sight transmission uses sky waves from the ionosphere.

b. A half-wave dipole is shorter for higher frequencies.

c. Multipath signals cause ghosts in the picture.

d. The higher the antenna, the longer the radio horizon distance.

11-8 SATELLITE TELEVISION

The best way to overcome the line-of-sight limitation is to put the transmitting antenna on a satellite in orbit high above the earth. The satellite serves as a relay station between earth stations at different locations. In this way, satellite communication is achieved easily over thousands of miles.

The elements of a satellite system are illustrated in Fig. 11-17. The first requirement is to rocket the satellite into space, where it orbits around the earth. In the United States, the rockets are supplied by the National Aeronautics and Space Administration (NASA), for private companies that own the satellite. Although the cost

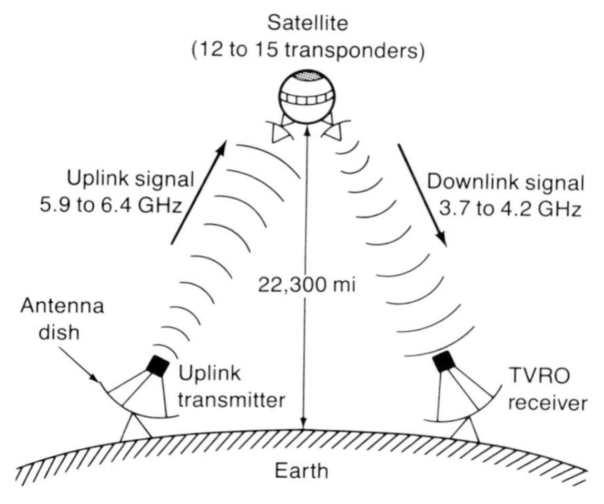

Fig. 11-17 Elements of a satellite communications system.

is great, the system of satellite communications is cheaper than a network of land stations covering the same area. Furthermore, satellite signals can easily span the oceans.

GEOSTATIONARY ORBIT The satellite height of 22,300 mi [35,887 km] is used because this radius provides a *geostationary,* or *synchronous, orbit.* The time for one orbit matches the 24 h of one rotation of the earth on its axis. As a result, the satellite appears to be still with respect to earth. Thus it is possible for the uplink transmitter to aim its antenna signal at the satellite. Also the earth receiving station can pick up the downlink signal by aiming the antenna dish. Different satellites have angular headings that differ by 3 to 5°.

UPLINK AND DOWNLINK FREQUENCIES Microwaves are used to permit accurate beaming of the radio signals to a satellite 22,300 mi [35,887 km] away. The frequencies are in the gigahertz (GHz) range. Note that 1 GHz = 10^9 Hz. Also, 1 GHz is 1000 MHz. The specific frequencies are as follows:

Uplink = 5.9 to 6.4 GHz. These frequencies are used for the earth transmitter to the satellite.

Downlink = 3.7 to 4.2 GHz. These frequencies are used for the satellite transmitter to the earth station receiver.

The satellite has 12 to 15 transponders for separate channels. Each transponder converts the uplink signal to a downlink signal for the TV receive only (TVRO) earth station.

As a relay station, the satellite picks up the signal from an earth station at one location and sends it back to earth, where it can be received at locations about halfway around the world. The power output is 5 to 8.5 W. The dc power requirements are supplied by solar cells.

TRANSPONDER CHANNELS The TV satellites have 12 transponders for different signals in separate channels. A transponder is a combined receiver and transmitter. Uplink signals are received, to be converted to downlink frequencies and then transmitted to the earth station receivers.

Actually 24 channels are available with 12 transponders. The signals for 12 channels use horizontal polarization, and vertical polarization is used for the other 12 channels.

SATELLITE COMMUNICATIONS Although television is very popular, it is only one application of satellite communication. Its uses include telephone, television, and data transmission. Regulation worldwide is provided by the *In*ternational *Tel*ecommunications *Sat*ellite (Intelsat) consortium. In the United States, satellites are operated by the *Com*munications *Sat*ellite Corporation (Comsat). Private companies such as RCA and Western Union also own domestic satellites. In Canada, the Anik satellites are used for Canadian television. For worldwide communications, there are satellites over the Atlantic, Pacific, and Indian oceans. Just a few of the more popular

TABLE 11-5
POPULAR SATELLITES

NAME	OWNER	ANGULAR HEADING	APPLICATIONS
Satcom IV	RCA	132°	Used by cable TV companies
Comstar 3	Comsat	95°	Telephone communications
Westar 3	Western Union	86°	Used by public TV stations
Anik B	Canada	109°	Canadian television

communications satellites are listed in Table 11-5.

RECEIVER EARTH STATION The main problem with receiver earth stations is the very weak signal from the satellite 22,300 mi [35,887 km] away. The power output from the satellite is generally 5 W. However, its antenna gain is typically 1000 for an effective radiated power (ERP) of 5000 W. Assuming a loss of -196 dB in transmission, signal at the receiver is only 1.2×10^{-16} W. Using a large antenna dish for a gain of 10,000, though, and a special low-noise amplifier (LNA) for the microwave signal, the TVRO station can receive the satellite signals. See Fig. 11-18.

The large antenna dish and special LNA are rather expensive for a hobbyist. The total cost for the complete receiver earth station can be $2000 to $10,000. For the business of TV satellite communications, though, these costs are small.

The television pictures from a satellite can have remarkable quality. Since FM is used, the picture has no noise. Also, with a 40-MHz channel the high-frequency definition can be much better than that for the standard 6-MHz channel. For broadcasting, though, the satellite signal at the earth station must be converted to a standard TV signal. Note that in the future, special satellite channels may be reserved for high-definition television (HDTV).

ANTENNA DISH A large parabolic or spherical reflector is used for the weak microwave signal in order to provide an antenna gain of about 10,000. The parabolic dish provides more gain. The gain must be provided before the signal is amplified. Otherwise, the signal-to-noise ratio is not good enough.

For the downlink frequencies of about 4 GHz, the antenna dish must be 10 to 12 ft [3.0 to 3.7 m] in diameter. This is big in terms of the antenna mounting. The dish's vertical elevation and azimuth angle (for aiming at the satellite) must be adjustable. One specific direction is used

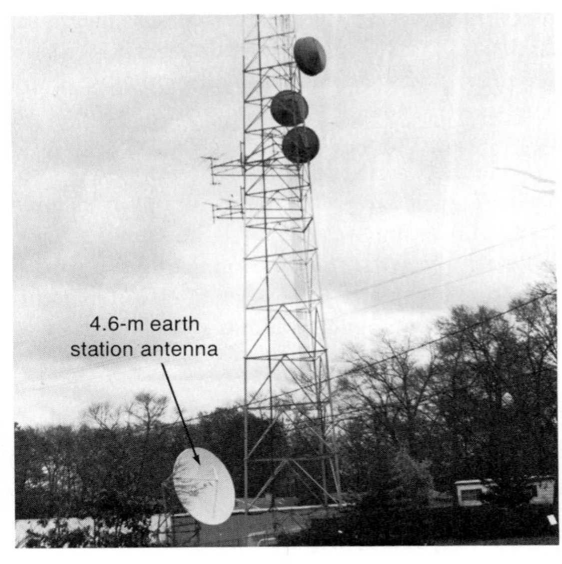

Fig. 11-18 Antenna tower and satellite dish for cable TV earth station.

for each satellite. A change of 3 to 5° brings in the next satellite in space. A method is provided to change between vertical and horizontal polarization so that all channels can be picked up on the satellite.

LOW-NOISE AMPLIFIER This unit is actually mounted on the antenna dish to receive the focused microwave signal. At 3.7 to 4.2 GHz, special microwave amplifiers are necessary. Typically the voltage gain is 300. The main requirement is low noise because of the extremely weak signal. The ratings in noise temperature are measured in degrees Kelvin. The lower the value, the better the amplifier is for low noise. A typical rating is 120 K, with 85 K being the best noise figure.

DIRECT-BROADCAST SATELLITES (DBS) The Comsat organization and other companies are planning to put TV satellites in orbit for broadcasting directly to individuals having their own receiver earth stations. This method would bypass the services of TV broadcast stations and cable distribution networks. The frequencies for DBS are higher, with 17.3 to 17.8 GHz for uplink and 12.2 to 12.7 GHz for downlink. Also, more satellite power output is planned, with an ERP of 1,000,000 W. The combination of higher frequencies and more power should make it possible to use a smaller antenna dish of about 3-ft [0.9-m] diameter. There will be 20 channels, each with a bandwidth of 25 MHz. Service is scheduled to start in 1986. The DBS service has been adopted to provide television for rural areas and special features such as high-definition TV and teletext.

Test Point Questions 11-8
Answers at End of Chapter

a. Is 6 GHz an uplink or a downlink frequency?
b. Is 4 GHz an uplink or a downlink frequency?
c. How many megahertz are there in 1 GHz?
d. By how many degrees do satellites differ in angular heading?

SUMMARY

1. The amplitude-modulated picture carrier signal has a symmetric envelope, which is the composite video signal used to modulate the carrier wave. The two main features of the transmitted picture carrier signal are negative polarity of modulation and vestigial sideband transmission.
2. Negative transmission means that the video modulating signal has the polarity required to reduce the carrier amplitude for the white camera signal. Darker picture information raises the carrier amplitude. The tip of sync produces maximum carrier amplitude for the 100 percent level.
3. Vestigial sideband transmission means that all the upper side frequencies, but only part of the lower side frequencies, are transmitted in the 6-MHz channel for the modulated picture carrier signal. The side frequencies below the picture carrier signal that are low enough to be outside the assigned channel are not transmitted.

4. Channels 2 to 6 are lowband VHF channels between 54 and 88 MHz; channels 7 to 13 are highband VHF channels between 174 and 216 MHz; channels 14 to 83 are UHF channels from 470 to 890 MHz. In all bands, the station broadcasts in a standard 6-MHz-wide channel.
5. The standard 6-MHz channel includes the AM picture carrier 1.25 MHz above the low end and the FM sound carrier 0.25 MHz below the high end, with 4.5 MHz between the picture and sound carrier frequencies. The color subcarrier signal is transmitted as a side frequency 3.58 MHz above the picture carrier.
6. The FM sound signal has a maximum frequency swing of ±25 kHz for 100 percent modulation.
7. The frequency tolerance for picture and sound carrier frequencies is ±1000 Hz. The tolerance is ±10 Hz for the 3.579545-MHz color subcarrier signal.
8. Radio waves in the VHF and UHF bands are propagated by line-of-sight transmission.
9. Communications satellites are in orbit 22,300 mi [35,887 km] above the earth. The satellite serves as a relay station. Its transponders receive uplink signals and transmit downlink signals to the earth station receivers. Different satellites have angular headings that differ by 3 to 5°.
10. Microwaves are used for satellite communications. Uplink frequencies are 5.9 to 6.4 GHz, and downlink frequencies are 3.7 to 4.2 GHz.

SELF-EXAMINATION

Answers at Back of Book

Choose (a), (b), (c), or (d).

1. The modulated picture carrier wave includes the composite video signal as the (a) average carrier level, (b) symmetric envelope of amplitude variations, (c) lower sideband without the upper sideband, (d) upper envelope without the lower envelope.
2. Which of the following statements is true? (a) Negative transmission means that the carrier amplitude decreases for black. (b) Negative transmission means that the carrier amplitude decreases for white. (c) Vestigial sideband transmission means that both upper and lower sidebands are transmitted for all modulating frequencies. (d) Vestigial sideband transmission means that the modulated picture carrier signal has only the upper envelope.
3. With a 2-MHz video signal modulating the picture carrier signal for channel 4 (66 to 72 MHz), which of the following frequencies are transmitted? (a) 66-MHz carrier frequency and 68-MHz upper side frequency; (b) 71.75-MHz carrier frequency with 69- and 73-MHz side frequencies; (c)

67.25-MHz carrier frequency with 65.25- and 69.25-MHz side frequencies; (d) 67.25-MHz carrier frequency and 69.25-MHz upper side frequency.

4. With a 0.5-MHz video signal modulating the picture carrier, (a) both upper and lower side frequencies are transmitted; (b) only the upper side frequency is transmitted; (c) only the lower side frequency is transmitted; (d) no side frequencies are transmitted.
5. In all standard television broadcast channels, the difference between the picture and sound carrier frequencies is (a) 0.25 MHz, (b) 1.25 MHz, (c) 4.5 MHz, (d) 6 MHz.
6. The difference between the sound carrier frequencies in two adjacent channels is (a) 0.25 MHz, (b) 1.25 MHz, (c) 4.5 MHz, (d) 6 MHz.
7. Line-of-sight transmission is a characteristic of propagation for the (a) VHF band and higher frequencies, (b) VHF band but not the UHF band, (c) radio frequencies below 1 MHz, (d) AM picture signal but not the FM sound signal.
8. In channel 14 (470 to 476 MHz), the 3.58-MHz color signal is transmitted at (a) 471.25 MHz, (b) 473.25 MHz, (c) 474.83 MHz, (d) 475.25 MHz.
9. The difference between the sound carrier and color subcarrier frequencies is (a) 4.5 MHz, (b) 1.25 MHz, (c) 0.92 MHz, (d) 0.25 MHz.
10. The maximum deviation of the FM sound signal, in kilohertz, is (a) 10, (b) 25, (c) 75, (d) 100.

ESSAY QUESTIONS

1. Define negative transmission. Give one advantage.
2. Name one advantage and one disadvantage of vestigial sideband transmission.
3. For each of the following, list the picture carrier and sound carrier frequencies and their frequency separation: channels 2, 5, 7, 13, 14, and 83.
4. Define the following terms: **(a)** offset carrier operation, **(b)** ghost in the picture.
5. Which television channel numbers are in the band of 30 to 300 MHz? Which are in the band of 300 to 3000 MHz?
6. Draw a graph similar to Fig. 11-9*b* that shows frequencies transmitted in channel 8, indicating the picture carrier, sound carrier, and color subcarrier with their frequencies.
7. Why is reflection of the transmitted carrier wave a common problem with the picture signal in television, but not in the radio broadcast band of 535 to 1605 kHz?
8. What is the effect in the reproduced picture of multipath signals caused by reflections?

9. What are the frequency tolerances for picture and sound carriers and the color subcarrier?
10. What is meant by offset-carrier operation for the picture signal?
11. List the FCC type designations for the picture and sound carrier signals.
12. What is meant by a cochannel station, a lower adjacent channel, and an upper adjacent channel?
13. Define the following terms in FM: center frequency, deviation, swing, percentage of modulation, and modulation index.
14. Why is antenna height important for television transmitters and antennas?
15. What is a horizontal half-wave dipole antenna?
16. How high above earth is a satellite in a geostationary orbit?
17. What are the uplink and downlink frequencies for television satellites?
18. Describe three important requirements for a television receive only (TVRO) earth station.

PROBLEMS

Answers to Odd-Numbered Problems at Back of Book

1. List the RF side frequencies transmitted with the picture carrier signal for the following modulations: **(a)** 0.25-MHz video modulation of channel 2 carrier, **(b)** 3-MHz video modulation of channel 5 carrier, **(c)** 0.5-MHz video modulation of channel 14 carrier, **(d)** 4-MHz video modulation of channel 14 carrier.
2. List the picture and sound carrier frequencies for channels 7, 8, and 9.
3. In negative transmission, what is the relative amplitude of the modulated picture carrier wave for **(a)** maximum white, **(b)** the tip of sync, **(c)** the blanking level, **(d)** black in the picture, **(e)** medium gray?
4. What is the frequency separation for **(a)** picture and associated sound carriers, **(b)** picture carrier and lower adjacent-channel sound carrier, **(c)** picture carriers in two adjacent channels, **(d)** sound carriers in two adjacent channels?
5. What is the frequency separation for the combinations of **(a)** picture carrier and color subcarrier, **(b)** sound carrier and color subcarrier?
6. List the picture and sound carrier frequencies for all channels from 2 to 14 inclusive.
7. What is the exact picture carrier frequency for channel 2 offset by −10 kHz?
8. Refer to Fig. 11-19. Indicate the picture and sound carrier frequencies for three VHF channels that are adjacent in frequency, other than 2, 3, and 4.

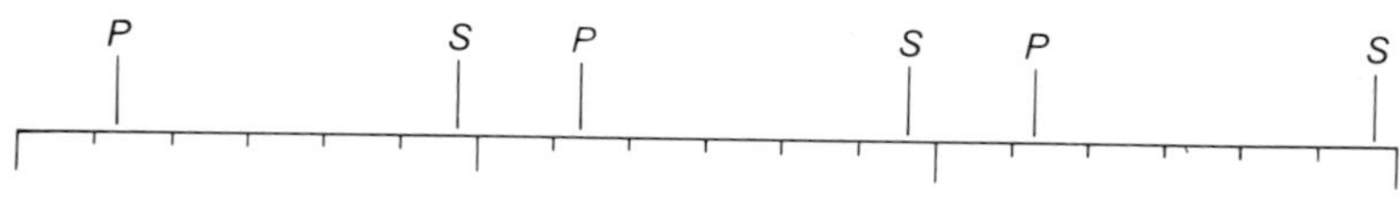

Fig. 11-19 For Prob. 8.

9. Calculate the percentage of modulation for the following frequency deviations in the FM sound signal for television: **(a)** 5 kHz, **(b)** 10 kHz, **(c)** 25 kHz.
10. Calculate the overall length, in feet, of a half-wave dipole antenna for 54 MHz.
11. A 5000-W radio signal is attenuated by −196 dB. How much is the resultant signal (in microwatts)?
12. The transmitter power of 5 W is increased by an antenna gain of 30 dB. How much is the effective radiated power (ERP)?

SPECIAL QUESTIONS

1. What is the main difference between the illustrations in Fig. 11-13*a* and *b*?
2. Calculate the minimum cost of all the equipment needed for a TVRO station.
3. Give several advantages of satellite television.

ANSWERS TO TEST POINT QUESTIONS

11-1 **a.** 10 to 15, or 12.5
b. 75
c. 100
11-2 **a.** T
b. F
c. T
11-3 **a.** T
b. F
c. F
11-4 **a.** 67.25 MHz
b. 70.25 MHz
c. 70.83 MHz
d. 71.75 MHz
11-5 **a.** 25 kHz
b. 4.5 MHz
c. 80 percent
11-6 **a.** ±1000 Hz
b. A5C
c. 10 kHz
11-7 **a.** F
b. T
c. T
d. T
11-8 **a.** Uplink
b. Downlink
c. 1000
d. 3 to 5°

12

TELEVISION RECEIVERS

The television circuits use three signals, including chroma for color. One is the FM sound carrier signal with an audio signal for the loudspeaker. Most important is the AM picture carrier signal, modulated with the video signal for the picture tube. In color receivers, the third signal is the 3.58-MHz colorplexed chroma signal, which is part of the picture carrier signal. In terms of baseband signals, the receiver needs audio, luminance video, and color video signals. The three signals make it possible to see the picture and hear the sound.

In addition to the signal circuits, the television receiver has horizontal and vertical deflection circuits to produce the scanning raster. Finally, once the picture is on the raster, synchronization is necessary. The deflection sync includes *H* and *V* pulses that time the scanning circuits to hold the picture steady on the raster.

Black-and-white receivers are explained first. Figure 12-1 shows a 12-in. monochrome receiver. The front view is shown in Fig. 12-1, and an inside view of the chassis components is shown in Fig. 12-2, with the rear cover off. Additional requirements for color television receivers are described in Chap. 14. Also, more details of sync and deflection circuits are analyzed in Chap. 13, for monochrome or color receivers. The topics in this chapter are:

12-1 Functional Blocks for the Signal
12-2 Functional Blocks for Sync and Deflection
12-3 Automatic Gain Control
12-4 DC Power Requirements
12-5 RF Section
12-6 IF Section
12-7 Video Detector
12-8 Video Amplifier Section
12-9 DC Component of the Video Signal
12-10 The 4.5-MHz Sound IF Section
12-11 Troubleshooting the Signal Circuits
12-12 TV Monitor with Modular Components

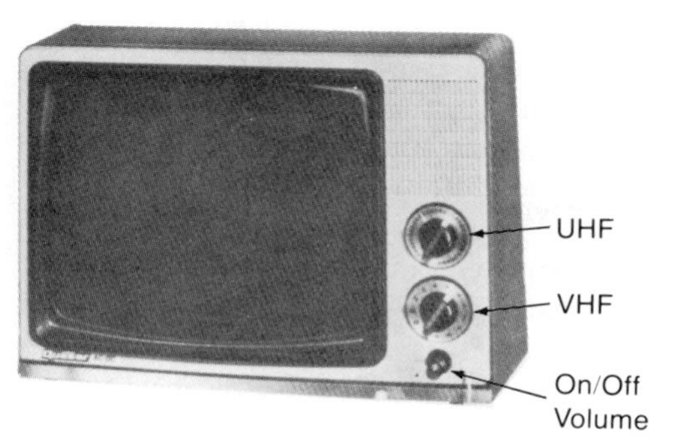

Fig. 12-1 A 12-in. monochrome receiver. Chassis shown in Fig. 12-2. (*Quasar Company*)

12-1 FUNCTIONAL BLOCKS FOR THE SIGNAL

Figure 12-3 shows the block diagram for a monochrome receiver. Those blocks in the shaded area indicate the RF-IF signal circuits. The receiver is basically a superheterodyne circuit. A local oscillator stage in the RF tuner, or front end, beats the RF signal down to the intermediate frequencies for the IF amplifier. Then all RF signals for different stations are converted to the same IF values of the receiver. The standard IF values for television receivers are:

45.75 MHz for the picture IF carrier signal

41.25 MHz for the sound IF carrier signal

Most of the signal amplification in the receiver is done by the IF amplifier sections.

The video signal first appears at the output of the video detector. The detector has modulated IF signal input and baseband signal output.

SOUND SIGNAL Included in the video detector output is a 4.5-MHz sound signal. This signal is produced by a second heterodyning process in which the sound IF signal at 41.25 MHz beats against the picture IF carrier at 45.75 MHz. The frequency difference is 45.75 − 41.25 = 4.5 MHz. The receiver is actually a double superheterodyne for the sound signal. In the video detector, the

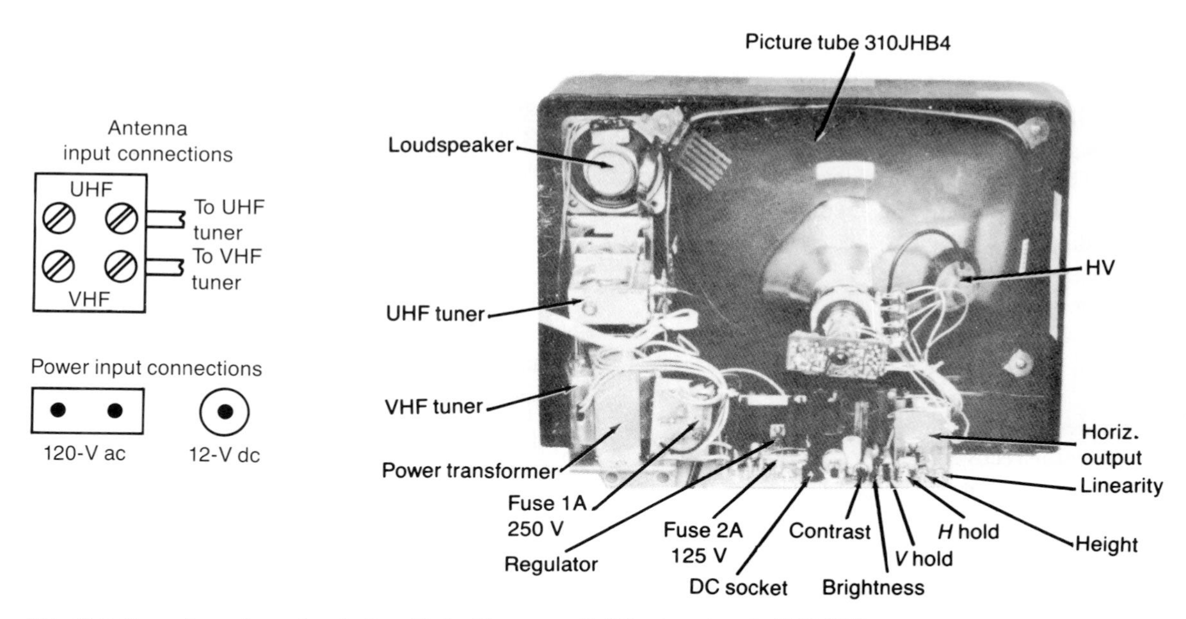

Fig. 12-2 Rear view of receiver in Fig. 12-1 with cover off. (*Quasar chassis 12TS-628*)

IF picture carrier serves as a local oscillator that beats with the IF sound signal.

The 4.5-MHz sound is still an FM signal with the original frequency modulation, but at a lower center frequency. Most important, the sound signal is independent of the exact local oscillator frequency in the RF tuner of the receiver, because 4.5 MHz is the difference between the carrier frequencies produced by the transmitter.

The sound signal is extracted by a 4.5-MHz trap and coupled to a narrowband IF amplifier tuned to 4.5 MHz. Then the original frequency modulation is recovered by an FM detector, such as the ratio detector, to produce the desired audio output. An audio amplifier provides the power needed to drive the loudspeaker. The front-panel volume control is usually at the input to the audio amplifier.

VIDEO DETECTOR OUTPUTS The detector is just a small semiconductor diode, but because of rectification the following three signals result:

1. Composite video signal for the video amplifier that drives the picture tube. In addition, the video amplifier supplies the signal for:
   a. The sync separator that strips the synchronizing pulses from the composite video signal
   b. The automatic gain control (AGC) circuit that controls the gain of the RF and IF stages
2. The 3.58-MHz chroma signal is used in the color circuits of color television receivers.
3. The 4.5-MHz FM sound signal is coupled to the 4.5-MHz sound IF section.

The video and chroma signals are produced as the detector recovers the modulation on the picture carrier signal.

VIDEO SIGNAL PATH The video signal for the picture tube controls the beam current and thus the brightness of the scanning spot. As a result, the intensity modulation of the beam reproduces the picture information. The video amplifier develops enough signal voltage, up to 200 V p-p, to drive the picture tube from cutoff for black and then close to zero grid-cathode voltage for peak white.

A front-panel contrast control varies the gain of the video amplifier. Adjusting the p-p ac signal drive for the picture tube varies the contrast. Note that the brightness control adjusts the dc bias.

SYNC SIGNAL PATH The sync separator is an amplifier circuit that is held in cutoff but made to conduct when the sync pulses are present. The input signal is the composite video signal from the video amplifier. The output is stripped sync, for both *V* and *H* scanning, without the picture information.

Then the separated sync is coupled to the vertical and horizontal scanning oscillators. The feed to the *H* deflection oscillator is total sync, since the phase-lock loop system that controls synchronization of the horizontal oscillator is unaffected by the wide vertical sync pulses. However, the feed to the *V* deflection oscillator contains an *RC* integrator circuit. This network is a low-pass filter because of the shunt capacitor. The integrator is not affected by the narrow horizontal sync pulses, but it builds up the required pulse output for the *V* sync. The capacitor is charged by the wide vertical pulse.

Test Point Questions 12-1

Answers at End of Chapter

What are the frequencies for the following signals?

a. Picture IF carrier
b. Second sound IF carrier
c. Chroma after the video detector
d. Vertical sync

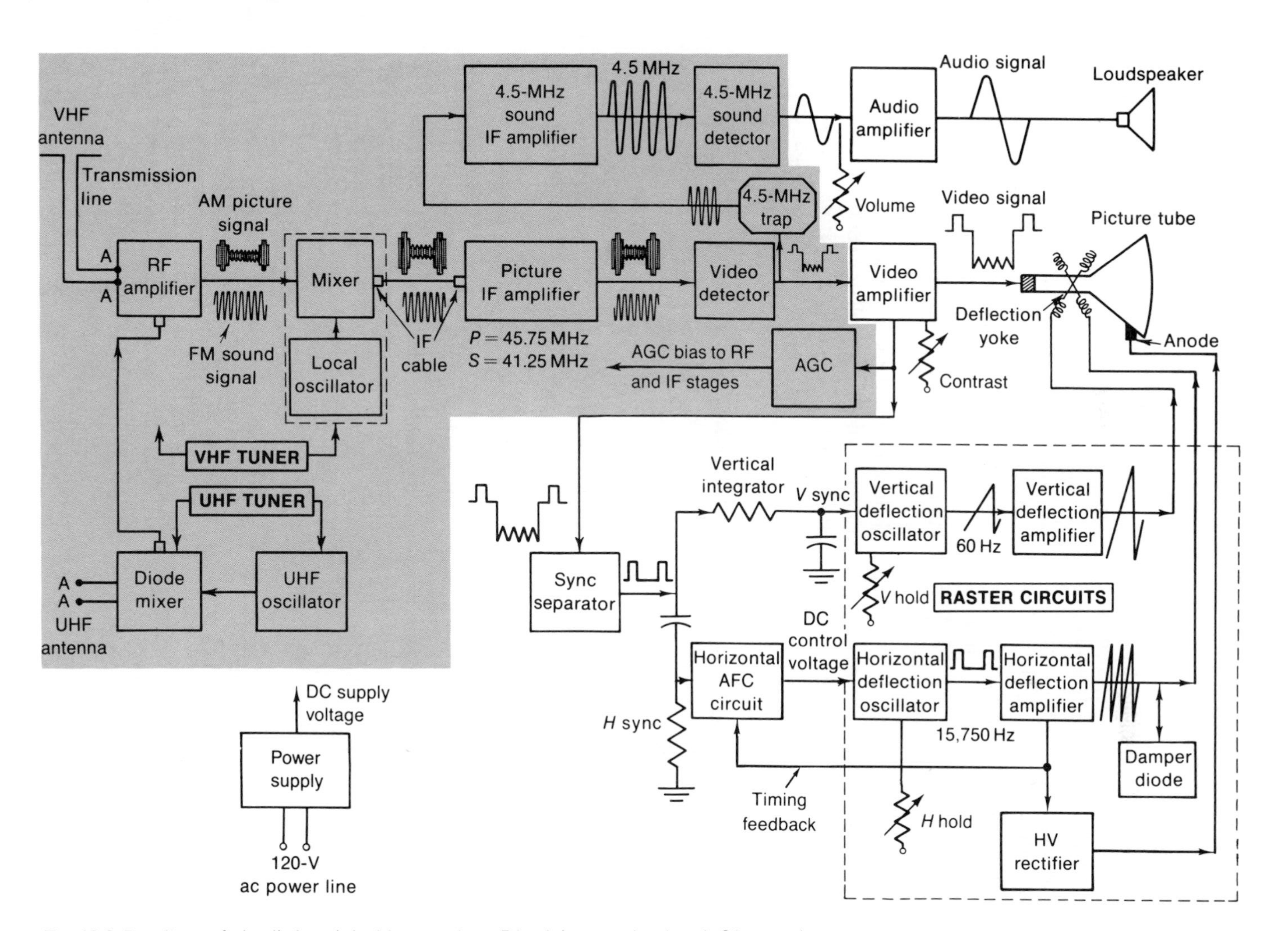

Fig. 12-3 Functions of circuits in a television receiver. *P* is picture carrier signal; *S* is sound carrier signal. Shaded area corresponds to RF-IF section. Waveshapes shown are not to scale.

12-2 FUNCTIONAL BLOCKS FOR SYNC AND DEFLECTION

We can think of the *V* or *H* deflection oscillator as the starting point for deflection. Each is a free-running oscillator circuit, which generates output with or without an input signal. However, sync input is used to control the oscillator frequency. The oscillator output drives a power amplifier, which serves as a scan generator to produce the required amount of sawtooth scanning current in the coils of the deflection yoke.

WHY USE A DEFLECTION OSCILLATOR? Actually, the separated sync pulses could be used to generate the required scan current directly. This idea is illustrated in Fig. 12-4, which shows a pulse-driven sawtooth generator. The capacitor *C* charges through resistor *R* from the dc supply voltage, while the transistor *Q*1 is cut off. Transistor *Q*1 is not conducting because it has no forward bias. When a positive sync pulse drives *Q*1 into conduction, however, *C* discharges rapidly through the transistor. The result is a sawtooth waveform of voltage across *C*. This method is the general circuit for generating a sawtooth voltage, with an *RC* time constant for charging that is long compared with the interval between the pulses.

However, a circuit such as Fig. 12-4 would produce no scanning current at all in the absence of a signal. Even a momentary loss of sync input would cause the deflection to collapse. The solution is to develop the scanning currents from deflection signals that are always present, with or without sync. This requires the use of free-running deflection oscillators that are locked by the separated sync pulses, but only for timing, to control the oscillator frequency.

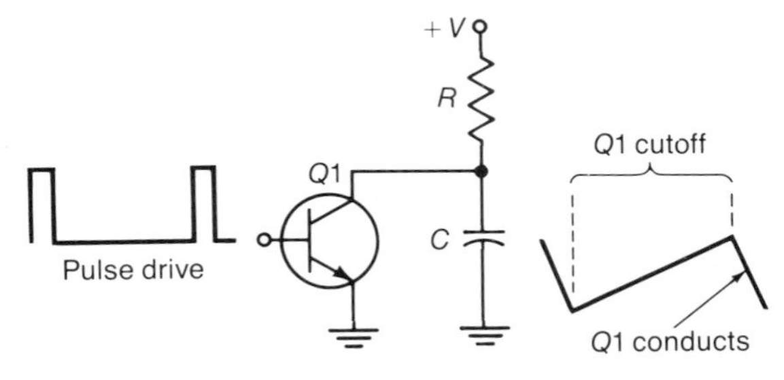

Fig. 12-4 Circuit for a pulse-driven sawtooth generator.

Refer to the receiver block diagram in Fig. 12-3. The vertical deflection oscillator is free-run ning and is controlled by *V* sync. Also, the horizontal deflection oscillator is free-running and is controlled by the horizontal AFC circuit. The deflection oscillator is usually a multivibrator (MV) or blocking oscillator (BO) circuit. These circuits are free-running oscillators that are relatively easy to synchronize, with either trigger pulses or dc control voltage for AFC.

SYNCHRONIZING THE DEFLECTION OSCILLATORS Direct triggering is used for the vertical oscillator. The separated *V* sync pulse is applied directly to the oscillator to lock it in at the 60-Hz sync frequency. What the pulse does is force the oscillator into conduction during the cutoff interval. The triggering occurs just before the oscillator would start to conduct by itself at the natural free-running frequency. The time at which the sync pulse triggers the oscillator is the start of retrace in scanning.

For direct triggering, the *V* oscillator must be set for a free-running frequency slightly lower than the sync frequency. Then each trigger pulse occurs at the right time, just before conduction. The *vertical hold control* is used to set the oscillator frequency at the point where the sync trigger pulses lock in the oscillator.

Loss of vertical sync causes the picture to roll vertically, as shown in Fig. 12-5. The picture rolls upward when the oscillator frequency is too low and downward when the frequency is too high. Note that the rolling black bar is vertical blanking. You can adjust the vertical hold control to lock in the picture.

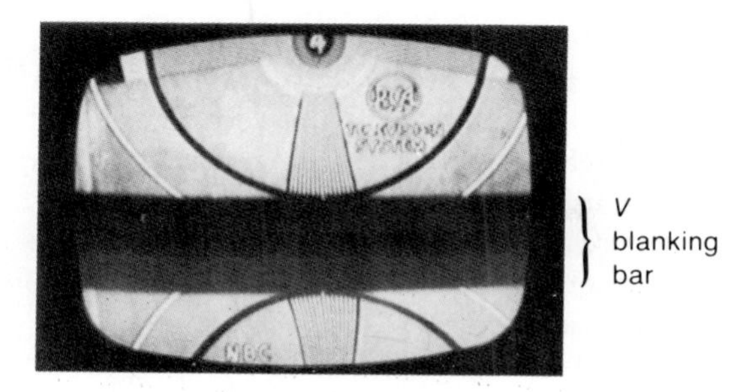

Fig. 12-5 Loss of *V* sync causes picture to roll up or down.

Direct triggering can be used for the vertical oscillator, without AFC, because the *RC* integrating filter for *V* sync also removes any high-frequency noise pulses in the signal. Noise is a big problem in synchronization because noise pulses can be mistaken for sync pulses.

The horizontal deflection oscillator is not triggered directly. The reason is that noise would interfere with synchronization, since *H* sync cannot be integrated as *V* sync can. Instead, the separated sync signal is applied to a phase-lock loop (PLL) for horizontal automatic frequency control (HAFC). Details of this system are shown in the block diagram in Fig. 12-6. Note the shaded block, which is the timing comparator. Generally this circuit uses two diodes to compare the timing of sync with a sample of the retrace pulses developed by the *H* oscillator. When the timing matches, the retraces coincide with the *H* sync pulses. Then the free-running oscillator is unaffected, and the picture is locked in horizontally. An error in timing caused by an error in the oscillator frequency produces a dc correction voltage for the oscillator. The dc control voltage can be filtered with an *RC* integrating filter to remove noise pulses.

A *horizontal hold control* provides adjustment of the free-running frequency for the *H* oscillator. Figure 12-7 shows how the picture tears into diagonal segments without horizontal synchronization. The picture may drift left or right just before it breaks up. Note that the diagonal black bars are parts of the *H* blanking bars.

It should be noted that many receivers now use a digital gen-lock system for the deflection oscillators. This method does not require hold controls. More details are explained in Sec. 13-7 in the next chapter.

SCANNING CURRENT IN THE YOKE The oscillator output must be amplified to produce enough current in the scanning coils. Producing the required power output is the function of the vertical deflection amplifier and the horizontal deflection amplifier, as indicated by the receiver block diagram in Fig. 12-3. We can compare this idea of power output with the more familiar example of audio signal. In audio equipment, the greater the output power, the louder the sound. Simi-

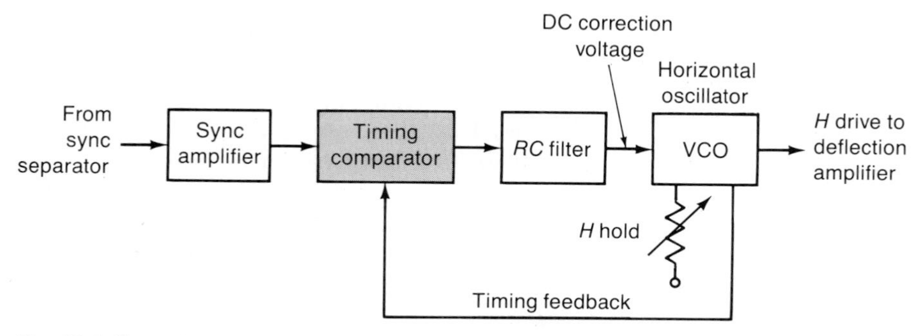

Fig. 12-6 Phase-locked loop (PLL) circuit for horizontal AFC.

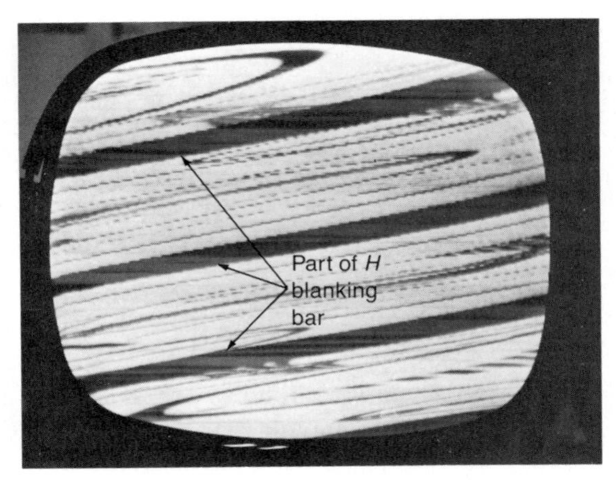

Fig. 12-7 Loss of *H* sync causes picture to break into diagonal bars.

larly, the power output for vertical scanning determines the height of the raster. Also, the horizontal power output determines the width of the raster.

The methods of producing *V* and *H* scanning current differ in principle, mainly because of the effect of the yoke inductance at the two different scanning frequencies. For *V* scanning at 60 Hz, the deflection coils are mainly resistive. However, for *H* scanning at 15,750 Hz, the deflection coils provide an inductive load, since the sharp changes in current produce a large value of self-induced voltage. In either case, though, sawtooth current is needed for linear scanning.

VERTICAL SCANNING CURRENT The inductive reactance of the vertical deflection coils at 60 Hz is small, compared with the effective resistance. So the vertical deflection amplifier is similar to a class A audio output stage. The vertical amplifier produces sawtooth current in the *V* scanning coils, with sawtooth driving voltage from the *V* oscillator. The oscillator uses an *RC* network to develop a sawtooth waveform of voltage.

The vertical output stage is a power amplifier. It acts as a current source to provide a linear rise in the deflection coils for vertical trace at the field-scanning rate. The stage is cut off for only the brief retrace time.

Two controls in the *RC* circuits that develop the sawtooth voltage are provided to adjust the amplitude and shape of the output waveforms. These controls at the back of the receiver are labeled

V size or height

V linearity (LIN)

The height control is adjusted so that the picture just fills the mask around the picture tube from top to bottom. The *V* linearity control is adjusted for uniform deflection, without stretching or compression of the picture. Figure 12-8 shows examples of incorrect *V* size and linearity.

HORIZONTAL SCANNING CURRENT The required sawtooth waveform presents a little different problem here because the inductive reactance of the yoke is high for the extremely fast rate of current change. A typical value for the horizontal deflection coils is a change of several amperes in about 58 μs. In this case, the *H* windings appear as almost pure inductance.

Consider the effect of a perfectly linear rise of current *I* in a pure inductance *L*. The flux of the magnetic field associated with *I* expands at a uniform rate. The resulting self-induced voltage *V* across the coil has a constant value. The voltage is constant because the rate of change of *I* is constant. The rate of change of *I* determines *V*.

If we look at this effect in the opposite way, then a constant voltage across the *H* scanning coils will produce a sawtooth rise in current. The function of the output circuit, then, is to supply a voltage pulse of constant amplitude for horizontal trace.

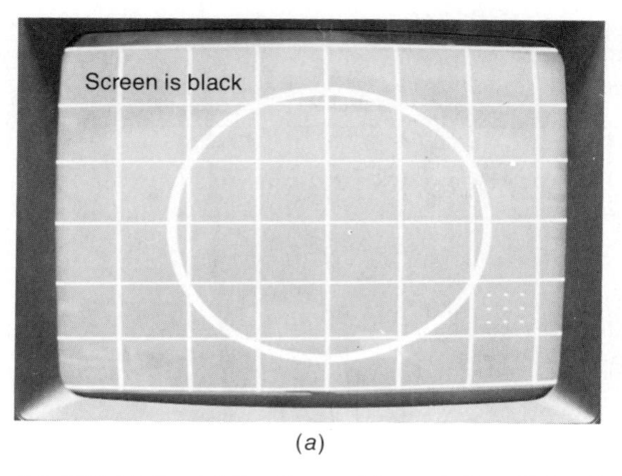

(a)

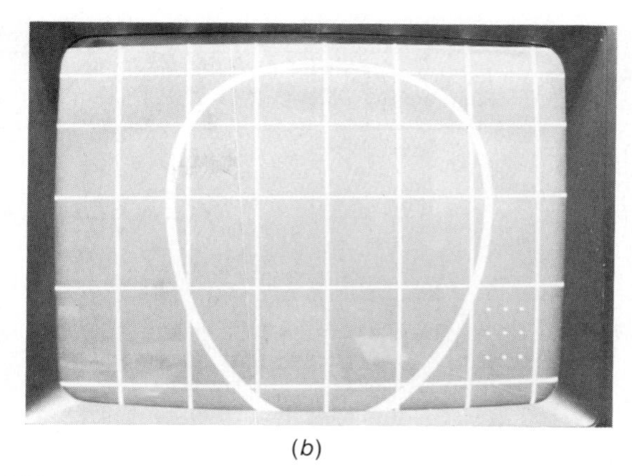

(b)

Fig. 12-8 Vertical deflection problems. (*a*) Insufficient height because of weak *V* scanning amplitude. Screen can be black at bottom or top or both. (*b*) Poor vertical linearity. Picture can be squeezed at bottom or top.

The *H* deflection amplifier is pulse-driven to be in either saturation or cutoff. The amplifier itself acts as a switch that is on or off.

In general, the voltage waveshapes in the horizontal output circuit are rectangular pulses, for a sawtooth waveform of scanning current. Specifically, though, additional special features are used to increase the efficiency and to produce flyback high voltage for the picture tube. More details are explained in Chap. 13. Note that the horizontal output stage consumes more than 75 percent of the total power used by the receiver.

Size and linearity controls are seldom used for the horizontal deflection circuits. The system is designed for maximum efficiency, which would only be reduced by any adjustments.

Test Point Questions 12-2

Answers at End of Chapter

a. Is the sync used for the deflection oscillator or the amplifier?

b. The *V* oscillator frequency is too low. Which control needs to be adjusted?

c. The screen has too much black area across the bottom. Which control would you adjust?

d. Is a sawtooth waveform of current needed in the *V* coils, *H* coils, or both?

e. Is AFC used for the *V* or *H* deflection oscillator?

f. Is high voltage for the picture tube anode produced by the *V* or *H* output circuit?

12-3 AUTOMATIC GAIN CONTROL

Refer to the receiver block diagram in Fig. 12-3 to see that the video signal is also applied to an AGC section. This circuit produces a dc bias for automatic gain control on the RF and IF amplifiers. The AGC circuit is a closed-loop system, which means that it has feedback. More details of the system are shown in the block diagram in Fig. 12-9. The AGC provides a fixed level of video signal at the output of the video detector, despite the widely varying levels of the RF signal supplied by the antenna. Reception conditions can vary from an antenna signal less

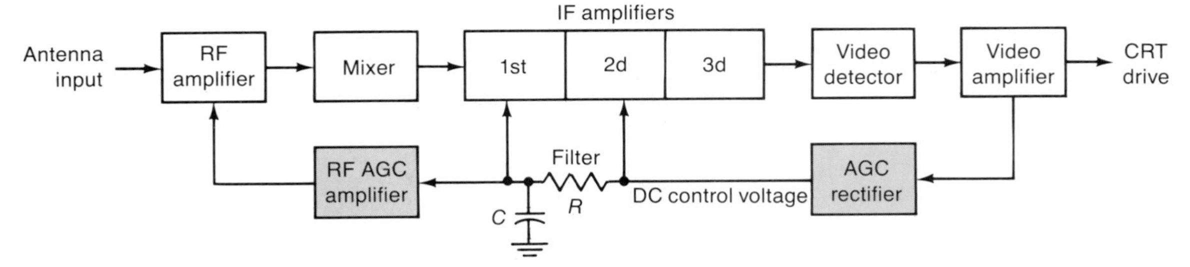

Fig. 12-9 Feedback loop of AGC circuit. The AGC bias controls RF and IF gain.

than 100 μV to one that is a few tenths of a volt. The amount of signal at the receiver depends on the transmitter power, the receiving antenna distance from the transmitter, and other factors. With AGC, though, the picture contrast is about the same when the receiver is switched to different stations.

PRODUCING THE AGC BIAS The AGC system develops a dc control voltage that is proportional to the peak value of the received signal. Since negative transmission, or downward modulation, is used at the transmitter, the peak value of the signal is the tip of sync. This level is unaffected by variations in picture content. The AGC rectifier in Fig. 12-9 produces the dc control voltage for the AGC bias. To eliminate ac signal variations, *RC* filters are used for the dc bias.

A peak rectifier, however, is susceptible to the effects of noise pulses added to the RF carrier signal. The impulse noise can affect the control bias from the AGC circuit, which acts as though there were more signal. The *RC* filter for AGC bias also minimizes the effects of noise.

DISTRIBUTION OF THE AGC BIAS As shown in Fig. 12-9, the dc bias from the AGC circuit is connected to the early IF amplifiers and to the RF amplifier in the tuner. These AGC-controlled stages are designed to change the gain with a change in dc bias. The results are as follows:

1. More antenna signal produces more AGC bias.
2. More AGC bias reduces the receiver gain.

The main thing is to reduce the gain the most for strong signals to prevent overloading with too much signal input for the RF and IF amplifiers. Gain is reduced less for weaker signals. The overall result of the AGC action is to maintain a constant level of video signal output from the video detector stage.

Test Point Questions 12-3

Answers at End of Chapter

Answer True or False.

a. The AGC rectifier is a peak detector.
b. More AGC bias results in more receiver gain.
c. The AGC action keeps the picture contrast approximately the same for different stations.

12-4 DC POWER REQUIREMENTS

All the amplifiers in the receiver need dc power. The reason is that an amplifier for ac signal input provides amplified output by controlling the dc values in the output circuit. A transistor needs dc electrode voltages in order to conduct any current at all. Refer to the receiver block diagram in Fig. 12-3. The power supply converts the ac power line input to dc supply voltage. Filters are used to eliminate ac ripple in the dc output.

Various dc voltages are required to fit the needs of the signal circuits, the deflection circuits, and the picture tube. A typical 19-in. black-and-white receiver needs the following:

1. *Low voltage.* About 12 to 35 V for small-signal amplifiers.
2. *Medium voltage.* About 200 V for the video output stage.
3. *Medium voltage.* About 150 V for the horizontal output stage.
4. *Medium voltage.* About 300 to 400 V for the screen grid of the picture tube and for the focus grid.
5. *High voltage.* About 15 to 18 kV of anode voltage for a monochrome picture tube.

The requirements for the video output stage and horizontal output stage are different. The video drive for the picture tube may be more than 100 V but with very little current. In the horizontal output circuit, the main factor is the load current, typically at 1 A or more.

In modern receivers, there is seldom one common power supply for the low-voltage and medium-voltage requirements. Common practice is to use several separate rectifiers, driven by either retrace or scan pulses in the output from the horizontal output stage. This method provides the required dc voltages for the signal circuits, where the current demand is small. The filtering is simplified because the ripple frequency is high at 15,750 Hz, instead of 60 Hz.

The dc supply voltage for amplifiers is called either V^+ or B^+, from the days when a B battery was used. A voltage regulator often is used for the V^+ supply. The regulator maintains a constant dc output voltage with changes in load current.

In portable equipment, the dc supply voltage is provided by a battery. Small television receivers often operate either from batteries or from the ac power line. In Fig. 12-2, the receiver has both types of connections for power input. The dc input jack is for +12 V, from a car or boat battery.

The plug for 120-V ac input is attached to the rear cover of the receiver. As a safety interlock, the plug comes off when the cover is removed. To operate the receiver temporarily without the cover, a *cheater cord* can be used, which has the same type of plug as on the cover. For receivers using a transformerless power supply, the plug is polarized with a wider pin for the grounded side of the ac input.

Test Point Questions 12-4

Answers at End of Chapter

a. Is a typical dc supply voltage for small-signal transistor amplifiers 18 or 400 V?
b. Is the anode high voltage for a color picture tube usually 400 V or 25 kV?
c. Is horizontal flyback the trace or retrace time?

12-5 RF SECTION

The RF tuner, or *front end,* is the frequency converter part of the superheterodyne receiver. The tuner accepts antenna signals at all channel frequencies. These signals are converted to a single band of frequencies in the IF passband for the fixed-tuned IF amplifier. The output of the RF tuner is the start of the IF section.

VHF AND UHF CHANNELS The tuner actually is composed of two units. One covers the VHF band of television channels 2 to 13. The other tunes the UHF band of television channels 14 to 83. However, channels 70 to 83 are now used for communications services. Both units are mounted as a common assembly, as shown for the receiver in Fig. 12-2. The assembly is mounted at the front of the receiver cabinet, where it is convenient to use the station selector. It should be noted, though, that for varactor tuners with pushbutton switches any position can be used for a VHF or UHF channel.

Note the two pairs of screw terminals for the antenna input connection in Fig. 12-2. One pair is for the 300-Ω, balanced twin-lead transmission line from the VHF antenna. These connections go to the VHF tuner. The other pair connect UHF channels to the UHF tuner.

Many receivers also have an input jack for cable TV. This connection is for 75-Ω coaxial cable. It goes to the VHF tuner, since only VHF channels are used for cable television. When the receiver does not have this jack for cable input, a small balun is used to convert from 75-Ω unbalanced to 300-Ω balanced connections for the receiver input. A balanced line does not have either side grounded.

The IF output of the RF tuner is connected to the main chassis by a short length of 75-Ω coaxial cable. The VHF tuner supplies the IF output. The UHF tuner feeds the VHF tuner.

BLOCK DIAGRAM OF VHF TUNER See Fig. 12-10. The first stage of the VHF tuner is the RF amplifier, or *preselector.* Its input is the RF signal for the TV channels, from either the antenna or the cable feed. The signal for the desired channel is amplified to drive the mixer stage.

The preselector is a tuned radio frequency (TRF) amplifier. Its tuned circuits are changed each time a new channel is selected. The bandwidth is great enough to cover the 6 MHz required in each channel to include the picture and sound carrier frequencies. These signals are marked *P* and *S* on the RF response curve.

The gain of the RF amplifier changes with the level of the input signal, because of the control by AGC bias. At low signal levels, less than 2 mV, the RF amplifier operates at maximum gain. This gain is very important to achieve a good *signal-to-noise ratio* into the mixer. In a superheterodyne circuit, the mixer is the main source of receiver noise, which produces snow in the picture. The level of RF signal applied to the mixer is the main factor in the overall signal-to-noise ratio of the receiver. Therefore, the RF stage should function as a low-noise amplifier for weak signals.

When a very strong antenna signal is coupled into the RF amplifier, it serves a different function. The stage should act as an attenuator, to ensure that the following stages are not overloaded with too much signal drive. The AGC bias controls the gain of the RF amplifier, as necessary for weak and strong signals.

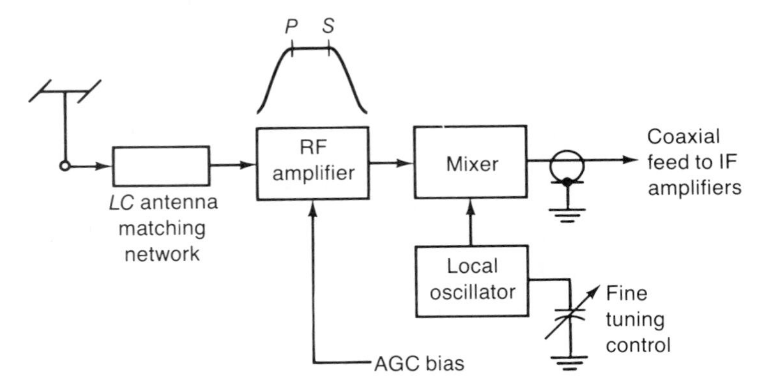

Fig. 12-10 Block diagram of VHF tuner.

The *mixer stage* is supplied with two input signals. One is the amplified channel signal from the preselector stage, and the other is the cw signal from the local oscillator. The oscillator is tuned to a specific frequency for each channel. Usually, the oscillator beats above the RF channel frequencies. The frequency difference is the IF value. For example, for the 175.25-MHz RF picture carrier signal in channel 7, the oscillator frequency is 175.25 + 45.75 = 221 MHz. It is the oscillator frequency that determines which channel signals come through the IF section. A vernier control, called *fine tuning,* provides precise oscillator tuning for the best picture.

The simple addition of two RF signals does not produce heterodyning. To produce output at the sum and difference frequencies, the mixer stage must rectify the combined waveform of the RF signal and the oscillator cw output. This means that the mixer stage is a nonlinear amplifier. Transistor mixers operate very close to zero bias, which results in class B amplification.

FREQUENCY INVERSION OF IF OUTPUT FROM THE MIXER When the local oscillator beats above the RF signal frequencies, the picture and sound carrier frequencies become reversed in the sense of which is higher. This action is illustrated in Fig. 12-11, with numerical values for channel 7. The channel is 174 to 180 MHz. Its RF picture carrier P is 175.25 MHz, with the sound S at 179.75 MHz. The local oscillator frequency is

$$175.25 + 45.75 = 221 \text{ MHz}$$
$$179.75 + 41.25 = 221 \text{ MHz}$$

The IF values are produced as the frequency differences resulting from P or S beating with the oscillator at 221 MHz. The value of S in the IF output is lower because the frequency is closer to the oscillator frequency, which means a smaller difference. The RF and IF carrier frequencies can be tabulated as follows:

	RF	IF
Picture	175.25	221 − 175.25 = 45.75
Sound	179.75	221 − 179.75 = 41.25

The P and S frequencies are still 4.5 MHz apart. However, the sound carrier signal is now 4.5 MHz lower at intermediate frequencies. The same reversal is true of video modulating frequencies. The frequencies of the high baseband video signals (those corresponding to fine details in the picture) are above the RF picture carrier frequency as the signal is transmitted. When converted to intermediate frequencies, however, the same high video frequencies are below the IF picture carrier frequency.

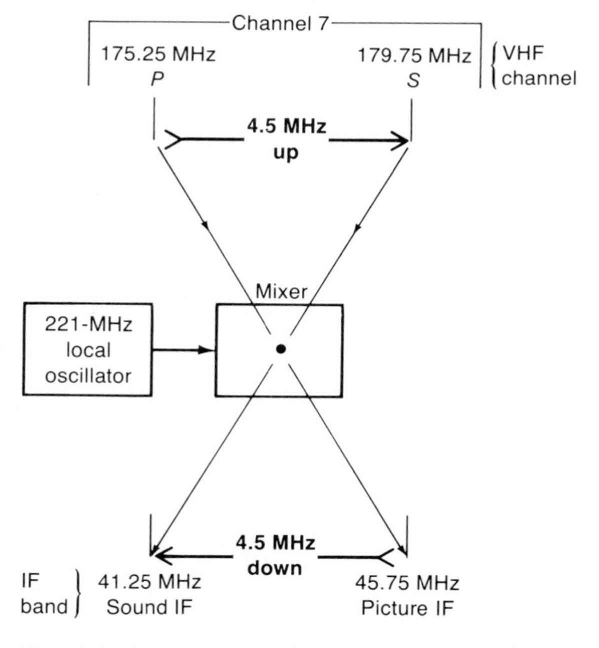

Fig. 12-11 The heterodyning process reverses relative positions of picture and sound carrier frequencies within 6-MHz channel.

ISOLATION BY THE RF AMPLIFIER In this important function, the RF stage separates the mixer from the antenna circuit. The reason is that the preselector is tuned to only the radio frequencies within the selected channel. Two problems are solved. First, any interfering RF signals outside the channel that exist in the antenna circuit are attenuated by the RF stage. Remember that one disadvantage of the superheterodyne circuit is the fact that any signal that beats with the oscillator to produce IF output will be received as well as the desired signal.

The second problem is the attenuation of the RF stage in the reverse direction, from the mixer to the antenna. This feature is very important in preventing the local oscillator signal, which is at the mixer input, from reaching the antenna. Any oscillator radiation from the antenna is a source of interference to other equipment. FCC certification requirements are aimed at preventing the TV receiver from transmitting interfering signals by oscillator radiation.

UHF TUNER The UHF tuner is basically similar to the VHF tuner, but its design requirements are different because of the higher frequencies in the UHF band. One difference is that often the UHF tuner does not include an RF amplifier stage. Low-noise RF amplifiers for the UHF band are costly. The mixer is generally just a high-frequency diode. As a result, the entire RF input circuit is passive, without any amplification. The local oscillator, though, uses a UHF transistor. As in the VHF tuner, the UHF oscillator beats above the RF signal—45.75 MHz higher than the picture carrier frequency of the selected UHF channel. FCC rules for local oscillator radiation are less stringent for UHF than VHF operation because many UHF tuners do not have the RF amplifier stage.

The IF output of the UHF tuner is not routed directly to the IF amplifier. Instead, the IF signal is fed to the VHF tuner. This circuit is transformed to two stages of additional IF amplification when the UHF tuner is in operation.

When the station selector is set to the UHF position for mechanically switched tuners, the following changes occur:

1. The RF amplifier and mixer input circuits on the VHF tuner are tuned to the IF passband.
2. The dc supply voltage is connected to the UHF tuner to activate its local oscillator.
3. The VHF local oscillator is turned off.
4. The VHF antenna feed is disconnected to substitute the IF output of the UHF tuner.

VARACTOR TUNERS The *varactor* is a diode that changes capacitance with the amount of reverse voltage. Then the oscillator frequency is changed by varying the dc control voltage on the varactor diode. Varactor tuners often have pushbutton switches for the channels, instead of a rotary station selector switch. Varactor-tuned circuits have a higher noise level than passive *LC* circuits.

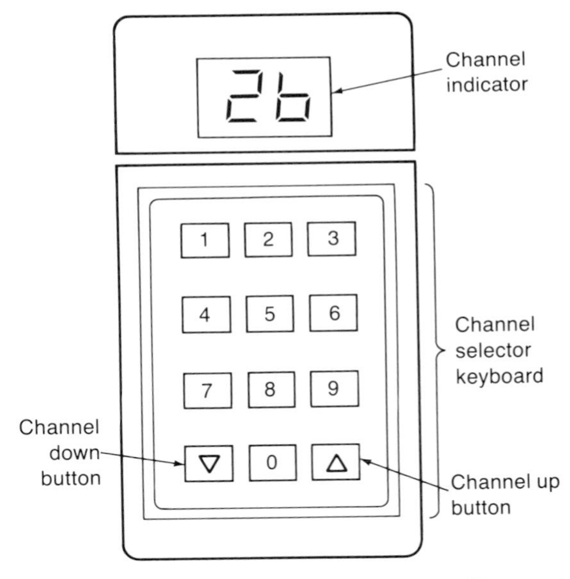

Fig. 12-12 Keyboard for selecting channels with varactor tuner. (*Quasar model TS-971*)

So an RF amplifier stage is needed in UHF varactor tuners to improve the signal-to-noise ratio.

The varactor tuners are more expensive than the rotary switch type, but they are commonly used for added convenience with remote-control operation and for fast tuning in changing channels. Figure 12-12 shows the keyboard for selecting channels with a varactor tuner. The electronic tuning with the varactor circuits enables quick selection of each channel. Note that the channels are selected by two-digit numbers, such as 04 for channel 4. Digital processing circuits are used for processing the keying signals for the channels. Channel 26 in Fig. 12-12 is for a cable TV channel. The same type of keyboard is used in a separate unit for remote-control tuning. The remote transmitter emits infrared light that is picked up at the receiver to activate the tuner.

Test Point Questions 12-5

Answers at End of Chapter

a. Does the local oscillator beat above or below the RF signal frequencies?

b. Which stage in the tuner is most effective in reducing oscillator radiation?

c. Which stage produces the greatest receiver noise?

d. What is the local oscillator frequency for tuning in channel 14?

e. Which stage in the receiver does the output signal of the VHF mixer feed?

12-6 IF SECTION

The IF amplifier accepts only the intermediate frequencies in the output of the mixer stage because these circuits are tuned for the IF signal. There just is no gain for the original RF input and the sum frequencies. Only the IF signal is amplified.

The primary function of the IF section is to raise the signal level to the point at which the AM envelope can be detected. A semiconductor diode generally is used as a half-wave rectifier to detect the IF signal. A signal level of at least 0.5 V is necessary for linear detection. Thus the IF section consists of two or three cascaded amplifiers for an overall voltage gain of approximately 10,000. For example, with a 0.2-mV IF signal from the mixer, the amplified output to the video detector equals 2 V. A block diagram of the IF amplifier section and video detector is shown in Fig. 12-13, along with the IF response curve. Note that both the 45.75-MHz picture IF signal and the 41.25-MHz sound IF signal are amplified in the common IF section. The colorplexed 3.58-MHz chroma signal is part of the picture signal.

IF BANDWIDTH In early TV receivers, a system of staggered tuning for the IF stages was used to achieve the necessary bandwidth. Now the shape of the overall IF response curve is determined mainly by the IF circuit coupling the mixer output in the tuner to the first IF amplifier. In this way, unwanted signals are rejected before they are amplified, which avoids the problem of cross modulation in later stages. In addition, wavetraps are used to reject interference from adjacent channels.

The mixer output circuit is typically an overcoupled double-tuned transformer. Traps are inserted in the secondary circuit. This part of the IF section is indicated as the input filter at the left in Fig. 12-13. A newer approach uses a special component called a *surface-acoustic-wave* (*SAW*) *filter,* which does not require *LC* resonant circuits.

IF WAVE TRAPS In addition to its gain for the desired signal, the IF amplifier provides the adjacent-channel selectivity of the receiver to reject interference. The IF response at the edges of the passband is determined by *LC* trap circuits. These circuits cut into the skirts of the response

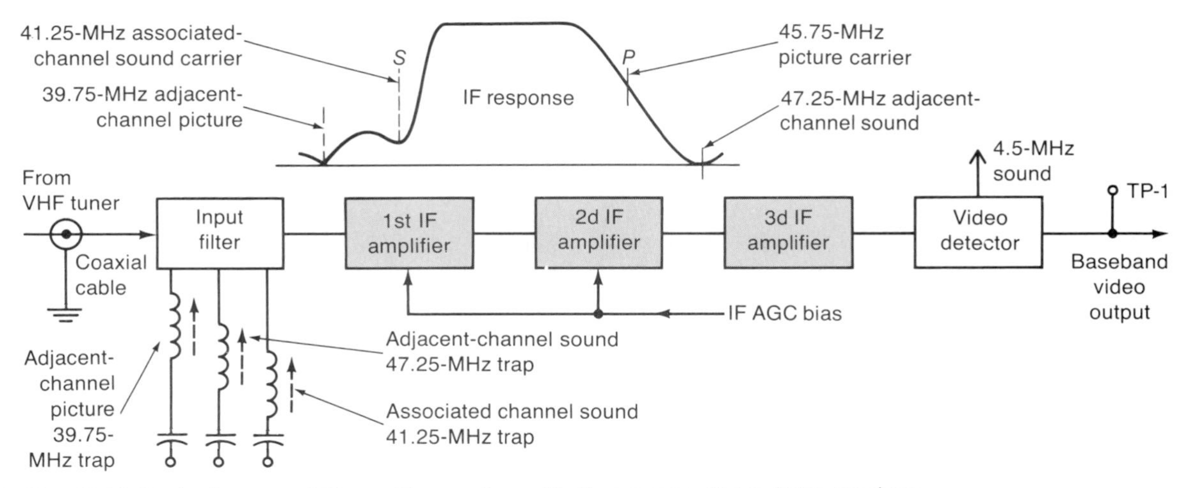

Fig. 12-13 Block diagram of IF amplifier section with IF response. Wave traps produce notches in the curve.

curve, by reducing the IF gain at the trap frequencies. As shown at the IF input filter in Fig. 12-13, the trap frequencies are:

39.75 MHz for the upper adjacent-channel picture carrier

41.25 MHz for the associated channel sound carrier

47.25 MHz for the lower adjacent-channel sound carrier

The frequencies for adjacent RF channels are discussed in Chap. 11. Since the RF tuner does not have enough selectivity to reject adjacent channels, the attenuation is done by the IF amplifier. Here, the adjacent channel interference for any channel is always at the IF trap frequencies. Therefore, they can be fixed-tuned, to shape the edges of the IF response curve.

50 PERCENT RESPONSE FOR IF PICTURE CARRIER In Fig. 12-13, the gain at 45.75 MHz is only one-half the value for frequencies in the flat part of the response. It may seem peculiar to have less gain for the picture carrier frequency, but this response is necessary to compensate for vestigial sideband transmission, as described in Chap. 11.

In the RF picture signal, double sidebands are transmitted for the lower video modulating frequencies, up to about 0.75 MHz. Higher video modulating frequencies up to 4 MHz are transmitted with only the upper sideband. The effect is a relative boost in energy for video frequencies ±0.75 MHz around the picture carrier frequency. With the IF response at 50 percent for *P*, though, the boost in RF energy is canceled by the reduced IF gain. In the overall system for the transmitter and receiver, then, all video frequencies are equalized in the output from the video detector.

Test Point Questions 12-6

Answers at End of Chapter

a. Is the 41.25-MHz IF sound signal 4.5 MHz above or below the picture signal?

b. Is the IF response at 45.75 MHz equal to 10, 50, or 100 percent?

c. Is the channel selectivity of the receiver determined by IF or RF traps?

d. Which stage in the television receiver is driven by the IF section?

12-7 VIDEO DETECTOR

The signal from the final IF amplifier drives the video detector as shown in Fig. 12-14. The detector is typically a high-frequency diode rectifier with a filter in its output circuit that bypasses the IF ripple component. The video detector output circuit is the first place where a baseband composite video signal can be viewed with an oscilloscope.

VIDEO DETECTOR POLARITY Polarity refers to positive or negative sync in the video signal output. There are two possibilities, depending on where the diode load resistor R_L is connected:

1. Resistor R_L can be in the diode cathode return. Then the sync is positive, with respect to chassis ground. Usually the IF signal input then is at the diode anode.
2. Resistor R_L can be in the diode anode circuit. Then the sync is negative. Usually the IF signal input then is at the diode cathode.

Remember that the modulated picture signal has its peak amplitude for the tip of sync. This amplitude produces the peak voltage output across R_L.

The detector polarity is chosen to fit the needs of the video amplifier driving the picture tube and to provide some degree of noise reduction. Cathode drive at the picture tube is almost universal. So the polarity of the signal output from the video amplifier is positive sync. The video amplifier itself is usually an inverting amplifier. Its input must be negative sync, then, for a single stage. Most black-and-white TV receivers with one video amplifier have negative sync output from the video detector, as shown in Fig. 12-14. An advantage of this polarity is that noise pulses that exceed the peak sync at the input of the video amplifier can be clipped by cutoff.

Color TV receivers may use two inverting video amplifiers. Then the video detector output has positive sync polarity. Two inversions provide positive sync drive at the cathode of the picture tube. Noise suppression still can be accomplished by using a PNP transistor for the first video amplifier.

DETECTOR FREQUENCY RESPONSE A low-pass filter is used in the output to remove the IF ripple but pass the baseband video signal. In addition, the 4.5-MHz second sound IF signal is taken from the video detector in monochrome receivers. The required bandwidth for the video detector output circuit is 0 Hz to 4.5 MHz. In Fig. 12-14, the 44-MHz bandstop filter in the video

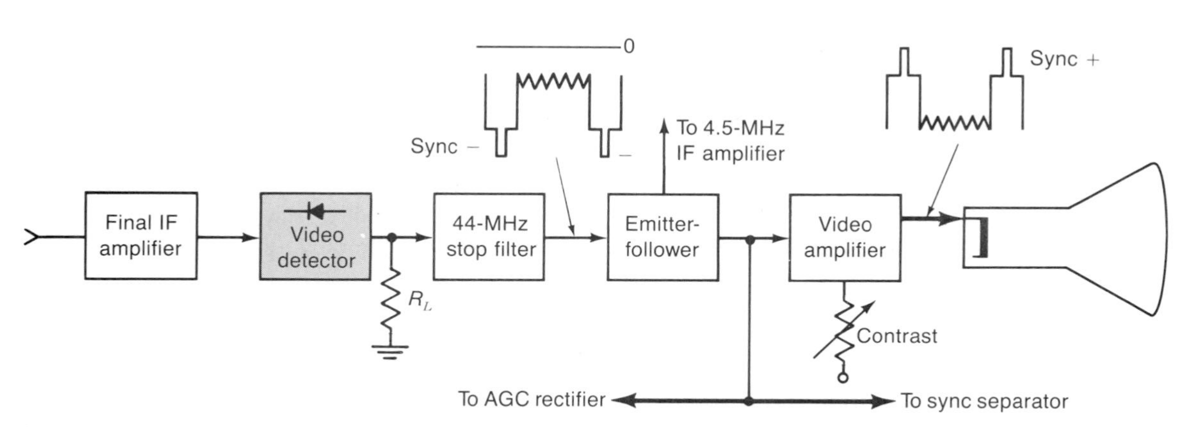

Fig. 12-14 Block diagram of video detector and video amplifier for black-and-white TV receiver. Emitter-follower does not invert polarity of video signal.

detector output prevents the IF signal from reaching the video amplifier.

The 0 Hz means direct current. In other words, the detector output has the dc level of the demodulated signal. Actually, the IF signal input to the detector can be checked by measuring the dc output with a dc voltmeter across R_L.

Test Point Questions 12-7

Answers at End of Chapter

Answer True or False.

a. Figure 12-14 shows negative sync output from the video detector.

b. The emitter-follower in Fig. 12-14 does not invert the signal polarity.

12-8 VIDEO AMPLIFIER SECTION

The primary function of the video amplifier is to provide the voltage swing needed to drive the picture tube from cutoff, for blanking, to practically zero grid-cathode voltage, for peak white. In p-p values, this signal swing may vary from about 30 V for small picture tubes to about 200 V. With about 1 V of signal from the video detector, the required voltage gain in the video amplifier is 30 to 200.

The dc supply voltage for the video amplifier must be more than the p-p signal swing. For this reason, the video amplifier in a solid-state receiver usually has its own dedicated power supply, just for the video output. Typically, the rectifier is driven by input pulses obtained from the horizontal output stage.

Usually control of gain is provided in the video amplifier to permit adjustment of the picture contrast. As illustrated in Fig. 12-14, the contrast control varies the amplifier gain for the ac video signal. The gain must be varied without altering the dc operating point, so that linear operation is maintained.

EMITTER-FOLLOWER AS A BUFFER STAGE In addition to driving the picture tube, the video amplifier section can be the feed point for the following:

1. AGC circuit
2. Sync separator
3. The 4.5-MHz sound signal

This arrangement is illustrated by the video section in Fig. 12-14 for a black-and-white receiver. In color receivers, a separate sound detector is used, instead of the video detector, for the 4.5-MHz second sound IF signal.

Note the use of an emitter-follower in Fig. 12-14 as a buffer stage between the video detector and the video amplifier. First, the emitter-follower does not invert the signal's polarity. The video amplifier still has a video signal with negative sync from the detector. Second, and most important, the emitter-follower provides impedance matching. It has high input impedance, which allows the video detector to work into a high-impedance load. The buffer stage also provides a low source impedance for feeding the AGC and sync separator circuits. This arrangement reduces amplitude distortion that can be caused by heavy load current during the sync peaks.

Note that the contrast control is in the video amplifier, not the buffer stage. Thus any variation of the control setting does not affect the amount of signal applied to the AGC and sync circuits.

VIDEO AMPLIFIER BANDWIDTH The relative amplitude and phase relations of the frequency components of the video signal must be preserved. Theoretically, the full 4.2-MHz bandwidth for video modulation can be used with the 6-MHz broadcast channel. In the picture, the smallest horizontal details correspond to the highest video frequencies. From a practical standpoint, however, very few TV receivers provide a picture with the highest resolution possible.

Most small-screen receivers provide a luminance resolution of about 250 lines. This value translates to a video bandwidth of about 3.2 MHz. Therefore, practical video amplifier circuits require high-frequency response up to 3.2 or 3.5 MHz. In color receivers, video response for the 3.58-MHz chroma signal is necessary. However, the luminance response still is generally for 250-line resolution. An exception is the trend toward high definition in projection receivers, where the wideband luminance signal is more important because the bigger picture usually has less contrast.

To achieve the required bandwidth in the video amplifier, the shunting effects of the junction capacitance and the wiring must be overcome. The shunt capacitance reduces the gain for high video frequencies. However, compensation is provided by video peaking coils.

Test Point Questions 12-8

Answers at End of Chapter

a. Is ac video signal drive varied by the contrast or the brightness control?

b. Is the input signal for the video amplifier supplied by the video detector or the sync separator?

c. Is the video amplifier bandwidth in a monochrome receiver generally 3.2 or 6.2 MHz?

12-9 DC COMPONENT OF THE VIDEO SIGNAL

The dc component of the video signal indicates relative brightness in the scene with respect to the blanking level. At the output of the video detector, the dc component of the video signal is intact, as transmitted. The reason is that the video signal is only in the modulation envelope of the AM picture signal in the RF and IF amplifiers. Detection is necessary to recover the video signal and its dc component.

To preserve the dc component, the video amplifier is often direct-coupled from the video detector output to the cathode of the picture tube. The direct coupling, or dc coupling, means that no coupling capacitors are used in series. A coupling capacitor passes the ac signal but blocks its average dc level. However, the dc component can be reinserted by a restorer circuit.

EFFECT IN THE VIDEO SIGNAL Loss of the dc component is shown in Fig. 12-15. In Fig. 12-15*a*, the video signal has its correct dc component, but it is blocked by an *RC* coupling circuit, which provides the signal in Fig. 12-15*b*.

The signal at the output side of the series coupling capacitor resolves itself around a zero axis. The total area above zero must equal the total area below zero, so that an average of zero is

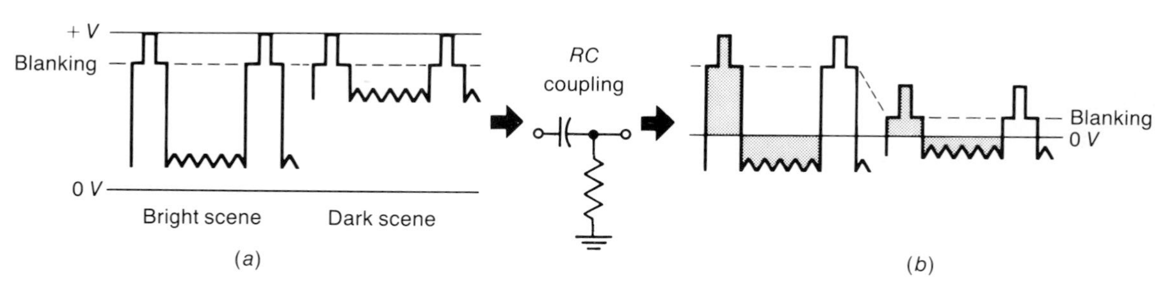

Fig. 12-15 How loss of dc component affects video signal waveform. (*a*) Sync and blanking pulses lined up with dc component. (*b*) The dc component blocked by *RC* coupling circuit.

obtained. As a result, the sync pulses and the blanking level are no longer lined up at a single voltage level. For the picture tube, in which the bias has been set to put blanking at the cutoff level for bright scenes, now the blanking level will be well into the conduction area for dark scenes. The undesired results are

1. Wrong brightness
2. Vertical retrace lines not being blanked by video blanking

In black-and-white receivers, these effects are not too obvious. All receivers use internal blanking to eliminate the retrace lines.

EFFECT IN THE PICTURE The wrong brightness can produce annoying visual effects. Figure 12-16 shows an example of a still picture mounted on a white wall. In Fig. 12-16*a,* the picture has a normal balance of black and white. In Fig. 12-16*b,* though, the camera lens was zoomed out to include much of the white wall in the background. The addition of so much white causes the darker parts of the picture to go beyond the cutoff voltage for the picture tube, so the picture looks too dark. Also, the dark gray details are not visible. The same thing would happen with a performer wearing dark clothing and standing in front of a white curtain.

In general, the picture information is either too dark against a light background or too light against a dark background. In many monochrome receivers these effects are tolerated, since *RC* coupling is used in the video amplifier, without any dc restorer.

In color receivers, though, loss of the dc component causes incorrect colors, which cannot be tolerated. For this reason, color receivers use direct coupling or dc restorers. You can compare the dc levels for receivers by watching at the instant when the picture goes to black between commercials. Properly adjusted sets with good dc retention really go black; the others retain a gray raster.

DC REINSERTION An alternative to direct coupling is to restore, or reinsert, the dc component blocked by capacitive coupling. The dc component is reinserted at the output of the video amplifier, in the circuit that drives the picture tube. A dc restorer is a clamp circuit. It clamps the sync tips to a fixed voltage level. Thus the video signal is restored to the original form it had at the video detector output.

(*a*)

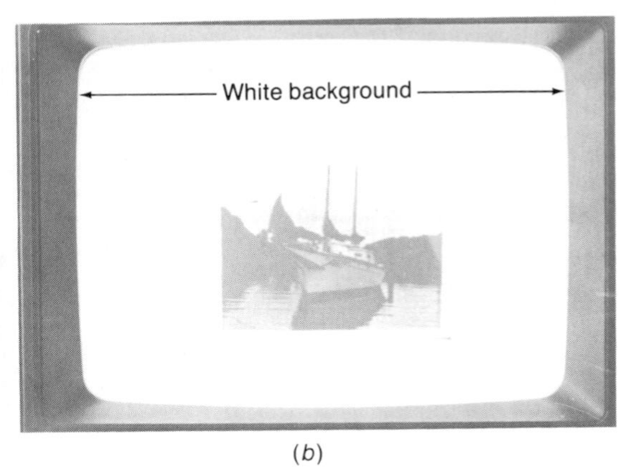

(*b*)

Fig. 12-16 Visual effects of dc component. (*a*) Correct brightness. (*b*) Loss of dc component.

The dc restorer circuit uses a diode to rectify the video signal itself. The rectified signal indicates how much dc level must be reinserted.

Test Point Questions 12-9

Answers at End of Chapter

a. Does the dc component of the video signal determine the brightness or the contrast in the picture?

b. Which method preserves the dc component, capacitive or direct coupling?

12-10 THE 4.5-MHz SOUND IF SECTION

The associated sound is transmitted as an FM signal in the TV broadcast channel, with a center frequency 4.5 MHz above the picture carrier frequency. The maximum frequency deviation is ±25 kHz above and below the sound carrier frequency. As explained in Chap. 11, "Television Transmission," FM is used for the sound signal because it is free from noise and interference. The principles of using FM for television sound apply in the same way as for FM radio in the broadcast band of 88 to 108 MHz, except that the frequency swing is ±25 kHz, instead of ±75 kHz, for 100 percent modulation. As in an FM receiver, the sound IF circuits require AM limiting and an FM detector for audio output.

SPLIT SOUND In very early TV receivers, the sound IF signal, then at 21.25 MHz, was split off at the output of the RF tuner and applied to a separate sound IF section tuned to 21.25 MHz.

The problems with this split-sound method are the tuning accuracy and frequency drift of the local oscillator. The sound IF signal has a very narrow bandwidth of 50 kHz, compared with approximately 4 MHz for the picture signal. As a result, local oscillator tuning or drift was critical for the sound IF carrier signal. The first effect noted is the distorted sound, before you can see any change in the picture. Tuning for the high-frequency channels was especially difficult. These old receivers were fine-tuned by listening to the audio, not by looking at the picture.

INTERCARRIER SOUND As shown by the block diagram in Fig. 12-17, the sound IF signal is amplified and detected as the 4.5-MHz beat between the picture and sound carrier frequencies. The advantage—and it is very important—is that the 4.5-MHz second sound IF signal is independent of the local oscillator frequency. As a result, tuning in the sound is easy for any VHF or UHF channel. When you have a picture, the 4.5-MHz sound is there also. The intercarrier sound system was invented in 1947 by R. B. Dome of General Electric.

The first 41.25-MHz sound IF signal and the 45.75-MHz picture IF carrier signal are both amplified in the common IF section. Both signals are coupled into the video detector. However, the sound signal has a much lower amplitude than the picture carrier. As a result, the picture carrier serves as a local oscillator to heterodyne with the sound signal. The difference between the carrier frequencies is 45.75 − 41.25 MHz. Then the FM sound signal is beat down to 4.5 MHz as the center frequency. It is still an FM signal, with the original modulation. An FM detector is needed to recover the audio signal.

Note that the 4.5-MHz difference depends on the transmitted carrier frequencies, not the local oscillator in the receiver. The tuning can be so far off that the picture is not good enough to watch but the sound remains. An interesting side effect, though, is that loss of the picture carrier at the transmitter also results in loss of sound at the receiver.

The video detector has the bandwidth needed to include the 4.5-MHz sound signal. This signal is separated by a 4.5-MHz trap in the video cir-

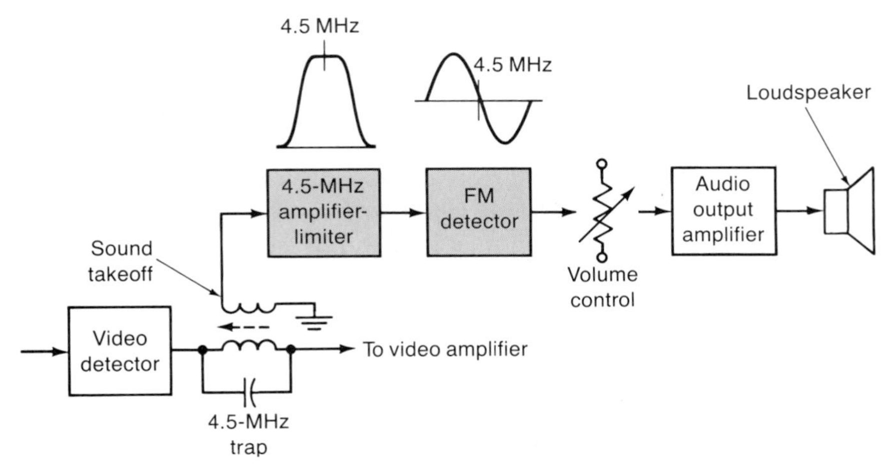

Fig. 12-17 The 4.5-MHz intercarrier sound system in monochrome receiver.

cuits. In monochrome receivers, the trap is the *sound takeoff,* which couples the signal to the 4.5-MHz sound IF section, as shown in Fig. 12-17. Generally one IF stage is enough for amplifying the 4.5-MHz sound IF signal. Then a circuit such as a ratio detector is used to recover the audio modulation. Amplitude limiting in the 4.5- MHz section rejects noise in the FM signal. Note that the entire sound section with IF amplifier, FM detector, and audio amplifier can be in one IC unit.

Audio deemphasis is used in the detector output to compensate for the preemphasis in transmission. The time constant for preemphasis and deemphasis is 75 μs.

Test Point Questions 12-10

Answers at End of Chapter

a. What is the frequency of the second sound IF signal when the receiver is tuned to UHF channel 14?

b. What is the resonant frequency of the sound takeoff trap in the video circuits?

c. What is the maximum frequency deviation of the FM associated sound signal?

12-11 TROUBLESHOOTING THE SIGNAL CIRCUITS

A break in the signal path between the antenna terminals and the picture tube results in no picture, with a blank raster. Keep in mind the fact that the raster is produced by the horizontal and vertical deflection circuits.

However, some observations can narrow the problem down to major sections for the signal. For example, a blank raster with normal sound points to a break in the signal path after the video detector, where the 4.5-MHz sound signal is taken off. This trouble is localized to the video amplifier.

Note, though, that the sound may not be normal because of loss of drive to the AGC system. The absence of AGC bias causes IF overload, producing a loud buzz in the sound.

Locating the problem between the video amplifier and the IF section is relatively easy with an oscilloscope. Check the output signal from the video detector. Its value is typically 0.5 to 1.5 V p-p. No detector output indicates either no IF signal input or a defective detector diode. The dc level of the detector output also can be checked with a dc voltmeter.

The appearance of snow indicates that the signal chain is intact for the mixer in the RF tuner, IF amplifier, video amplifier, and the picture tube. The break, then, is ahead of the mixer, or in the local oscillator. In the path before the mixer are the RF amplifier and antenna circuits.

The total absence of snow points to a break in the IF section, rather than the RF section. This effect also indicates trouble in the video section, but we have determined that the video detector has no IF signal input.

Loss of gain in the signal path reduces the picture contrast. Here again, the receiver noise is a clue to the trouble. If the picture is weak but snowy, the fault lies in the RF circuits ahead of the mixer. If the picture has no snow, then the loss of gain is in the IF or video signal. To locate the problem between the IF and video sections, checking the signal level out of the video detector provides the key clue.

AGC troubles are the most difficult to localize because the AGC circuit is a closed-loop system with feedback. The video section supplies the input signal to the AGC rectifier, but its dc bias in the output controls the gain of the IF and RF sections.

An AGC trouble that produces too much control voltage can result in the no-picture symptom. The result is the same as failure of the IF amplifier. Remember that AGC bias always works in the direction of reducing the receiver gain.

The opposite trouble—no AGC bias—causes strong signals to overdrive the IF amplifier. Then the sync is compressed. The picture appears very dark, possibly reversed in black and white, and totally out of sync (Fig. 12-18). Loud buzz in the sound caused by cross modulation between the sync and sound signals is another sign of overload. The buzz is produced by vertical sync pulses in the sound signal.

To locate AGC problems, it is necessary to break the closed loop. Substitute a manual bias voltage for the control bias normally provided by the AGC system. If normal operation can be restored in this way, then the RF and IF sections are normal and the trouble lies in the AGC circuit.

Fig. 12-18 Overloaded picture.

Test Point Questions 12-11
Answers at End of Chapter

Answer True or False.

a. The video detector is the main source of receiver noise.
b. A break in the IF section can cause the symptom of no picture on a clean raster without snow.
c. A break in the antenna circuit can cause the symptom of no picture but with snow.
d. An overload picture is usually out of sync.

12-12 TV MONITOR WITH MODULAR COMPONENTS

Figure 12-19 shows a modular TV system with a 19-in. monitor. The idea is similar to using modules as separate components for a stereo sound system. In fact, this modular system has provisions for audio signal, included with the equipment for video processing and television reception. The purpose of modular units is to allow flexibility in setting up a system for TV reception,

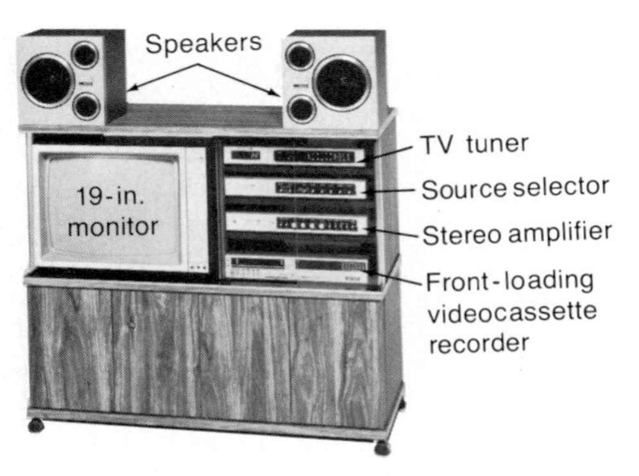

Fig. 12-19 Modular TV system with video monitor. (*Zenith Radio Corp.*)

VCR recording and playback, video disk playback, the use of video games, and a home computer.

TV MONITOR At the top of Fig. 12-19, the monitor is like a TV receiver, with the picture tube and its associated circuits but without the RF tuner and IF section. In the monitor unit are the sync and deflection circuits with the high-voltage supply to produce the scanning raster on the picture tube screen. Also included are the video amplifiers. The standard level of composite video input is 1 V p-p, with negative sync polarity, from 75-Ω coaxial cable. The monitor does not have antenna input connections, but receives the video signal from the source selector below the tuner in Fig. 12-19.

For use with a computer, the monitor provides amplifiers for red, green, and blue video signals, fed from a separate input jack. With *RGB* inputs, the screen brightness can be reduced one-half by an internal jumper wire. Less brightness may be better for the computer display because of the steady image produced.

TV TUNER MODULE This unit has the RF tuner for TV reception. Included are the IF amplifier and detector circuits needed for video and audio outputs. The input and output connections are as follows:

VHF antenna terminals

UHF antenna terminals

Two audio outputs

Two video outputs

The VHF antenna input is for 75-Ω coaxial cable.

All the outputs go to the source selector. This unit is essentially the same as the signal switching box shown in Fig. 1-23. The source unit supplies the signal to the TV monitor. Note that the videocassette recorder is included.

The RF tuner is a varactor tuner, with digital readout of the selected channel. A keyboard is used for manual and remote operation of the tuner. Video blanking is inserted when the channel is changed.

Test Point Questions 12-12

Answers at End of Chapter

Answer True or False.

a. A TV monitor does *not* have an RF tuner.
b. The standard level of composite video signal for connections between modular units is 75 V.
c. A high-voltage supply for the picture tube is included in the TV monitor.

SUMMARY

The functions of all stages in a television receiver are summarized by their input and output signals, listed in Table 12-1. First, the signal stages are given for the RF tuner, including VHF and UHF operation. Then the IF, video detector, and sound sections are listed. Next are the video circuits, followed by the sync separator. The 3.58-MHz chroma section in color receivers is listed here also but more details are explained in Chap. 14. Note the abbreviations: *P* for picture signal, either RF or IF at 45.75 MHz, and *S* for sound signal, RF or IF at 41.25 and 4.5 MHz. Also, *C* is the chroma signal at 3.58 MHz.

Then come the vertical and horizontal deflection circuits, including the high-voltage supply derived from the horizontal flyback voltage. More details on the sync and scanning circuits are given in Chap. 13. Last on the list is the low-voltage power supply needed for all the amplifiers.

TABLE 12-1
FUNCTIONS OF STAGES IN A TELEVISION RECEIVER

STAGE	INPUT SIGNAL	OUTPUT SIGNAL	NOTES
RF amplifier for VHF band	*P* and *S* from antenna	Amplified RF signals to mixer	Low noise for no snow; also is IF amplifier for UHF tuner
Local oscillator for VHF band	None	To VHF mixer	Tunes 45.75 MHz above *P*
VHF mixer	*P* and *S* plus oscillator output	*P* and *S* for IF amplifier	Also is IF amplifier for UHF tuner
Local oscillator for UHF band	None	To UHF mixer	Tunes 45.75 MHz above P
UHF mixer	*P* and *S* at RF plus oscillator output	IF values of *P* and *S* to VHF tuner	RF amplifier optional for UHF tuner
Picture IF, video IF, or common IF section	*P* and *S* from VHF mixer	Amplified *P* and *S* for video detector	$P = 45.75$ MHz, $S = 41.25$ MHz
Video detector	Amplified *P* and *S* from IF section	Composite video signal; also *S* at 4.5 MHz and *C* at 3.58 MHz	Picture detector or second detector
Sound IF amplifier	*S* at 4.5 MHz from video detector	*S* at 4.5 MHz to FM sound detector	4.5 MHz is intercarrier sound frequency
FM sound detector	Amplified *S* at 4.5 MHz	Audio signal to audio amplifier	Has deemphasis network
Audio section	Audio signal from FM detector	Audio power output to loudspeaker	Two audio channels needed for stereo

TABLE 12-1 *(Continued)*

STAGE	INPUT SIGNAL	OUTPUT SIGNAL	NOTES
Video amplifier	Composite video signal from video detector	Amplified video signal for picture tube, AGC, and sync circuits	Is the *Y* video amplifier in color receivers
AGC amplifier	Composite video signal	DC bias for RF and IF amplifiers	Automatic gain control for *P* and *S*
Chroma section	3.58-MHz *C* signal from video amplifier	Red, green, and blue video for tricolor picture tube	More details in Chap. 14
Sync separator	Composite video from video amplifier	To *V* sync integrator and horizontal AFC	Separates and amplifies sync pulses
Horizontal AFC	*H* sync pulses	DC control voltage to *H* oscillator	Two diodes as phase detector
Horizontal oscillator	DC control voltage from AFC circuit	15,750-Hz drive for *H* amplifier	Operates with or without sync
Horizontal amplifier	15,750-Hz drive produced by *H* oscillator	15,750-Hz sawtooth current in *H* coils of deflection yoke	Class C power amplifier, also supplies high-voltage rectifier and damper
Damper	From *H* output stage	Rectified deflection voltage for boosted B^+	Diode power rectifier
Vertical oscillator	60-Hz *V* sync from integrator	60-Hz drive for *V* amplifier	Operates with or without sync
Vertical amplifier	60-Hz drive from *V* oscillator	60-Hz sawtooth current in *V* coils of deflection yoke	Similar to class A power amplifier; may be push-pull circuit
High-voltage rectifier	Flyback pulses from *H* amplifier	DC anode voltage for picture tube	10- to 30-kV output; needs *H* output for operation
Low-voltage supply	120-V ac power and *H* flyback pulses	DC electrode voltages for all amplifier stages	12- to 200-V output; scan supply needs *H* output for operation

SELF-EXAMINATION

Answers at Back of Book

Part A. Match the functions listed at the left with the circuits at the right.

1. Contrast of picture	**a.** Mixer
2. Audio signal output	**b.** AGC
3. Gain control of RF and IF	**c.** FM detector
4. IF conversion	**d.** Video amplifier
5. Synchronization of picture	**e.** High-voltage supply
6. Brightness of raster	**f.** Low-voltage supply
7. DC electrode voltages	**g.** RF amplifier
8. Snowy picture	**h.** IF wave traps
9. Adjacent-channel selectivity	**i.** Sync separator
10. Baseband video signal	**j.** Video detector

Part B. Match the troubles listed at the left with the circuits at the right.

1. Normal sound but no brightness	**a.** Local oscillator
2. Normal picture but no sound	**b.** High-voltage rectifier
3. Picture in diagonal bars, out of sync	**c.** IF amplifier
4. No picture or sound but normal raster	**d.** 4.5-MHz amplifier
5. Wrong channel numbers	**e.** Horizontal AFC

Part C. Match the controls at the left with the functions at the right.

1. Fine tuning	**a.** Tunes RF, oscillator, and mixer stages
2. Contrast	**b.** Varies frequency of local oscillator
3. Volume	**c.** Adjusts RF and IF gain
4. Brightness	**d.** Varies audio level
5. Station selector	**e.** Varies gain of video amplifier
6. AGC level	**f.** Overload
7. Buzz	**g.** Varies frequency of vertical oscillator
8. Vertical hold	**h.** Varies dc bias for picture tube

ESSAY QUESTIONS

1. Divide a TV receiver into no more than six main sections, with an extra section for color.
2. Subdivide the TV receiver further with no more than 10 sections.

3. What is the difference between a video monitor and a TV receiver?
4. List the functions of the antenna and the transmission line.
5. What are the channel numbers for the VHF tuner and UHF tuner?
6. List at least five dc electrode voltages produced by the low-voltage power supply.
7. What is the function of the high-voltage power supply? Why is it called a *flyback* supply?
8. **(a)** Name three functions of the composite video signal in a monochrome receiver. **(b)** What is the extra function in a color receiver?
9. What is the advantage of the 4.5-MHz intercarrier sound, compared with the split-sound system?
10. Why can the sync separator be considered part of the signal circuits?
11. Classify all the stages listed in Table 12-1 under the following headings: picture and sound, picture alone, sound alone, synchronization of the picture, illuminated raster.
12. What are the circuits for the following controls? Station selector, fine tuning, contrast, volume, AGC level, H hold, V hold.
13. Name the use of each of the following frequencies? 55.25, 59.75, 45.75, 41.25, 42.17, 4.5, and 3.58 MHz.
14. Why is the dc component of the video signal important in picture reproduction?
15. Explain the purpose of a wave trap. Why is an LC circuit used?
16. Give an example of a sound takeoff circuit in a monochrome receiver.
17. Where would you connect an oscilloscope to see the voltage waveshapes in Fig. 12-14.
18. Which is the one stage that tunes in the desired station for VHF channels 2 to 13?
19. Name the one stage that is most important for minimum snow in the picture.
20. What is the purpose of using a scanning supply for low voltage?
21. How much video signal input is required for a video monitor?
22. Give three examples of accessory equipment used with a video control center.

PROBLEMS

Answers to Odd-Numbered Problems at Back of Book

1. Calculate the oscillator frequencies for tuning in **(a)** channel 6, **(b)** channel 7, **(c)** channel 13, and **(d)** channel 14.
2. What is the frequency difference in each of the following pairs? **(a)** 83.25 and 87.75 MHz, **(b)** 45.75 and 41.25 MHz, **(c)** 45.75 and 42.17 MHz, **(d)** 4.5 and 3.58 MHz.
3. The input signal to the IF section is 0.2 mV from the mixer. The IF output

is 2 V to the video detector. **(a)** Calculate the voltage gain A_V. **(b)** How much is this voltage gain in decibels?

4. The signal input at the first video amplifier is 1.5 V p-p. The cathode drive at the picture tube is 150 V p-p. How much voltage gain is necessary in the video amplifier section?
5. A fluctuating dc signal waveform varies between 132 and 48 V, with an average level of 70 V. **(a)** How much is the p-p voltage? **(b)** How much is the dc component?
6. Give an example, with calculations, of lower adjacent-channel interference at 47.25 MHz in the IF section.

SPECIAL QUESTIONS

1. Name one advantage and one disadvantage of having modular components with a TV monitor instead of just a TV receiver.
2. Give the typical dc supply voltage for **(a)** a small-signal transistor, **(b)** a linear IC unit, **(c)** a digital bipolar IC unit, **(d)** power transistors.

ANSWERS TO TEST POINT QUESTIONS

12-1 **a.** 45.75 MHz **b.** 4.5 MHz **c.** 3.58 MHz **d.** 60 Hz

12-2 **a.** Oscillator **b.** *V* hold **c.** Height **d.** Both **e.** *H* oscillator **f.** *H* output circuit

12-3 **a.** T **b.** F **c.** T

12-4 **a.** 18 V **b.** 25 kV **c.** Retrace

12-5 **a.** Above **b.** RF amplifier **c.** Mixer **d.** 517 MHz **e.** IF amplifier

12-6 **a.** Below **b.** 50 percent **c.** IF **d.** Video detector

12-7 **a.** T **b.** T

12-8 **a.** Contrast **b.** Video detector **c.** 3.2 MHz

12-9 **a.** Brightness **b.** Direct

12-10 **a.** 4.5 MHz **b.** 4.5 MHz **c.** 25 kHz

12-11 **a.** F **b.** T **c.** T **d.** T

12-12 **a.** T **b.** F **c.** T

13
RASTER CIRCUITS AND SYNC

The sync is part of the composite video signal, but the separate synchronizing pulses are used for timing the deflection circuits that produce the scanning raster. In the raster circuits, the vertical oscillator drives the vertical amplifier to fill the screen with the horizontal scanning lines, top to bottom. The *V* sync pulses trigger the oscillator to lock in the frequency at 60 Hz. For horizontal deflection, the scanning lines are produced by the horizontal oscillator and amplifier. The oscillator frequency is locked in by the horizontal AFC circuit, with *H* sync pulses at 15,750 Hz. Note that the deflection circuits produce the raster, while the sync only makes the picture hold still.

The function of sync in timing the scanning is the same for color or monochrome. In color television, however, the exact frequency is 15,734 Hz for *H* sync and scanning. Also, the frequency for *V* sync and scanning is exactly 59.94 Hz. The nominal frequencies generally are considered as 60 or 15,750 Hz, though, for *V* or *H* sync and scanning, respectively.

An interesting point about synchronization is that the time needed for the transmitted signal to travel to the receiver has no effect on the timing by the sync. The reason is that the sync pulses must be present at the same time as the camera signal variations in the transmitted composite video signal. Actually, the sync times the scanning in the raster with respect to the picture information in each horizontal line and vertical field. Thus a lack of sync can make the picture roll up or down and tear apart horizontally, without affecting the raster itself. These topics are discussed in the following sections:

13-1
AMPLITUDE AND WAVEFORM SEPARATION OF THE SYNC

The synchronizing pulses use the peak amplitudes of the transmitted composite video signal. Included are the *H*, *V*, and equalizing pulses. Specific details of the sync pulse waveforms are described in Chap. 7, "Video Signal Analysis," but the main points are as follows:

1. The *H* sync pulses are narrow, having a 4.75-μs pulse width. They are repeated at the 15,750-Hz line-scanning frequency.
2. The *V* sync pulses are much wider. Each serrated *V* pulse includes six half-line pulses for a total width of three lines, which equals 190.5 μs. The *V* sync pulses are repeated at the 60-Hz field-scanning rate.
3. The equalizing pulses at 31,500 Hz are repeated at half-line intervals, as are the serrations in a *V* sync pulse. A group of six equalizing pulses occurs just before and after each *V* sync pulse, to make the vertical synchronization the same in even and odd fields for good interlacing.

The sequence of sync separation is illustrated in Fig. 13-1. First, the amplitude separation removes all the sync pulses from the composite video signal. The stage that amplifies just the sync amplitudes is a sync separator or just the sync amplifier. The total sync output includes horizontal, vertical, and equalizing pulses.

The integrator is an *RC* filter whose purpose is to remove all but the *V* sync pulses. A long *RC* time constant, compared with the *H* pulse width, allows *C* to charge only during the time of the vertical sync pulse. The output of the integrator provides trigger pulses to hold the vertical oscillator at 60 Hz. Without vertical synchronization, the picture rolls up or down the screen. To correct this problem, you can adjust the vertical hold control.

The horizontal AFC circuit is a phase-locked loop (PLL) that provides dc control voltage to hold the horizontal oscillator at the frequency of the *H* sync pulses. This method has the advantage of being insensitive to noise pulses, compared with triggered sync. Noise is more of a problem with horizontal synchronization because the *H* sync frequency is higher than the *V* sync frequency. Without horizontal hold, the picture tears apart into diagonal segments. To correct this problem, adjust the horizontal hold control.

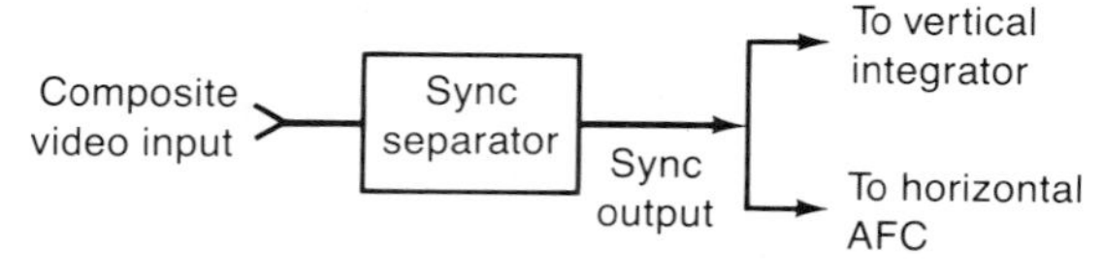

Fig. 13-1 Sequence of amplitude and waveform separation of sync pulses.

Test Point Questions 13-1
Answers at End of Chapter

Answer True or False.

a. All the sync pulses have the same amplitude.
b. The synchronizing pulses produce the scanning raster.
c. The *V* sync pulse has the lowest frequency.

13-2
SYNC SEPARATOR

Normally the stage is held in cutoff. However, the composite video signal is applied in such polarity that only the sync amplitudes drive the amplifier into conduction. As a result, the output is sync—separated from the composite video input.

The video input to a typical sync separator is shown at the top of Fig. 13-2. The composite video has sync in the negative direction. This polarity can drive the base electrode of a PNP

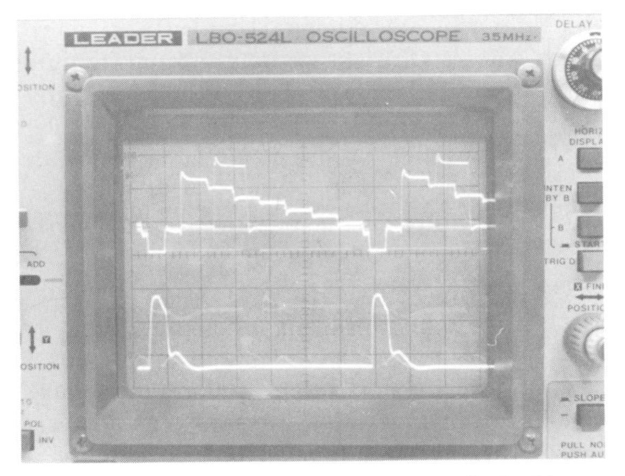

Fig. 13-2 Sync separator action, shown with dual-trace oscilloscope. At top is composite video input for color-bar signal without chroma. At bottom is separated sync. Oscilloscope sweep is set to show *H* sync pulses.

transistor into conduction. The separated sync output is shown at the bottom of Fig. 13-2. The output is total sync, including horizontal, vertical, and equalizing pulses. Note that the sync pulses are in the positive direction, because the sync separator functions as an inverting amplifier. The circuit is usually a common-emitter (CE) amplifier with a resistive load. In terms of components, the sync circuits are often part of an IC unit for processing the video signal.

The sync output consists of clean, squared-off pulses without any signals between pulses. In most cases, the sync separator is driven between cutoff and saturation. Then the p-p swing of the sync output is very nearly equal to the supply voltage.

The separator can operate at any level between blanking and tip of sync, since this area has only the sync amplitudes. The pulse edges have the required timing.

NOISE IN THE SYNC Signal bias is used in the sync separator stage so that the separation is self-adjusting according to changes in the amount of video drive signal. In general, the signal bias varies with the amount of input signal. Then the tip of sync is clamped at a specific level, even with different amounts of signal. However, the *RC* coupling circuit for signal bias is sensitive to impulse noise. Large noise spikes in the signal can build up larger values of bias. In severe cases, the excessive bias can disable the sync separator for a short interval, causing the loss of several sync pulses. The temporary loss of synchronization is actually worse than any noise streaks in the picture. For this reason, the receiver must have noise-reduction circuits for the sync separator.

SYNC TROUBLES Complete failure of the sync separator causes the loss of both vertical and horizontal hold. The picture rolls vertically and breaks into slanting bands at the same time. Careful readjustment of the vertical and horizontal hold controls might produce a complete picture momentarily. Then the picture will roll up or down and drift sideways until it breaks up again. The fact that a still picture can be produced, even for an instant, shows that the vertical and horizontal deflection oscillators can run at the correct scanning frequencies.

Another possibility is partial failure of the sync separation, such that the conduction threshold sinks into the area of the video signal. Then some of the black video information is in the sync signal. The result is a bend in the picture or a weaving effect, caused by synchronization that is affected by picture content. This trouble can be caused by a defect in the sync separator itself or compression of the sync in the picture IF amplifier section. Specifically, AGC overload is a typical problem. The AGC bias is not enough for the signal level, which causes excessive drive in the IF amplifiers. When the problem is severe, synchronization is lost entirely and usually the picture is reversed in black-and-white values.

Test Point Questions 13-2

Answers at End of Chapter

Answer True or False.

a. The sync separator is a class A amplifier.

b. The separated sync includes all the sync pulses.

c. In Fig. 13-2, the separated sync is inverted from the pulses in the composite video signal.

13-3 VERTICAL SYNC INTEGRATOR

The vertical synchronizing pulses are separated from the total sync by using the difference in time duration of the *V* and *H* pulses. The filtering is done by an integrator circuit, which is basically an *RC* filter, as shown in Fig. 13-3. Since *C* is in a shunt path, the filter is a low-pass type. The buildup of charge in a shunt capacitor is called *integration* because of the additive effect on the voltage across *C*.

The input waveform shown at the top of Fig. 13-3 is total sync. This photograph has been obtained by synchronizing the oscilloscope to show the beginning of the vertical blanking interval. The output waveform at the bottom of Fig. 13-3 shows the separated vertical sync pulse. Then the integrated *V* sync pulses are used to trigger the *V* deflection oscillator at the 60-Hz field-scanning frequency.

The waveform separation of the integrator depends on its time constant *RC*. With $R = 10$ kΩ and $C = 0.005$ μF, each *RC* section has a time constant of 50 μs. This time is long compared with the 4.7-μs *H* pulse width. Therefore, *C* cannot charge much from the *H* pulses. Also, *C* discharges in the time between pulses. However, during the wider vertical pulses, *C* has enough time to charge. It loses very little charge in the narrow interval provided by the serrations. The result is integrated vertical sync across *C*.

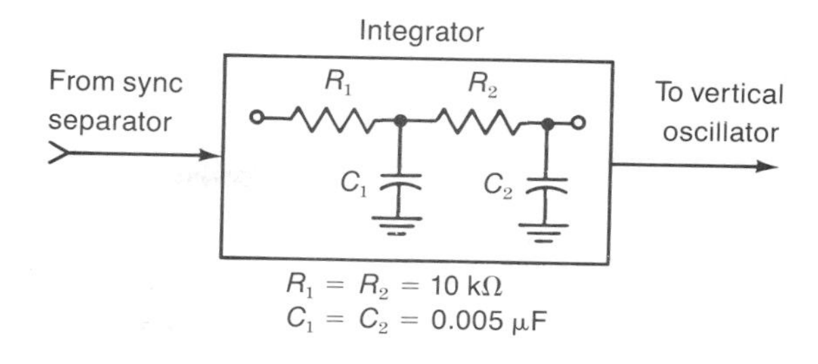

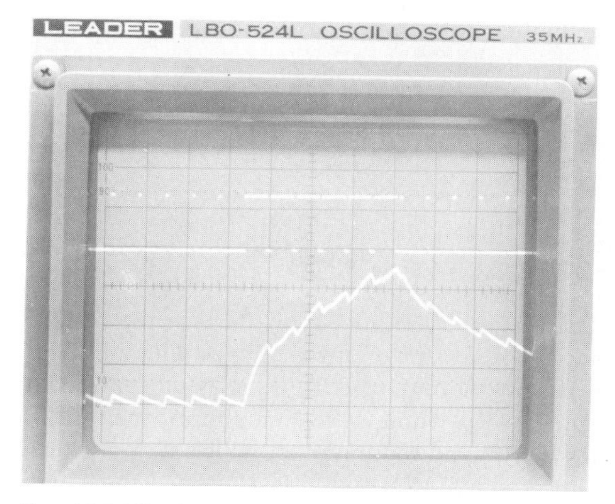

Fig. 13-3 Effect of *RC* filtering by vertical integrator, shown with dual-trace oscilloscope. Total sync input at top. Integrated *V* sync at bottom goes to vertical deflection oscillator.

Keep in mind that the serrations are there only to keep the horizontal oscillator synchronized during the three-line interval of the *V* sync pulse. At the end of vertical sync, the capacitor has time to discharge completely, to be ready for integration of the next vertical pulse.

A failure in the integrator circuit causes loss of vertical sync only. The picture rolls vertically up or down the screen. However, adjustment of the vertical hold control can make the picture roll either way or stop rolling for a moment. The fact that the picture can be stopped and made to roll either up or down shows that the vertical oscillator can run at the correct frequency. The trouble is loss of vertical sync.

Test Point Questions 13-3

Answers at End of Chapter

a. Is the input for the *V* integrator taken from the sync separator or the video amplifier?
b. Is the output from the *RC* integrator the voltage across *R* or *C?*
c. Is a typical time constant for the vertical integrator 5 or 50 μs?

13-4 VERTICAL DEFLECTION

The vertical scanning circuit starts at the vertical oscillator, as shown in Fig. 13-4*a.* The oscillator generates output whether it is synchronized or not. For the whole deflection circuit, the oscillator drives a power amplifier, which is the vertical output stage. In between is a wave-shaping network to provide the amplifier drive needed for sawtooth current in the vertical deflection coils.

The deflection oscillator is a relaxation type that uses either the blocking oscillator or the multivibrator circuit. These oscillators switch between two unstable states of conduction and cutoff at the free-running frequency. The oscillator is *astable,* meaning there is no stable state. Because of the astable operation, this type of oscillator is easy to synchronize. In the vertical oscillator circuit, the cutoff state is ended before its natural period by application of the integrated vertical sync pulse. Then the oscillator is locked in by the sync to hold at 60 Hz.

With this method of triggered sync, the oscillator must have a cutoff period larger than the time between sync pulses. In short, the free-running frequency of the vertical oscillator must be below 60 Hz. With a picture on the screen, you can adjust the vertical hold control to lock in the picture while it is rolling upward slowly.

Following the oscillator stage is a wave-shaping network that produces a linear ramp for the sawtooth voltage. Basically, an *RC* circuit is needed. The capacitor *C* charges slowly in one path for a linear rise and discharges fast in another path for the rapid flyback. However, the drive for the vertical amplifier is not exactly sawtooth because the shape is predistorted to compensate for distortion produced in the output circuit.

The wave-shaping network in Fig. 13-4*a* has two functions. First, a capacitor is used to provide a linear rise in voltage. This ramp is for linear scanning during the trace. Because of this function, it is called the *sawtooth capacitor.* Second, a pulse or spike is added to the sawtooth waveform, to ensure that the vertical amplifier is cut off during retrace time. The combination of sawtooth and pulse shown for the vertical stage is called a *trapezoidal waveform.*

The output stage is a large-signal power amplifier. Although it is cut off during retrace time, the amplifier uses most of the current swing between cutoff and saturation for the active scanning period. This is like an audio output stage in that it provides the large amount of current needed in the vertical scanning coils, typically more than 1 ampere. Either class A operation, during the active scanning only, or class B push-pull circuits are used for the vertical output stage. Push-pull distortion is illustrated in Fig. 13-4*b.*

In some systems, the entire vertical deflection circuit is one oscillator feedback system. A feedback loop may be taken from the output circuit back to the first stage, as indicated by the dashed line in Fig. 13-4*a.* It is common practice to call the first stage the *oscillator,* even though two or three cascaded amplifiers are included in the feedback loop. This type of circuit is actually a form of multivibrator.

Note the three controls for vertical scanning

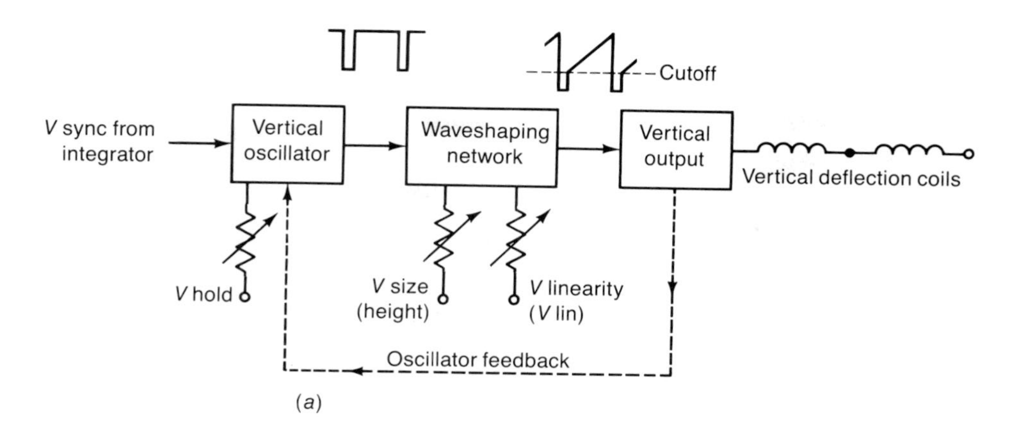

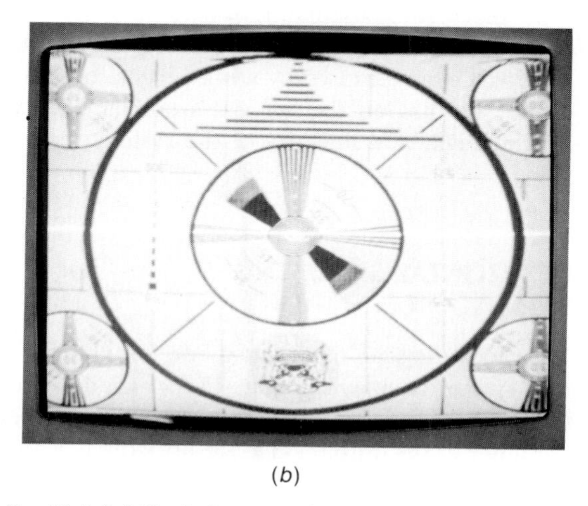

(b)

Fig. 13-4 (*a*) Block diagram of vertical deflection. (*b*) White line across center shows crossover distortion in push-pull vertical amplifier for output stage.

shown in Fig. 13-4*a*. Their functions are as follows:

V hold Varies the vertical oscillator free-running frequency. Set it just below 60 Hz so that the *V* sync locks in the oscillator to make the picture stop rolling.

V size or height Varies the amount of output from the vertical amplifier. Set it to fill the screen top to bottom with the scanning lines.

V linearity, or V lin Varies the linearity of the sawtooth ramp. Set it to eliminate crowding or spreading of the scanning lines at the top or bottom of the screen. Note that improved circuits allow elimination of the *V* linearity control in some receivers.

The three controls can affect one another. Make sure the final result is a locked-in picture that fills the height of the screen with good linearity top to bottom.

Test Point Questions 13-4

Answers at End of Chapter

Refer to Fig. 13-4*a*.

a. Which control makes the picture stop rolling?
b. Which stage supplies the scanning current in the *V* deflection coils?
c. Which stage can use a circuit such as a class B push-pull amplifier?

13-5 TROUBLES IN VERTICAL SCANNING

Loss of the deflection current in the vertical coils results in no vertical scanning. Then the raster collapses into a single, bright horizontal line across the center of the screen. The trouble can be caused by failure of the oscillator or amplifier or a defect in the coupling circuits or yoke.

In color receivers, the pincushion correction and convergence circuits are connected to the vertical output. So a defect in these circuits can cause no vertical deflection also.

There is a big difference between the problem of no oscillator output and that of the oscillator's running at the wrong frequency. Incorrect oscillator frequency only makes the picture roll. The trouble can be in the oscillator or a loss of vertical sync. However, with trouble in the oscillator, the *V* hold control may vary the speed of rolling, but it cannot change the direction up or down.

Insufficient height or poor vertical linearity can be caused by a defect in the wave-shaping circuits or a drastic change in the dc bias on the vertical output stage. In any case, it is a problem of weak output, amplitude distortion, or both, in the vertical amplifier. Usually these troubles are not caused by the oscillator itself, because it does not supply the power output.

It can be helpful to compare the vertical output with the audio circuits. Just as more audio power makes louder sound, more vertical output produces more height in the raster. Less height means reduced vertical output. In many cases, nonlinearity is associated with weak output.

Test Point Questions 13-5

Answers at End of Chapter

Answer True or False.

a. A single bright line across the center of the screen can be caused by incorrect frequency of the vertical oscillator.
b. Too much black space at the bottom of the screen can be caused by weak vertical output.
c. The dc bias on the vertical amplifier affects the height and linearity of the raster.

13-6 HORIZONTAL SYNC AND DEFLECTION

The block diagram of a typical horizontal deflection system is shown in Fig. 13-5. Included are the *H* deflection oscillator, driver, and a power amplifier in the output stage for horizontal scanning. The oscillator uses the blocking oscillator or multivibrator circuit. This stage generates a 15,750-Hz drive signal for the deflection that produces the horizontal scanning lines. Basically, the idea is similar to that of the vertical scanning circuit, but because of the higher frequency for *H* scanning, there are important differences:

1. The *H* oscillator frequency is synchronized by automatic frequency control, not triggered sync.
2. The horizontal output stage is more like a class C power supplier that produces output pulses. The output is switched on for horizontal scanning in each line.
3. The horizontal output is used for the high-

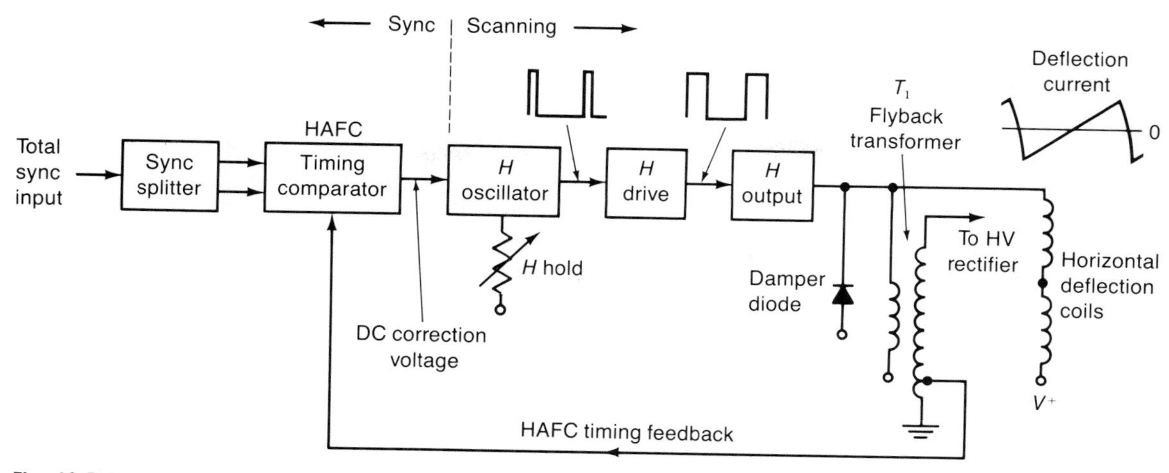

Fig. 13-5 Block diagram of horizontal deflection. HAFC is horizontal automatic frequency control.

voltage rectifier that produces anode voltage for the picture tube. Without horizontal scanning there cannot be any brightness on the screen.

4. The horizontal output needs a damper diode to minimize shock-excited oscillations in the horizontal scanning current.

The damper diode has two more important uses, besides damping. One function is to provide *boosted* B^+ voltage for the horizontal amplifier. This effect is produced as the diode damper rectifies the H deflection output in a circuit that adds the rectified voltage in series with the dc voltage from the power supply. A higher dc supply voltage for the horizontal amplifier allows more ac power output. The circuit is self-starting, but the horizontal amplifier cannot have dc supply voltage unless the damper diode is conducting.

As another function, the damping current of the diode is used to provide part of the horizontal scanning, at the left side, just after flyback. The system, called *reaction scanning,* produces about one-third the horizontal trace. This technique is the reason why the horizontal output stage can be cut off for part of the trace time, as in a class C amplifier. While the amplifier is not conducting, the reaction scanning produces trace from the left edge of the screen toward the right. Then the amplifier is driven into conduction to complete the trace to the right edge. The reaction scanning and boosted B^+ features offer a tremendous increase in efficiency for the horizontal output circuit. Efficiency is important here because the horizontal output requires most of the power in the receiver.

HAFC The horizontal oscillator frequency is controlled by a dc correction voltage developed by a phase comparator or timing comparator, as shown at the left in Fig. 13-5. Generally two diodes are used for the comparator circuit. Typically, the comparator is supplied with push-pull horizontal sync pulses from a phase-splitter or sync-splitter stage. In addition, another input needed for the comparator is a sawtooth voltage waveform as a sample of the oscillator frequency. This feedback is taken from the horizontal output circuit as a pulse that is formed into a sawtooth by an RC network in the feedback path.

The output of the comparator is dc correction voltage that indicates whether the oscillator is at the correct frequency. When H sync arrives at the center of retrace, no correction voltage is produced. However, if the oscillator frequency is too high or too low, a dc correction voltage will be produced to pull the oscillator into the sync frequency. It is really a phase-locked loop (PLL) system that is called *horizontal automatic frequency control* (HAFC) in this application.

The function of the HAFC is to hold the picture together horizontally. The H oscillator can produce horizontal scanning, however, with or without the AFC. Note the dashed line at the top of Fig. 13-5 that divides the circuits into two sections: scanning to produce the horizontal lines and sync to hold the picture together. Without horizontal synchronization by the AFC circuit, the picture tears apart into segments with diagonal black blanking bars. The horizontal hold control in the oscillator circuit is adjusted to lock in the picture.

HORIZONTAL DRIVE The oscillator output is a rectangular pulse that is reshaped in the driver to provide the required pulse input to the output stage. This stage functions as a switch. Its conduction time determines how long the dc supply voltage is connected to the H coils in the yoke for each horizontal scan. The width of the pulse drive for the horizontal output is critical. For this reason, there are generally no controls to adjust the horizontal scanning.

HORIZONTAL OUTPUT With transistors in this stage, the horizontal scanning current is supplied directly to the yoke coils. In older receivers with tubes, a voltage step-down transformer is used. For both cases, a damper diode is needed to reduce oscillations at the start of each horizontal scan. This time is at the left side of the raster. Most important, though, the damper diode supplies part of the trace current in each line.

FLYBACK TRANSFORMER Note the flyback transformer T_1 at the right in Fig. 13-5. The primary is in parallel with the yoke to conduct the horizontal scanning current. The secondary is a step-up winding to produce high voltage from the sharp drop in current during retrace, or flyback. This high voltage is rectified to produce the dc anode voltage for the picture tube. The high-voltage rectifier can be a single diode or a voltage multiplier circuit.

Taps at different points on transformer T_1 also can be used to provide pulse drive for other lower-voltage power supplies. In addition, one tap provides pulse feedback to the comparator for HAFC. Another tap can be used to supply H pulses for a keyed AGC circuit.

Test Point Questions 13-6

Answers at End of Chapter

Refer to Fig. 13-5.

a. Is HAFC for horizontal sync or scanning?

b. Is T_1 for horizontal sync or high voltage?

c. Does the output stage operate similar to the class A or class C type of amplifier?

13-7 GEN-LOCK SYSTEM FOR SYNC AND DEFLECTION

This name indicates a method of locking in the V and H deflection generators at their correct frequencies by means of digital techniques. The use of IC chips makes it possible to have the gen-lock system in TV receivers. A single IC chip dedicated for this purpose includes noise protection, sync separation, and both the vertical and horizontal deflection oscillators. An example is shown in Fig. 13-6. The gen-lock system is used in television cameras and other studio equipment to provide the V and H drive signals.

In Fig. 13-6, a single master oscillator operates at 31.5 kHz. This frequency is twice the H line

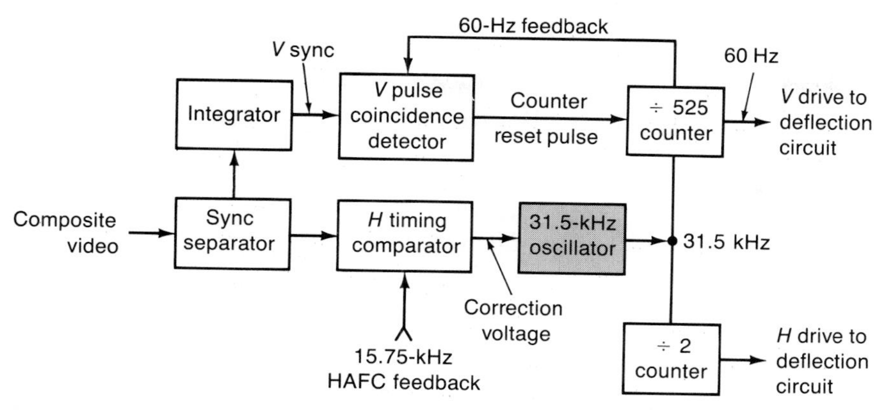

Fig. 13-6 Simplified block diagram of gen-lock circuit for *H* and *V* drive generators.

frequency, since 2 × 15,750 Hz = 31,500 Hz = 31.5 kHz. The oscillator drives two countdown dividers. At the bottom of the diagram, division by 2 produces the 15,750-kHz horizontal drive signal. This pulse is used directly for the horizontal deflection circuits. The other counter divides by 525 to develop the 60-Hz vertical field signal. Note that 31,500/525 = 60, or 60 × 525 = 31,500. The 60-Hz drive signal is used to develop the vertical scanning waveform.

For frequency dividers, the system starts with the highest frequency. Then it can be divided down by digital counters, in any exact submultiple. The frequency of the equalizing pulses or the *V* serrations, also with half-line spacing, is 31,500 Hz.

The division establishes the correct scanning frequencies but not the synchronized phase needed for retrace time with respect to picture information. For instance, a black bar across the screen can be produced by vertical blanking anywhere from top to bottom. Also, the *H* blanking bar can drift across the screen.

To establish correct phasing for vertical scanning, the separated sync is integrated to extract the *V* sync pulse. Then this pulse is compared with the *V* drive signal developed by the counter. The pulse coincidence detector has this function. When the two pulses are timed correctly, the count is not disturbed. However, if the two *V* pulses are not coincident in time, a reset pulse is developed for correction. The reset means that the count is turned back to zero. In this way, the *V* counter starts at the beginning of a field each time a reset is called for. Thus the *V* count is produced only when the phasing is correct.

Although the master oscillator operates at 31.5 kHz, the *H* timing comparator has 15,750-kHz pulses. The inputs to the comparator include separated *H* sync and *H* flyback pulses from the flyback transformer in the horizontal output circuit. Then the sync is always compared with retrace. The correction voltage controls the frequency of the 31.5-kHz master oscillator.

The gen-lock system provides excellent interlacing. Furthermore, this method has extremely good noise immunity in terms of vertical sync. To illustrate the possibilities, the reset pulse comparator can be set up to make the timing comparison every 10 fields, for example. During the time that there is no comparison, the system is immune to any outside influence. So most of the time the vertical synchronization cannot be affected by noise pulses.

Test Point Questions 13-7

Answers at End of Chapter

Answer True or False for the gen-lock circuit in Fig. 13-6.

a. The whole circuit can be contained in one dedicated IC chip.

b. The master oscillator operates at 15.75 kHz.

c. No vertical hold control is used.

13-8 WHY THE PICTURE ROLLS VERTICALLY

The explanation of a rolling picture is illustrated in Fig. 13-7 for the case of too high a vertical oscillator frequency. Note the relative timing of vertical blanking in the composite video signal and vertical retrace in the sawtooth vertical deflection current. When both are at exactly the same frequency, every vertical retrace occurs within the vertical blanking time. Then vertical blanking is not visible at the top and bottom edges of the frame. However, when the vertical frequency is too high, the sawtooth cycles advance in time with respect to the 60-Hz blanking pulses. Then vertical blanking occurs during trace time instead of during retrace. Furthermore, each sawtooth advances into trace time for succeeding blanking pulses. As a result, the black bar produced across the screen by the vertical blanking pulse drops lower and lower down the screen for successive cycles.

Remember that the information for the top of the picture as it is transmitted always comes immediately after vertical blanking. When the vertical oscillator is locked in sync, each frame is reproduced over the previous frame, and then the picture holds still. However, when the picture information and blanking in each frame are reproduced lower on the screen than in the previous frame, the picture appears to roll down. The same idea applies to rolling up.

The further the vertical scanning frequency is from 60 Hz, the faster the picture rolls. The upward rolling usually is slower than the downward rolling because the oscillator frequency changes more gradually at the high-resistance end of the hold control for low frequencies. If the vertical oscillator frequency can be made as low as 30 or 20 Hz, which are factors of 60 Hz, two or three duplicate pictures will be seen one above the other. If the frequency is raised to 120 Hz, the bottom half of the picture will be superimposed on the top half.

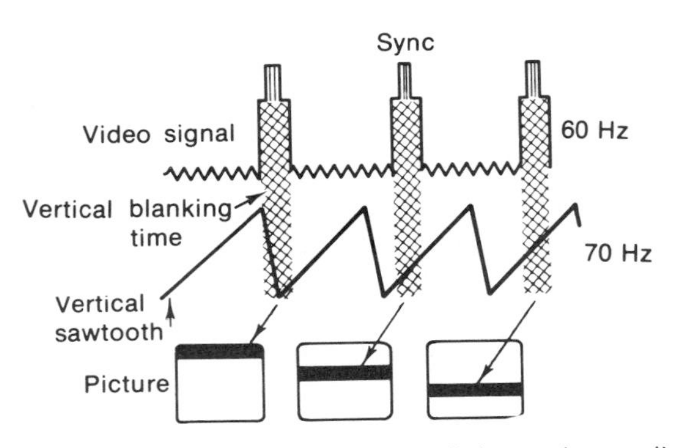

Fig. 13-7 Why picture appears to roll down when vertical scanning is too fast with respect to vertical blanking pulses. Picture rolls up when vertical oscillator frequency is too low.

Test Point Questions 13-8

Answers at End of Chapter

Refer to Fig. 13-7.

a. Do the black bars represent *V* or *H* blanking?

b. Is the oscillator frequency too high or too low?

13-9 DIAGONAL BLACK BARS IN THE PICTURE

When the horizontal oscillator is locked into the 15,750-Hz sync frequency the line structure holds together to show a complete picture, and horizontal blanking is invisible at the left and right edges. If the oscillator is off the correct frequency, though, the picture will tear into diagonal segments. The diagonal black bars are produced by horizontal blanking pulses. The picture is in segments because the horizontal AFC circuit prevents individual horizontal lines from tearing apart, since the frequency cannot change from line to line. When the number of diagonal bars is continually changing, this is evidence that the AFC circuit is not controlling the oscillator. When the bars are steady, the AFC circuit is holding the oscillator but at the wrong frequency.

In either case, the horizontal blanking pulses produce diagonal black bars when the horizontal oscillator is off the correct frequency. If the frequency differs from 15,750 Hz by 60 Hz, there will be one diagonal bar. Every 60-Hz difference between the oscillator frequency and 15,750 Hz results in another diagonal bar. As the bars increase in number, they become thinner and have a less steep slope. The bars slope down to the left when the oscillator frequency is below 15,750 Hz and up to the left when above 15,750 Hz.

The reason for the diagonal bars is illustrated in Fig. 13-8 for the case of too high a horizontal oscillator frequency. Note how successive sawtooth cycles advance in time with respect to the blanking pulses transmitted at 15,750 Hz. Each blanking pulse is 10 μs wide, reproducing black for about one-sixth of every line. Remember that the left edge of the picture is always immediately after horizontal blanking. Furthermore, the blanking goes more into trace time for successive sawtooth cycles. For each successive line, then, the black is more to the right.

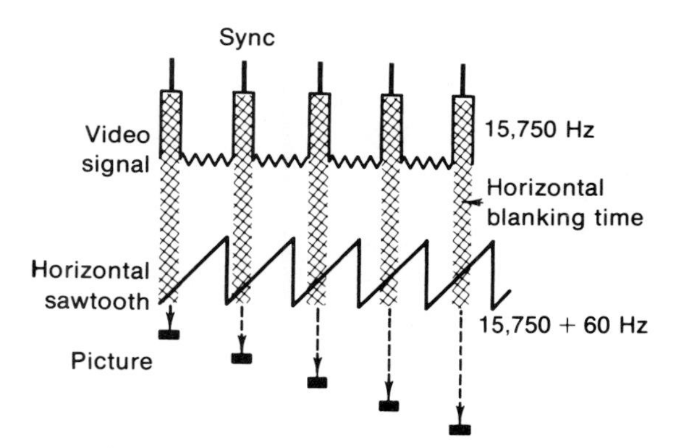

Fig. 13-8 Why picture tears into diagonal bars when horizontal scanning is too fast with respect to horizontal blanking pulses. One diagonal bar is produced by 60-Hz error. Bar has opposite slope, down to the right, when horizontal oscillator frequency is too low.

Since vertical scanning is occurring at the same time, the black area moves down as it progresses to the right. Only five scanning lines are illustrated here. But if all the lines were shown, the result would be one diagonal black bar from the top left to the bottom right corner. Then the same action is repeated over the previous diagonal bar. The same idea applies to the case of too low an oscillator frequency, but the black would start at the top right corner and progress diagonally down to the bottom left.

Between the black diagonal bars, the picture information is reproduced in the wrong position to such an extent that the picture usually cannot be recognized. Near the bottom of each bar, the picture information is actually reversed in its left-right position. Also, the horizontal flyback during visible time stretches black or white information all the way across the screen.

Test Point Questions 13-9

Answers at End of Chapter

Refer to Fig. 13-8.

a. Does the diagonal black bar represent *V* or *H* blanking?

b. Is the oscillator frequency too high or too low?

13-10 POWER SUPPLIES

A power supply rectifies its ac input to provide dc output. The television receiver has several power rectifiers for the required dc operating voltages. High voltage is needed for the anode, or ultor, of the picture tube. Low voltage is needed for the small-signal amplifiers, such as sync amplifiers, IF amplifiers, chroma processing, and the stages in the RF tuner. The different requirements are shown in this list of dc supply voltages for a typical 19-in. color TV receiver:

25 kV for picture tube anode, or ultor

5 kV for picture tube focusing grid ($G3$)

700 V for picture tube screen grid ($G2$)

200 V for video output stage

130 V for horizontal output stage

18 to 35 V for amplifiers using small-signal transistors and IC units

All these voltages are produced by the power supply rectifiers in the circuit of Fig. 13-9. Except for the picture tube requirements, the dc supply voltages are used for the ac signal amplifiers.

FLYBACK HIGH-VOLTAGE SUPPLY In Fig. 13-9, the horizontal output transformer T_1 has a high-voltage winding that provides about 8.5 kV of pulse input to the voltage tripler. This unit has three internal rectifiers. The flyback pulse is generated by the fast horizontal flyback. The dc output from the tripler, at about 25 kV, is connected to the ultor button on the picture tube. Its capacitance of approximately 1500 pF is the filter capacitor.

In addition, a tap on the transformer is used for the focus rectifier $D1$. This method is used

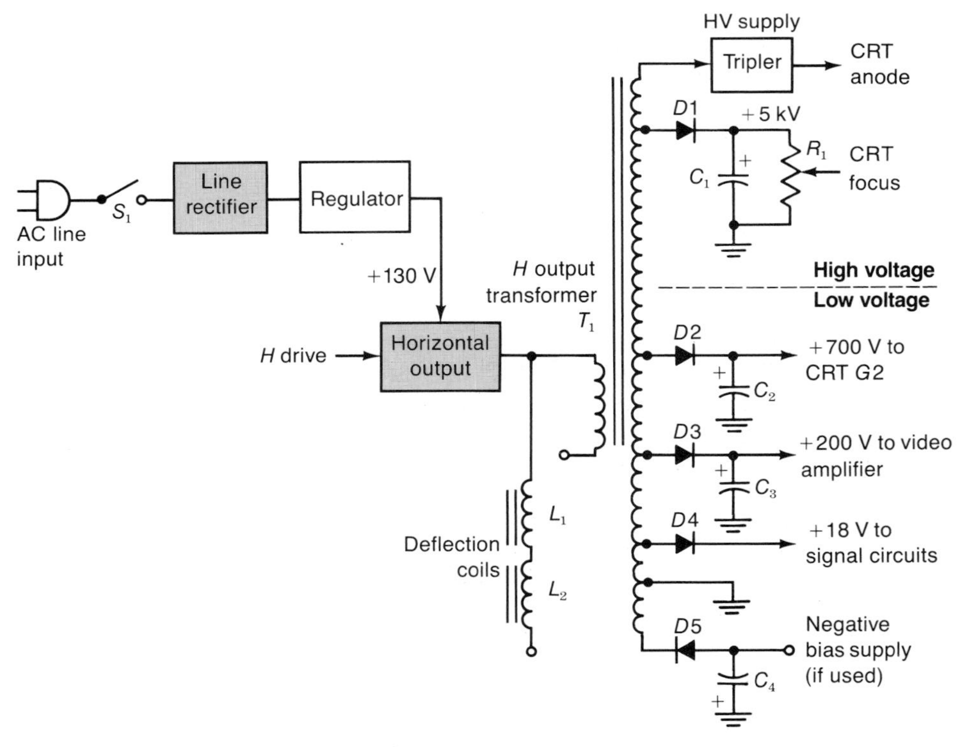

Fig. 13-9 Low-voltage and high-voltage power supplies in television receiver.

for color picture tubes with high-voltage focusing. The dc output is about 5 kV, adjusted by R_1 for best focus in the picture.

LOW-VOLTAGE SUPPLY Refer to Fig. 13-9. The required lower values for the dc supply voltage are produced by a combination of a line rectifier that has input from the ac power line and rectifiers connected to different taps on the horizontal output transformer T_1. The line rectifier can use a half-wave circuit, voltage doubler, or bridge rectifier. In the horizontal output circuit, diodes $D2$ to $D5$ supply different values of dc output voltage. Included is an inverted supply with negative dc output, if necessary, for negative bias. These low-voltage rectifiers use the horizontal scanning voltage produced during trace time. This method is often called a *scan-voltage supply.*

There are several advantages in using the scanning-voltage method. First, different dc supply voltages can be obtained easily from different taps on the horizontal output transformer. This method is much more efficient than a tapped bleeder resistor or voltage-drop resistor, because no I^2R power is wasted in heating the resistors. Second, the ac ripple is at the 15,750-Hz horizontal scanning frequency, which is much easier to filter than the 60-Hz power-line frequency.

The line rectifier generally uses a voltage regulator for the dc output, as in Fig. 13-9. Its purpose is to allow a steady value of rectified dc output voltage with changes in the amount of load current. Some regulators use a *series-pass transistor* in the path for the load current. The conduction is varied by an error-control voltage to regulate the dc output. A more efficient method uses *switching-mode regulation.* In this system, the output load current is pulsed on and off at the switching rate. The efficiency is very high because the output is regulated by control of the duty cycle of current pulses delivered to the load. The regulator dissipates little power because it is either on with very low resistance or off with zero current.

The line rectifier in Fig. 13-9 provides the dc supply voltage for the horizontal output amplifier. This stage produces the power for the scanning-voltage supplies. Eventually, though, all the dc power comes from the ac power line.

Test Point Questions 13-10

Answers at End of Chapter

Refer to Fig. 13-9.

a. Is the tripler for high voltage or low voltage?
b. Which diode is for the focus voltage?
c. Which diode is in an inverted power supply?
d. Is the voltage regulator used for the line rectifier or the focus rectifier?

13-11 TROUBLES IN HORIZONTAL SCANNING AND HAFC

Because of the flyback high voltage, problems in brightness may be related to the horizontal deflection circuits. Without horizontal scanning, there is no anode voltage for the picture tube and no brightness on the screen. Frequency errors in the H oscillator make the picture tear apart into diagonal segments. The horizontal AFC is actually a sync circuit, but it is so closely related to the horizontal oscillator that they are considered together.

NO HORIZONTAL OUTPUT This trouble can be caused by a defect in the horizontal oscillator, driver, or output stage. You do not see a single vertical line, however, corresponding to the single horizontal line without vertical deflection. Instead, the symptom is total loss of the raster, since the flyback high voltage depends on the horizontal output. You may see a single vertical line for an instant at the time of failure because of the high voltage stored in the anode capacitance of the picture tube.

SCANNING-VOLTAGE SUPPLIES In many receivers, some of the low-voltage supplies also are taken from the horizontal output. Then the results of no horizontal output are even more general. The receiver is completely dead—no raster, no picture, no sound.

HORIZONTAL-FREQUENCY ERRORS The result of horizontal-frequency errors is a mass of slanting black bars as the picture is torn into diagonal segments. Each bar is a piece of horizontal blanking. When sync is the problem, you can adjust the horizontal hold or frequency control to produce a single upright picture. But the picture slips rapidly to one side or the other. This effect shows that the horizontal oscillator can run at the correct frequency but is not locked in by *H* sync. The same effects are seen when the *H* feedback pulse is not supplied to the AFC system. Both the sync and the feedback pulses are needed for the timing comparator circuit.

A frequency error in the horizontal oscillator circuit produces the same effect of diagonal black bars. However, the *H* hold or frequency control may not have enough range to correct the error. A large frequency error results in a large number of black bands. They are thin and almost horizontal, as shown in Fig. 13-10*a*. As the correct frequency is approached, the number of diagonal bars becomes smaller and each is wider, as in Fig. 13-10*b*. Note that the width and high voltage can be affected when the *H* oscillator is far off its correct frequency.

Frequency errors are produced by changes in the components of the oscillator circuit. Another cause is a severe imbalance in the diode circuits of the timing comparator. This trouble produces too much dc correction voltage for the oscillator.

HORIZONTAL HOLD-DOWN CIRCUIT A third cause of large frequency errors is an automatic circuit that forces the *H* oscillator off its correct frequency as a protection against excessive high voltage that can produce x-rays. Other overvoltage protection circuits actually stop the horizontal oscillator in the event of excessive high voltage. This results in complete loss of high voltage. Any circuit failure that could raise the high voltage abnormally activates the hold-down circuit. Receivers with anode voltages above 15 kV have a hold-down or shut-down circuit. This feature is necessary in color receivers to comply with federal regulations to either reduce the high voltage or make the picture unintelligible if there is any danger of x-ray emission.

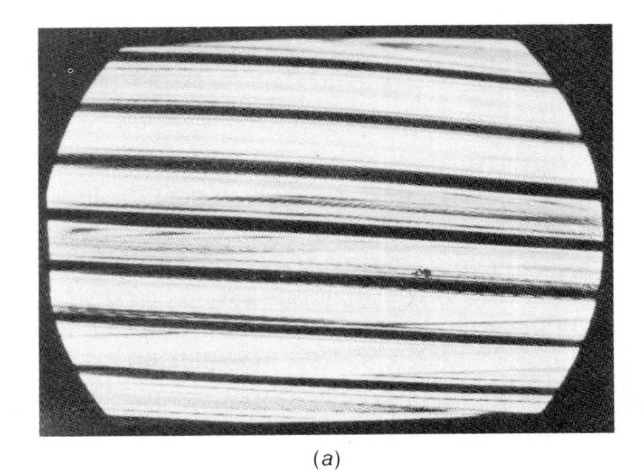

(*a*)

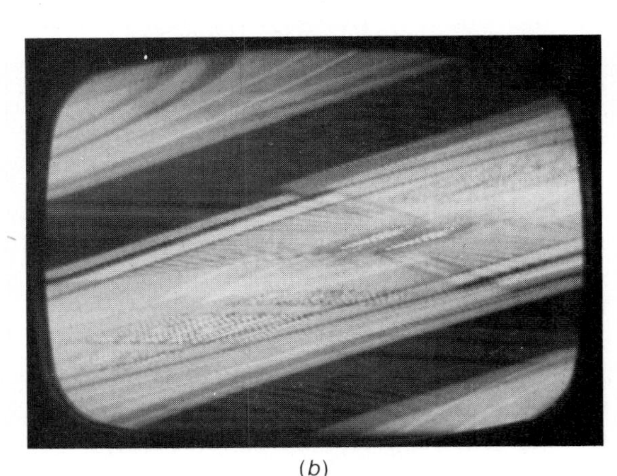

(*b*)

Fig. 13-10 Visual effects of frequency errors in horizontal oscillator. (*a*) Large error. (*b*) Small error.

Test Point Questions 13-11

Answers at End of Chapter

Answer True or False.

a. No horizontal output usually results in one bright vertical line on the screen of the picture tube.

b. The horizontal scanning circuits generally do not have a frequency control.

c. A larger frequency error is shown in Fig. 13-10*b* than in Fig. 13-10*a*.

SUMMARY

The functions of stages in the sync and scanning circuits are summarized in Tables 13-1 to 13-3. Some receivers use the gen-lock method illustrated in Fig. 13-6, where digital circuits are used to lock in the *H* and *V* oscillator at the

TABLE 13-1
FUNCTIONS OF CIRCUITS FOR SYNC

STAGE	INPUT	OUTPUT	NOTES
Sync separator	Composite video	Total sync without video	Sync includes *H*, *V*, and *E* pulses
V sync integrator	Total sync	*V* sync alone to *V* oscillator	*RC* low-pass filter
Horizontal AFC	*H* sync	DC control voltage to *H* oscillator	Dual-diode phase detector

TABLE 13-2
FUNCTIONS OF CIRCUITS FOR VERTICAL SCANNING

STAGE	INPUT	OUTPUT	NOTES
V oscillator	*V* sync from integrator	60-Hz pulses to wave-shaping network	Operates with or without sync; includes *V* hold control
V wave-shaping network	Pulses from *V* oscillator	Trapezoidal voltage to *V* amplifier	*RC* networks; includes *V* linearity and height controls
V amplifier	60-Hz drive from wave-shaping network	60-Hz sawtooth scanning current in *V* coils of deflection yoke	Similar to class A power amplifier; may be push-pull circuit

sync frequencies. No *H* and *V* hold controls are necessary in this system. Note that receivers with anode voltages above 15 kV have a horizontal hold-down or shut-down circuit as a protection against excessive high voltage that can cause x-ray emission.

TABLE 13-3
FUNCTIONS OF CIRCUITS FOR HORIZONTAL SCANNING

STAGE	INPUT	OUTPUT	NOTES
H oscillator	DC control voltage from AFC diodes	15,750-Hz pulses to driver stage	Operates with or without sync; includes *H* hold control
H driver	Narrow pulses from *H* oscillator	Wider drive pulses for *H* amplifier	Pulse width determines conduction time of *H* amplifier
H amplifier	15,750-Hz drive pulses	15,750-Hz linear ramp of current in *H* coils of deflection yoke	Class C amplifier; conduction time about 50%; also supplies high-voltage rectifier and damper
High-voltage rectifier	Flyback pulses from *H* output	DC anode voltage for picture tube	May use voltage tripler or quadrupler
Damper	Scanning voltage from *H* output	Rectified deflection voltage for boosted B^+	Diode power rectifier
Low-voltage rectifier	Scanning voltage from *H* output	Rectified deflection voltage for dc supply	Diode power rectifier

SELF-EXAMINATION

Answers at Back of Book

Part A. Answer True or False.

1. The sync pulses are part of the composite video signal.
2. The *V* and *H* oscillators can operate with or without sync.
3. The frequency of the equalizing pulses is 120 Hz.
4. Flyback high voltage is taken from the *H* output circuit.

5. The gen-lock system does not need V and H hold controls.
6. No vertical deflection results in a single horizontal line across the center of the screen.
7. No horizontal deflection results in no high voltage and no brightness.
8. No sync results in no brightness and no raster.
9. Noise pulses in the sync signal can make the picture roll up or down.
10. The sync separator has video input and sync output.

Part B. Choose the correct answer.

1. Is an RC integrator used for V or H sync?
2. Is the V hold control in the oscillator or the amplifier stage?
3. Are dual diodes used for horizontal AFC or the sync separator?
4. Is the damper diode in the V or H output circuit?
5. The picture is in diagonal segments. Should the V control or H hold control be adjusted?
6. There is too much black area at the top and bottom of the screen. Should the V hold or the height control be adjusted?
7. Is the boosted B^+ voltage produced in the output circuit of the damper or the H oscillator?
8. Is the waveform of scanning current in the V and H coils of the deflection yoke sawtooth or trapezoidal?
9. Are the linearity and size controls usually not provided for the V or the H deflection circuits?
10. People appear in the picture with elongated legs. Should you adjust the V or the H linearity control?

ESSAY QUESTIONS

1. List the functions of the sync separator, horizontal AFC circuit, and vertical integrator.
2. List the function of each stage in the vertical deflection circuit.
3. What is the function of each stage in the horizontal deflection circuit?
4. Explain briefly how flyback high voltage is produced for the anode of the picture tube.
5. What is meant by a scan-voltage supply for low voltage?
6. What is a gen-lock system for deflection?
7. Why is noise a problem in the sync?
8. List three controls in the V deflection circuits and explain the function of each.
9. Why are no controls provided for the horizontal output circuit?

10. Why is the sawtooth waveform required for scanning current in the deflection coils?
11. What is a trapezoidal voltage waveform?
12. What is the function of the vertical integrator circuit?
13. What is the function of the horizontal AFC circuit?
14. Which stage in the deflection circuits requires the most power?
15. Describe briefly two sync troubles.
16. Name two problems in the V deflection circuits.
17. List three troubles in the H deflection circuits.
18. What two problems can cause incorrect oscillator frequency for V or H scanning?
19. What makes the picture roll up or down the screen?
20. What makes the picture tear into segments with diagonal bars?
21. List the functions of three rectifiers in Fig. 13-9.
22. What is the function of a voltage regulator in the power supply?

PROBLEMS

Answers to Odd-Numbered Problems at Back of Book

1. Calculate the RC time constant with R 10 kΩ and $C = 0.01$ μF.
2. Compare the RC time constant of 100 μs with the width of the H sync pulse.
3. A horizontal output stage has an average I_C of 2 A and $V_C = 24$ V. How much is the dc power dissipation?
4. A damper diode rectifier produces 180-V dc output, connected series-aiding with 34 V from the low-voltage supply. How much is the boosted B^+ voltage?
5. A horizontal output stage is cut off for retrace and 40 percent of trace. For how many microseconds is the transistor conducting?
6. Vertical scanning coils have inductance $L = 40$ mH with $R = 50$ Ω. Calculate the inductive reactance X_L for sine-wave current at 60 Hz.
7. Horizontal scanning coils have inductance $L = 10$ mH with $R = 12$ Ω. Calculate the inductive reactance X_L for sine-wave current at 15,750 Hz.

SPECIAL QUESTIONS

1. List two troubles you have seen in the television picture that are related to deflection sync.
2. Why are the controls that vary the *V* or *H* oscillator frequency called *hold* controls?
3. Why are troubles in deflection sync essentially the same in monochrome and color receivers?
4. Explain the difference between deflection sync and color sync.
5. Explain the difference between class A and class C operation in an amplifier.
6. Compare a push-pull amplifier with a single-ended circuit.
7. Why is the sync separator considered a stage in the signal circuits, not the raster circuits?

ANSWERS TO TEST POINT QUESTIONS

13-1 **a.** T **b.** F **c.** T
13-2 **a.** F **b.** T **c.** T
13-3 **a.** Sync separator **b.** *C* **c.** 50 μs
13-4 **a.** *V* hold **b.** Output **c.** Output
13-5 **a.** F **b.** T **c.** T
13-6 **a.** Sync **b.** High voltage **c.** Class C
13-7 **a.** T **b.** F **c.** T
13-8 **a.** *V* **b.** High
13-9 **a.** *H* **b.** High
13-10 **a.** High voltage **b.** *D*1 **c.** *D*5 **d.** Line rectifier
13-11 **a.** F **b.** F **c.** F

14

COLOR TELEVISION RECEIVER CIRCUITS

The main difference between monochrome and color receivers, besides the picture tube, is that the color receiver has a 3.58-MHz chroma section. As illustrated in Fig. 14-1, the video detector supplies the colorplexed video signal for a buffer amplifier. Then the 3.58-MHz chroma signal goes to the color circuits that provide red, green, and blue video signals for the color picture tube. The reproduced picture is shown in color plate I. (All color plates can be found in Chap. 8.)

In the chroma section, the modulated 3.58-MHz subcarrier signal is selected and amplified in a color amplifier that drives the color demodulator circuits. In the demodulator, the modulated chroma signal beats with 3.58-MHz cw output from the color oscillator to recover the red, green, and blue information needed for the color picture tube. The chroma section regenerates the 3.58-MHz subcarrier signal needed for demodulation.

The luminance (Y) signal also is needed for the black-and-white information. Then the color video signals superimpose a full-color display on the monochrome image. The special requirements for the luminance signal in a color receiver and the circuits in the 3.58-MHz chroma section are explained in the following sections:

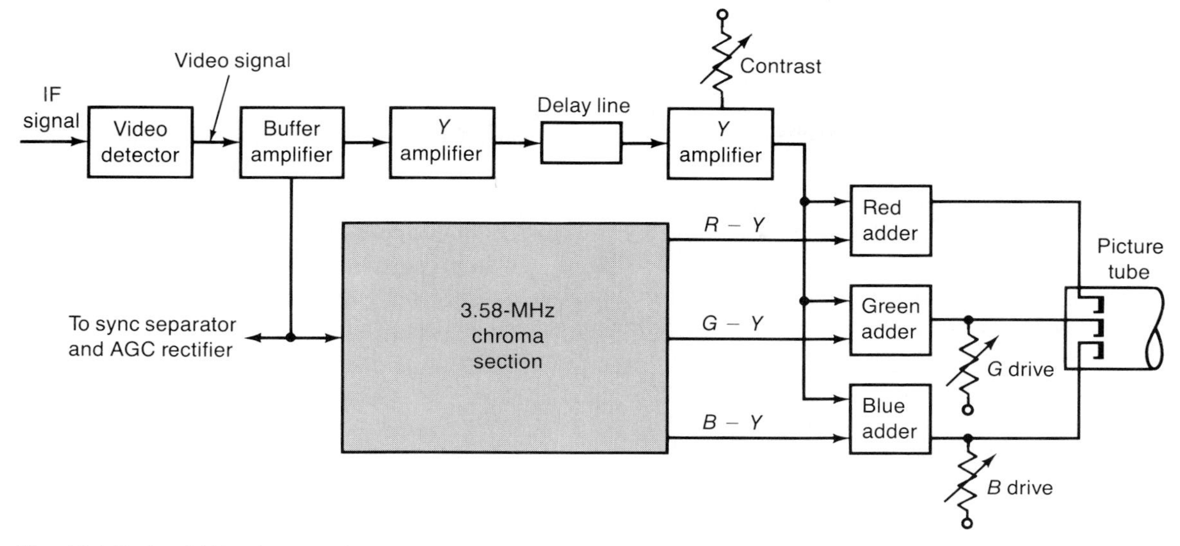

Fig. 14-1 Path of *Y* luminance signal that produces black-and-white image in color TV receiver.

14-1 PRODUCING THE LUMINANCE IMAGE

The foundation on which the full-color picture is built is the luminance, monochrome, or black-and-white image. In effect, the color is added. Furthermore, color is added only for the larger areas of the picture, those that correspond to video frequencies of 0.5 MHz or less. The system can be compared to a coloring book where the details are imaged by sharp black-on-white outlines and the color is added by blunt crayons for the larger areas.

In older color receivers, a single *Y* video output stage was used to drive the three electron guns. The usual method now, though, is to use three parallel-driver output stages, as in Fig. 14-1. These stages also serve as adders to combine the *Y* signal and color-difference signals.

During monochrome reception or when the color is turned off in the chroma section, a negative *Y* signal is applied to the three cathodes. Note that the −*Y* signal at a cathode corresponds to a positive *Y* signal at the control grid. The reproduced picture, then, is a neutral, colorless image. Although only a black-and-white picture is produced by the *Y* signal, it is the basis to which color is added.

***R, G,* AND *B* DRIVE CONTROLS** If the light-emitting efficiency were the same for all three phosphors, the required ratio of video drive voltages would be 1:1:1 for all three guns. Do not confuse these values with the 30:59:11 proportions of *R, G,* and *B* that make up the *Y* signal. The *Y* ratios produce a gray scale that appears natural, as determined by the visual response of the human eye. However, the phosphors in the picture tube are not equally efficient in light output. Therefore, some adjustment must be made to balance the beam currents at peak white to produce a neutral white. This function is accomplished by *R, G,* and *B* drive controls in the video output-adder stages. The controls are setup adjustments, usually located at the back of the receiver.

A typical arrangement is to have two drive controls, as shown in Fig. 14-1, instead of three. The color channel with the lowest efficiency, generally red, is driven with fixed maximum gain. Then the *G* and *B* drive controls can be adjusted to reduce green and blue for balance, as indicated by a neutral peak white.

The balancing is checked visually by turning off the color and watching the brightest parts of the picture. Adjust the drive controls to produce a neutral, colorless white in the highlights. It is best to make these adjustments on a monochrome picture. Remember that either the background bias or the screen-grid controls are set for neutral gray in the dark parts of the picture.

CONTRAST CONTROL The contrast control is in the *Y* video amplifier, as shown in Fig. 14-1. It is on the front panel in most receivers, so it can be adjusted by the viewer. The contrast control has only a narrow range in color receivers because changing the luminance amplitude also changes the saturation of the color picture. Actually, a change in contrast setting requires a corresponding change in chroma gain, by means of the color saturation control. In many receivers, a separate color control is mechanically ganged with the contrast control to make the luminance and chroma track with changes in the contrast setting. Such a combination control may be labeled *picture control,* instead of *contrast.*

VIDEO BANDWIDTH To achieve the full luminance resolution that the TV system is capable of, the *Y* amplifier should have a high-frequency response that extends flat to approximately 4.2 MHz. This response is seldom found in color receivers, however. One problem is the interference between the color subcarrier signal retained in the *Y* channel and the residual subcarrier ripple produced by the chroma section, where the 3.58-MHz subcarrier signal is regenerated for demodulation. To prevent this interference, generally a 3.58-MHz trap is used in the *Y* amplifier chain.

Because of the 3.58-MHz trap, the *Y* signal bandwidth is limited to 3.2 MHz. This video frequency allows a maximum horizontal resolution of 250 lines approximately.

To improve the resolution, a comb filter may be used in top-of-the-line receivers such as large-screen and projection models. The comb filter removes the color subcarrier sideband signals while leaving the high-order luminance harmonic frequencies intact. As a result, the *Y* video response can be extended to 4.2 MHz without chroma interference. This frequency response corresponds to 325-line resolution. The same comb filter that removes chroma components from the luminance chain also is used to take off the 3.58-MHz color signal to feed the chroma section.

EFFECT OF DC COMPONENT ON COLOR At the low end of the video-frequency passband is the dc component that varies very slowly with changes in the average scene brightness. The effect of loss of the dc component on a black-and-white picture is not too serious. In a color picture, however, loss of the dc component changes the color. The reason is that the balance of red, green, and blue is affected by the gamma characteristic of the picture tube. With a gamma exponent of 2.2, the picture tube practically squares the peak values for the video signals. For example, consider a color made of 1 part red, 2 parts green, and 3 parts blue. The effect of gamma is to produce beam current ratios of 1:4:9 for peak video drive signals. These values produce a much different color than values with the proportions of 1:2:3. The required gamma correction is in the video signal, but the dc component must be preserved to retain the balance. For this reason, direct coupling is generally used for the *Y* video amplifier stages between the video detector and the picture tube. Direct coupling is used also in the chain from the chroma demodulators into the color video amplifiers that drive the picture tube.

When the dc level is blocked by capacitive coupling, pedestal clamp circuits are necessary to restore the dc component. The circuit may use a diode rectifier or be just one function of an IC that reinserts a dc level proportional to the amount of missing dc component. This arrangement is called a *dc restorer,* or *clamp, circuit.*

Test Point Questions 14-1

Answers at End of Chapter

a. Does the *Y* signal produce a monochrome or color picture?

b. Are the drive controls adjusted for white or dark gray?

c. Which primary color generally does not have a drive control?

14-2 HINTS FOR TROUBLESHOOTING COLOR RECEIVERS

The main idea to remember is that the color is superimposed on a monochrome picture which is produced on a white scanning raster. White is the main color to check because it is made in the tricolor picture tube by combining red, green, and blue in the proper proportions. The requirements for the electron guns are illustrated in Fig. 14-2:

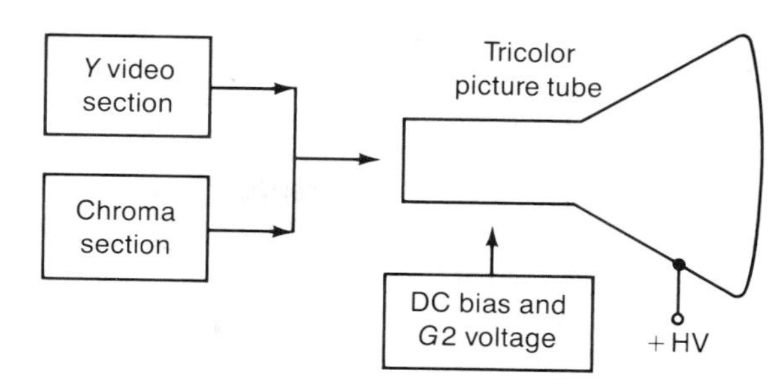

Fig. 14-2 Signal requirements for color superimposed on monochrome image on white raster.

1. Each gun must have the correct bias and *G*2 screen voltage. The result is a neutral white or gray raster.
2. Each gun must have a *Y* signal to produce a monochrome picture. The monochrome signal is supplied by the *Y* video amplifier section.
3. Each gun is supplied with *R, G,* and *B* video signals for the color picture. The chroma section processes the 3.58-MHz signal to supply the color video for the picture tube.

It is impossible to get a correct color picture if the receiver does not show a neutral black-and-white picture when the chroma circuits are turned off. Furthermore, the monochrome picture cannot be neutral unless the raster is neutral also.

Whenever the color appears wrong, the first thing to do is turn off the color and inspect the black-and-white image. In many receivers, it may be necessary to switch off the automatic color circuits before the color can be completely removed by turning down the front-panel color control.

For example, consider the case of a dead red gun in the picture tube. The picture will be missing red where it is expected in the color image. Turning off the color, though, will show a cyan-black image instead of a white-black image. Also, the raster will be cyan if the *Y* signal is removed. Such a problem should not be considered as a problem with color. The fault lies not in the chroma processing circuits but in the sections that make a monochrome picture on a white raster.

A fundamental rule, then, is to inspect the monochrome picture first. Black-and-white reproduction is the most difficult because this process requires that all the colors be in the correct proportions.

Failure in one of the three video output-adder stages will drastically affect the color balance, making the monochrome picture take on a predominant hue. Not only is it a problem of the missing ac signal, but also the dc values can be affected. For instance, consider an open green-adder stage. The cathode of the green gun rises to the supply voltage, which cuts off the beam current for this color. The result is a picture in magenta instead of black and white.

A shorted transistor in the green output stage has the opposite effect. Now the cathode bias for the green gun is removed completely. The high value of the beam current makes the picture appear definitely green. In some cases, the excessive beam current may load down the high-voltage supply to produce the symptom of no brightness and no raster at all.

A break in the *Y* video amplifier chain before the adders has the effect of removing the luminance information. However, the color information will remain, provided the break occurs after the takeoff point for the 3.58-MHz signal to the chroma section. When the color control is turned down, though, the result is no picture. The reason is that there is no luminance signal and no color signal.

Test Point Questions 14-2

Answers at End of Chapter

Answer True or False.

a. When the blue gun is dead, the monochrome picture and raster will be yellow.

b. A monochrome picture cannot be produced without the 3.58-MHz chroma section.

c. An open in the green output-adder stage results in a magenta picture.

14-3 NEED FOR LUMINANCE DELAY

The luminance and chrominance signals take separate paths following the video detector. They are rejoined as *Y* signal and decoded color-difference signals at the output-adder stages, as shown in Fig. 14-1. The luminance path is wideband, with the frequency range of approximately 0 to 3.2 MHz. However, the chroma signal has the much smaller bandwidth of ±0.5 MHz. The value of 0.5 MHz is the practical bandwidth of either sideband of the modulated chroma signal and for video frequencies in the demodulated color signals. Low-pass filters follow the color demodulators in order to restrict the bandwidth to 0.5 MHz.

As a result of reduced bandwidth, the narrowband color video signals have more time delay than the luminance video signal. The color signals reach the picture tube too late compared with the luminance signal. Or, the *Y* signal arrives too early. The *Y* signal needs to be delayed so that the luminance and color information are reproduced at the same time. The *Y* delay time needed is approximately 0.8 μs.

Figure 14-3 shows an example of phase delay and the resulting time delay with a square wave applied to a simple *RC* low-pass filter. The filter is a low-pass type because the output is taken across the shunt *C*. If the time constant is short

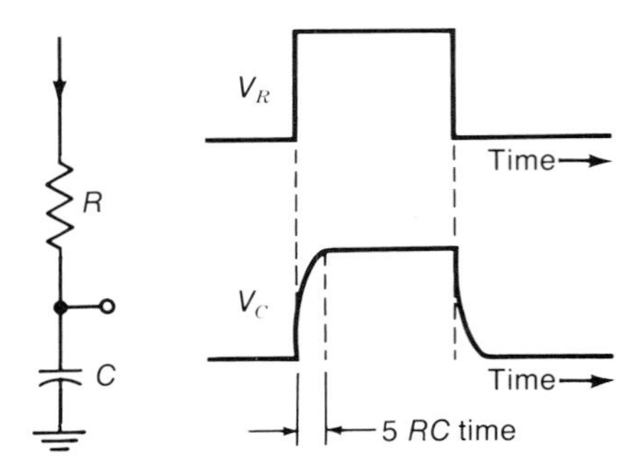

Fig. 14-3 Delay effect of a simple *RC* low-pass filter.

compared with the period of the square wave, then the capacitor will be fully charged in $5RC$ time approximately. After the pulse has passed, C will also discharge in $5RC$ time. As a result, the square wave at the input has a time lag at the leading and trailing edges in the output waveform across C. The effective part at the top of the waveform is delayed in time, as shown by a shift to the right on the time axis.

This same sort of time delay takes place in the narrowband color video circuits. Then the wideband luminance signal arrives at the picture tube too soon. If this discrepancy is not corrected, the color parts of the image will not fit into the sharp outlines provided by the luminance signal. Since the color arrives late and scanning goes from left to right, the color parts of the picture are displaced to the right. Also, the leading edges of objects in the picture are missing the color. The combination makes the color bleed or spill over the right edges. This effect would be especially evident on colored letters of the alphabet and numbers, as used in titles on the screen. The result is illustrated in Fig. 14-4 for the letter X.

The solution to this problem is to introduce a time delay into the Y video amplifier chain. The inserted time delay for the Y video is made equal to the natural time delay for the color video, approximately 0.8 μs, or 800 ns.

The required time delay is provided by a delay line, such as the long coil shown in Fig. 14-5.

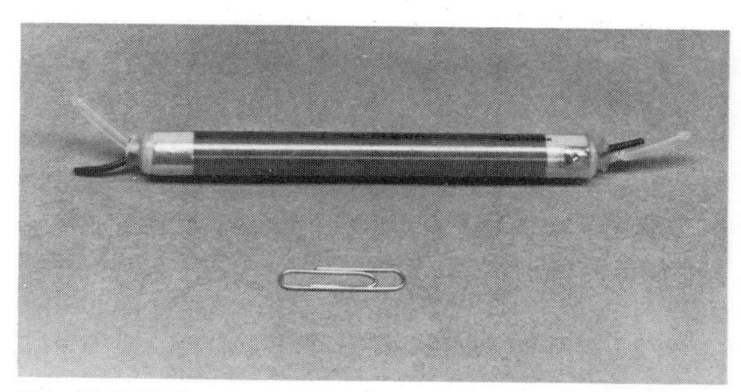

Fig. 14-5 Helix-wound, center-conductor type of *Y* delay line. Length is 6 in. [152.4 mm].

It corresponds to a transmission line where the delay is the time of propagation from the input end to the output end. In addition to the required 0.8-μs delay, the line should have the relatively high characteristic impedance of 1000 to 2000 Ω. The impedance must be high to avoid voltage loss for the signal at the input and output. Ideally, the impedance should be matched at both ends of the line.

In Fig. 14-5, the delay line is made with many turns of fine wire on the insulating cylinder. Also, a conductive coating around the cylinder serves as a shield. The shield is connected to chassis ground, while the conductor signals are at the input and output terminals. Besides the shielding effect, the shunt capacitance of the shield makes the conductor act as a long line. Another type is shown in Fig. 14-6 with lumped L and C constants for the delay line. The size is smaller, but

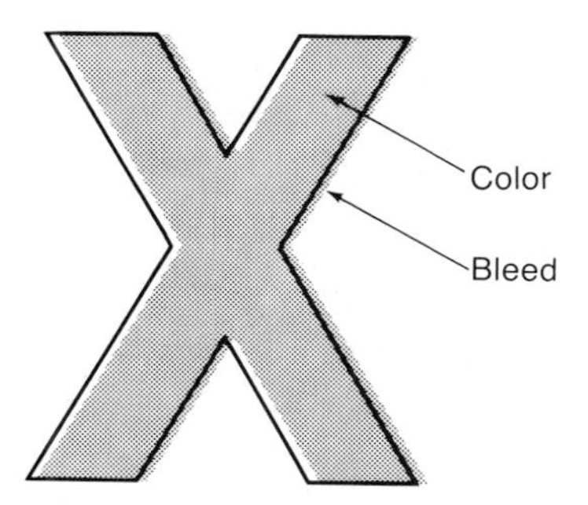

Fig. 14-4 Visual effect of chrominance time delay.

Fig. 14-6 Encapsulated lumped-constant type of *Y* delay line. Width is 1½ in. [38.1 mm].

Fig. 14-7 Effect in picture with an open ground in *Y* delay line.

it also provides the required time delay and impedance characteristics.

Failure to terminate the delay line in its characteristic impedance causes signal reflections. Figure 14-7 shows the picture when the ground return of the shield is open. An open circuit is the most extreme case of an impedance mismatch. When the inside wire conductor is open, however, the trouble is no *Y* video signal.

Figure 14-8 shows how the delay line is connected in series with the *Y* video amplifier chain. The delay line has three terminals. One is for the input signal, another is for the output signal, and the third goes to the chassis ground. At the input side, the *Y* video is coupled by an amplifier to drive the delay line with the required *Z*. At the output side, the delay line feeds the signal to the final *Y* video amplifier. Its input impedance is the termination of the delay line.

An obscure color problem can result from incorrect delay. The time added by the delay line is fixed. It matches the 0.8-μs delay normally introduced in the color processing circuits. However, a change in color bandwidth caused by misalignment can alter the delay time for the color signal. Less bandwidth corresponds to more time delay. The reduced bandwidth affects the color resolution, but also the picture looks as if the *Y* delay time were too short. Actually, the color delay is too long. In either case, the picture has poor color fit, as shown in Fig. 14-4.

Test Point Questions 14-3

Answers at End of Chapter

Answer True or False for the delay line in Fig. 14-8.

a. It has a 0.8-μs delay time.

b. The characteristic impedance is 15 Ω.

c. An open conductor results in no *Y* video signal.

d. An open ground return results in multiple outlines in the picture.

14-4 SPECIAL FEATURES OF THE IF CIRCUITS

In a color receiver, the part of the IF spectrum that includes the color subcarrier frequency is very important. This color IF value is $45.75 - 3.58 = 42.17$ MHz. The chroma sidebands extend

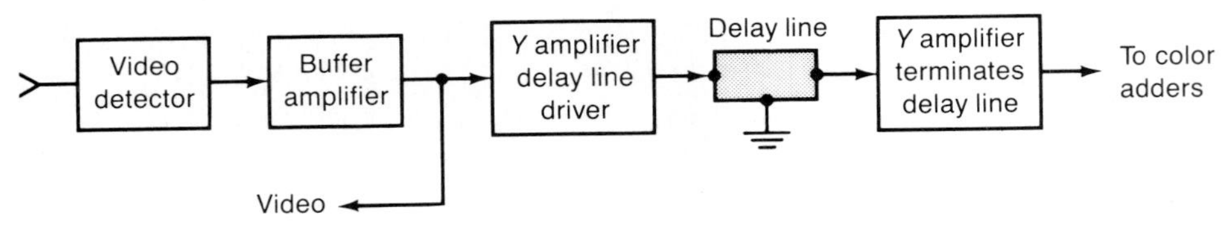

Fig. 14-8 Location of *Y* delay line in video circuits. Delay line $Z = 1$ to 2 kΩ.

±0.5 MHz above and below 42.17 MHz with all the color information. At the low end, 42.17 − 0.5 MHz = 41.67 MHz, which is very close to the 41.25-MHz sound IF carrier.

REDUCED IF GAIN FOR COLOR It is difficult to extend the IF passband flat down to 41.67 MHz because a sharp corner would be formed where the associated sound trap cut into the response curve. Such abrupt changes in amplitude response are accompanied by a nonlinear phase shift. The phase distortion causes incorrect hues in small areas of the picture and at vertical edges. The solution is to provide a gradual drop in amplitude response, with the 42.17-MHz color IF subcarrier at 50 percent response, as shown in Fig. 14-9*a*.

An interesting note here is that both the IF picture carrier and the IF color subcarrier have 50 percent relative gain in the IF response curve. The 45.75-MHz picture carrier is at the high-frequency side, and the 42.17-MHz color subcarrier is at the low-frequency side.

As a result of reduced IF response, the color subcarrier signal out of the video detector has about one-half its normal amplitude in the colorplexed composite video signal. Furthermore, the 0.5-MHz sideband frequencies close to the associated sound receive even less amplification, while the upper sideband frequencies have more than 50 percent response. These gain values are reversed in the chroma section, however, to restore the correct relative response for the 3.58-MHz chroma signal.

CHROMA FREQUENCY COMPENSATION The chroma takeoff circuit that feeds the chroma section has a peaking effect that complements the effects of the IF amplifier. As shown in Fig. 14-10, the chroma signal is applied to the bandpass amplifier. A single-tuned circuit at the input resonates at 4.1 MHz. This resonance effect puts the 3.58-MHz color subcarrier on the slope of

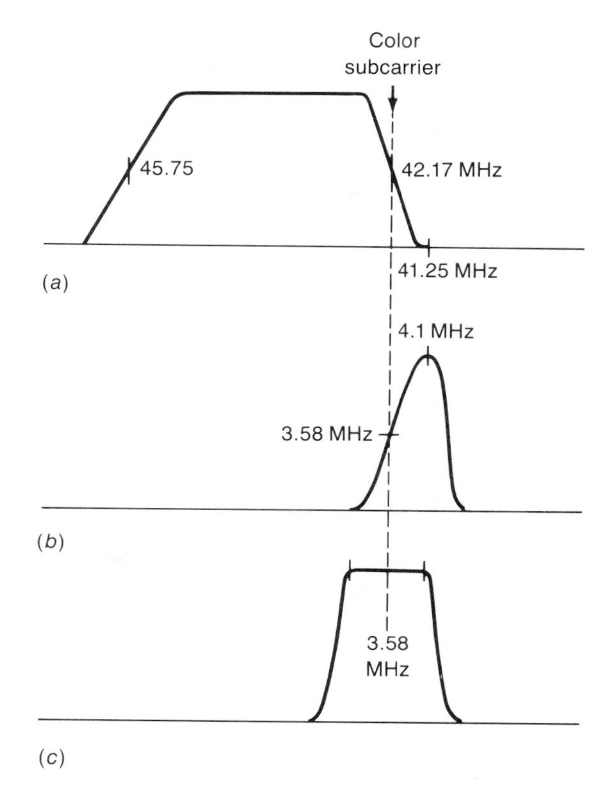

Fig. 14-9 How the response of first bandpass amplifier complements IF response to provide uniform gain ±0.5 MHz either side of color subcarrier frequency. (*a*) IF response curve. (*b*) Input to bandpass amplifier. (*c*) Overall response for 3.58-MHz chroma signal.

the response curve shown in Fig. 14-9*b*. Here the upper sideband of the 3.58-MHz chroma signal is near the peak while the lower sideband is attenuated. The slope is the same but in the opposite direction of the IF response curve. As a result, the overall effect for the chroma signal is the uniform response shown in Fig. 14-9*c*. Then 3.58 MHz is at the center of the curve, with symmetric response ±0.5 MHz above and below the chroma subcarrier.

A special alignment technique is necessary to ensure that the IF gain and chroma response match properly for uniform amplification of both chroma sidebands. The remaining circuits in the

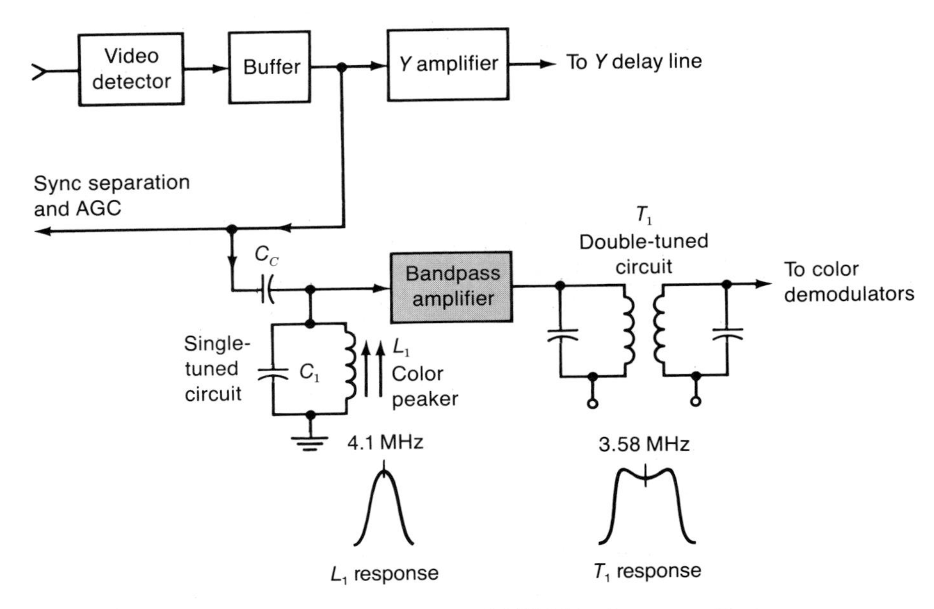

Fig. 14-10 Bandpass amplifier is beginning of 3.58-MHz chroma section.

bandpass amplifier have flat response, broadly tuned to 3.58 MHz. Note the symmetric response of the bandpass amplifier shown in Fig. 14-10 for output transformer T_1.

The single-tuned trap with L_1 in Fig. 14-10 is often called the *color takeoff circuit* because it feeds the chroma signal to the bandpass amplifier. The adjustable coil L_1 is also called a *peaker* because it emphasizes the upper sideband of the chroma signal.

THE 920-kHz SOUND BEAT Another problem in color receivers is the 920-kHz beat between the color and sound carrier frequencies. The separation between them is

$$4.5 - 3.58 = 0.920 \text{ MHz} = 920 \text{ kHz}$$

This 920-kHz sound beat can produce interference in the picture.

If both the sound and color carriers are present in the video detector, the 920-kHz beat will appear. The heterodyning effect is essentially the same as the way in which the 4.5-MHz sound signal is produced. Once the 920-kHz beat is produced, it cannot be removed by filters because the frequency is in the normal video passband.

The visual effect of the 920-kHz beat can be observed by misadjusting the fine-tuning control of the receiver. The interference appears as a herringbone pattern in color areas of the picture. This effect is shown in color plate XII. The 920-kHz frequency corresponds to approximately 58 diagonal bars. The herringbone pattern is the visual effect of audio modulation. Since there is no color subcarrier for neutral white or gray parts of the picture, the beat interference appears in the color areas only.

Although an IF chroma signal is necessary to produce the beat, it appears in the luminance part of the signal because the beat frequency is 920 kHz. This frequency is outside the 3.58-MHz passband. You will continue to see the beat interference even if the color is turned off at the front-panel control.

The solution is to remove the 41.25-MHz associated sound signal at the input to the video detector. Elaborate cancellation traps are used for this purpose. Their response is very deep in attenuation and very narrow in frequency. In fact, the visual proof of correct fine-tuning in a color receiver is disappearance of the 920-kHz beat in highly saturated parts of the color picture. At that point, the RF tuner is converting the sound carrier to the precise frequency of 41.25 MHz, to which the trap is tuned.

SEPARATE 4.5-MHz SOUND DETECTOR Elimination of the associated sound from the video detector means that it cannot supply the 4.5-MHz beat for the sound signal. Another diode detector is needed, therefore, just for the sound. The two detectors are shown in Fig. 14-11. The video detector supplies the composite video signal, including both luminance and chrominance. The other diode, generally called the *sound IF detector,* produces the 4.5-MHz sound signal.

The IF input to the 4.5-MHz sound detector is taken before the 41.25-MHz trap. Both the sound and picture carriers are needed for the 4.5-MHz beat. The IF response at the input to the sound detector is similar to the overall IF response at the video detector in monochrome receivers.

Test Point Questions 14-4

Answers at End of Chapter

a. What is the value of the beat frequency between the associated sound carrier and color subcarrier?

b. What is the beat frequency between the associated sound carrier and the picture carrier?

c. What is the resonant frequency of L_1 and C_1 in Fig. 14-10?

d. What is the relative gain for 42.17 MHz in the IF amplifier?

14-5 THE 3.58-MHz CHROMA SECTION

An overall view of the 3.58-MHz chroma section is shown in Fig. 14-12. The 3.58-MHz chroma signal is in the colorplexed composite video, usually obtained from an emitter-follower buffer that follows the video detector. Although it has been frequency-distorted by the downward slope of the IF response, the chroma signal is corrected by the upward slope of the chroma takeoff circuit at the input to the chroma section. In the bandpass amplifier, the chroma sidebands of ±0.5 Hz on either side of 3.58 MHz are amplified uniformly. It is a bandpass amplifier (BPA) because the bandwidth is a relatively large percentage of the resonant frequency. Two stages are shown

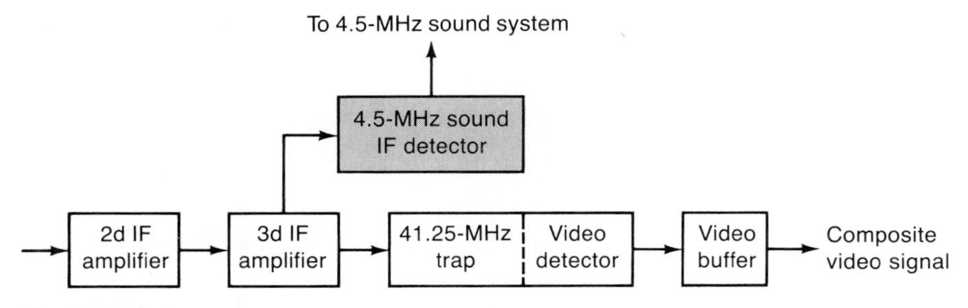

Fig. 14-11 Color receivers need a separate IF detector diode to feed 4.5-MHz sound system.

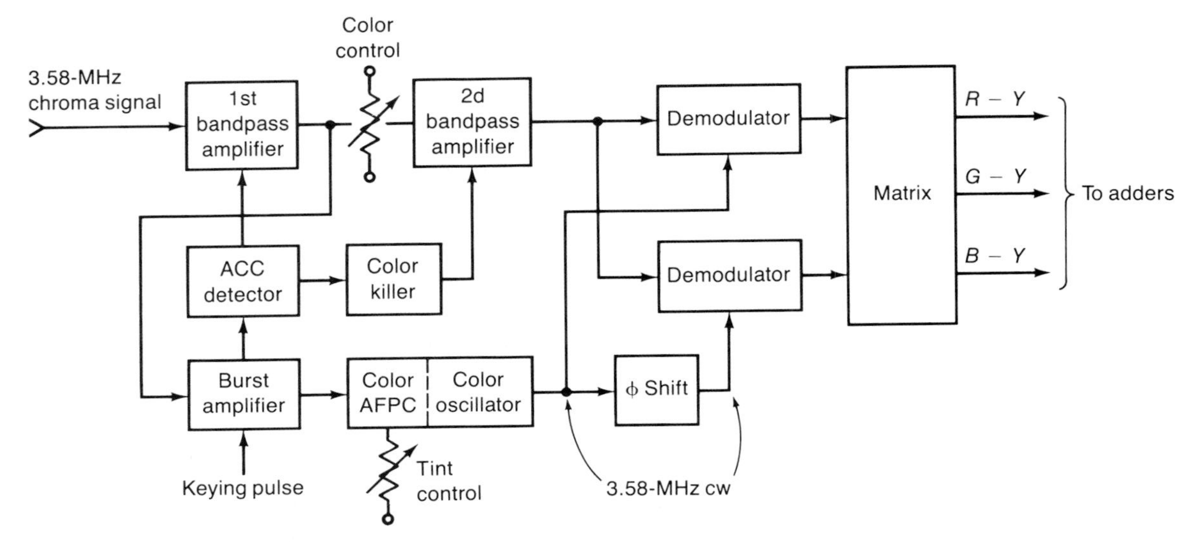

Fig. 14-12 Block diagram of chroma section.

in Fig. 14-12. The bandpass amplifier is often called the *color amplifier.* Its gain determines the color saturation. The output of the color amplifier is the 3.58-MHz chroma signal for the color demodulators.

Figure 14-13 shows the oscilloscope waveform at the *H* rate for a 3.58-MHz chroma signal in the bandpass amplifier. Note that lower-frequency signals such as deflection sync and parts of the *Y* signal below 3.08 MHz have been rejected. You see only color burst and the color subcarrier signal, both at 3.58 MHz. However, it is not correct to consider that the chroma is totally separated from the luminance at this point. There still remain high-frequency luminance components in the frequency range of 3.08 to 4.08 MHz.

COLOR CONTROL A gain control in the bandpass amplifier controls the amplitude of the chroma signal output to the demodulators. The control specifically varies saturation, from weak to intense colors, but is generally labeled *color,* or *color intensity.* At one end, fully counterclockwise, the control turns off the chroma signal. Then the picture is reproduced in monochrome. When the color control is set fully clockwise, enough gain is provided in the bandpass amplifier to produce some degree of oversaturation.

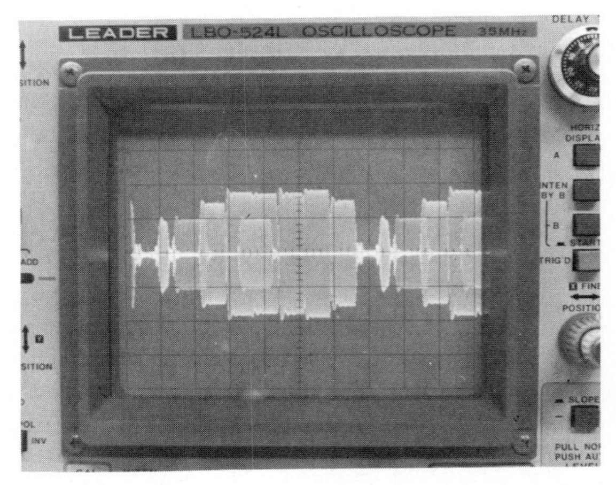

Fig. 14-13 Oscilloscope waveform at *H* rate of standard color-bar signal at output of bandpass amplifier. Luminance and deflection sync are missing; chroma and burst remain.

AUTOMATIC COLOR CONTROL This function can be considered as automatic gain control (AGC) for the color amplifier. In Fig. 14-12, note that the automatic color control (ACC) detector block controls the first bandpass amplifier. The automatic control is in addition to the manual color control.

The ACC is needed to make up for variations in level of the 3.58-MHz chroma signal caused by the following:

1. Different RF responses in the tuner for different channels
2. Nonuniform frequency response in the antenna
3. Different amounts of signal strength at the antenna for different channels

The ACC circuit sets the gain of the bandpass amplifier by monitoring the amplitude of the color burst. This level is the one factor in the chroma signal that is unaffected by picture content. As shown in Fig. 14-12, the ACC detector has input from the burst amplifier. The amount of burst input determines how much gain the ACC circuit allows in the bandpass amplifier.

COLOR DEMODULATORS The output of the bandpass amplifier drives the two color demodulators in Fig. 14-12. Each demodulator requires two inputs:

1. The 3.58-MHz chroma signal. Its sidebands have the color information.
2. Unmodulated 3.58-MHz cw signal from the color oscillator. This signal is reinserted to take the place of the subcarrier suppressed in transmission.

The color demodulators are synchronous amplitude detectors. They are synchronous because the amount of detected output depends on the phase of the reinserted cw signal compared with that of the chroma signal.

In terms of the synchronous phase, there are many ways to operate the color demodulators. The detected color output depends on the phase of the cw input. Also, there can be either two or three demodulators.

Some receivers use two demodulators to detect the I and Q video signals as they are transmitted. A matrix circuit then develops the three color-difference signals $R - Y$, $G - Y$, and $B - Y$.

Many receivers demodulate $R - Y$ and $B - Y$ video signals directly. Then a matrix is used to develop the $G - Y$ video signal.

Some receivers use two demodulators, called X and Z for specific phase angles. Then the detector output is converted to $R - Y$, $B - Y$, and $G - Y$ video.

Some receivers use three demodulators to produce $R - Y$, $G - Y$, and $B - Y$ video signals directly.

For any method, each demodulator must have the 3.58-MHz chroma signal from the BPA plus the 3.58-MHz cw signal at a specific angle. In color television, the phase angle determines the hue of the color. The hue of the detected video depends on the phase of the reinserted subcarrier signal.

In all cases, the output of the color demodulators provides $R - Y$, $G - Y$, and $B - Y$ color-difference signals. They go to the adders to be combined with Y signal for R, G, and B video at the picture tube.

SUBCARRIER REGENERATOR The lower part of Fig. 14-12 shows the subcarrier regenerator, which includes a 3.58-MHz color oscillator. Also included is the color automatic frequency and phase control (AFPC) system. The purpose of the subcarrier regenerator is to generate a 3.58-MHz cw signal for the color demodulators.

The color oscillator is crystal-controlled with a crystal that resonates at 3.579545 MHz. Furthermore, the AFPC system locks in the oscillator to the frequency and phase of the reference for the system, which is color burst.

To start with, the subcarrier regenerator needs 3.58-MHz burst without the remainder of the signal. In Fig. 14-12, the block at the lower left is the *burst separator* or *burst amplifier.* This stage is a narrowband amplifier tuned to 3.58 MHz. However, it is biased to cutoff. Horizontal flyback pulses, or delayed sync pulses, are applied to key the stage into conduction during retrace time only. At this time the color burst is present in the video signal. Remember that the 3.58-MHz color burst is on the back porch of horizontal blanking. Thus the output of the burst amplifier is the 3.58-MHz color burst, separated from the video signal and amplified for the AFPC system.

The AFPC system includes a phase-locked loop (PLL) circuit. A sample of the 3.58-MHz output from the color oscillator is compared with the burst in a phase detector. Its output is the dc control voltage that corrects both the frequency and the phase of the oscillator.

The output of the color oscillator is a 3.58-MHz cw signal to be reinserted in the color demodulators. This carrier regeneration is needed because the 3.58-MHz subcarrier is suppressed in transmission. The sidebands cannot be demodulated without the subcarrier. In Fig. 14-12, the oscillator output goes to one demodulator directly. The other path has a fixed phase shift, indicated by the greek letter ϕ (phi), in order to demodulate a different hue.

TINT, OR HUE, CONTROL This control is located on the front panel of the receiver to permit the viewer to adjust the phase angle of the cw feeds to the demodulators. Different phase angles correspond to different hues. The hue is what most people call the color. However, whether the sky is reproduced in blue or green is a question of hue specifically, rather than saturation. The hue control is often labeled the *tint control,* because it is a more familiar name.

The tint contol may be in the burst amplifier, the AFPC, or the color oscillator output. In any case, the PLL circuit just follows the phase shift inserted by the tint control. Rotation of the tint control provides a phase shift of ±30 to ±45°. This range is broad enough to change the yellow in the standard color-bar pattern from green to orange. In terms of pink flesh tones, they can be changed from green at one end of the tint control to purple at the opposite end.

Set the control for tints you know, such as green grass, blue sky, and proper flesh tones. When these are correct, the other tints are determined automatically by their relative phase.

Many receivers have design modifications to emphasize orange for pink flesh tones that cannot have too much green or purple. Also, some receivers use the vertical interval reference signal (VIRS) to lock in both tint and saturation.

CRYSTAL-RINGER SYSTEM An alternative to AFPC is the method of shock-excitation for the 3.58-MHz crystal. The color burst is applied directly to the crystal. Then the crystal produces oscillations temporarily. However, the crystal continues to ring between bursts. In this method, the oscillator that follows the crystal is locked in by the burst directly, instead of a PLL system with dc control voltage being used. The 3.58-MHz cw output of the color oscillator is used to drive the color demodulators. The crystal-ringer circuit is discussed later with Fig. 14-25.

Test Point Questions 14-5

Answers at End of Chapter

Answer True or False.

a. The bandpass amplifier is tuned to 3.58 MHz with a typical bandwidth of ±0.5 MHz.
b. The color control varies the gain of the bandpass amplifier.
c. The burst amplifier is off during *H* flyback time.
d. A synchronous demodulator needs two input signals.
e. The AFPC circuit provides dc control voltage for the color oscillator.
f. The tint control varies the amount of output from the color oscillator.

14-6 TROUBLES IN CHROMA CIRCUITS

The following are problems for the color picture only. The receiver can produce a monochrome picture on a white raster.

NO COLOR, WEAK COLOR, OR TOO MUCH COLOR A failure in the bandpass amplifier stops the flow of the chroma signal to all the demodulators. Then no color-difference signals can be produced, and the adders have only the Y signal. The result is a monochrome picture without any color. The picture looks the same as it would if the color were turned off by rotating the color control completely counterclockwise.

A loss of gain in the bandpass amplifier simply reduces the amount of color saturation. The colors appear pale, and they are not vivid or strong.

A failure in the ACC system can have the opposite effect. Certain troubles permit the BPA to operate at maximum gain. The result is oversaturation. Then the colors are too vivid. Furthermore, there is excessive color snow, called *confetti.* The confetti is coarse, though, because of the narrow ± 0.5-MHz band of the color processing circuits.

Two inputs are needed for a color demodulator—the chroma signal and the cw output from the color oscillator. If either one is missing, the demodulator cannot produce any output. Therefore, failure of the color oscillator means there is no color video output from the demodulators. So the trouble of no color in the picture has two possible causes. The failure can be in either the color oscillator or the BPA. Also, the color-killer circuit can be the cause of no color, as explained in Sec. 14-8.

INCORRECT COLORS Consider these possibilities. The color oscillator can be operating in the wrong phase. Or one demodulator can be out of operation. Or a color-difference signal can be missing from the matrix output. There are specific symptoms for these troubles, though. Incorrect phase usually produces all the colors, but they are in the wrong place. For instance, the sky is red instead of blue, and the grass is magenta instead of green. Failure of a demodulator, however, results in particular colors being missing. Without $G - Y$, for example, the picture is missing green and magenta. Remember that magenta is minus green, at the opposite end of the $G - Y$ hue axis.

CHANGING COLORS Failure of the AFPC system to lock in the subcarrier produces a unique symptom. Now the phase of the oscillator cw signal for the demodulators is able to change continuously with respect to the chroma signal from the BPA. The objects in the picture change hue, as a result, at a rate determined by the frequency error. For instance, a 1-Hz error will cause a face on the screen to go through all the colors in the rainbow once each second. The frequency error is usually higher. When it gets to 60 Hz, which is the field-scanning rate, the color changes through 360° for the entire rainbow spectrum from the top of the picture to the bottom.

At still higher values of frequency error in the color oscillator, the colors break into diagonal bands with a complete rainbow in each band. The number of bands equals the number of rainbows stacked vertically multiplied by the 60-Hz field-scanning rate. For example, five rainbow bands represent a frequency error of $5 \times 60 = 300$ Hz. The bands are confusing and difficult to identify in a typical TV picture, except with solid colors, as seen in the titles for programs. See color plate VI. In a picture that has vertical color bars, the rainbow bands are easy to see.

The loss of color lock indicates a failure of the PLL system. The cause can be no burst input, no feedback from the color oscillator, or failure of the phase comparator itself. Another possibility is a frequency error in the color oscillator that is too much for the PLL system to correct.

Test Point Questions 14-6

Answers at End of Chapter

a. Name two circuits that can cause the trouble of no color

b. Will a fixed phase error in the color oscillator cause no color or wrong hues?

c. If the $R - Y$ demodulator fails, which colors will be missing from the picture?

14-7 COLOR BANDPASS AMPLIFIER

Two stages of amplification are shown in Fig. 14-14, with both tuned to 3.58 MHz. The first stage includes the single-tuned peaker circuit to correct for the slope of the IF response curve.

Since the chroma signal out of the first amplifier is at a relatively low amplitude, the AGC for the color level can be applied here. Several different methods are used for the ACC, but the basic requirements are as follows:

1. Dc control voltage for bias to control the gain automatically
2. ACC variable-bias voltage proportional to the burst amplitude in the received signal

In some cases, a simple peak detector diode is used for the ACC bias. It is driven from a sample of the separated burst signal out of the burst separator, as shown in Fig. 14-14.

With a crystal-ringer system, the ACC detector is driven from the ringing crystal itself. The amplitude of this cw signal is directly proportional to the burst amplitude. The sample of burst is more immune to noise because the crystal does not respond to noise as much as it does to burst. This advantage can be important for very weak signals.

The front-panel *color saturation* control is usually between the two bandpass amplifiers, as in Fig. 14-14. The color level control acts as a volume control in a radio. More chroma signal means more color saturation, just as a greater audio signal makes the volume louder.

In some receivers, a subcolor control is used that is mechanically ganged with the contrast

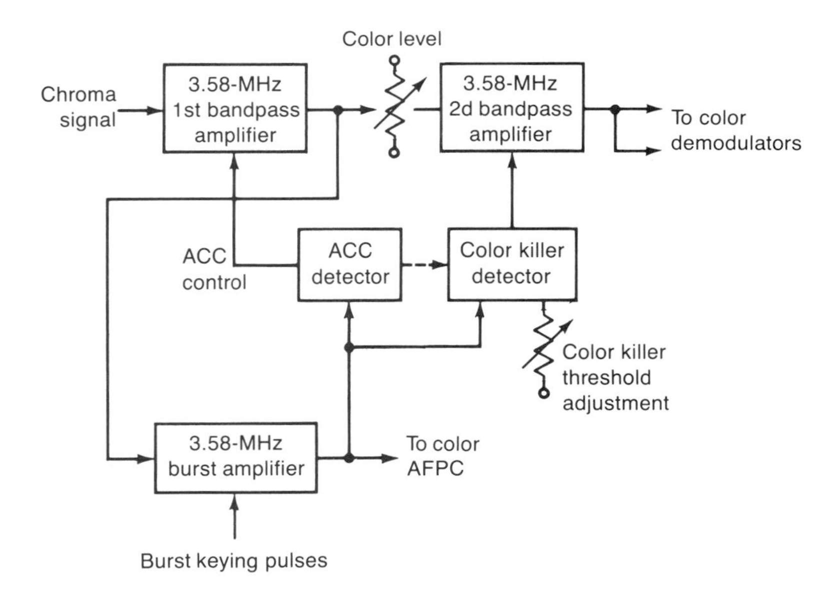

Fig. 14-14 Details of color bandpass amplifier with automatic color control (ACC).

control. Another method uses a control that varies a dc voltage to make the color level track with the contrast setting. Then the contrast control is also a picture control.

Many receivers have one-button automatic operation for color. A fixed resistive divider restricts the range of the manual color and tint controls in the automatic position. Then, it is usually not possible to turn off the color completely with the color control, in order to check on a monochrome picture. First you must make sure the button is not in its automatic position.

The second BPA is a power output stage to supply the 3.58-MHz chroma signal to the color demodulators, all in parallel. There may be two or three demodulators. Each one needs chroma signal input and the 3.58-MHz cw signal from the color oscillator.

Test Point Questions 14-7

Answers at End of Chapter

a. Does the ACC circuit vary the gain of the first or second BPA?

b. Does the manual color control vary the amplitude or the phase of the 3.58-MHz chroma signal?

c. Does the output from the BPA feed the demodulators or the color oscillator?

d. Is the burst amplitude used to determine the ACC bias or the oscillator phase?

14-8 COLOR-KILLER CIRCUIT

In all color receivers, the color-killer circuit shuts down the color BPA completely when a monochrome signal is being received. This method uses the presence or absence of the burst signal to determine whether the program is in color. No burst means no color. To cut off the 3.58-MHz chroma signal, the color-killer circuit biases the second BPA out of operation (Fig. 14-14). Specifically, the color-killer circuit uses a detector diode to provide dc bias for the color amplifier. The sequence of operation can be summarized as follows:

For color: Burst is on. The color-killer diode provides normal bias for the BPA. Its 3.58-MHz chroma signal goes to the color demodulators.

For monochrome: There is no color burst. The diode bias from the color-killer circuit cuts off the BPA.

The reason for killing the color amplifier for monochrome programs is that the demodulators try to make color out of the luminance information between 3 and 4 MHz that still remains in the BPA. Luminance signals near 3.58 MHz can show in the picture, especially in fine-line patterns. Examples are stripes or plaids in clothing, or even spaces between the teeth when a person is smiling. This effect varies with the distance to the camera because of the different video frequencies in the picture information. You see a tiny rainbow of color in a sparkling pattern, which corresponds to high-frequency luminance signal variations.

The dominant color of this luminance interference is magenta. The reason is that the $B - Y$ signal has the most gain in the color video amplifiers in the receiver, in order to compensate for the way in which the colors are encoded at the transmitter. In terms of phase angle, the hue of magenta, or purple, is close to the $B - Y$ video signal. Furthermore, the color snow, called confetti, that appears on the screen when the antenna is disconnected also is predominantly magenta. In general, any uniform signal not preemphasized for specific colors is reproduced by the receiver mainly as magenta.

The color-killer circuit often includes a threshold control to set the value of burst that will open the color amplifier for normal operation on color. This control can be misadjusted to kill the color on a color program. Normally, the threshold is set at the point that just produces color. Also, the setting should kill any color confetti on the screen when there is no picture.

The color-killer detector is designed to ignore noise. Otherwise, the noise could act as a burst signal to turn on the color amplifier. A properly operating color killer will kill confetti noise in a snowy raster when the antenna is removed or the receiver is switched to an unused channel.

The color-killer circuit adds an important factor that must be considered in troubleshooting the chroma circuits. For instance, we said earlier that loss of burst causes the color AFPC system to unlock from the color sync. This effect is true but it might not be the symptom noticed on the screen. The reason is that loss of burst is interpreted by the color killer as a monochrome program. As a result, the BPA is cut off and the symptom is quite different—no color.

To isolate the cause of a no-color condition, first it is necessary to disable the color killer. If the color returns but is out of sync, the fault must be in the color burst separator.

Test Point Questions 14-8

Answers at End of Chapter

Answer True or False.

a. The color killer bias is on the BPA.

b. Burst is used to produce the dc bias from the color-killer diode detector.

c. Color snow, or confetti, is predominantly magenta.

14-9 COLOR DEMODULATORS

The schematic diagram of one type of chroma demodulator is shown in Fig. 14-15 to illustrate how it is sensitive to only a designated axis of phase angles. This circuit with two diodes is used in many color receivers. Note the two input signals. The cw input from the 3.58-MHz color oscillator is shown at the left, coupled by transformer T_1 to the diodes. At the center, T_2 couples the 3.58-MHz chroma input signal from the BPA.

Consider the condition of no input signal from the BPA. The color is turned off. However, the cw drive from local oscillator is always present. Refer to Fig. 14-15*a*. During the half-cycles when the cw polarities are as shown, the diodes conduct to charge C_1 and C_2. Each is charged to the peak voltage. The rectified voltage is positive at the cathode side or negative at the anode side of the diodes. Then the two capacitor voltages are equal and opposite because the circuit is balanced. During the next half-cycle of cw drive, when the T_1 polarities reverse, both diodes are cut off.

The capacitors serve as equal but opposing sources of dc voltage. At the output terminal at the junction of R_1 and R_2, the net output voltage is zero.

In Fig. 14-15*b*, the chroma signal is applied in the same phase as the cw drive from the oscillator. Note the polarities shown for T_1 and T_2. The two input signals are series-aiding and so add for *D*1, but series-opposing and so subtract for *D*2. Then C_1 has a larger voltage, and the output is positive.

Reverse the phase of the signal by 180° in the feed from the chroma BPA, and the condition shown in Fig. 14-15*c* results. Now the signal voltages for *D*2 are additive. The voltage across C_2 is larger, and the output is negative.

Just as important is the case in which the chroma signal is out of phase by 90 or 270° with respect to the oscillator cw signal. Although not shown here, this condition allows the diode detectors to remain balanced. The chroma signal is going through zero at the center of the half-cycle of conduction produced by the oscillator signal. For both diodes, the input signals are aiding during a quarter-cycle and opposing during a quarter-cycle. Thus the circuit stays balanced, and the output is zero.

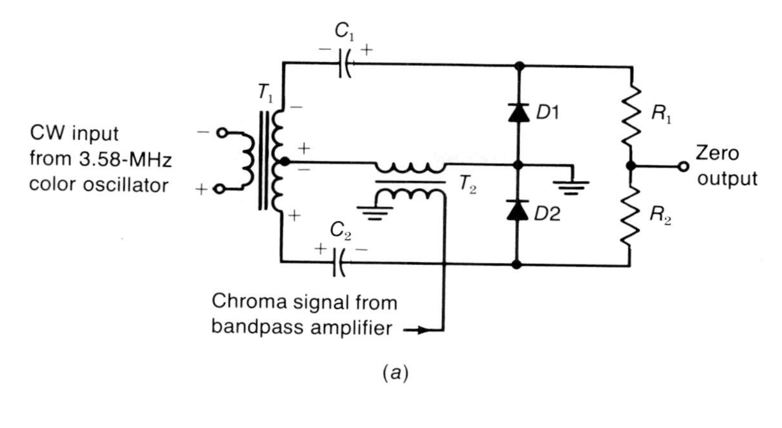

(a)

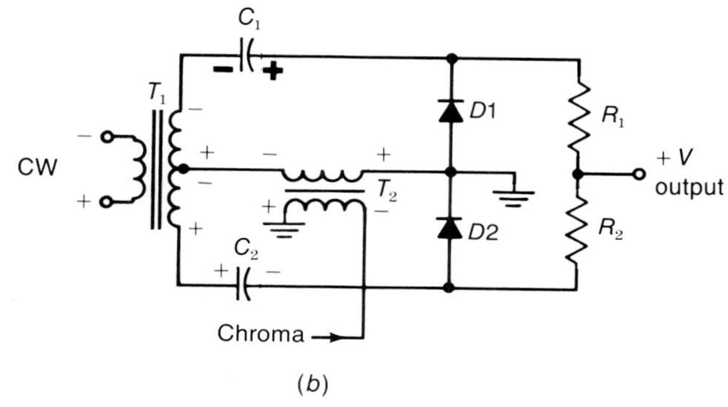

(b)

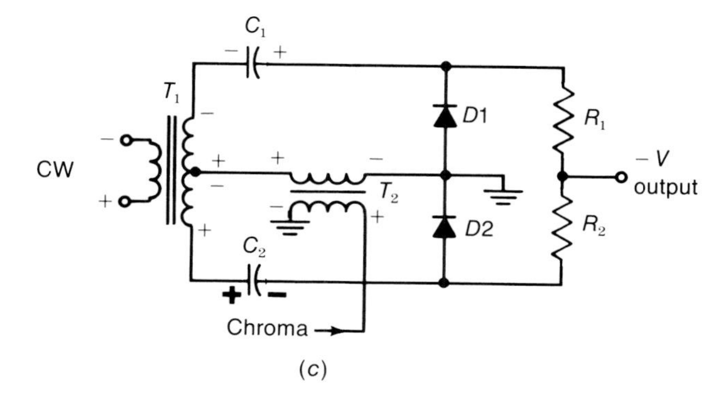

(c)

Fig. 14-15 A basic type of color demodulator circuit with balanced diodes. (*a*) No input from bandpass amplifier means no demodulator output. (*b*) Signal from bandpass amplifier in phase with 3.58-MHz cw from color oscillator. (*c*) Bandpass amplifier signal 180° out of phase with oscillator cw.

In summary, the demodulator produces output for 0 and 180° phase between the chroma and cw signals but not for quadrature phase at 90 or 270°. This explains why two demodulators are often 90° out of phase. Then there is minimum crosstalk interference between the circuits.

With intermediate phase angles, between 0 and 90° or 180 and 270°, the demodulator output varies between the extremes of zero and maximum. For sine-wave variations in phase, the de-

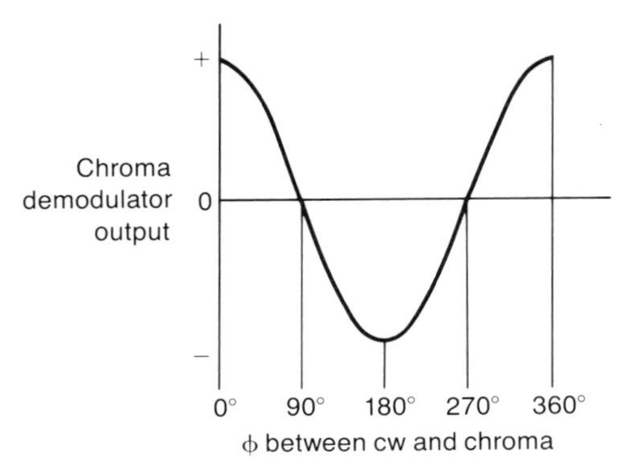

Fig. 14-16 How demodulator output voltage varies as chroma signal from bandpass amplifier shifts in phase (ϕ) with respect to fixed phase of oscillator cw signal.

modulator output has the sine-wave variations in output voltage shown in Fig. 14-16. The main point to remember is that the circuit is sensitive to in-phase or out-of-phase signals, but ignores quadrature signals. Between these two extremes, the chroma demodulator output is proportional to the phase angle between two input signals.

***I* AND *Q* DEMODULATORS** The hue of the detected color video signal depends on the phase of the oscillator cw signal, which serves as the 3.58-MHz subcarrier for the demodulation. An obvious method is to make the two demodulators in the receiver operate with the same phase axes used for the *I* and *Q* signals in the encoding in the camera. This system allows the highest degree of color resolution. The reason is that the orange-cyan *I* signal has a maximum bandwidth of 1.3 MHz, compared with 0.5 MHz for all other color video signals. However, *I* and *Q* demodulators have seldom been used in receivers because of extra complications in the circuits for the *I* signal. The added color resolution of the *I* signal is difficult to see in typical pictures, with the possible exception of large-screen projection-model receivers.

The problems in an $I - Q$ demodulation system can be seen from the block diagram in Fig. 14-17. Note the difference in bandwidths. The *Q* signal has double sidebands ±600 kHz from 3.58 MHz. The *I* signal also has double sidebands in this range but has only the lower sideband for frequencies from 600 kHz to 1.3 MHz. Therefore, two separate BPAs are needed. One feeds the signal to the *Q* demodulator. The other is in the feed line to the *I* demodulator. Its response

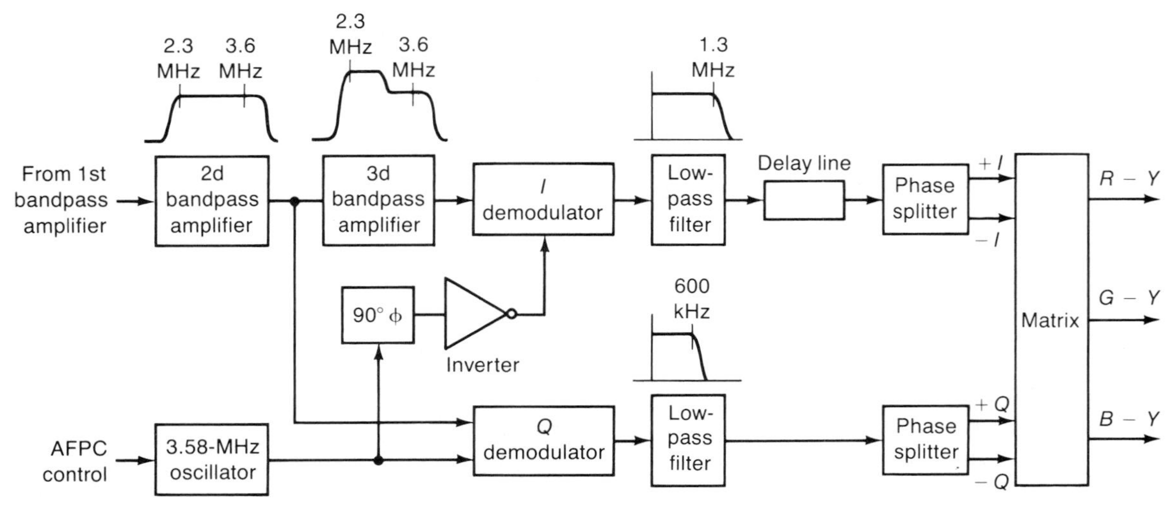

Fig. 14-17 Basic requirements of the $I - Q$ demodulator system.

is not flat but boosts the frequencies where only the lower sideband exists. This effect is needed to make up for the suppressed part of the upper sideband.

The I and Q demodulators are fed oscillator cw signals that are 90° out of phase. The inverter stage puts the I oscillator phase at 270° with respect to Q, so that the demodulation is on the $+I$ axis.

A low-pass filter following the I demodulator restricts the color video bandwidth in that channel to 1.3 MHz. Another filter in the output of the Q demodulator limits the bandwidth to 600 kHz.

Note that a delay line is needed for the I signal. The reason is the difference in bandwidths of the I and Q channels. As a result, this type of receiver has two delay lines—one to slow down the I signal to match the Q signal and the other to delay the Y signal to match both color signals.

Phase splitters in the color video output circuits develop $\pm I$ and $\pm Q$ signal polarities. The resistive matrix then selects the proportions needed to develop the color-difference signals. Finally, $R - Y$, $G - Y$, and $B - Y$ video signals are fed to the picture tube with the Y signal to reproduce the picture in luminance, red, green, and blue.

JUDGING THE COLOR RESOLUTION The thing to look for in judging color resolution is saturated color letters in program titles, especially when the letters become small. An example is shown in Fig. 14-18 for the capital letter E. It will have color in the longer horizontal bars at top and bottom, but it might have little color in the vertical leg. You can judge the color resolution between receivers in side-by-side tests by comparing color titles of this type. Keep in mind, though, that the maximum color video bandwidth of 0.5 MHz for most receivers corresponds to a horizontal distance no less than one-fiftieth of the picture's width.

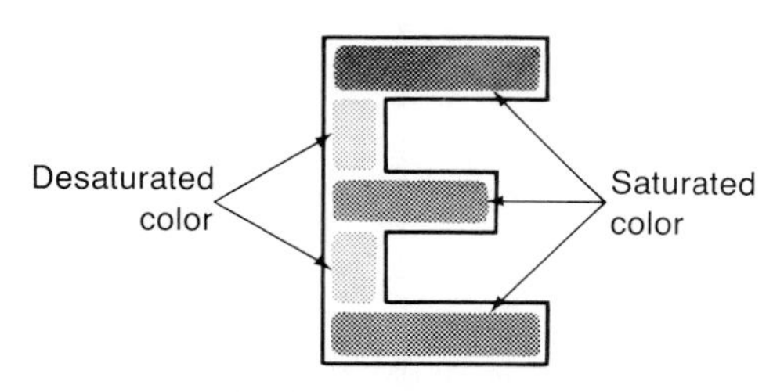

Fig. 14-18 Color letters in titles can be used as a test pattern to judge color resolution.

$R - Y$ AND $B - Y$ DEMODULATORS A shift of 33° in the demodulation axes permits $R - Y$ and $B - Y$ color video signals to be decoded directly. To see how this is done, consider the phase-angle diagrams in Fig. 14-19. In Fig. 14-19*a*, a fully saturated magenta vector is shown. Its components in terms of I and Q signals are indicated by the length of the I and Q vectors. These values are produced by I and Q demodulators. Note that the magenta vector is resolved in terms of quadrature components.

In Fig. 14-19*b* the same magenta vector is shown, but now it is resolved into $R - Y$ and $B - Y$ components. The length of these two vectors indicates the values of the video signal produced by the $R - Y$ and $B - Y$ demodulators. The difference between the vectors in Fig. 14-19*a* and *b* is that the phase of the oscillator cw signal is shifted 33° from $+Q$ to match the phase of $B - Y$. Also, 90° from $B - Y$ is the phase of $R - Y$. By selection of the demodulator axes it is possible to decode any desired set of color values.

Figure 14-20 shows a block diagram of this system that demodulates the $B - Y$ and $R - Y$ video signal directly. The oscillator cw phase is shifted 90° for the $R - Y$ demodulator. This method is much simpler than $I - Q$ demodulation. The color amplifier bandwidth is 0.5 or 0.6 MHz in both color channels, and no color delay is needed. Note that $G - Y$ is developed by means of the divider with R_1 and R_2. The circuit solves the equation shown for $-(G - Y)$, and then the inverter changes the phase to $G - Y$.

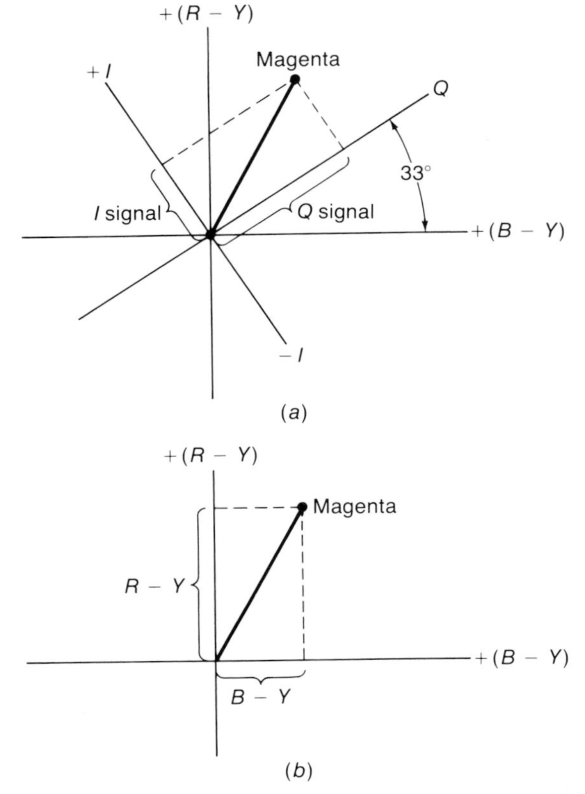

Fig. 14-19 The hue of magenta in chroma signal decoded by two different demodulation systems. (*a*) Magenta resolved into *I* and *Q* components. (*b*) Magenta resolved into $R - Y$ and $B - Y$ components.

THREE-DEMODULATOR SYSTEM In Fig. 14-21, the $B - Y$, $R - Y$, and $G - Y$ video signals are demodulated directly. Two phase shifters are necessary for the oscillator cw drive. The 90° phase is for the $R - Y$ demodulator. For the $G - Y$ demodulator an inverter is used for 180°, and an additional 56.6° makes $180 + 56.6 = 236.6°$ for the $G - Y$ axis.

One advantage of using three demodulators is that the *Y* signal can be added directly to the demodulator output. Then the signal output includes *R*, *G*, and *B* video that can be used for the picture tube.

***X* AND *Z* DEMODULATORS** The *X* demodulator name is for the color axis 12° from $-(R - Y)$. The *Z* axis is 27° from the burst phase, which is the same as $-(B - Y)$ phase. The *X* and *Z* demodulators are approximately 51° apart. The $X - Z$ demodulation system has been used because it offers the advantage of a balanced circuit for forming the $R - Y$, $B - Y$, and $G - Y$ signals in the demodulator output circuit.

COLOR EMPHASIS Often the color video signals are altered from their theoretical values for practical reasons. The departure from color fidelity is done to avoid the appearance of green or violet flesh tones even when a burst-chroma phase error

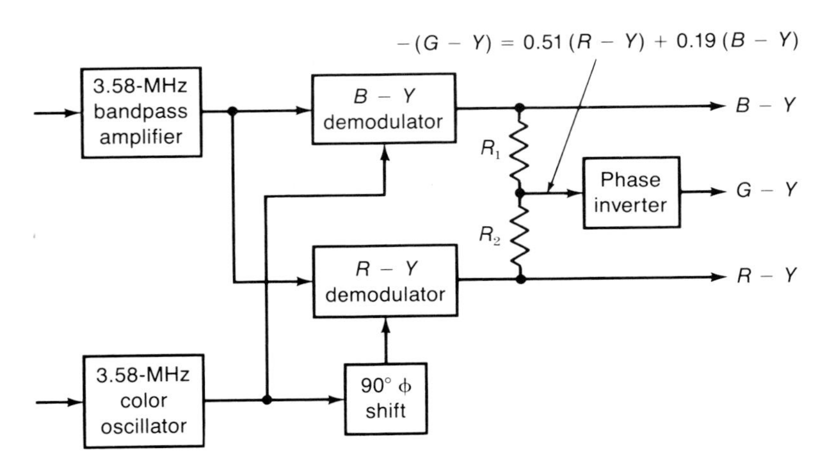

Fig. 14-20 Block diagram of $R - Y$ and $B - Y$ demodulator system.

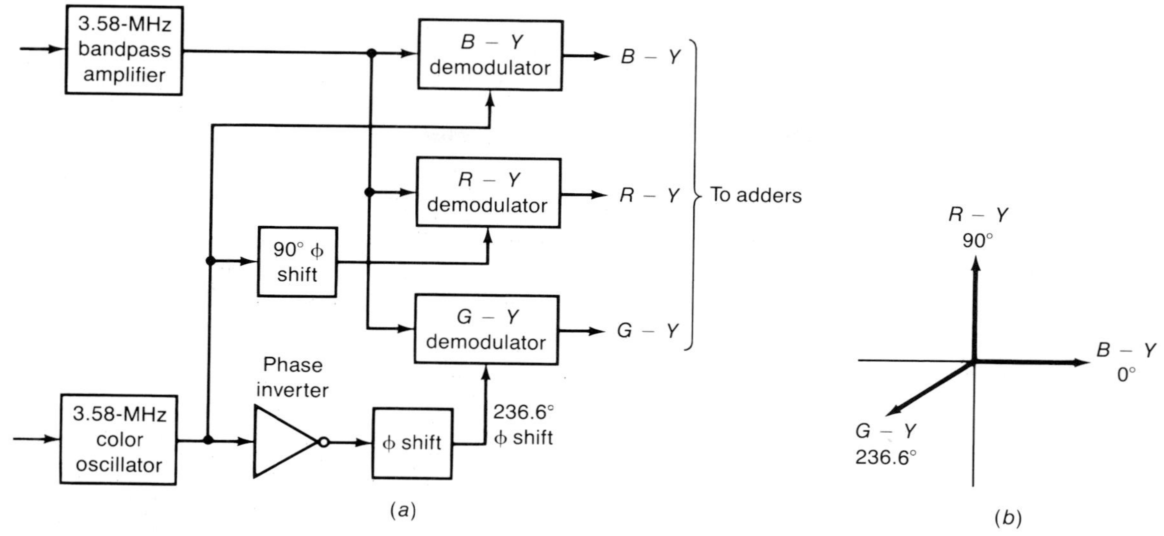

Fig. 14-21 Block diagram of system with three demodulators. The $B - Y$, $R - Y$, and $G - Y$ color video signals are decoded directly. (*a*) Circuit. (*b*) Phase-angle axes.

is introduced in the network transmission links. This practice is evidenced in the predominance of orange and blue in many television pictures. The emphasis can be accomplished in the chroma demodulators and the color video matrix circuits.

TROUBLESHOOTING HINTS FOR THE COLOR DEMODULATORS Keep in mind that the demodulators are often dc-coupled through the adders to the picture tube. The reason is to preserve the dc component of the color video signals.

Refer to the diode demodulator circuit shown in Fig. 14-15. It becomes unbalanced if one of the diodes should fail. Then the steady dc voltage in the output will alter the white balance for the picture tube. Troubleshooting is mainly a question of checking dc voltages, therefore, when a demodulator problem is suspected. There are very few ways for a demodulator to fail that will not change the dc output.

Another useful hint is that the 3.58-MHz color oscillator operates continuously to drive the demodulators, even during a monochrome program. The reason is related to the balance in the modulators. They are seldom balanced perfectly. There is always some residual dc output voltage even without chroma signal input. This small imbalance is taken care of when the picture tube is set up with the gray-scale tracking adjustments. If the color oscillator did not operate at all times, there would be one set of gray-scale conditions for color and another for monochrome. These factors can help to diagnose the trouble. For instance, the trouble of no color can be caused by a failure in either the chroma BPA or the subcarrier oscillator. However, if the problem also causes a change in white balance, failure in the color oscillator is indicated. The change in white balance makes a monochrome picture too green, magenta, or some other hue, instead of being a neutral white.

Test Point Questions 14-9

Answers at End of Chapter

a. What is the phase angle between $R - Y$ and $B - Y$?
b. Is the bandwidth of the I signal 1.3 or 0.5 MHz?
c. In Fig. 14-15, which transformer couples the cw input?
d. In Fig. 14-17, does the I signal or the Q signal have a delay line?
e. Is dc coupling often used for the demodulator output or the cw input?

14-10 AFPC SYSTEMS FOR COLOR SYNC

The AFPC system for color sync involves having the color oscillator locked in frequency and phase by the color sync burst. Remember that the color sync is a burst of 8 to 11 cycles at 3.58 MHz on the back porch of each H blanking pulse. The phase of the color burst is at $-(B - Y)$, which is a yellow-green hue. Phase angle is hue in color television.

In general, the AFPC circuit is like automatic frequency control (AFC) in other applications. In one application, the horizontal AFC locks in the horizontal deflection oscillator. In another application, the AFC is on the local oscillator in the RF tuner for automatic fine-tuning (AFT).

The color oscillator regenerates the 3.58-MHz subcarrier for detection of the chroma signals in the demodulators. A crystal sine-wave oscillator is used, and its frequency and phase can be varied by a dc control voltage. VCO indicates a voltage-controlled oscillator. Usually, the dc voltage changes the capacitance of a varactor to control the oscillator. A crystal oscillator with voltage control is abbreviated as VXCO. Although a crystal is used for stability, the frequency and phase of the oscillator can be varied by parallel capacitance.

The dc control voltage generally is produced by a phase comparator or detector with two diodes. The circuit compares the 3.58-MHz cw output produced by the oscillator with the 3.58-MHz color sync burst. Then the dc control voltage produced by the comparator can hold the color oscillator at the correct frequency and phase. A typical AFPC circuit is shown in Fig. 14-22.

PHASE DETECTOR Details of the phase detector in Fig. 14-22 are shown in the circuit of Fig. 14-23. Diodes $D1$ and $D2$ compare the phase of a sample of the cw output produced by the VXCO with the separated color burst from the burst amplifier. Balance in this circuit is similar to the principle of balanced diode demodulators shown in Fig. 14-15. The two diodes are balanced to produce zero output at the junction of R_1 and R_2 when the two input signals are 90° out of phase. Then they combine so that both diodes have equal amounts of input signal. Any phase relation between the two input signals that deviates from 90° results in either positive or negative dc output. The polarity of this dc correction voltage depends on the direction of the phase change. How much correction is needed depends on the amount of phase change. The polarity of the circuit is designed to make the correction voltage force the VXCO back into the condition of quadrature phase compared with burst.

Note that the phase comparator is inserting a phase shift of 90° into the oscillator cw signal for the color demodulators. This phase angle is taken into account for the rest of the color circuits. When the 3.58-MHz burst amplifier is tuned, for example, it is just set for the condition where the demodulators produce the correct color video signals.

SEPARATING THE COLOR SYNC BURST The burst amplifier in Fig. 14-22 is really a burst separator. Its input is either composite video or

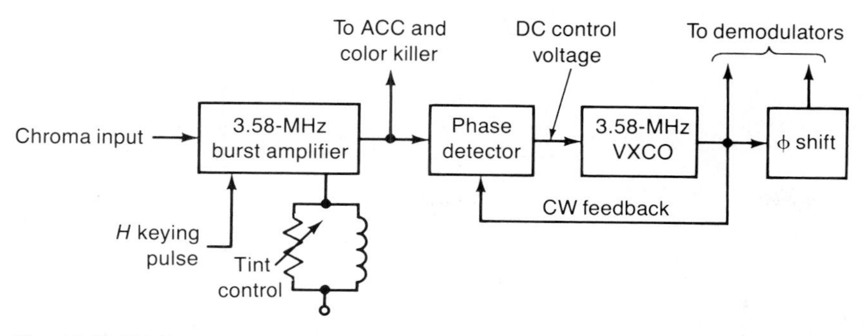

Fig. 14-22 PLL type of AFPC system for color sync. VXCO is voltage-controlled crystal oscillator.

a sample of the 3.58-MHz chroma signal, which also contains the sync burst. In many cases, the feed to the burst amplifier is taken from the output of the first BPA, as shown in Fig. 14-14.

Normally held in cutoff, the burst amplifier is made to conduct for only the short time while burst is present. A keying pulse turns on the separator during *H* flyback time. One keying method uses a sample of the *H* flyback pulse, taken from a winding on the horizontal output transformer. The pulse straddles the time interval of the color sync burst. However, this method allows some errors in gating. The *H* retrace pulse can be too long compared with the burst. Also, there may be a phase error in the horizontal AFC system for *H* deflection. The result of incorrect burst gating is that some chroma signal at the start of *H* trace mixes with the burst signal coupled to the phase detector in the AFPC circuit. This effect can be seen in the picture as a slight shift in hue when the horizontal hold control is rotated.

An improved method derives the burst gating pulses from delayed horizontal sync pulses. In this sytem, the burst separation is not affected by different settings of the horizontal hold control.

Oscilloscope waveforms for the burst separator are shown in Fig. 14-24. The input is shown at the top of Fig. 14-24. It contains a sample of chroma signal from the BPA and the delayed *H* sync pulse for gating. The gating pulse is a sine wave because the delay network uses an *LC* circuit. At the bottom of Fig. 14-24, the output is the separated burst signal alone, without the chroma signal. The separated burst goes to the AFPC circuit, which locks in the color oscillator to hold the correct hues steady in the picture.

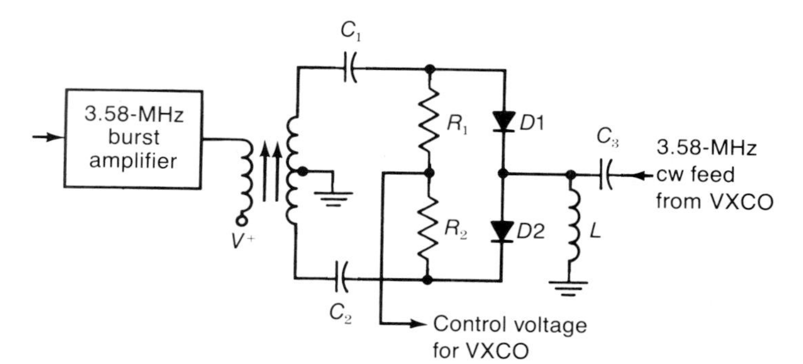

Fig. 14-23 Balanced phase detector with *D*1 and *D*2 to compare color burst with oscillator sample.

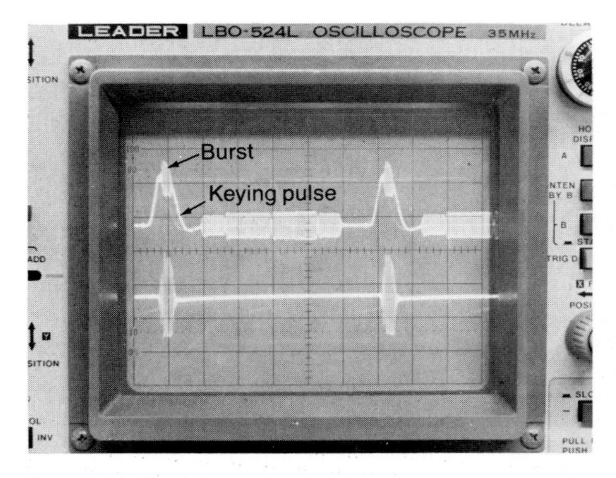

Fig. 14-24 Waveforms for burst separator or amplifier on dual-trace oscilloscope. Top shows signal input; bottom shows burst output.

CRYSTAL-RINGER CIRCUIT Figure 14-25 shows a block diagram for this type of AFPC. The crystal is not in the color oscillator. Instead, separated burst is applied directly across the 3.58-MHz crystal. During the 8 to 11 cycles of burst, the crystal is excited so that it oscillates in the same phase as the burst. At the end of the burst, the crystal continues to ring. The shock-excited oscillations, called *ringing*, continue with only slightly reduced amplitude until the next burst. This action can be produced by the crystal because it is equivalent to a resonant *LC* circuit with very high *Q*, meaning little losses.

The waveform for a typical crystal ringer is shown in Fig. 14-26. Note the slight drop in amplitude in the interval between bursts.

The crystal ringer in Fig. 14-25 is followed by a buffer amplifier that has high input impedance. Its function is to prevent loading the crystal, which would lower the *Q*. The main feed from the buffer stage is applied to the color oscillator, at the right in the diagram. This circuit is generally an *LC* oscillator, although a second crystal can be used also. The oscillator is injection-locked by the cw drive from the buffer amplifier, derived from the ringing crystal.

Following the oscillator in Fig. 14-25 is a driver stage to supply 3.58-MHz cw drive to the demodulators. The hue, or tint, control is in this circuit. The control varies the phase shift in the subcarrier signal for both demodulators. The phase control is separate from the fixed phase shift used for one demodulator with respect to the other.

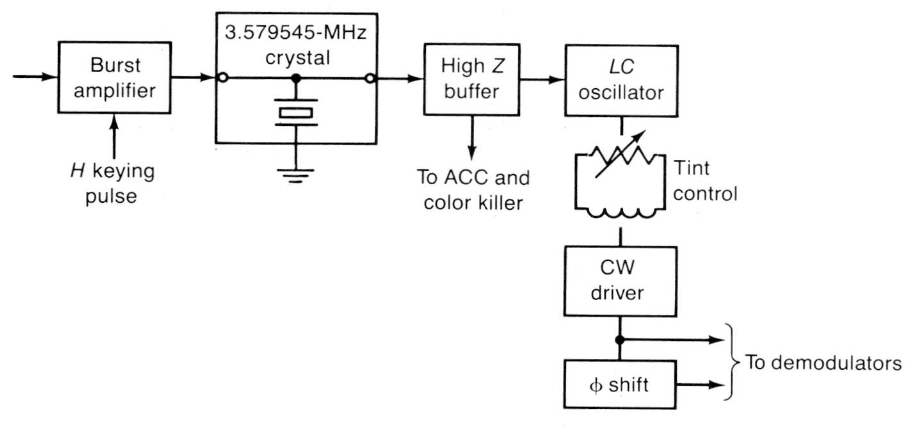

Fig. 14-25 Crystal-ringer type of AFPC system.

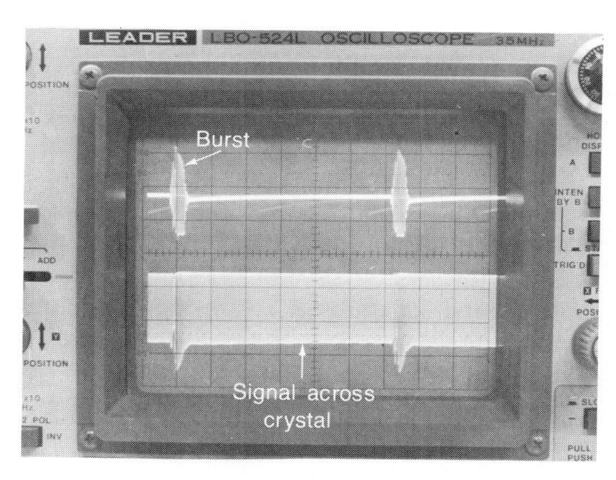

Fig. 14-26 Oscilloscope waveform at *H* rate for signal across ringing crystal.

Note the separate feed line from the buffer stage in Fig. 14-25 to the ACC and color-killer circuits. The crystal-ringer system has some advantages for this application. The amplitude of the cw signal in the buffer is proportional to the burst amplitude. So this signal can be used to drive a peak detector. The rectified dc output is the gain-control voltage for ACC on the chroma BPA.

In addition, the buffer cw output can be used for the color killer. A threshold detector indicates a cw amplitude that exceeds a specified value when the burst is on for a color program. This effect provides on-off control for the color killer. Such a system is immune to noise because of the crystal. For this circuit, the color-killer threshold adjustment is set by switching the receiver to an unused channel or removing the antenna connection and varying the control until the color is killed. The color confetti disappears, and the snow in the picture is black and white.

TROUBLESHOOTING HINTS FOR COLOR SYNC Loss of color sync is a common problem in older receivers. The hues change slowly, or color bars drift through the picture. There are two possibilities. Either there is no color sync, or the color oscillator cannot operate at the correct frequency.

Loss of color sync can occur if the burst separator fails. However, then the first symptom is no color at all in the picture, owing to the action of the color killer without burst. To solve the problem, it is necessary to disable the color killer. This can be done for some receivers by rotating the color-killer threshold control. For others it is necessary to consult the service manual.

To check whether the color oscillator can run at the right frequency, the burst should be removed. A 0.05-μF capacitor inserted from the input of the burst amplifier to ground will short-circuit the signal. Next, the color killer must be disabled. Then the frequency adjustment for the color oscillator is varied to produce a *zero-beat* condition. This effect occurs when the color oscillator is within a few cycles of the correct frequency. Colors seem to float vertically through the picture. For parts of the picture in solid colors, such as the background, the colors do not move but change hue. A complete rainbow of hues is produced for each cycle of frequency error. When a color-bar signal is used, the hues of the bars change slowly but remain unbroken from top to bottom. These effects in the picture show that the oscillator is capable of running at the correct frequency. If the color oscillator can produce the zero-beat effects but still cannot be locked in color sync, the trouble lies in the burst amplifier or phase detector.

Crystal-ringer circuits are easier to troubleshoot. It is just a question of checking waveforms with an oscilloscope to make sure the crystal is ringing.

Modern receivers use integrated circuits for the color processing. A single IC can replace many transistors. With color sync troubles, then, the IC is replaced.

COLOR OSCILLATOR AS A SOURCE OF FREQUENCY CALIBRATION A television receiver with the subcarrier oscillator locked into the color burst of the transmitted signal is an excellent source of signal with a very accurate frequency. It can be used for calibrating frequency counters. Use the low-capacitance probe of the oscilloscope to prevent loading and detuning of the oscillator circuit. After connecting the oscilloscope, check that the picture is still locked into color sync. The oscillator frequency locked into sync is equal to 3.579545 MHz exactly. The television networks use atomic standards to establish the subcarrier frequency, and the tolerance is far better than most practical needs.

Test Point Questions 14-10

Answers at End of Chapter

Answer True or False.

a. The crystal ringer is shock-excited by color burst.

b. In an AFPC phase detector, the burst and oscillator cw signals are 180° out of phase.

c. The burst separator is off during horizontal trace time.

d. No color sync means that colors drift through the picture.

SUMMARY

1. A color television picture consists of a black-and-white image with red, green, and blue information added for larger areas that corresponds to color video frequencies up to 0.5 MHz.
2. The luminance (*Y*) video signal with monochrome information for the black-and-white image is applied to all three cathodes of the tricolor picture tube.
3. The proportions of *Y* video signal are determined by the *R*, *G*, and *B* drive controls. Adjust for neutral white in a monochrome picture.
4. The contrast control is in the *Y* video amplifier in order to vary the gain of the luminance signal.
5. A delay line is needed in the *Y* video amplifier to provide 0.8-μs delay time. Then the luminance and color information arrive at the same time at the picture tube.
6. The color information is provided by the 3.58-MHz chroma section. These circuits process the modulated 3.58-MHz chroma signal to recover the red, green, and blue information for the three guns of the picture tube.
7. The chroma BPA amplifies the modulated 3.58-MHz chroma signal.
8. The color control varies the gain of the 3.58-MHz chroma BPA. Adjust for enough color in the picture without too much saturation.
9. The 3.58-MHz color oscillator regenerates the subcarrier needed for demodulation of the chroma signal.
10. The synchronous demodulators detect the 3.58-MHz chroma signal to provide red, green, and blue information as $R - Y$, $G - Y$, and $B - Y$ video.
11. The phase of the oscillator cw signal for the demodulators is synchronized by the color burst at 3.58 MHz.
12. The burst amplifier separates sync burst from the colorplexed composite video signal.

13. The AFPC for the color oscillator holds it synchronized with the phase of color burst. A crystal-ringer circuit has the same function. Without color sync, the picture has drifting color bars.
14. The tint, or hue, control adjusts the phase angle for the demodulated color video signals. Adjust for correct colors such as green grass, blue sky, and natural skin tones.
15. Generally dc coupling is used in the *Y* video and color video amplifiers from the point of detection to the picture tube. The dc component is necessary to achieve the correct color values.
16. The color-killer circuit cuts off the chroma BPA when there is no chroma signal, which is indicated by no color burst. The purpose is to eliminate color snow, or confetti, in a monochrome picture.
17. The ACC circuit varies the gain of the chroma amplifier to achieve a constant color level in the picture.
18. When you are troubleshooting color receivers, first check to see whether a normal monochrome picture can be produced on a neutral white raster.
19. Remember that a problem in dc coupling can alter the dc electrode voltages for the picture tube.
20. Weak color or no color at all is a problem with the 3.58-MHz chroma signal, since it includes red, green, and blue in the one signal.
21. Remember that the 3.58-MHz color oscillator is necessary for all the color demodulators.
22. For incorrect colors, the oscillator may be operating in the wrong phase. This problem affects all colors.
23. When specific colors are missing, one demodulator or a color-difference amplifier may be faulty.
24. The problem of changing colors indicates a failure in the AFPC system for color synchronization.
25. The functions of all stages for the chroma section in Fig. 14-12 are summarized in Table 14-1.

TABLE 14-1
FUNCTIONS OF STAGES IN CHROMA SECTION (FOR FIG. 14-12)

STAGE	INPUT	OUTPUT	NOTES
Color amplifier, or bandpass amplifier (BPA)	3.58-MHz chroma signal	To color demodulators	Gain determines the color saturation
Automatic color control (ACC)	Color burst	DC bias on color amplifier	Automatic gain control for color
Color killer	Detected burst	Cutoff bias on color amplifier	Kills color when there is no burst
Color demodulator	Chroma signal and oscillator cw	Detected color video signal	Two or three demodulators used

TABLE 14-1 (*Continued*)

STAGE	INPUT	OUTPUT	NOTES
Color oscillator	No signal input	3.58-MHz cw to demodulators	Phase locked in by AFPC
Burst amplifier or separator	Video signal with burst	Separated burst	Tuned to 3.58 MHz but conducts only for burst
Color AFPC or crystal ringer	Burst	Controls frequency and phase of color oscillator	Keep the hues steady, in sync with burst phase
Matrix	Detected color video signal, from demodulators	$R - Y$, $G - Y$, and $B - Y$ signals to adders	Passive resistance networks

SELF-EXAMINATION

Answers at Back of Book

Choose (a), (b), (c), or (d).

1. Which of the following applies for a monochrome picture? (a) Chroma amplifier on, (b) chroma amplifier off, (c) picture tube off, (d) delay line open.
2. Which of the following is *not* tuned to 3.58 MHz? (a) Burst amplifier, (b) video preamplifier, (c) chroma amplifier, (d) color demodulator input.
3. The contrast control is in the (a) chroma amplifier, (b) color killer, (c) Y video amplifier, (d) delay line.
4. The color level control is in the (a) demodulator, (b) BPA, (c) AFPC, (d) $G - Y$ amplifier.
5. The color oscillator does not operate. The trouble is (a) incorrect hues, (b) excessive confetti, (c) no color, (d) no picture.
6. The balance for Y video signals to the three guns in the picture tube is set by the (a) screen controls, (b) tint control, (c) contrast control, (d) drive controls.
7. Which signal needs a 0.8-μs time delay? (a) 3.58-MHz chroma, (b) $B - Y$ video, (c) Y video, (d) color burst.
8. The output of the burst separator feeds the (a) color demodulators, (b) $G - Y$ adder, (c) AFPC for color oscillator, (d) Y video amplifier.
9. The output of the color oscillator feeds the (a) chroma BPA, (b) color demodulators, (c) picture tube, (d) burst separator.
10. Drifting color bars in the picture indicate trouble in the (a) Y video amplifier, (b) chroma BPA, (c) color killer, (d) AFPC for color oscillator.

11. The beat frequency between the 3.58-MHz color subcarrier and the 4.5-MHz sound signal is (a) 0.92 MHz, (b) 3.58 MHz, (c) 4.8 MHz, (d) 4.5 MHz.
12. Which control varies the phase angle of the demodulated color video signal? (a) Color level, (b) tint, (c) drive, (d) picture.
13. Which of the following stages must be on during horizontal flyback time? (a) Y video amplifier, (b) chroma BPA, (c) burst separator, (d) $R - Y$ video amplifier.
14. Which of the following stages has bias from the ACC and color-killer circuits? (a) $R - Y$ demodulator, (b) $R - Y$ video amplifier, (c) chroma BPA, (d) color oscillator.
15. A crystal-ringer circuit is used for the (a) Y video amplifier, (b) AFPC on color oscillator, (c) color demodulators, (d) chroma BPA.

ESSAY QUESTIONS

1. List three requirements of a color picture tube in reproducing a monochrome picture.
2. Describe briefly the function of the 3.58-MHz chroma section in Fig. 14-1.
3. Name the functions of the following controls: contrast, brightness, color, tint, *RGB* drive, and *RGB* screen.
4. What is the function of the Y delay line? Why is it in the luminance circuit and not the color video section?
5. List the functions of the following stages: video preamplifier, video output, BPA, color oscillator, synchronous demodulator, and red adder.
6. What is the function of the color-killer circuit?
7. What is the function of the ACC circuit?
8. What is the function of the AFPC circuit for the color oscillator?
9. List the chroma circuits that are tuned to 3.58 MHz.
10. Why is the burst amplifier keyed into conduction during horizontal flyback time?
11. What are the input and output signals for the following stages? Video detector, video preamplifier, BPA, burst amplifier, color oscillator, $R - Y$ demodulator, and red adder.
12. Why does a color receiver have a separate 4.5-MHz sound detector stage?
13. Explain briefly how 920-kHz beat interference can be produced.
14. Approximately how much p-p video signal voltage is required to drive a 19-in. color picture tube?
15. How does the picture look without color sync?

16. Why does the trouble of no sync burst cause no color in the picture?
17. Draw the response curve of the 3.58-MHz chroma BPA.
18. Describe the two signals for input to an $R - Y$ demodulator.
19. Draw a schematic diagram of a burst amplifier circuit.
20. Describe three problems in the picture caused by a failure in the 3.58-MHz chroma section.
21. Give three possible causes of no color in the picture.
22. Name five troubles in the picture or raster caused by a failure that is not in the 3.58-MHz chroma section.
23. How does a synchronous demodulator circuit differ from an ordinary AM diode detector?
24. What are the phase angles between the following pairs of axes? $R - Y$ and $B - Y$, burst phase and $R - Y$, $B - Y$, and $-(G - Y)$.
25. What is meant by a ringing crystal? Which chroma circuit uses this system?
26. Draw a circuit of a balanced phase detector with two diodes for AFPC on the color oscillator.
27. Why are video signals usually coupled to the cathodes of the three guns in the picture tube, rather than to the control grids?
28. Why is dc coupling used generally for the video signals to the picture tube?
29. Draw a block diagram of the Y video amplifier chain from the video detector to the picture tube.
30. Draw a block diagram of a complete 3.58-MHz chroma section that includes $R - Y$ and $B - Y$ demodulators, RGB adders, and AFPC for the color oscillator.

PROBLEMS

Answers to Odd-Numbered Problems at Back of Book

1. How many picture elements correspond to a 0.8-μs delay time?
2. How many bars can be produced by a 920-kHz video signal?
3. Find the beat frequency for the following pairs of IF values: **(a)** P at 45.75 and S at 41.25 MHz, **(b)** P at 45.75 and C at 42.17 MHz, **(c)** S at 41.25 and C at 42.17 MHz.
4. In a 3.58-MHz crystal, $Q = 5000$. The parallel C is 2 pF. Calculate the equivalent inductance L of the crystal as a parallel resonant circuit.
5. What are the lower and upper side frequencies for 200-kHz color video modulation in the 3.58-MHz bandpass amplifier?

SPECIAL QUESTIONS

1. Why is white the hardest color to reproduce in a color receiver?
2. Name one trouble you have seen in a color picture and explain what the cause could be.
3. Compare the advantages and disadvantages of an $I - Q$ receiver with those of a $B - Y$, $R - Y$ receiver.
4. Give an example of an integrated circuit that is used for color processing, and list the circuits in the IC unit.

ANSWERS TO TEST POINT QUESTIONS

14-1 **a.** Monochrome **b.** White **c.** Red

14-2 **a.** T **b.** F **c.** T

14-3 **a.** T **b.** F **c.** T **d.** T

14-4 **a.** 920 kHz **b.** 4.5 MHz **c.** 4.1 MHz **d.** 50 percent

14-5 **a.** T **b.** T **c.** F **d.** T **e.** T **f.** F

14-6 **a.** Bandpass amplifier, color oscillator, and color killer **b.** Wrong hues **c.** Red and cyan

14-7 **a.** First **b.** Amplitude **c.** Demodulators **d.** ACC bias

14-8 **a.** T **b.** T **c.** T

14-9 **a.** 90° **b.** 1.3 MHz **c.** T_1 **d.** I signal **e.** Demodulator output

14-10 **a.** T **b.** F **c.** T **d.** T

15

CABLE TELEVISION

Cable televison (CATV) started as a means of providing signals to communities that could not receive broadcast stations, either because of distance or shadow areas in which the signal was too weak. Then a community antenna was used at a remote location to feed TV signals to receivers in the area. Today, cable TV has developed far beyond that into huge systems that cover large areas, even for locations having good reception. The reason is that cable TV does not have the restriction of channel allocations for broadcasting. The cable systems offer up to 36 channels. A cable converter box permits selection of the desired channel. Premium pay services such as Home Box Office, Spotlight, Prism, Cinemax, and others also offer current movies and sports events not available on broadcast television. These programs reach the cable operator via satellite transmission. More details of the cable channels, distribution systems, and CATV equipment are described in the follow sections:

15-1 Cable Frequencies
15-2 Coaxial Cable for CATV
15-3 Characteristic Impedance
15-4 Cable Losses
15-5 Cable Distribution System
15-6 The dBmV Unit for Losses and Gains
15-7 Distortion in the Cable Signal
15-8 Two-Way Cable Systems
15-9 Cable TV Converters
15-10 Wave Traps and Scrambling Methods
15-11 Long-Distance Links
15-12 Fiber Optics

15-1 CABLE FREQUENCIES

Many older cable systems distribute TV signals on the same VHF channel frequencies that are used for broadcasting. The UHF channels are converted to VHF channels for distribution because cable losses are too high in the UHF band. This method is a 12-channel system, including the lowband and highband VHF channels 2 to 13. Subscribers in the system do not need a converter. Direct cable connections are made to the TV receiver, where the RF tuner can be used to select the desired channel.

ADJACENT CABLE CHANNELS With a 12-channel system, some receivers may have adjacent-channel interference, since all the VHF channels are used. The ability to reject adjacent-channel frequencies depends on the IF selectivity of the receiver. The interference produces a windshield-wiper or venetian-blind effect in the picture. See Figs. 11-7 and 11-8 in Chap. 11.

In the cable system, interference is minimized by balancing the signals for all channels at a common level. Also, compared with TV broadcast signals, the sound carrier level is usually much lower than the picture carrier signal.

MIDBAND AND SUPERBAND CABLE CHANNELS Since the cable signal is not radiated, at least not intentionally, the cable system can use frequencies that are assigned to other radio services without interference. Therefore, the midband cable channels are used in the gap between VHF channels 6 and 7. These frequencies from 88 to 174 MHz include 88 to 108 MHz for the FM radio broadcast band plus various marine and aircraft communications services. However, the FM radio band generally is not used for TV cable channels.

As listed in Table 15-1, the midband cable TV channels start with number 14 or letter designation A for 120 to 126 MHz, with the video or picture carrier frequency set at 121.25 MHz. Although not listed, the sound carrier frequency is automatically 4.5 MHz higher, or 125.75 MHz. Included are channel numbers 14 to 22 or letters A to I.

Additional midband channels are numbers 00, 01, and 54 to 59. Channels 00 and 01 are above the FM radio band. Double digits are used for all cable channel numbers to allow for a digital control board for tuning. Channels 54 to 59 occupy spot frequencies in gaps of the regular midband channel allotments.

Superband just means cable TV channels above the VHF broadcast channel 13. This band starts with cable channel letter J or number 23. The letters continue to Z and the numbers to 53.

The use of VHF broadcast channels 2 to 13 and cable channels 14 to 37 provides 12 + 24 = 36 channels in a typical large cable TV system. These frequencies are up to approximately 300 MHz. Systems using the higher cable channels up to 400 MHz are more sophisticated. They require special cable and better amplifiers with closer spacing to offset greater losses at the higher frequencies.

TUNING TO THE CABLE CHANNELS In conventional TV receivers, the RF tuner usually is not made to select the midband and superband cable channels. Therefore, the cable operator provides a separate converter unit. It converts all cable frequencies to a designated VHF channel, such as channel 2, 3, or 4. The subscriber keeps the receiver tuned to the specified channel, and all channel selection is done at the converter.

CABLE-READY TV RECEIVERS Many late-model receivers offer a tuner that can select the midband and superband cable channels directly without the need for a converter. However, there is another practical problem. The premium pay services usually have a signal that is scrambled electronically. The circuits required for descrambling are built into the converter or attached to it.

TABLE 15-1
CABLE TV CHANNELS

LETTER DESIGNATION	NUMBER	VIDEO CARRIER, MHz	NUMBER	VIDEO CARRIER, MHz
Midband channels			**Superband channels without letters**	
A	14	121.25	40	319.25
B	15	127.25	41	325.25
C	16	133.25	42	331.25
D	17	139.25	43	337.25
E	18	145.25	44	343.25
F	19	151.25	45	349.25
G	20	157.25	46	355.25
H	21	163.25	47	361.25
I	22	169.25	48	367.25
			49	373.25
Superband channels			50	379.25
			51	385.25
J	23	217.25	52	391.25
K	24	223.25	53	397.25
L	25	229.25	**Additional midband assignments**	
M	26	235.25		
N	27	241.25		
O	28	247.25	54	89.25
P	29	253.25	55	95.25
Q	30	259.25	56	101.25
R	31	265.25	57	107.25
S	32	271.25	58	97.25
T	33	277.25	59	103.25
U	34	283.25	**Nominal channel numbers for use with digital readout converters**	
V	35	289.25		
W	36	295.25		
X	37	301.25		
Y	38	307.25	A-2 or 00	109.25
Z	39	313.25	A-1 or 01	115.25

As a result, the system-oriented converter would be needed anyway to watch the scrambled-signal premium channels.

CABLE RADIATION The cable operator must be especially careful that the system does not radiate TV signals. Radiation can occur if cables are open, short-circuited, or even partially mismatched at their termination. Damage to the cables may result from strong winds, storms, or other accidents.

To detect radiation, a selected midband channel may be used just for an FM tone-modulated indicator signal. Then a simple portable FM radio can be used as a "sniffer" to locate any radiation, just by riding along the cable route in the service truck.

Some midband channels are particularly sensitive to the radiation problem. For instance, the band for channel A or 14 includes the aircraft distress frequency at 121.5 MHz. Some cable operations may not use that channel when the possibility of interference exists.

HARMONICALLY RELATED CHANNELS Cable systems have the option of operating slightly off the frequencies assigned for TV broadcasting, but close enough to allow TV receivers and converters to tune to the frequencies. One such choice is harmonically related channels (HRCs), where all the picture carrier frequencies are an integral multiple of 6 MHz. These are listed in Table 15-2. Note that channel 04 with the 66-MHz harmonic picture carrier is only 1.25 MHz away from the 67.25-MHz broadcast carrier frequency. The advantage of using the HRC system in cable systems is simplification of the frequency synthesis circuits used for tuning at the head end and in the converter.

Test Point Questions 15-1

Answers at End of Chapter

a. What is the superband channel number just above VHF broadcast channel 13?

b. To which VHF broadcast channel does a TV receiver with a cable converter stay tuned?

TABLE 15-2
HARMONICALLY RELATED CARRIERS FOR CABLE TV CHANNELS

CHANNEL NUMBER	VIDEO CARRIER, MHz	CHANNEL NUMBER	VIDEO CARRIER, MHz
00	108.00	30	258.00
01	114.00	31	264.00
02	54.00	32	270.00
03	60.00	33	276.00
04	66.00	34	282.00
05	78.00	35	288.00
06	84.00	36	294.00
07	174.00	37	300.00
08	180.00	38	306.00
09	186.00	39	312.00
10	192.00	40	318.00
11	198.00	41	324.00
12	204.00	42	330.00
13	210.00	43	336.00
14	120.00	44	342.00
15	126.00	45	348.00
16	132.00	46	354.00
17	138.00	47	360.00
18	144.00	48	366.00
19	150.00	49	372.00
20	156.00	50	378.00
21	162.00	51	384.00
22	168.00	52	390.00
23	216.00	53	396.00
24	222.00	54	72
25	228.00	55	90
26	234.00	56	96
27	240.00	57	102
28	246.00	58	402
29	252.00	59	408

15-2 COAXIAL CABLE FOR CATV

The conduit used for distributing the CATV signals at RF channel frequencies is coaxial cable. It is an efficient wideband transmission line that has the advantage of shielding. There are several types of coaxial line, generally called *coax,* but all are constructed as in Fig. 15-1. A central wire is surrounded by a cylindrical or tubular

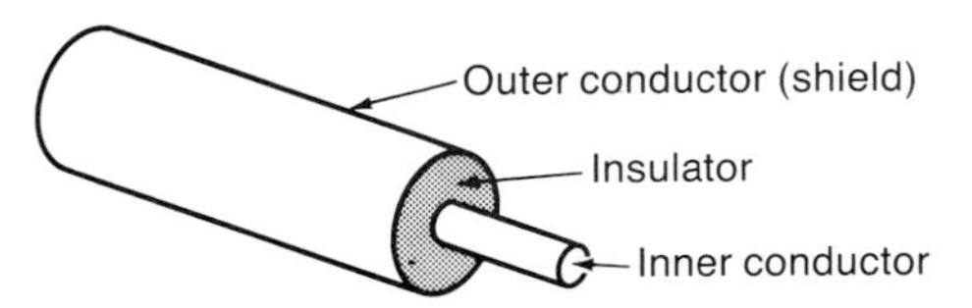

Fig. 15-1 Coaxial cable consists of inner conductor at center of outer tubular conductor.

conductor, and the two conductors are separated by an insulator.

The type of cable generally used in a main signal route, called a *trunk line,* is shown in Fig. 15-2. It consists of a heavy central aluminum conductor that is copper-clad, meaning that it is coated with copper. The outer conductor or shield is also aluminum and is shaped in a solid tube. A polyethylene foam fills the internal space and supports the inner conductor exactly at the center. The cable diameter is about 3/4 in. [19.1 mm]. Some other types of trunk cable are hollow, with the inner conductor supported by plastic beads at regular spacings. The larger the cable diameter, the less the attenuation. However, large cables are not flexible and are difficult to install.

For installations with a long, unsupported span of cable, a steel *messenger cable* is encased within the outer jacket. The steel wire actually supports the weight of the cable.

Trunk cables also are made with a waterproof polyethylene jacket for use underground or underwater. In addition, armored cables with a spiral layer of steel are used.

In some systems, two cables are combined in a single outer jacket. These are called *Siamese cables.* They can be used in two-cable systems in which each cable carries different programs in the range of channel 2 to channel 13. Then the system has a capacity of 24 channels without the need for a cable converter. A simple two-position A-B switch can be used by the subscriber to choose one cable or the other, for 12 channels on each.

The cable used in the branch lines from the main trunk are similar to that in Fig. 15-2 but smaller in diameter. Thinner cable can be used because the run is not too long.

The line from a branch to the subscriber is called a *drop line.* The drop line is generally RG-59U coaxial cable, as shown in Fig. 15-3. This cable is flexible because a copper braid is used for the outer shield. Its diameter is ¼ in. [6.35 mm], including the outer polyethylene jacket to make the cable weatherproof.

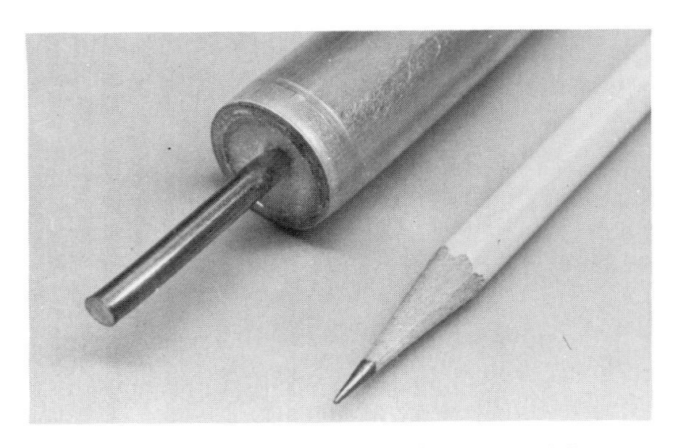
Fig. 15-2 Type of coaxial cable used for trunk lines.

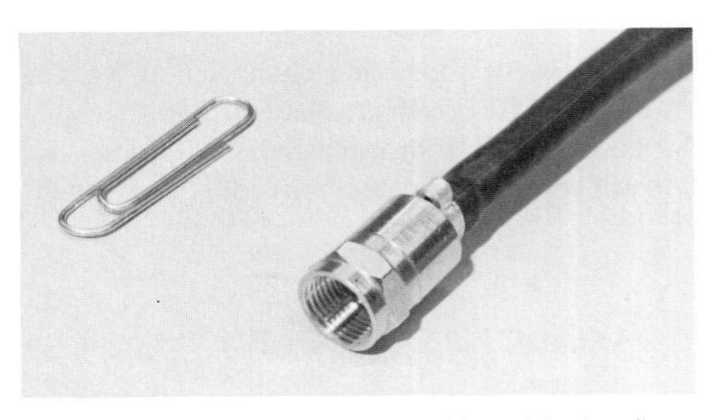
Fig. 15-3 RG-59U flexible coax used for cable drop lines. The F connector at end is standard for CATV use. Diameter is ¼ in. [6.35 mm].

Test Point Questions 15-2

Answers at End of Chapter

Answer True or False.

a. The inner conductor of coaxial cable serves as a shield.

b. Generally RG-59U cable is used for the drop line.

c. Thinner cable has greater losses.

15-3 CHARACTERISTIC IMPEDANCE

Coaxial cable is one type of transmission line, which means a line with uniform distance between the two conductors. Any transmission line has a characteristic impedance, or *surge impedance,* because of the constant conductor spacing. The symbol for the surge impedance is Z_O. Different types of line have different values of Z_O, but for any one type Z_O is the same for any length of line.

The coaxial cable used for CATV in general, and the RG-59U specifically, has a characteristic impedance of 72 to 75 Ω. Generally 75 Ω is considered as the nominal value. Note that 50-Ω coaxial cable also is common in applications for communications equipment such as CB radio. Also, for the flat twin-lead cable generally used for antenna input to TV receivers $Z_O = 300\ \Omega$. Although not coaxial cable, the twin-lead cable is a transmission line.

The Z_O is resistive, without a reactive component, but it is an ac value that cannot be measured with the ohmmeter. However, you can check the low dc resistance for continuity to see whether the line is open.

WHAT IS THE MEANING OF Z_O? As the name says, Z_O is a characteristic for a particular type of line. Its value depends on the size of conductors, their spacing, and the type of insulator between them. In general, wider spacing with the same conductors provides a higher Z_O. One definition of Z_O is the impedance the line would have as a load connected to an ac voltage source at one end and infinitely long at the other end. The line must be considered infinitely long so that no energy can be reflected from the end to interfere with the energy supplied by the source to the line. It may seem impractical to have an infinitely long line, but the same effect can be produced by terminating the end with a resistance equal to Z_O.

Consider the equivalent circuit of a transmission line shown in Fig. 15-4. This circuit is a *lumped-constant* model, for L and C represent the concentrated values of inductance and capacitance for any unit length of the line, corresponding to the L and C distributed over that length.

The battery in Fig. 15-4 represents a dc source just to supply energy, and the meters give readings of the voltage and current. When the switch S is closed, each of the capacitances C is charged by the voltage source. Since C is uncharged initially, the capacitance is like a short circuit as it takes a high charging current. However, the series L opposes the increase in current. So a finite time is taken to charge C_1 in the model. As C_1 charges to some value of V, it serves as a source to charge the next section with L_2 and C_2. Since the L and C values are extremely small, the charging process propagates down the line very rapidly. The velocity is close to the speed of light in space. Still, the voltage across the two conductors travels as a wavefront out to the end of the line.

Assume, now, that the line in Fig. 15-4 is infinitely long. If such a line could be made, it would go on charging forever, toward the open end. At the input end connected to the source, though, the voltage and current readings settle at specific values of V and I. This ratio of V/I is the characteristic impedance Z_O of that line.

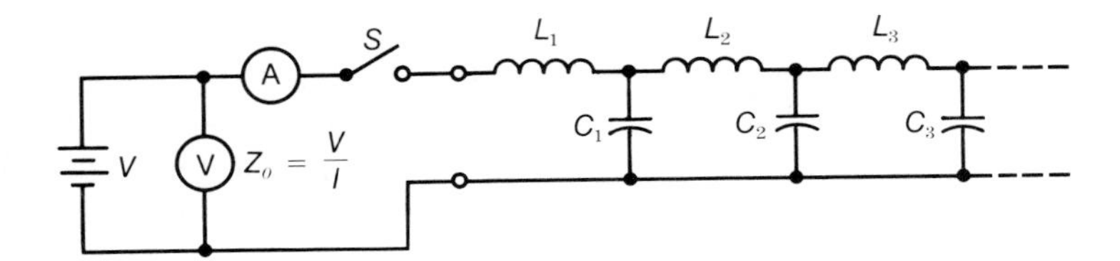

Fig. 15-4 Lumped-constant model of a coaxial cable transmission line.

FORMULAS FOR Z_O The value of Z_O is specified by L and C, since these characteristics determine how much charging current is produced. Specifically,

$$Z_O = \sqrt{\frac{L}{C}} \quad \Omega \qquad \textbf{(15-1)}$$

With L in henrys and C in farads per unit length, Z_O is in ohms. The L is for both sides of the line in series. For example, assume for a 1-ft length that $L = 0.12\ \mu\text{H}$ and $C = 21$ pF. Then

$$\begin{aligned} Z_O &= \sqrt{\frac{0.12 \times 10^{-6}}{21 \times 10^{-12}}} \\ &= \sqrt{0.0057 \times 10^{6}} \\ &= 0.076 \times 10^{3} \\ &= 76\ \Omega \end{aligned}$$

Formula 15-1 is stated in terms of L and C for the electrical characteristics of the line. These values are determined by the physical characteristics of conductor size and spacing and the dielectric. For coaxial line with an air dielectric between the two conductors,

$$Z_O = 138 \log \frac{D}{d} \quad \Omega \qquad \textbf{(15-2)}$$

where d is the diameter of the inside conductor and D is the diameter of the outside conductor, which really indicates the spacing. The values to be compared must have the same units. For example, consider No. 18 gage wire with $d = 0.04$ in. for the inner conductor. Let $D = 0.25$ in. for the outer conductor for 1/4-in. RG-59U cable. Then

$$\begin{aligned} Z_O &= 138 \log \frac{0.25}{0.04} \\ &= 138 \log 6.25 \\ &= 138(0.796) \\ &= 110\ \Omega \end{aligned}$$

The 110-Ω value is for an air dielectric. Use of a foam or plastic insulator between the conductors reduces Z_O about 66 percent, to a value of $110 \times 0.66 = 72.6\ \Omega$. The 0.66 is the *velocity factor* of the line.

TERMINATING THE LINE IN Z_O Suppose that we cut the "infinitely long" line in Fig. 15-4 at a point 10 ft [3.0 m] from the switch and then connect across the open end of the line a resistor having the same value as the characteristic impedance of the line. Now, when the line capacitance is fully charged, the resistor at the end will produce the same meter readings for V and I. The line terminated with R equal to Z_O acts just like an infinitely long line. For the source that feeds the line, the load impedance is the same. Most important for ac signals, all the energy in the line is used at the termination, and no signal is reflected from the end. This factor explains why the distribution lines in CATV must always be terminated in their characteristic impedance, which is generally 75 Ω.

MISMATCH WITH AN OPEN OR SHORT-CIRCUITED LINE When the line is not terminated in Z_O an impedance mismatch results. One extreme case is a line open at the end, as shown in Fig. 15-5*a*. The driving source here is an ac

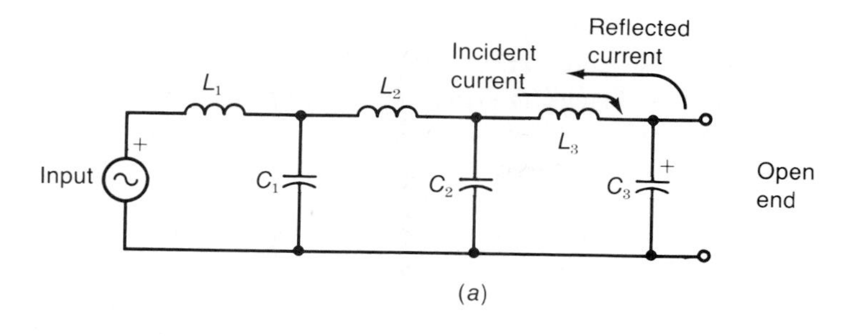

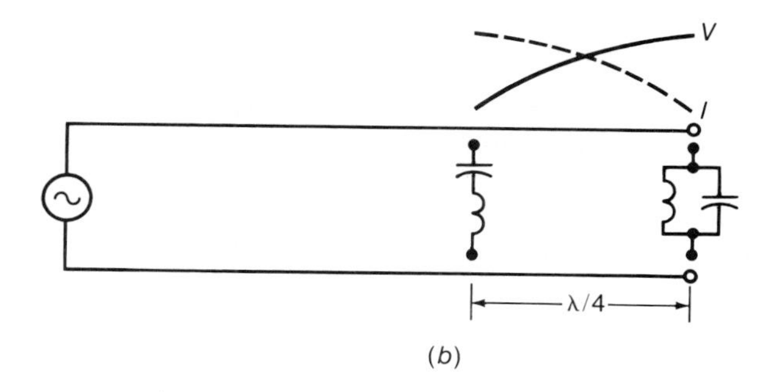

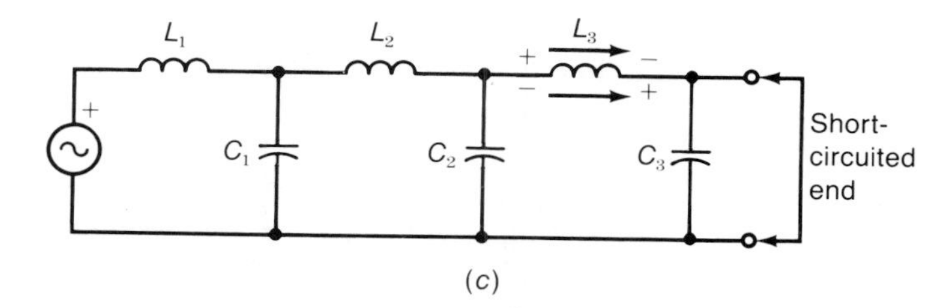

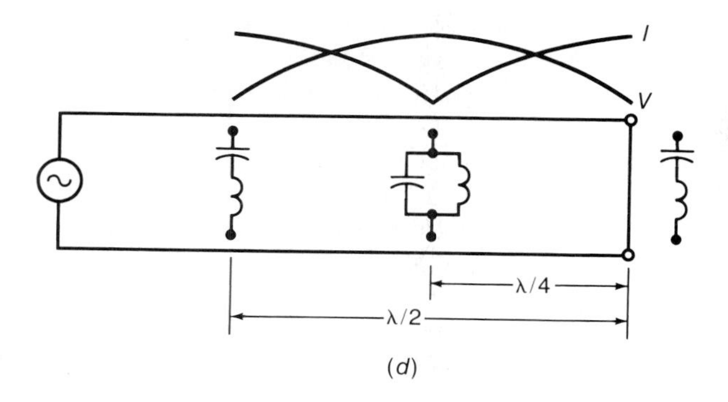

Fig. 15-5 Effects of an open circuit and short circuit at end of transmission line. (*a*) Model line terminated in an open circuit. (*b*) Effect a quarter-wave back from the open end. (*c*) Model line terminated in a short circuit. (*d*) Effect a quarter-wave back from short-circuited end.

generator to supply signal on the line. Note that the last lumped capacitor on the line, indicated as C_3, has a signal voltage of the same polarity as the source. Therefore, C_3 acts as a source to send a voltage wave back from the end toward the input source. Capacitor C_3 sends back a wave of discharge current, in the opposite direction from the incident charging current. These effects are illustrated by the standing-wave patterns of V and I in Fig. 15-5*b*.

In the line with an open end, therefore, standing waves of V and I are set up along the line. A standing wave means that different points along the line have a specific V and I as an ac signal in either peak or root mean square (rms) values. A maximum on the standing wave occurs where the incident and reflected values have the same phase, with respect to distance along the line. A node occurs where the incident and reflected values are out of phase and so cancel. With respect to time, however, the ac values of V and I are continuously changing.

For a specific frequency of ac signal on the line, the distances can be considered in terms of the wavelength. One-quarter wave back from the open end, the voltage waves are 180° out of phase, and a voltage null results. The current is additive here, though, which makes I double the value of a matched line. At this point on the line, therefore, it is equivalent to a series resonant circuit. The reason is that I is high and V is low for a specific frequency. At the open end of the line, the current is nulled and voltage is doubled. The open end corresponds to a parallel resonant circuit, with high Z at a specific frequency.

The relative values of V and I reverse at quarter-wave distances back to the source. At each peak or null on the standing wave, the V/I ratio for Z is resistive and has a maximum or minimum value. At intermediate points, the line is reactive and has intermediate values of impedance.

The conclusion is, then, that an open coaxial cable acts as a tuned circuit. Such a resonant response means different results for different frequencies. Furthermore, all the energy supplied to a lossless line would be reflected to the source at the input. When long line runs are used, the resulting time delay in the reflected signals can produce ghosts in the TV picture. Note that if the driving source does not have a 75-Ω impedance, then the signal reflected from the open end is also reflected again from the source, which creates multiple ghosts.

The example of a line short-circuited at the end is shown in Fig. 15-5*c*. The last component on the line is inductance L_3, since C_3 is bypassed by the short circuit at the end. After a current peak has been produced by the driving source, the inductance tends to keep the current flowing. Therefore, energy is reflected from the end of the line. This time, though, the reflected current is in the same direction as the incident current. Also, the polarity of the self-induced voltage is reversed. The resulting standing waves of V and I are shown in Fig. 15-5*d*. They correspond to the standing waves in Fig. 15-5*b* for the open line, but the V and I patterns are reversed in terms of peaks and nulls.

In summary, an open end always has high V and low I because of the capacitance of an open circuit. A quarter-wave back, conditions reverse with a peak of I and null of V. For the opposite case, a short-circuited end always has high I and low V because of the short circuit. Conditions reverse with a peak of V and null of I a quarter-wave back. The standing-wave pattern continues the reversals for every quarter-wave. Remember that high I and low V for a specific frequency create the same effect as series resonance. Also, high V and low I mean high Z for the effect of a parallel resonant circuit. These effects illustrate why quarter-wave and half-wave sections of transmission line can be used as low-loss tuned circuits, particularly for wave traps, at frequencies in the VHF and UHF bands.

Furthermore, the fact that a mismatched line

has standing waves means that the amount of signal at the end depends on where you cut the line. A foot more or less can make a big difference. If a line is correctly terminated in its Z_O, however, its length is not critical.

VOLTAGE STANDING-WAVE RATIO The examples of an open, or short-circuited, line are the extremes of mismatch, in which almost all the energy is reflected from the end. However, reflection also occurs with a poor termination not equal to the characteristic impedance Z_O. Then part of the energy is reflected. As a result, the voltage is less than double at the peaks in the standing-wave pattern, and the nulls are more than zero. For this reason, the degree of cable match can be expressed as the ratio of voltage at the peaks to voltage at the nulls. The proportion is the voltage standing-wave ratio (VSWR):

$$\text{VSWR} = \frac{V_{\text{max}}}{V_{\text{min}}} \qquad \textbf{(15-3)}$$

When the line is perfectly matched with a termination equal to its own Z_O, there are no standing waves. Then V_{max} and V_{min} are equal, and VSWR = 1. Any other termination, however, yields a VSWR greater than 1.

Test Point Questions 15-3

Answers at End of Chapter

a. What value of R should be used to terminate RG-59U coaxial cable for impedance matching?

b. Does a line with more C per unit length have a higher or lower Z_O?

c. Does an open end of transmission line correspond to a series or parallel resonant circuit?

d. What is the value of the VSWR when a cable is terminated in its Z_O?

15-4 CABLE LOSSES

In our imaginary lossless line, all energy sent down the line from the source is consumed in the terminating load. With practical lines, though, some energy is dissipated in the line itself. The result is attenuation of the signal. There are three causes of attenuation:

1. I^2R losses produced by current in the conductors.
2. Dielectric losses in the insulator between conductors. Remember that the signals are high radio frequencies in the VHF band.
3. Skin effect. The RF current flows more on the circumference of the conductor than its center. Because of the smaller area for current, the ac resistance of the conductor increases.

The aluminum cable in Fig. 15-2 has a copper coating around the inside conductor to reduce losses from the skin effect.

LOSSES INCREASE WITH FREQUENCY Specifically, the losses increase in proportion to the square root of frequency f. For a practical case, compare channel 13 at 210 to 216 MHz which is about four times higher in frequency than channel 2 at 54 to 60 MHz. At $4f$, the line losses for channel 13 equal $\sqrt{4}$, or double the losses for channel 2. The values of cable attenuation for several different types of CATV cable are listed in Table 15-3 for frequencies from 5 to 500 MHz.

CABLE DISTANCE Designers of cable distribution systems think in terms of signal attenuation per unit distance of line. For example, suppose that a particular cable has an attenuation of 1 dB per 100 ft [30.5 m]. The loss is 6 dB for 600 ft [183 m] and 20 dB for 2000 ft [610 m]. Incidentally a 6-dB loss in voltage means one-half the signal.

Rather than continuously make the conversion

TABLE 15-3
ATTENUATION OF TRUNK AND DISTRIBUTION CABLES (dB/100 ft AT 68°F)

FREQUENCY, MHz	T4412	T4500	T4625	T4750	T4875	T41000*
5	0.19	0.16	0.13	0.11	0.09	0.08
50	0.62	0.51	0.41	0.34	0.30	0.27
216	1.31	1.08	0.88	0.74	0.64	0.59
240	1.39	1.14	0.93	0.78	0.68	0.62
260	1.45	1.19	0.97	0.82	0.71	0.65
270	1.48	1.22	0.99	0.83	0.73	0.66
300	1.56	1.29	1.05	0.88	0.77	0.70
325	1.63	1.34	1.09	0.92	0.80	0.74
350	1.69	1.40	1.14	0.96	0.84	0.77
375	1.75	1.45	1.18	1.00	0.87	0.80
400	1.81	1.50	1.22	1.03	0.90	0.83
450	1.93	1.59	1.30	1.10	0.96	0.89
500	2.04	1.69	1.38	1.17	1.02	0.94

* The T41000 is 1-in. trunk cable.
Courtesy Times Fiber Communications Inc.

from decibel loss to distance, it is more convenient to work in terms of cable loss directly. In our example, the cable 2000 ft [610 m] long is referred to as a 20-dB run. It is the function of the trunk amplifiers to make up for the cable losses and restore signal levels to standard values throughout the cable system.

Test Point Questions 15-4
Answers at End of Chapter

Answer True or False.

a. Cable losses increase at higher frequencies.
b. Coaxial cable does not have I^2R losses.
c. A 2-dB loss reduces the signal level by one-half.

15-5 CABLE DISTRIBUTION SYSTEM

Refer to Fig. 15-6. The starting point for cable signals is called the *head end.* Here the broadcast signals picked up by the antenna are amplified, adjusted for level, and fed into the trunk lines. The UHF channels are converted to VHF channels. Also included are local-origination signals from a studio. The video and audio signals modulate separate carriers in a VHF channel not being used. The main routes of signal from the head end are the trunk lines.

TRUNK AMPLIFIERS The trunk amplifiers are inserted at regular intervals along the trunk route to make up for cable losses. For the example in Fig. 15-7, a 20-dB amplifier is placed at the end of a cable run with a loss of 20 dB. The decibel unit used for cable signals is dBmV, which means "decibels above 1 mV." Amplifiers are placed at regular intervals to keep the signal up to the standard level of 1 to 3 mV.

Figure 15-8 shows a weatherproof housing for a trunk amplifier in an *aerial system,* which is mounted on a pole. Power is obtained from a tap on electric service lines on the same pole.

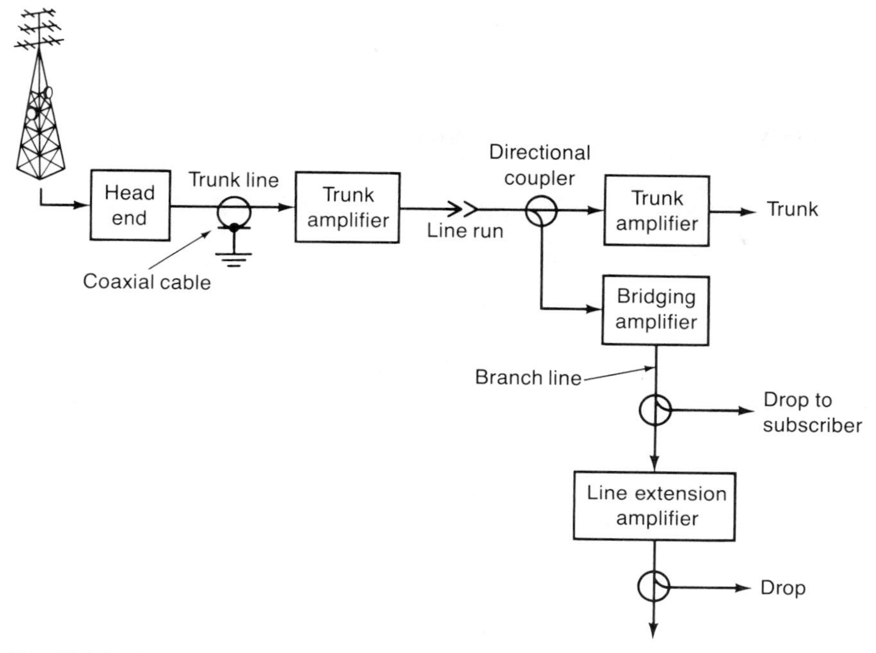

Fig. 15-6 Basic distribution system for cable television. Note symbol for directional coupler.

BRIDGING AMPLIFIERS This type of amplifier is for a branch from the main trunk to feed a particular neighborhood in the cable system. The typical gain is 20 to 40 dB. The output is for the branch lines to individual subscribers.

In many cases, the trunk and bridging amplifiers are located in the same weatherproof housing. An additional attenuator may be used at the input to the bridging amplifier to balance the signal levels.

LINE AMPLIFIERS Long line runs from the bridging amplifier may require that line-extender amplifiers be inserted in the branch line to make up for cable losses in that branch. This amplifier extends the number of drop lines that can be used on a branch line. The typical gain for a line amplifier is 20 to 40 dB.

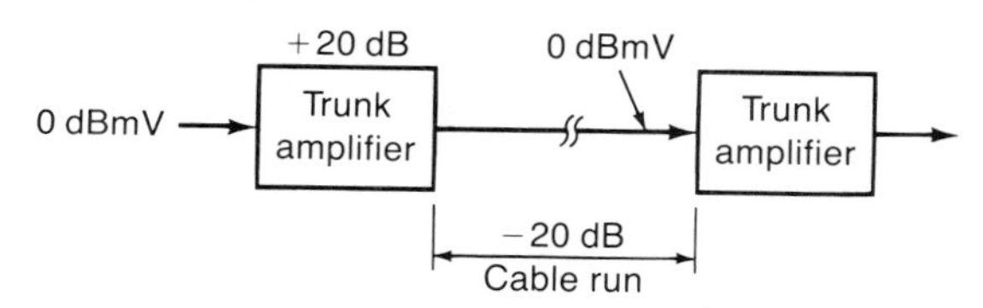

Fig. 15-7 Trunk amplifiers correct for losses in cable run.

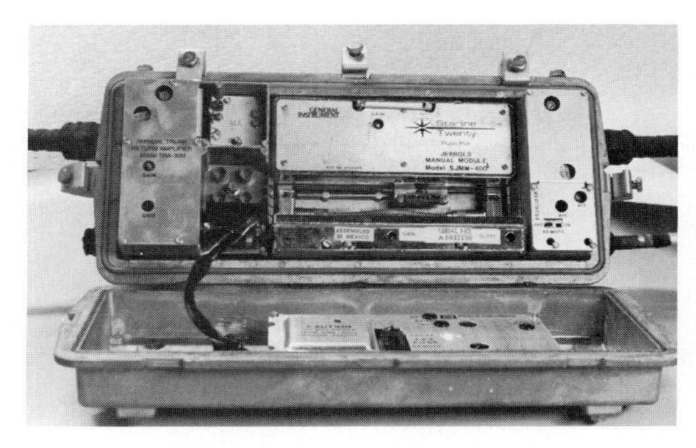

Fig. 15-8 Typical trunk amplifier unit, for outdoor pole mounting. Front cover removed for internal view. Width is 14 in. [355.6 mm].

DIRECTIONAL COUPLERS Signal power taken from the trunk must be kept very small so that the line is not loaded by all the branches. The device used to tap off the signal is a *directional coupler.* Its construction is illustrated in Fig. 15-9*a,* and its symbol is shown in Fig. 15-9*b.* It is a three-terminal device. One terminal is for signal input. Another carries the signal through the trunk line. The third terminal has tapped output signal for a branch.

The directional coupler is so named because it feeds a sample of the direct, downstream signal out at the tap but ignores reflected energy in the trunk line. This is accomplished by a small loop placed in the wall of the coaxial assembly, as shown in Fig. 15-9*a.* The loop is terminated with a 75-Ω resistor. The loop acts as both a capacitor and an inductor. Its capacitance charges to the potential difference between the inner and outer conductors at that point on the line. As a one-turn coil, the loop is magnetically coupled to the center conductor to tap off the signal.

Directional couplers have a very small *insertion loss* between the input and output signals on the trunk line. A typical value is −1 dB for insertion loss at 300 MHz. The *tap loss* from input to output at the tap is typically −13 dB, but this loss is made up in the bridging amplifier.

POWER SUPPLIES The cable amplifiers are solid-state and require little power. The power supplies may be placed at long intervals and the cable itself used to carry the dc power. Input for the power supply is 120 V ac tapped from the power line on the same pole in an aerial system. The typical dc supply voltage for the cable amplifiers is 24 V.

The power supply module often is located in the same weatherproof housing that encloses the trunk and bridging amplifiers. In some cases, storage batteries are kept on constant charge, with two 12-V batteries in series to make 24 V. They are switched into service when there is a failure in ac power.

LINE TAPS The final tap on the system feeds the drop line for the subscriber, usually with RG-59U cable. Figure 15-10 shows a multitap with four taps for four houses close to one another. As with directional couplers, the line tap has a low insertion loss but high tap loss.

The tap-to-tap loss is made high to provide isolation between the individual subscriber lines. Isolation is necessary so that a misterminated cable at the subscriber's TV receiver will not set up reflections in the cable system. Two possible terminations are a cable that is not connected or leads that are short-circuited. The tap units

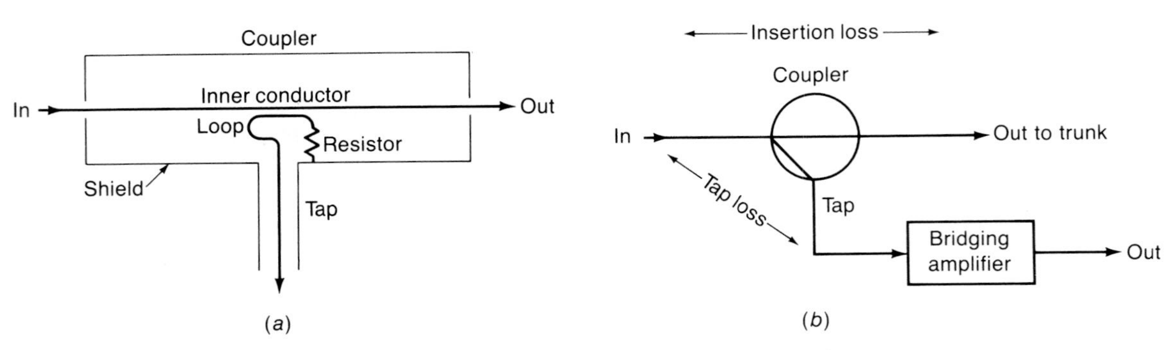

Fig. 15-9 Directional coupler tapping off signal from trunk line. (*a*) Schematic diagram. (*b*) Symbol.

Fig. 15-10 A four-tap unit for outdoor mounting. Size is 4 × 6 in. [101.6 × 152.4 mm].

are available with many values of tap loss, so the signal levels can be balanced for different subscriber drop lines along the branch.

BALUN UNITS The word *balun* is actually an abbreviation of *bal*anced-to-*un*balanced connections. A typical unit is shown in Fig. 15-11*a*. Most TV receivers are designed for 300-Ω balanced input at the antenna connections, for twin-lead transmission line with neither side grounded. The coaxial cable in a CATV system, however, is single-ended or unbalanced with one side grounded. The balun is used to match the 75-Ω coaxial cable to the 300-Ω receiver input.

As shown in Fig. 15-11*b*, the balun is constructed as two sections of 150-Ω line, usually coiled to make the unit smaller. The lines are connected in parallel at the 75-Ω side and in series at the 300-Ω side. Actually, the balun can match the impedances in either direction.

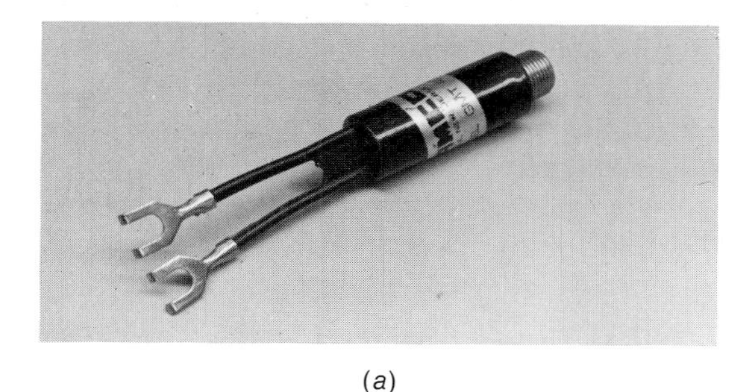

(*a*)

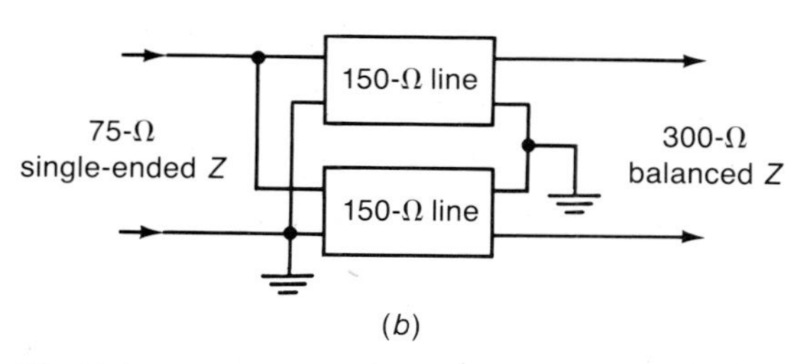

(*b*)

Fig. 15-11 The balun matches 75-Ω single-ended *Z* of cable to 300-Ω balanced *Z* of antenna input circuit of receiver. (*a*) Typical unit. Size is 2 × ½ in. [50.8 × 12.7 mm] without leads. (*b*) Schematic diagram.

F CONNECTOR The coaxial connector for the 75-Ω line in Fig. 15-11*a* is the standard F connector used in cable work. Its advantage is that no soldering is required. The solid center wire of the cable is the center pin of the connector. Also, the grounded sleeve slides into the braided shield of the cable. Either the sleeve of the plug is screwed onto the jack, or a press-fit connector can be used. Many TV receivers have an input jack for an F connector so that a direct cable connection can be made without the need for a balun.

Test Point Questions 15-5

Answers at End of Chapter

Answer True or False.

a. The head end of a cable system is the starting point of cable signals.

b. A trunk cable is the main line for cable signals.

c. The insertion loss is higher than the tap loss for line taps.

d. A balun converts impedances between 75 and 150 Ω.

15-6 THE dBmV UNIT FOR LOSSES AND GAINS

Because the cable signal voltages are always measured across the same 75-Ω impedance, it is convenient to express voltage levels in decibels. The reference used for CATV is 1 mV across 75 Ω. With this reference the units are indicated as dBmV. This reference is an arbitrary value, but 1 mV happens to be just about the minimum signal voltage measured across 75 Ω that a receiver needs for a noisefree picture. Across 300 Ω, the minimum is 2 mV.

Signal voltage can be converted to dBmV units by the formula

$$\text{dBmV} = 20 \log \frac{\text{mV}}{1 \text{ mV}} \qquad \textbf{(15-4)}$$

Since the denominator is 1 mV for the reference, you just find the logarithm of the signal level in millivolts and multiply by 20. For example, to convert a 10-mV signal level:

$$\begin{aligned} \text{dBmV} &= 20 \log 10 \\ &= 20(1) \\ &= 20 \end{aligned}$$

The dBmV method is convenient for calculations because the logarithmic units can be added or subtracted for voltage gains and losses. Consider an amplifier with a voltage gain of 10 driving a cable with an attenuation factor of 0.5, as shown in Fig. 15-12. In Fig. 15-12*a*, the voltage gain of 10 multiplies the 1-mV signal input to get 10-mV output. The cable reduces the signal level by one-half. Thus the final output is 10 × 0.5 = 5 mV.

The 5-mV signal output corresponds to 14 dBmV because

$$\begin{aligned} \text{dBmV} &= 20 \log 5 \\ &= 20(0.7) \\ &= 14 \end{aligned}$$

In Fig. 15-12*b*, all values are indicated in dBmV. Just add dBmV for a gain and subtract for a loss. The values in Fig. 15-12*b* are as follows:

0 dBmV is the input signal level of 1 mV

20 dBmV is the amplifier gain of 10

−6 dBmV is the cable attenuation of 0.5

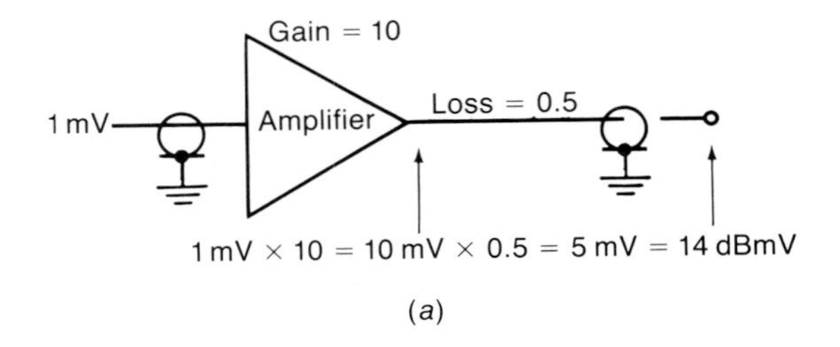

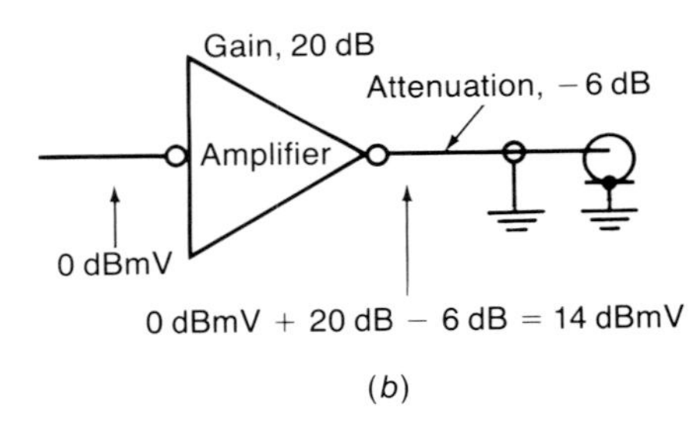

Fig. 15-12 Calculation of gain (*a*) in millivolts; (*b*) in dBmV units.

The end result is 0 + 20 − 6 = 14 dBmV for the signal level at the output. Note that the amplifier gain and attenuation can be in just regular decibels, since these values are voltage ratios without any reference.

Test Point Questions 15-6

Answers at End of Chapter

a. What is the reference level for the dBmV unit?

b. How much is the signal level of 2 mV in dBmV units?

c. How much is the signal level of 0.5 mV in dBmV units?

15-7 DISTORTION IN THE CABLE SIGNAL

The cable amplifiers should provide maximum signal to make up for the cable losses and still provide a good signal-to-noise ratio for no snow in the picture. However, the signal levels must be held within narrow limits because the amplifiers produce serious distortion with excessive signal.

HARMONIC DISTORTION When an amplifier is overdriven, harmonic distortion appears in the output. The harmonics are multiples of the signal frequencies being amplified. Harmonic distortion is actually a result of amplitude distortion, for changes in the waveform generate new frequencies.

Second-order harmonics are not too serious in a 12-channel system because the second harmonic of channels 2 to 6 falls in the range of 110 to 176 MHz. These frequencies are in the midband range between channels 6 and 7. The harmonics can cause interference problems, however, in cable systems using midband and superband channels.

The cable amplifiers use push-pull operation. Second harmonics generated in the push-pull circuit are canceled in the output. The cancellation is effective but not complete because perfectly balanced push-pull circuits are difficult to achieve.

CROSS MODULATION Third-order harmonics and the effects of cross modulation are more serious results of overload distortion. The nonlinear amplifier characteristic causes an overloaded amplifier stage to operate as a mixer stage, the input signals are detected, and the modulation is extracted. A transfer of the modulation to another carrier frequency can then occur.

The effect of cross modulation on the picture is a jumble of lines and the appearance of video from another channel. The interfering picture may be a negative. It shows most clearly when the channel you are watching goes to black between commercials.

However, the easiest symptom of cross modulation to recognize is the maximum modulation of the interfering signal, which is sync. This appears as vertical bars in the picture (Fig. 15-13).

Fig. 15-13 Symptoms of cross-modulation distortion in cable amplifier.

The bars may be stationary or may drift across the picture, depending on the stability of the sync generator for the interfering channel. Note that the bars are produced by sync and blanking pulses.

SPURIOUS SIGNALS Another effect of amplifier overload is the production of spurious frequencies that are not harmonically related to the desired signal. Harmonics of all the signal frequencies are produced, as well as the sum and difference frequencies, caused by the mixer action with nonlinear operation. Furthermore, these frequencies can beat with each other. The result is a wide range of unwanted signal frequencies. Computer solutions to the complex problem of numerical values for the spurious frequencies have shown that a large number show up on channel 4 at 66 to 72 MHz.

TEMPERATURE EFFECTS Another problem is that the signal level changes because of the effect of temperature on cable losses. The attenuation increases for higher temperatures, at an approximate rate of 1 percent per 10°F rise. This loss may not seem significant, but in very long cable runs the variation in signal level could be

100 dB in the expected temperature range for the northeast United States. The double trouble is a reduction in signal-to-noise ratio in hot weather and the probability of amplifier overload when it snows.

AUTOMATIC GAIN CONTROL To compensate for temperature changes and other variable factors, some trunk amplifiers have an AGC circuit to vary the gain. A typical arrangement is shown in the block diagram of a trunk amplifier in Fig. 15-14. The system uses a cw pilot carrier inserted at a frequency selected just for the AGC system. A pilot frequency of 73 MHz is indicated here, but other frequencies are in the range of 72 to 76, 100 to 120, 160 to 174, or 216 to 230 MHz.

The narrowband amplifier at the bottom of Fig. 15-14 is tuned to the pilot frequency. Then the AGC detector produces dc control voltage proportional to the amplitude of the pilot signal. The dc control voltage varies the attenuation of the cable signal into the preamplifier. A manual control is also provided by R_1 for the initial adjustment.

AUTOMATIC SLOPE CONTROL The cable attenuation increases for higher frequencies. Therefore, the overall frequency response of the cable tilts down for higher-frequency channels. To compensate for this effect, the frequency response of the amplifier is made to slope upward for the higher channel frequencies. The desired result is a uniform or flat frequency response for signals in all the channels.

The automatic slope control (ASC) is an AGC system designed to increase the amplifier gain just for higher channel frequencies. The ASC system uses another pilot carrier with a frequency at or near the top of the channel range. In Fig. 15-14 the ASC pilot frequency is 270 MHz. The narrowband amplifier and ASC detector are tuned to this frequency to provide dc control voltage that varies the gain of the slope-control amplifier. A manual control is provided by R_2 for the initial adjustment. The R_2 control for ASC and R_1 for AGC are set to balance the system to achieve a uniform signal on all channels. Then the automatic control circuits can maintain the balance.

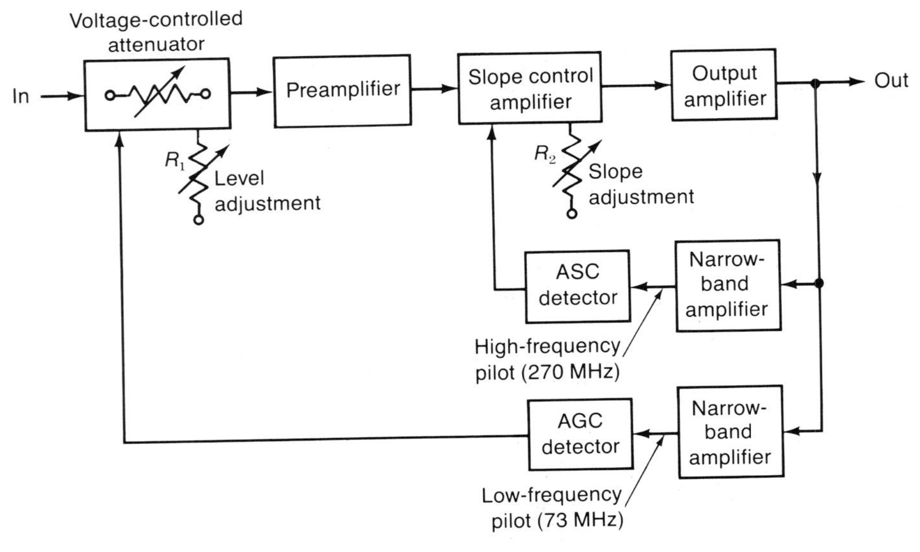

Fig. 15-14 Block diagram of trunk amplifier. ASC is automatic slope control.

Test Point Questions 15-7

Answers at End of Chapter

Answer True or False.

a. Sync and blanking bars from another channel can be caused by overload distortion.

b. Temperature has no effect on cable attenuation.

c. A slope-control circuit increases the amplifier gain for higher-frequency channels.

15-8 TWO-WAY CABLE SYSTEMS

In addition to downstream signals from the head end to subscribers, many cable systems are designed for upstream service from subscribers to the head end. The same cable is used for both directions. However, separate amplifiers are needed for the upstream signal, as shown in Fig. 15-15. Upstream communication is in the band of frequencies between 5 and 30 MHz.

For the downstream path at the top in Fig. 15-15, diplexers with a high-pass filter are used for the downstream signal. Filtering is necessary to remove any upstream signal. At the bottom of the diagram, low-pass filters separate the return signal in the 5- to 30-MHz band. Only the upstream signal is used in the return amplifier. The converter unit at the subscriber end supplies the upstream signal.

TWO-WAY APPLICATIONS Some communities permit home burglar alarm systems to be connected to a central receiving station in the return line of the cable system. Most important, the system provides two-way communications with subscribers for billing, surveys, shop-at-home service, and pay per view for special programs. The system acts as an electronic box office for collecting money from all the subscribers.

The subscriber reply can be made with a few pushbuttons on the cable TV converter unit. As many as 99 coded replies are possible by using a calculator type of keypad.

POLING SIGNAL The pay-per-view system requires that a poling signal be sent downstream to communicate with only the appropriate converter units. The frequency of the poling signal is in the 107- to 119-MHz range. Frequency-shift keying (FSK) is used with a 16-bit word as modulation for the particular address. When poled, the converter replies with data set up at the keypad. For example, punching in 55 can indicate that the subscriber wants to view a special program that evening. The reply to the poling signal

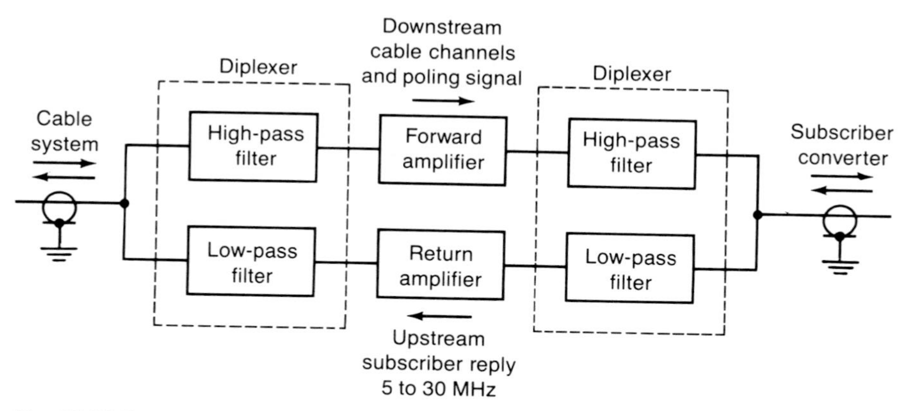

Fig. 15-15 Two-way cable amplifier system.

is sent back to the head end by means of a small modulator operating in the 5- to 30-MHz range for the upstream signal.

An affirmative reply to the head end sends a coded signal back downstream to operate the descrambler in the subscriber's converter unit, on the correct channel at the specified time. Also, data are entered into the cable operator's business computer for billing purposes.

A digital address for each subscriber is set in a read-only memory (ROM), which cannot be changed, when each converter unit is installed. If the converter is stolen, the electronic address will show up at the wrong location.

Although two-way cable systems are basically simple, they are difficult to put into service practically. The main problem is interference from the upstream signal at 5 to 30 MHz. The entire cable system, covering a huge area, acts as an antenna for the return signal. Particular attention must be paid to proper termination of the lines, good grounding, and low-loss cable fittings. Any parts of the system that radiate signals also pick up interfering frequencies. Elaborate digital switching methods are used to isolate any branches that pick up interference. A particular problem is that the subscriber's modulator may be stuck in the transmit mode, which can shut down the entire poling system. Provisions are made to switch to another poling frequency when this trouble occurs.

Test Point Questions 15-8

Answers at End of Chapter

Answer True or False.

a. Two-way cable systems require two separate cable systems for downstream and upstream signals.

b. The upstream signal is in the band of 5 to 30 MHz.

c. The poling signal is in the band of 107 to 119 MHz.

15-9 CABLE TV CONVERTERS

The converter on top of the TV set, or close to it, is an RF tuner used to select the desired channel. All the cable channels are heterodyned to a specific frequency band chosen to be one of the lowband VHF channels. Usually, channel 3 or 4 is the choice, depending on which is not an active broadcast channel in the area.

However, a simple frequency conversion to channel 3 or 4 presents some problems. For channel 3 conversion, the local oscillator (LO) in the converter would operate 61.25 MHz above the selected channel. Note that 61.25 MHz is the picture carrier frequency for channel 3. Suppose that channel 4 is selected by the converter. Then the LO operates at $61.25 + 67.25 = 128.5$ MHz. This LO frequency is inside the cable midband channel B or 15 at 126 to 132 MHz. In addition, there are several other frequency combinations in which the LO signal can be a source of interference—especially since the broadband preselector in the converter is not very selective for RF tuning owing to the wide range of cable channels. The solution to these problems is to use a double-superheterodyne circuit for the cable converter, with a UHF intermediate frequency.

UP-DOWN CONVERTERS Refer to the block diagram in Fig. 15-16. In this double-superheterodyne circuit, first the cable channels are heterodyned up to the IF value of 374 to 380 MHz in the UHF band. The oscillator frequencies are not in any band for cable TV channels. Second, the IF signal is converted down to the frequency for either channel 3 or 4.

Two mixer stages are used in Fig. 15-16. The first mixer with the varactor-tuned local oscillator converts all incoming channels to the IF value of the converter. The IF band here is 374 to 380 MHz, but some converters use 608 to 614 MHz for the IF signal. A bandpass filter in the output circuit of the up converter selects only

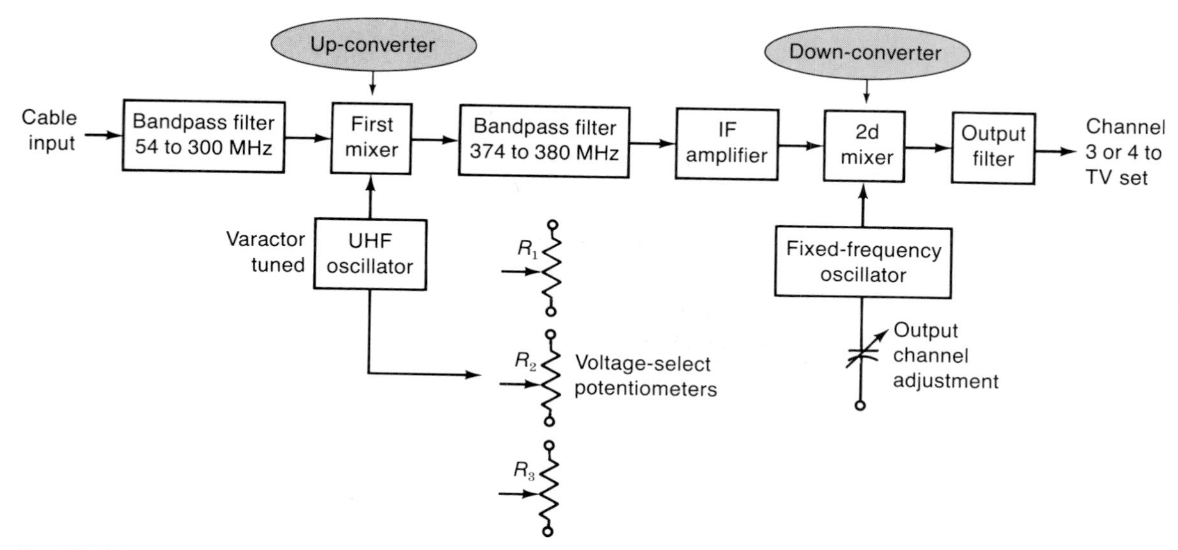

Fig. 15-16 Basic block diagram of up-down cable TV converter.

the IF signal, which is the desired channel tuned in by the UHF local oscillator.

The second mixer, with a fixed frequency oscillator, is the down converter. It heterodynes the IF signal at its UHF values down to either channel 3 or 4 for the TV receiver. An adjustment in this oscillator is set for either output channel.

The frequency that is used in the second LO for down conversion stays the same for all channels. The IF signal is always in the fixed IF passband of the converter. Each of the selected channels has already been selected by tuning the first LO frequency in the up converter, which heterodynes all the cable channels up to the IF band.

CHANNEL SELECTION Each channel is tuned by varactor control of the local oscillator frequency in the up converter. A varactor is a capacitive diode. Its capacitance decreases with the amount of reverse dc voltage. Since the frequency is varied by dc bias, the circuit is a voltage-controlled oscillator (VCO).

A typical arrangement for the cable converter is shown in Fig. 15-17. The pushbutton switches S_1 to S_6, at the right in the diagram, are identified with the channel numbers. When they are pushed in, the switches insert the variable resistors R_1 to R_6 into the circuit. The dc bias voltage is supplied through the three-position band switch with sections S_A, S_B, and S_C. Each potentiometer, or "pot," is preset to provide dc voltage that makes the VCO operate at the frequency needed to tune in a specific channel. The three-position band switch, with 12 pushbutton switches and 12 potentiometers, allows tuning for $3 \times 12 = 36$ channels. Only six pushbutton switches are shown in Fig. 15-17, for simplicity.

FREQUENCY SYNTHESIZER The block diagram in Fig. 15-18 shows the complete circuit for an up-down converter using frequency synthesis. The synthesizer section illustrates how the frequency is set for the VCO as the first local oscillator for the up converter. An 8-MHz crystal-controlled oscillator is the reference. The advantage of frequency synthesis is that many oscillator frequencies can be supplied with the accuracy of crystal control.

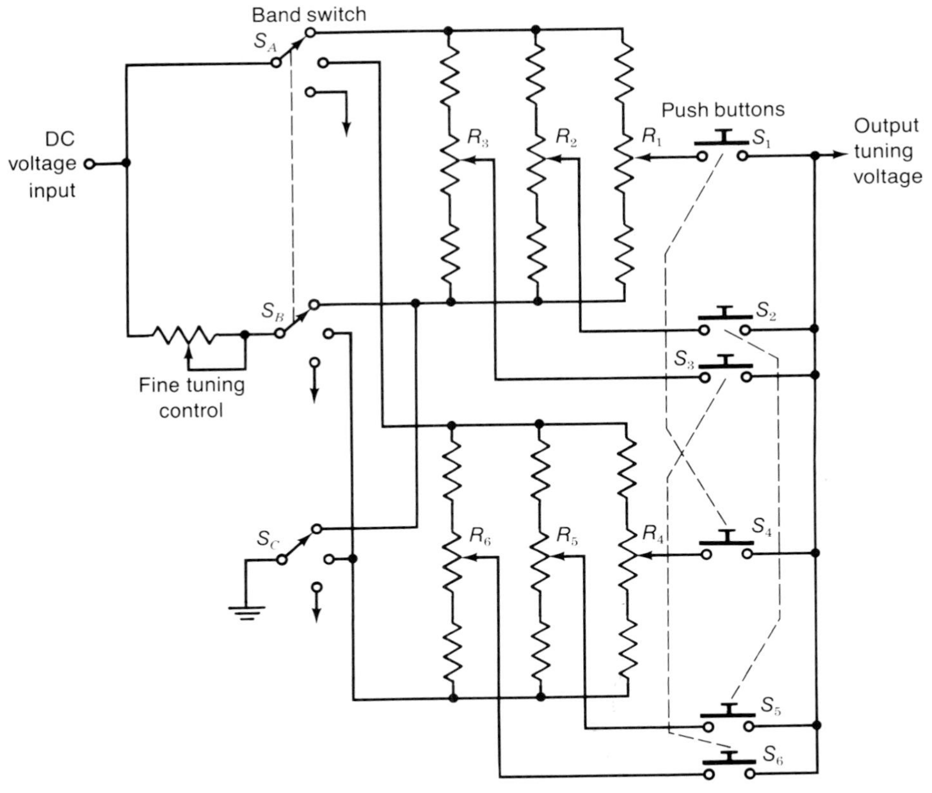

Fig. 15-17 Voltage-control for varactor tuning with variable-*R* potentiometers. System uses 36 potentiometers, 12 pushbuttons, and three-position band selector for 36 channels. Only six channels are shown here.

In Fig. 15-18, the 8-MHz oscillator in the synthesizer is divided by 1024 to produce 7.8125-kHz signal into a phase detector or comparator. The other input to the comparator is a sample of the signal from the VCO in the up converter. This sample is divided first by 256 and then by a factor *N* that is set in the programmable counter. The idea is to divide by whatever *N* is needed to provide 7.8125 kHz for comparison with the reference signal in the phase detector.

The factor *N* can take any value between 334 and 454. The actual count is determined by an 8-bit binary code set with the pushbutton switches, on either the counter or a remote unit. Remote operation is provided with a long wire to the converter, for convenience of the subscriber. Or a wireless infrared control system can be used, much as the remote tuner is used for TV receivers.

We can calculate the frequencies needed in the converter for a specific example. Superband channel 36 has a video carrier frequency of 295.25 MHz, as listed in Table 15-1. The video IF carrier frequency is 612.75 MHz for the converter in Fig. 15-18. Thus the required VCO frequency, beating above the mixer input signal, is

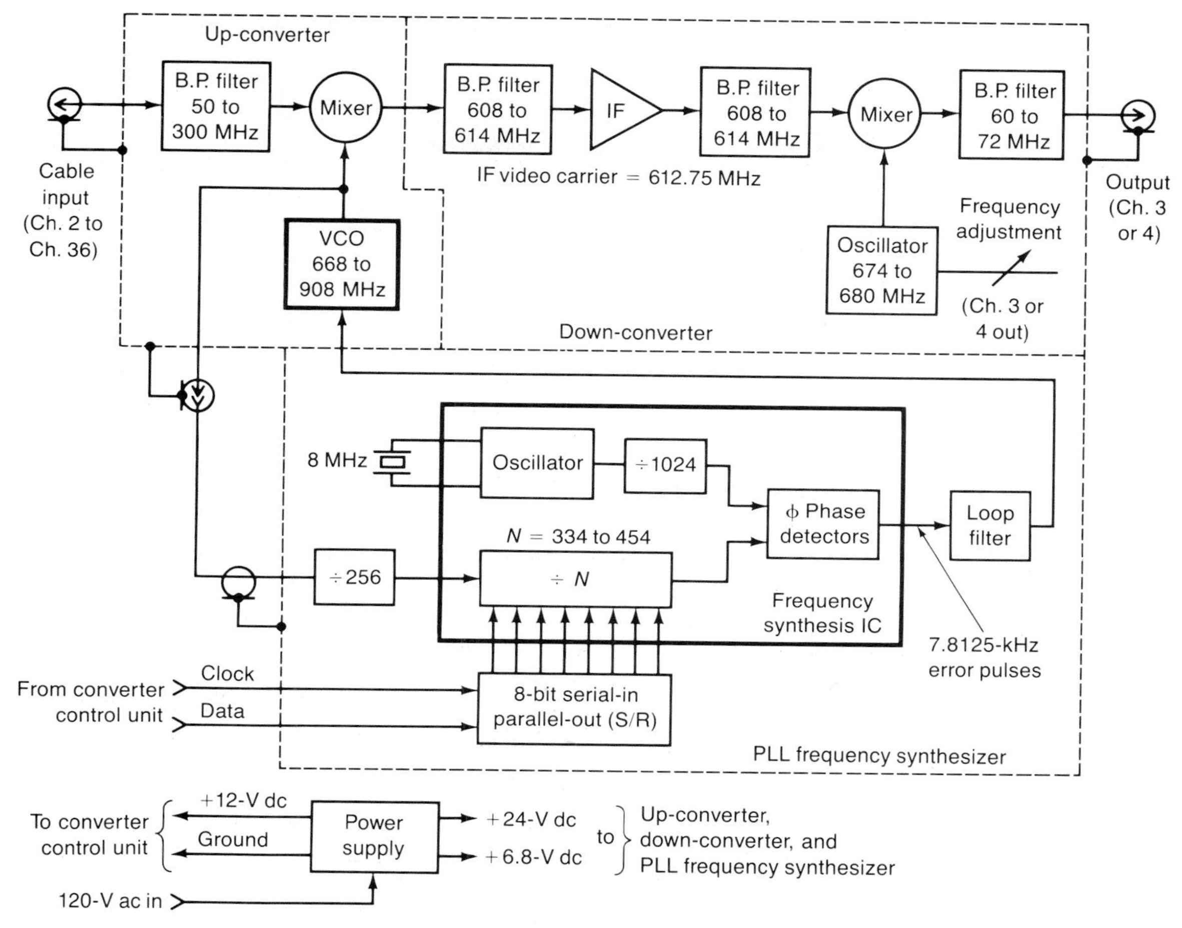

Fig. 15-18 Cable converter unit using frequency synthesis for first local oscillator in up converter. B.P. indicates bandpass filters used to remove spurious signals. (*Sylvania CATV Transmission Systems*)

$$295.25 + 612.75 = 908 \text{ MHz}$$

The 908-MHz oscillator output is supplied to the first mixer, but a sample is also taken for the synthesizer IC unit. First the 908-MHz LO frequency is divided by 256, which gives 3.546875 MHz. Then the programmable counter is set to divide by 454:

$$\frac{3546.875 \text{ kHz}}{454} = 7.8125 \text{ kHz}$$

The divided VCO signal and reference oscillator signal are compared in the phase detector. Its output is the dc control voltage to correct the VCO frequency. The feed to the VCO is through a filter to eliminate noise. This system is actually a phase-lock loop (PLL), and it is used in many applications for frequency control. If there is any error in frequency, the control voltage corrects the VCO to make its divided value at 7.8125 kHz exactly the same as the reference from the crystal oscillator. As a result, the VCO in the up converter has the same accuracy as the standard crystal oscillator for any selected channel.

Note that the video IF carrier at 612.75 MHz is at the upper end of 608 to 614 MHz for the IF passband, 1.25 MHz from the top. The reason is that any heterodyning that occurs where the oscillator beats above the mixer input frequencies produces inversion of the IF signal frequencies. This frequency inversion is illustrated in Fig. 12-11 in Chap. 12. However, the cable converter unit has another frequency inversion in the down converter. As a result of the double inversion, in the output signal on channel 3 or 4 the picture and sound carriers are at the same frequencies as in a regular TV broadcast channel.

Figure 15-19 shows a popular cable converter that uses frequency synthesis. The RF shield covers are removed to show the coaxial units needed for tuning with ultra-high frequencies.

Fig. 15-19 Frequency-synthesizer converter. RF circuit for up-down conversion. Width is 10 in. [254 mm]. Shields removed from up-down converter show coaxial type of tuning.

Test Point Questions 15-9

Answers at End of Chapter

Answer True or False.

a. The cable converter uses two local oscillators.
b. The video IF carrier in a cable converter is generally 45.75 MHz.
c. The local oscillator for the up converter operates in the UHF range.
d. Each cable channel is selected by setting the frequency of the VCO for the up converter.

15-10 WAVE TRAPS AND SCRAMBLING METHODS

Cable systems offer for a minimum fee the so-called basic service, which includes the local TV broadcast channels, some out-of-town stations, and local-origination programs. In addition, premium services are offered, such as Home Box Office, Spotlight, Cinemax, Rainbow, and others. They feature special sports events and movies, uncut and without commercial interruptions. However, these premium channels require a fee to be paid that is added to the basic charge. To serve only those subscribers who pay for the extra service, two techniques are used. One method is to insert a wave trap that attenuates the pay channel. The trap is in the feed line to each subscriber who does not have premium service. Figure 15-20 shows such a trap for aerial mounting on the outside pole. The trap method is not used much anymore, though, because it requires work on the pole to change the service. Also, the wave

Fig. 15-20 Channel trap used in aerial systems. Shown mounted on multitrap unit.

traps can be bypassed by illegal tampering at the subscriber tap on the feed line.

Today, the preferred method of security is to scramble the signal. The picture is not intelligible unless it is descrambled with a unit supplied by the cable operator.

SCRAMBLING The most common method of scrambling the signal is known as *sync suppression.* Sync is compressed only in the RF modulation envelope of the video carrier in the cable channel. Then the receiver cannot lock in with the sync-suppressed signal. The picture is usually out of sync, both vertically and horizontally, as evidenced by rolling and diagonal bars. In addition, the loss of sync upsets the receiver AGC circuit and produces the effects of AGC overload distortion. The picture is dark, possibly reversed in white and black values, like a negative, and out of sync. Figure 15-21 shows such a scrambled picture.

DESCRAMBLING The descrambler unit reverses the effect of the scrambler at the head end by restoring sync to the RF signal. Sync is restored by means of a keyed RF attenuator bypassed with a diode switch, indicated as R_A and S in Fig. 15-22. In this method, the pulses needed for the switched attenuator are sent to the descrambler unit by a separate route. A *pilot carrier signal* having a frequency below that of the channel is used. An example of the pilot carrier frequency is 114 MHz for midband channel A at 120 to 126 MHz. Other choices are possible, though, and cable operators choose their own pilot frequencies for security reasons.

Fig. 15-21 How the picture looks for channel using sync-suppression method of scrambling.

In Fig. 15-22, the descrambler contains a narrowband receiver tuned to the assigned pilot frequency. The receiver has an amplitude detector and pulse-shaping circuits to drive the diode switch. The decoding pulse in the pilot signal is the sync needed for descrambling. As a result, sync is restored in the RF signal for the TV receiver.

IN-BAND DESCRAMBLERS A more recent method uses the same idea of a pilot signal for descrambling, but the decoding pulses are sent inside the passband of the scrambled channel. These descrambler units are used with the cable converter, connected as shown in Fig. 15-23. For an in-band system, the FM sound carrier signal in a scrambled channel is amplitude-modulated with the decoding pulses. Keeping the percentage of modulation low prevents interference.

Since the converter changes all cable channels to a single channel such as 3 or 4, the descrambler unit in Fig. 15-23 contains a narrowband receiver tuned just for the sound carrier frequency of the designated channel in the converter output. Other than that, the descrambler operates just as the pilot carrier system illustrated in Fig. 15-22.

The advantage of the in-band method is that it allows as many scrambled channels as the cable operator wants to offer. Systems with four and more scrambled channels are common. Note that a change in the designated channel output of the converter, from 3 to 4 or vice versa, requires a different descrambler. Both the converter and the descrambler must operate on the same channel.

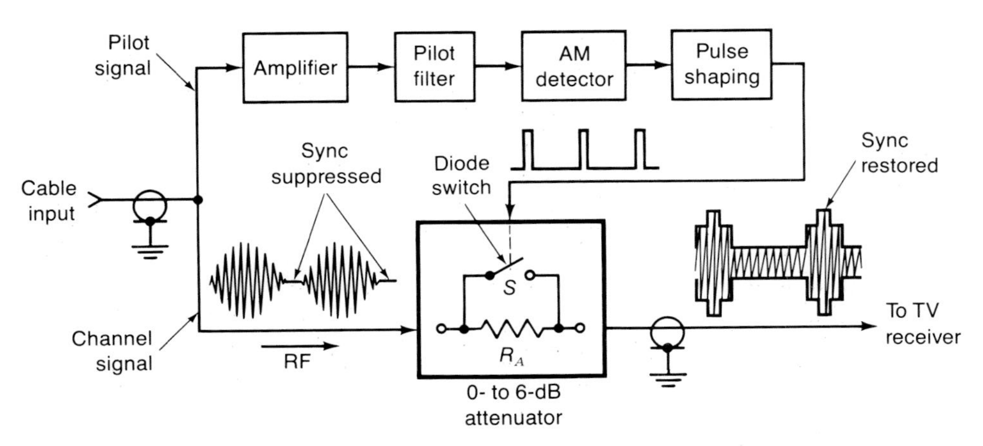

Fig. 15-22 Block diagram of basic descrambler.

Test Point Questions 15-10

Answers at End of Chapter

Answer True or False.

a. Wave traps to attenuate premium channels are usually located behind the TV receiver.

b. A scrambled channel usually has excessive snow in the picture.

c. A scrambled channel needs decoding pulses to restore the sync.

15-11 LONG-DISTANCE LINKS

Large cable systems often cover long distances which could result in prohibitive cable attenuation. Examples include the distance from a remote antenna tower to the head end and that from the head end to major hubs, which are the distribution points for local service. The methods used by the cable operator to reduce losses for long-distance links include supertrunks, microwave links, and fiber-optic links using light waves.

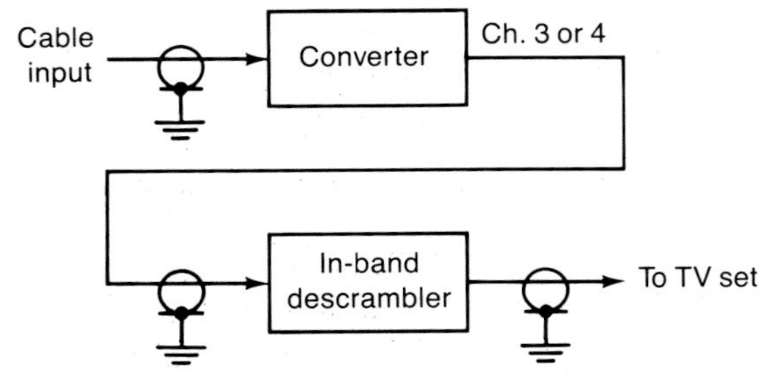

Fig. 15-23 Connections for in-band descrambler.

SUPERTRUNKS In this method, larger cables are used and the cable channels are heterodyned down to lower frequencies. Both techniques reduce the cable losses.

As shown in Fig. 15-24, the cable channels are changed to 6 to 78 MHz in the down converter. This band has space for 12 channels. Cable losses in the supertrunk are reduced for the lower frequencies, in proportion to the square root of the frequency change. For instance, 54 MHz, when reduced by a factor of 9 to 6 MHz, would have one-third the cable losses.

Note that a second heterodyne circuit is needed as an up converter in Fig. 15-24, to provide the cable channels at their standard frequencies. From the hub, channels 2 to 12 are fed to the cable distribution system.

In the supertrunk line, special low-loss cable is used. For example, a 1-in. [25.4-mm] coaxial

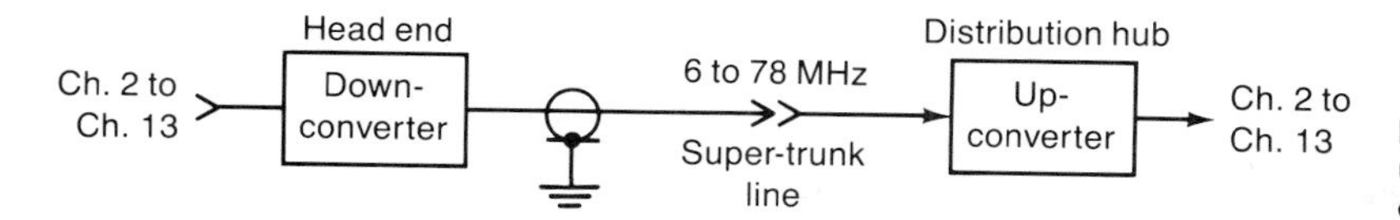

Fig. 15-24 Supertrunk system uses lower frequencies to reduce cable losses.

cable with fused insulator disks has an attenuation of only 0.32 dB per 100 ft [30.5 m] at 78 MHz. The low attenuation allows wider spacing between amplifiers on the trunk.

MICROWAVE LINKS Frequency allocations by the FCC permit operation in the band of 12.7 to 13.2 GHz. Relay stations of this type are called community antenna relay services (CARS).

Note that 1 GHz = 1000 MHz = 1×10^9 Hz. Frequencies in the range of 0.3 to 300 GHz are called the *microwave band* because the short wavelengths are a fraction of 1 m. The advantage of microwave transmission is that parabolic reflector dish antennas can be used to provide very high gain with a very narrow beam. In effect, the energy travels in a pencil-like beam from the transmitter dish antenna to the receiver dish. The line-of-sight transmission requires that no physical obstructions be in the path between transmitter and receiver. Microwave propagation is similar to light radiation, since the microwave frequencies are not much lower. However, microwaves are not visible.

Some typical signal levels can be calculated for a microwave link operating at 13 GHz. The transmitter output is 1 W, or 1000 mW. With a 1-mW reference for dBmW units, this power is 30 dBmW. Antenna gain in decibel units for a dish with 6-ft [1.8-m] diameter is 43, in either decibels or dBmW. The antenna gain applies at the transmitter and receiver for a total of $2 \times 43 = 86$ dBmW. Attenuation of the microwave signal for a 20-mi [32.2-m] distance can be taken as −146 dBmW. This value is the approximate free-space loss at 13 GHz, as listed in reference tables. The resulting signal at the receiver is

$$30 + 86 - 146 = -30 \text{ dBmW}$$

The signal power at −30 dBmW below the reference of 1 mW is equal to 0.001 mW, or 1 μW. In terms of voltage across 75 Ω, $V = 0.115$ mV of signal. Special low-noise amplifiers are required for the receiver in the microwave link. Note that individual transmitter-receiver combinations are used for the different cable channels.

Either a frequency-modulation link (FML) or an amplitude-modulation link (AML) can be used. The FML generally has a better signal-to-noise ratio, especially if preemphasis and deemphasis are used for the baseband video signal. However, the AML can actually have superior performance compared with an FM system using a narrow frequency deviation.

Test Point Questions 15-11

Answers at End of Chapter

Answer True or False.

a. Supertrunks have the cable channels at upconverted frequencies.

b. The frequency of 13 GHz is in the microwave band.

c. FM can be used for microwave links for television.

15-12 FIBER OPTICS

The latest type of communications link uses a cable made with thin glass fibers that serve as a conduit for light over long distances with little losses. In this system with a fiber-optic link, the full cable-channel bandwidth can be used for amplitude modulation of the light source. For transmission, a modulated light beam is the source that introduces light into the glass fibers. At the receiving end, a photoelectric detector converts the variations in light amplitude back to the cable signals. The light serves as a super carrier wave for the entire cable passband.

There are important advantages to using fiber-optic cable as a long-distance link. The cable is not as heavy as copper conductors, making it convenient for installation. Attenuation of the light is much less than the losses with conduction or radiation of an RF carrier wave. A big factor is that the exceptionally high frequency for light makes it possible to have modulation that includes a tremendous range of frequencies.

REFRACTION AND INTERNAL REFLECTION OF LIGHT The reason for the low attenuation is the internal reflection of light inside the fiber cable. Thus no light can escape, and the losses are extremely small. To analyze this effect, the basic laws of refraction of light are illustrated in Fig. 15-25*a*, and internal reflection is shown in Fig. 15-25*b*. Light rays are shown going from air into a slab of glass. The velocity of light is reduced in the glass because it is a denser medium.

In Fig. 15-25*a*, light rays enter at an angle from the *normal line*. This direction is perpendicular to the interface where light enters or leaves the glass. Going into the denser medium, the light rays do not continue their original angular direction. Instead, they are bent to an angle closer to the normal line because of the reduced velocity of the rays. As each wavefront of light reaches the air-glass interface, the effect is like a squad of people abreast marching in a line. The first one to hit the interface begins going slower, but the last continues with the original speed up to the interface. As a result, the line of the wavefront turns to its right, and the light beam bends toward the normal.

At the bottom of the glass slab, the light going out is bent away from the normal. This direction is opposite to the bending of the incident light. The reason is that the light goes to a less dense medium that allows it to travel at higher velocity.

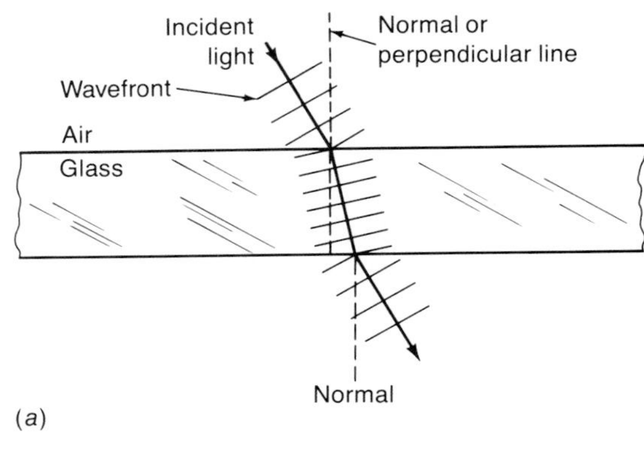

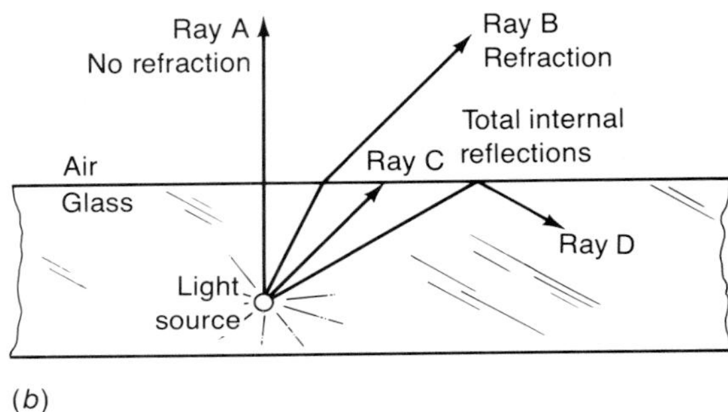

Fig. 15-25 Refraction of light and total internal reflection. (*a*) Refraction, or bending, of light rays. (*b*) Rays bent at less than a critical angle are completely reflected inside the denser medium.

The bending of the light is called *refraction*. How much the light bends when it meets a different medium is determined by the index of refraction, whose symbol is η. Its value is

$$\eta = \frac{\text{speed of light in vacuum}}{\text{speed of light in the medium}}$$

Typical values of η are 1 for air or vacuum, 1.8 for glass, 2.4 for diamond, and 1.3 for water.

Now consider a light source actually inserted in the slab of glass, as in Fig. 15-25*b*. The light radiates in all directions. The light ray marked A approaches the interface at a right angle. Such rays along the normal are not refracted. Ray B is refracted but still leaves the glass. Note that

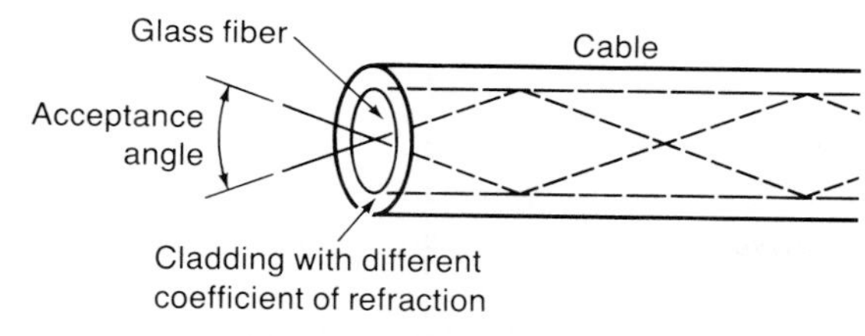

Fig. 15-26 Fiber-optic cable. Only light within the acceptance angle is reflected internally.

refraction bends the light away from the normal line. For ray C, however, the refraction is just enough to make the light follow along the glass surface. At D and smaller angles for the rays, the light is reflected internally. None of these light rays can leave the glass. The angle at which the internal reflection begins is the *critical internal angle.*

The corresponding action is shown in Fig. 15-26 for fiber-optic cable. Light entering the conduit at angles less than twice the critical angle will be reflected internally. Then the light is propagated along the cable in zigzag directions, bouncing off the walls but without leaving the glass. This angle that allows complete internal reflection is the *acceptance angle.* All incident light with a smaller angle, or along the central axis, is transmitted in the optic cable.

MODAL DISPERSION Light going into the optical cable or the central axis takes the shortest route. At other angles within the acceptance angle, the light must travel a longer path because of the internal reflections. The time difference between the direct and reflection paths is called the *modal dispersion.* This factor limits the bandwidth of the cable.

To minimize the modal dispersion, practical optic cable is made with fine fibers of small diameter. In addition, the fiber is encased in a *cladding* material that has a high index of refraction in order to increase internal reflections. In effect, all the fibers are in parallel to provide a cable with very low losses.

OPTIC TRANSMITTER The light source is often a special light-emitting diode (LED), operating in the infrared part of the spectrum, where the wavelength is greater than that for visible light. In construction, the LED is at the bottom of a conical pit to produce light in the cable. The LED current and its light output can be modulated with the full passband of all the cable channels. Actually, the LED is the limiting factor. The bandwidth of the cable itself is far greater than the bandwidth of the LED modulation circuits.

Another method of transmitting the optic signal uses an injection laser diode as the light source. This system can accept modulating frequencies well into the UHF range.

CABLE CONNECTORS One of the problems with fiber optics is splicing, or joining, cables. Care must be taken to make precise optical alignment at the connection, or excessive light loss will result. However, special connectors are available to join the cables and still keep light losses within tolerable limits.

Test Point Questions 15-12

Answers at End of Chapter

Answer True or False.

a. Fiber-optic cable has very low losses.
b. A light-modulated signal is limited to narrow bandwidth in the modulation.
c. Refraction means the bending of light waves.
d. Fiber-optic cable makes use of internal reflections of light.

SUMMARY

1. The midband cable TV channels are mainly A to I or 14 to 22 in the space between broadcast channels 6 and 7. Superband channels are J to Z or 23 to 39, plus channels 40 to 53, in the space above broadcast channel 13. The frequencies are listed in Table 15-1.
2. Coaxial cable is used for cable distribution systems because the shielding minimizes radiation of the signal and pickup of interference.
3. The standard level for cable signals at the TV receiver is 1 to 3 mV.
4. The characteristic impedance Z_O is the impedance a cable would have if it were infinitely long. Terminating a line in its Z_O results in maximum power transfer to the load, no standing waves, and no reflections on the line. Then the length of the line is not critical because there are no standing waves. The standard Z_O in cable TV is 75 Ω.
5. Standing waves of V and I are set up on a line not terminated in its Z_O. The length of such a line is critical because it has peaks and nodes of signal. The voltage standing-wave ratio is equal to V_{max}/V_{min}.
6. Attenuation of signal in the cable is produced by I^2R losses and the skin effect in the conductors and by dielectric losses. The losses increase as the square root of the frequency. Also, the losses increase with higher temperature.
7. In the cable distribution system, the head end supplies signals to the trunk, which is the main line. The trunk feeds branch lines for the drop lines to subscribers' TV receivers.
8. Trunk amplifiers, bridging amplifiers, and line amplifiers are used to make up for cable losses.
9. A directional coupler taps off signal from the cable. The insertion loss is very low for minimum attenuation. The tap loss is higher to provide isolation from the line.
10. A balun provides a match between 75-Ω unbalanced coaxial cable and 300-Ω balanced connections at the TV receiver input.
11. The dBmV unit uses the reference level of 1 mV across 75 Ω for 0 dB.
12. Weak signal causes snow in the picture, which is produced by random noise in the signal.
13. Overload distortion in the cable amplifiers can produce cross modulation in which the picture from one channel interferes with that from another channel.
14. The cable amplifiers have automatic slope control for the gain to compensate for increased losses at the higher-frequency channels.
15. Two-way cable systems use the same cable in both directions, but the return signal is on different frequencies. A poling signal is sent downstream to communicate with cable converters in the system.
16. Cable converter units use the double-superheterodyne circuit. The input channels are converted up to a higher IF signal in the UHF band. Then

the IF signal is converted down to either channel 3 or 4 for output to the TV receiver.

17. Wave traps and scrambling methods are used for the premium channels to make these signals unintelligible to subscribers who do not have this extra service. Usually, the sync is attenuated to make the picture out of sync and look like AGC overload. The picture is descrambled with a unit supplied by the cable operator to restore the sync level.
18. Long-distance links for cable television use supertrunks, which are larger cables with low losses, microwave links in the 12.7- to 13.2-GHz band, and fiber-optic cables.
19. Fiber-optic cables make use of internal reflections in the cable to transmit light with very low losses. The light can be modulated with a very wide band of signal frequencies to include all the cable TV channels.

SELF-EXAMINATION

Answers at Back of Book

Choose (a), (b), (c), or (d).

1. Which of the following is a midband cable TV channel? (a) 6, (b) 7, (c) A or 14, (d) J or 23.
2. Coaxial cable for distribution systems has an impedance of (a) 50 Ω, (b) 75 Ω, (c) 150 Ω, (d) 300 Ω.
3. The cable converter output for the TV receiver is usually on channel (a) 3, (b) 6, (c) 7, (d) 9.
4. The VSWR for a line terminated in its Z_O is (a) 0, (b) 1, (c) 1.5, (d) 2.
5. How many dBmV units correspond to a 1-mV signal level? (a) 0, (b) 1, (c) 3, (d) 6.
6. A tap for the subscriber drop line has a (a) high insertion loss, (b) high tap loss, (c) low tap loss, (d) 300-Ω impedance.
7. The most popular plug for RG-59U coaxial cable is the (a) RCA phonograph plug, (b) 4-pin DIN connector, (c) F connector, (d) banana pin.
8. Which of the following is true? (a) Excessive signal causes snow in the picture. (b) A weak signal causes cross-modulation distortion. (c) A weak signal causes snow in the picture. (d) A scrambled signal has excessive sync amplitude.
9. The upstream signal in two-way cable systems has the frequency of (a) 5 to 30 MHz, (b) 3 to 300 MHz, (c) 500 MHz, (d) 13 GHz.
10. A typical value for the IF signal, in megahertz, for up-down cable converters is (a) 45.75, (b) 300, (c) 500, (d) 612.75.
11. Frequency synthesis is used for (a) VCO in the up converter, (b) the trunk amplifier, (c) fiber-optic cable, (d) microwave links.

12. For in-band descramblers, the decoding pulses are sent on the (a) color subcarrier, (b) sound carrier, (c) picture carrier, (d) H sync pulses.
13. Which of the following is *not* true? (a) Microwave links can use FM. (b) Fiber-optic cables have very high losses. (c) Supertrunk lines use large cable for low losses. (d) The value 13 GHz is in the microwave band.
14. A trunk cable run has a loss of −20 dBmV. To make up for this loss, the voltage gain of the next amplifier should be at least (a) 10, (b) 100, (c) 200, (d) 300.

ESSAY QUESTIONS

1. What is meant by the midband and superband cable TV channels?
2. Why is coaxial cable used for distribution systems?
3. What is the advantage of converting a UHF-broadcast channel to a VHF cable channel?
4. Name two types of losses in a cable system.
5. List two types of amplifiers in a cable system.
6. What is a directional coupler?
7. Explain the difference between insertion loss and tap-off loss.
8. What are the functions of the head end and the trunk line?
9. **(a)** Define the characteristic impedance Z_O. **(b)** What is Z_O for coaxial line in cable TV? **(c)** Why is the line terminated in Z_O?
10. What is meant by a flat or nonresonant line? Why is the length of line not critical?
11. Why is it not possible to measure Z_O with an ohmmeter?
12. Describe how you would check a line with an ohmmeter to see whether it were open, or short-circuited.
13. Define VSWR. Why is the length of line critical when it has standing waves?
14. Describe briefly how open or short-circuited sections of transmission line correspond to resonant circuits.
15. What is the cause of snow in the reproduced picture?
16. What is meant by aerial mounting for cable TV equipment?
17. What is the convenience of using the F connector for coaxial cable?
18. Show how a balun would be used at the TV receiver.
19. **(a)** What is the voltage reference for dBmV units? **(b)** How much signal voltage corresponds to 0 dBmV?
20. What is meant by inversion of the IF signal frequencies when the local oscillator beats above the mixer input signal?
21. What is meant by overload distortion and cross modulation?
22. Explain how a double-superheterodyne circuit operates.
23. Why is ASC used in a trunk amplifier?
24. Name two features of a two-way cable system.

25. List the function of each stage in the block diagram of the up-down converter in Fig. 15-16.
26. What is the advantage of frequency synthesis for a local oscillator stage?
27. Name two methods of providing pay TV channels to only those subscribers who have the service.
28. List two features of the in-band scrambling method.
29. What are two advantages of fiber-optic links compared with microwave links?
30. Name two features of a fiber-optic link for cable TV.

PROBLEMS

Answers to Odd-Numbered Problems at Back of Book

1. For a line $L = 0.24\ \mu H$ and $C = 10.5$ pF/ft. Calculate Z_O.
2. Coaxial cable has an outside diameter of 0.5 in. [12.7 mm] and 0.08 in. [20.3 mm] for the inner conductor. Calculate Z_O.
3. A line has standing waves with a voltage maximum of 30 mV and minimum of 20 mV. Calculate the VSWR.
4. Calculate the length of an open quarter-wave stub at 200 MHz for coaxial cable with a velocity factor of 0.66.
5. A cable run has a loss of −20 dB at 50 MHz. How much is the loss at 200 MHz?
6. Refer to Fig. 15-18. What VCO frequency is needed to tune in the channel 2 picture carrier at 55.25 MHz?
7. Calculate the dBmV value corresponding to **(a)** 1 mV, **(b)** 2 mV, **(c)** 3 mV.
8. A 20-dBmV signal level is attenuated in a −18-dBmV line run and then amplified by 22 dBmV. What is the final signal level in dBmV and in volts?

SPECIAL QUESTIONS

1. List two advantages and one disadvantage of cable TV compared with television broadcasting.
2. Explain why a scrambled picture looks as it does.
3. Give at least one application of two-way cable systems.
4. Compare the frequencies for infrared light and 13 GHz in the microwave band.
5. Why are losses very low in fiber-optic cable?

ANSWERS TO TEST POINT QUESTIONS

15-1 **a.** 23
b. 2, 3, or 4

15-2 **a.** F
b. T
c. T

15-3 **a.** 75 Ω
b. Lower
c. Parallel
d. 1.0

15-4 **a.** T
b. F
c. F

15-5 **a.** T
b. T
c. F
d. F

15-6 **a.** 1 mV
b. 6 dBmV
c. −6 dBmV

15-7 **a.** T
b. F
c. T

15-8 **a.** F
b. T
c. T

15-9 **a.** T
b. F
c. T
d. T

15-10 **a.** F
b. F
c. T

15-11 **a.** F
b. T
c. T

15-12 **a.** T
b. F
c. T
d. T

16

TELEVISION AND VIDEO SERVICING

The diagnosis of problems in video equipment and television receivers usually can be localized to a major section by observing the raster and picture and by listening to the sound. TV receivers exhibit specific signs for some definite troubles. For instance, no high voltage with normal sound means no brightness on the screen.

Localizing the trouble to one stage and a specific component generally requires the use of test equipment, such as the multimeter, oscilloscope, and dot-bar signal generator. Just a simple ohmmeter can indicate an open resistor or short-circuited capacitor, once the trouble has been narrowed down to a suspected component.

In all cases safety precautions are important. Besides the high voltage of the picture tube, the power-line voltage can be a hazard if there are exposed metal parts. The main factors about safety, a review of symptoms, and the steps to follow in localizing the trouble are described in the following sections:

16-1 SAFETY

When you are working on a TV chassis outside its protective cabinet, there are several potential sources of electric shock. First, the high-voltage supply of 10 to 30 kV is a danger. This high dc voltage can cause a jolting shock. Also the ac input to the high-voltage rectifier can produce a serious skin burn. In terms of safety, though, the high-voltage power supply has the advantages of poor regulation and limited load current because the high-voltage rectifier is fed from the horizontal output circuit. The dc output drops sharply when it is partially short-circuited by someone touching the high-voltage circuit.

Although the low-voltage supply has much lower dc output voltage, a line-connected rectifier can supply appreciable current. The scanning-voltage rectifiers have limited output because they are supplied from the horizontal output circuit. In general, more than 30 V is usually required to produce enough current through the body to create an electric shock.

A real shock hazard exists from any exposed power-line voltage. One side of all 120-V electrical service is returned to earth ground in the power distribution system. Should someone come in contact with the other side, which is the hot side, the result is a 120-V difference in potential, as illustrated in Fig. 16-1. How serious the electric shock can be depends on the series resistance that determines the amount of current through the person's body. The R can be low when the person is on a damp, concrete floor, as in Fig. 16-1*a*. The higher R in Fig. 16-1*b* corresponds to a dry rubber mat on a dry wood floor.

However, the grounded objects that are all around us can supply a low-resistance grounded path. Examples are appliances with a three-wire grounded plug. The third wire goes to earth ground through the power distribution system, in order to ground the metal case. A bench oscilloscope is usually grounded. Touching the case and the hot side of the power line will produce a serious shock. Other grounded objects are heating radiators, hot- and cold-water pipes, and the appliances that are grounded to them.

ISOLATION OF A POWER TRANSFORMER A power supply that uses a transformer with separate primary and secondary windings provides isolation from the power line. Either side of the secondary may be connected to the chassis, but it will not be hot with respect to the ac power line. This connection is a chassis ground but not earth ground.

Figure 16-2 illustrates the isolation with a power transformer. The primary has one side at earth ground. However, either side of the secondary has 0 V to earth ground. The 120 V across

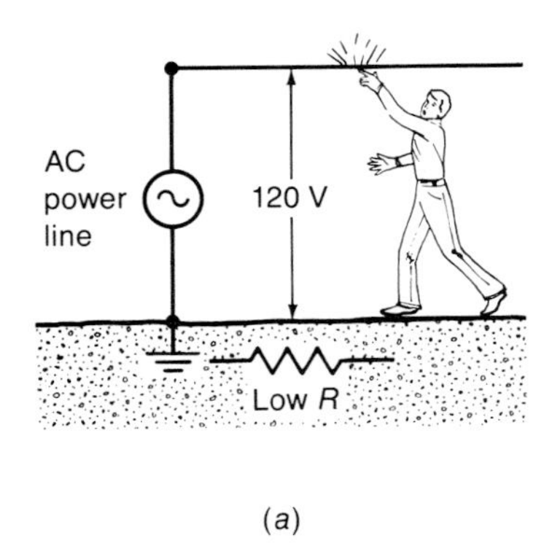

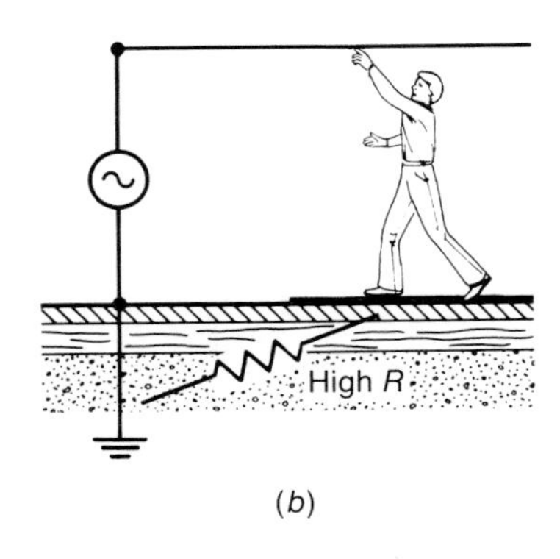

Fig. 16-1 Shock hazard from hot side of ac power line depends on resistance in ground return. (*a*) Low resistance on a damp floor. (*b*) High resistance with insulating mat on dry floor.

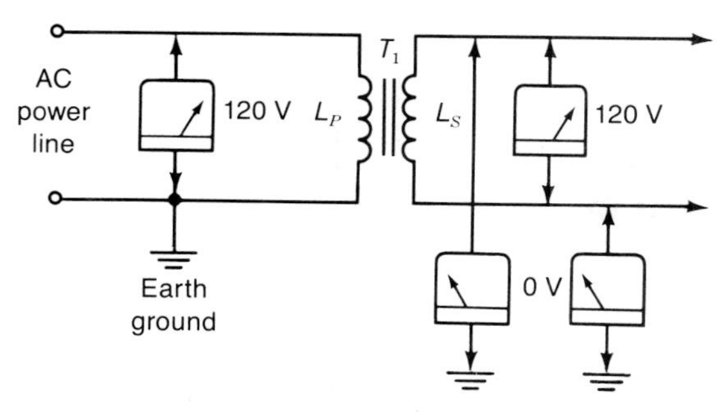

Fig. 16-2 Transformer with separate secondary winding provides isolation from ac power line. Meters in the secondary show 120 V across winding L_S but 0 V from either side to ground.

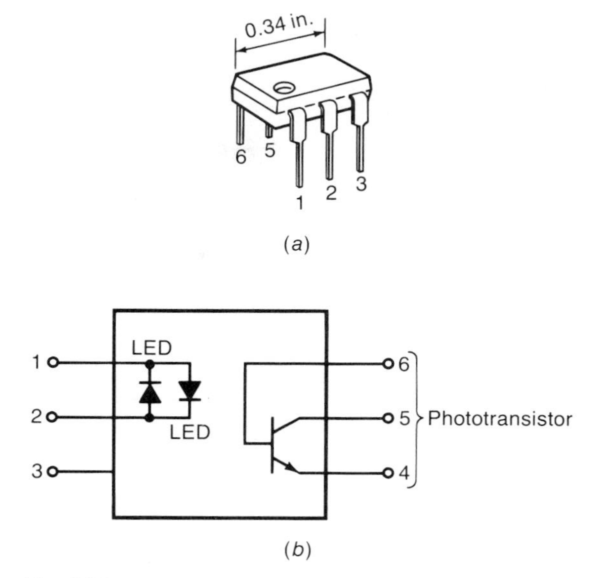

Fig. 16-3 Electro-optical coupler, used for isolation of ground return with coaxial cable connection. (*a*) Outline. (*b*) Pin connections. (*Motorola Semiconductor Products*)

L_S is a result of electromagnetic induction produced by the current in L_P, which is independent of any ground connections.

TV monitors usually have a power transformer for isolation, so that the chassis ground can be used as a common connection for the jacks that take coaxial cable input. The outer conductor of the cable is grounded to its plug, the input jack, and the monitor chassis. If power transformers are not used, other forms of isolation must be provided for the cable feeds. One method uses the electro-optical coupler shown in Fig. 16-3.

Although transformer-powered equipment is assumed to be inherently safe, keep in mind that the isolation between the primary and secondary windings is provided by only a thin layer of insulation, which is usually varnished paper. A puncture of this thin layer, caused by arc-over or an undetected pinhole, can result in a hot chassis. Then all cables connected to the equipment become a real hazard for electric shock.

STATIC DISCHARGE A resistor of 1 or 2 MΩ often is connected from the chassis to one side of the ac power line, with or without a power transformer. This *R* is between chassis ground for the B-minus return and earth ground through the power line. The purpose is to drain off static charge through *R* and the power wiring to earth ground. An example is several thousand volts accumulated by the action of dry snow blowing across an outdoor antenna. The antenna input terminals have a dc path to chassis ground.

RF BYPASS CAPACITOR A capacitor of about 0.1 μF may be connected from chassis ground to the power line for earth ground. The purpose of this bypass capacitor is to keep the chassis from being a source of RF interference. Such a capacitor must have special voltage ratings. Also, it is designed to prevent any fire hazard in case of a failure. An exact replacement is necessary.

SAFETY-SENSITIVE COMPONENTS It is standard practice to identify these special components by shading in the diagram as in Fig. 16-4 or some other keying system. Included are *RC* networks and *LC* filters for the ac power input connections and components in the high-

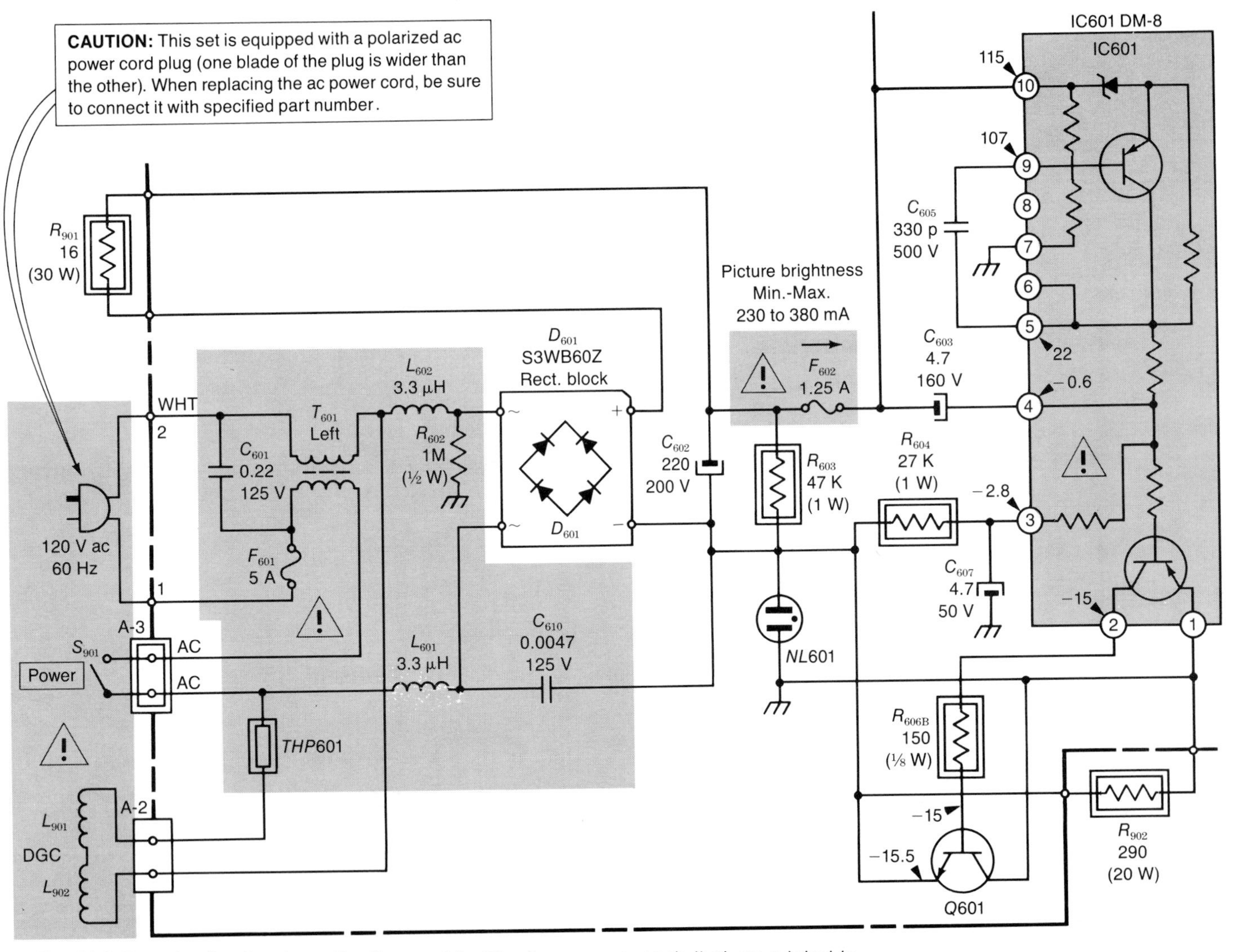

Fig. 16-4 Gray shading in schematic diagram identifies those components that are related to safety. Use only exact replacement parts. (*From Sony KV-1207 receiver*)

voltage supply. Their special characteristics are related to fire hazard, arcing, or x-ray emission. When replacement is necessary, use the manufacturer's part numbers. *Make no substitutions.*

HOT CHASSIS Many TV receivers do not have a power transformer. They rectify the ac line voltage directly to provide the dc supply voltage. Two examples of such a line-connected power supply are shown in Fig. 16-5. The advantages are less weight and space and greater economy for the receiver. However, the chassis could be hot with ac line voltage because of the connection to one side of the power line.

For the half-wave rectifier circuit in Fig. 16-5*a*, the B-minus return of the power supply is connected directly to the ac input. This chassis could be at the 120-V potential if the power plug were inserted with the chassis side connected to the hot side of the ac power.

In the bridge rectifier circuit in Fig. 16-5*b*, the chassis is always at a potential above earth ground that is one-half the ac line voltage. This potential is 60 V for 120-V ac input.

Note the *LC* filters in Fig. 16-5*a* and *b* to reduce the RF interference. Generally these components are shaded in schematic diagrams to indicate safety-related parts at risk for fire hazard.

Hot-chassis receivers use heavy blocks of insulation to insulate the chassis from the cabinet. No fasteners accessible from outside the cabinet make any direct electric connection to the chassis. In addition, the controls are isolated by the use of plastic knobs and plastic shafts. A special problem is the use of input and output jacks grounded to the chassis. Television receivers undergo strict tests by Underwriters Laboratories, in terms of shock hazard and fire protection.

POLARIZED PLUG As shown in Fig. 16-6, a polarized plug can be inserted only one way into the standard ac power receptacle. The wider blade of the plug connects to the grounded side of the power line. In the receptacle, the grounded

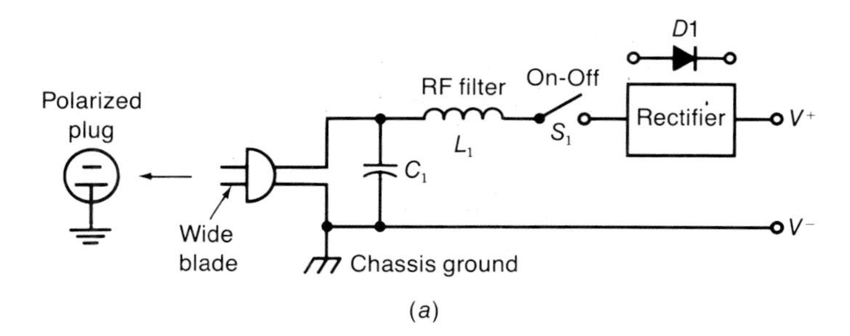

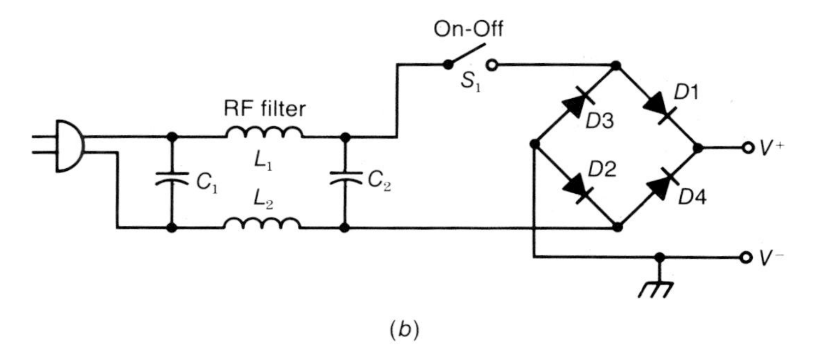

Fig. 16-5 Example of line-connected power supply that does not have an isolation transformer. (*a*) Half-wave rectifier. (*b*) Full-wave bridge circuit.

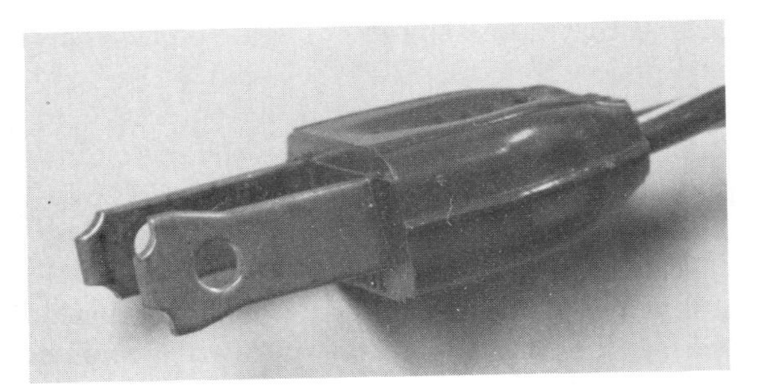

Fig. 16-6 Polarized line plug for ac power line. Wider blade is grounded side.

side has a white wire. In the receiver, the chassis is connected to the wider blade of the plug. As a result, the polarized plug ensures that the chassis is connected to the grounded side of the ac power line. Hot-chassis receivers made since about 1975 are required to use a polarized ac line plug. The polarization refers to the grounding, not to any voltage polarity.

ISOLATION TRANSFORMER When any TV receiver chassis is on the workbench, the exposed chassis can be dangerous if it is above ground potential. The shock hazard is especially bad with a hot-chassis receiver. In addition, a serious burn can result if the grounded lead of the oscilloscope is connected to a hot chassis. This accident causes ground leads to vaporize and service fuses to blow.

To eliminate the shock hazard for hot-chassis receivers, or those suspected of being hot, use a bench-type isolation transformer (Fig. 16-7). It provides the isolation of separate primary and secondary windings. The turns ratio is generally 1:1 to provide the standard line voltage at the secondary outlet. The power transformer must be rated to handle the power of any equipment connected to it. Typical ratings are 250 to 500 W.

Fig. 16-7 Isolation transformer used for safe bench work. Width is 3 in. [76.2 mm].

Test Point Questions 16-1

Answers at End of Chapter

Answer True or False.

a. An isolation transformer has separate primary and secondary windings.

b. The bridge rectifier circuit in Fig. 16-5*b* cannot have a hot chassis.

c. The wider blade in a polarized ac line plug connects to the chassis in receivers with a line-operated half-wave rectifier.

16-2 LEAKAGE TESTS

To ensure that the TV receiver is properly assembled and presents no shock hazard to the user, technicians should routinely perform the UL leakage test described in Fig. 16-8. The setup includes a 1.5-kΩ resistor bypassed with a 0.15-μF capacitor. Resistor R_1 develops voltage from any 60-Hz leakage current. Capacitor C_1 bypasses the resistor for higher frequencies. One side of the *RC* network is returned to the power-line earth ground. The third pin on a three-wire ac receptacle that is properly grounded provides a convenient place. Then the probe on the other

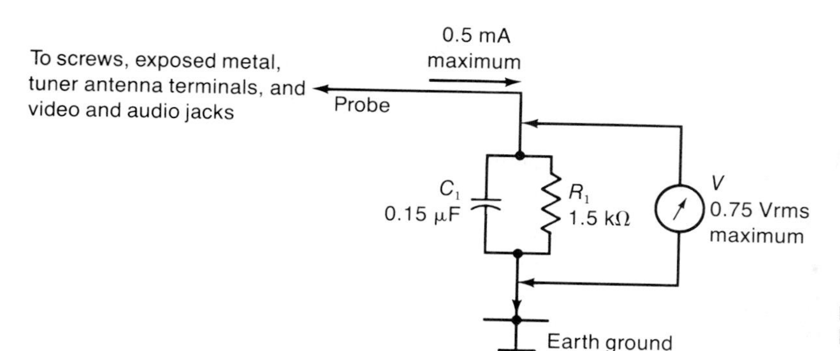

Fig. 16-8 Test for ac leakage. Maximum voltage reading across R_1 is 0.75 V rms.

side of the *RC* network is connected to all exposed metal parts on the cabinet. Included are antenna terminals, heads of metal fasteners, and video and audio jacks. In hot-chassis receivers, audio jacks are isolated by transformers and video jacks by transformers or optical couplers.

The antenna terminals in hot-chassis receivers are isolated from chassis ground by small capacitors, typically 100 pF, in series with both sides of the antenna feed. In parallel with each *C* is a 2-MΩ resistor that provides a path for static charge on the antenna.

The amount of leakage current from any exposed metal part to earth ground must not exceed 0.5 mA rms. A voltmeter across the 1.5-kΩ *R*, therefore, must not read more than 0.75 V. This voltage is 0.5 mA × 1.5 kΩ = 0.75 V. The voltmeter should have a sensitivity of at least 20 kΩ/V for ac voltage readings.

Many ac voltmeters are not accurate at this low reading. The meter should be checked against another meter or voltage source with known accuracy.

Test Point Questions 16-2

Answers at End of Chapter

For the test of ac leakage in Fig. 16-8:

a. How much is the maximum current?
b. How much is the maximum voltage?

16-3 METER MEASUREMENTS

The basic tests required for servicing use a multimeter and an oscilloscope. A multimeter measures voltage, current, and resistance. The oscilloscope is also a voltmeter, but it produces a graph of voltage versus time to show the waveshape. Keep in mind that dc values are easier to measure than ac values. Except for the 60-Hz ac power line, usually it is preferable to use the multimeter for dc voltages and resistances. Use the oscilloscope for ac signal voltages.

VOLT-OHM-MILLIAMMETER (VOM) This instrument measures volts, ohms, or milliamperes (Fig. 16-9). It is basically a dc meter, but a built-in rectifier adapts the VOM to read ac values of voltage and current. Also, an internal battery serves as a voltage source when the meter is used as an ohmmeter.

The sensitivity rating of the VOM for dc voltage readings is typically 20 kΩ/V, with a 50-μA meter movement. This rating means that the internal multiplier resistances provide 20 kΩ of *R* for every 1 V of full-scale deflection. Note that 1/(50 μA) equals 20,000 Ω.

To find the resistance of the voltmeter on a particular range, multiply the full-scale voltage by 20 kΩ. For examples,

$$\text{10-V range} = 10\text{ V} \times 20\text{ k}\Omega/\text{V} = 200\text{ k}\Omega$$
$$\text{250-V range} = 250\text{ V} \times 20\text{ k}\Omega/\text{V} = 5000\text{ k}\Omega$$

Fig. 16-9 Typical volt-ohm-milliameter. (*Simpson Electric Products*)

The voltmeter resistance for a given range is the same for any reading on the scale. Note that the VOM sensitivity for the ac voltage ranges usually is less than that for the dc ranges because of the internal rectifier circuit.

CIRCUIT LOADING The voltmeter resistance is a possible source of error in voltage measurements, because the meter introduces parallel resistance across the circuit being tested. This shunting effect lowers the equivalent resistance and increases the current, which means loading down the circuit. A theoretically perfect voltmeter should have infinitely high resistance because voltage is always measured across two points at different potentials. For the opposite case, a meter to measure current should have low resistance because it is connected as a series component.

The loading effect of a voltmeter was more important when vacuum-tube circuits were used because they have higher resistances than transistor circuits. With NPN and PNP transistors, the loading effect of a VOM is negligible. In fact, low-voltage ranges are more important than the meter loading. An advantage of the VOM is that it does not plug into the ac line for power, which is convenient for portability. Also either test probe can be connected to chassis ground.

In terms of accuracy for the meter movement itself, typical values are 2.5 percent of full-scale deflection for the VOM and 5 percent for the vacuum-tube voltmeter (VTVM) type.

VTVM AND FET MULTIMETER Nowadays the field-effect transistor (FET) is used instead of a tube for the internal amplifier circuit. This type of meter needs operating power, from either the ac power line or internal batteries for a portable instrument. The main features are very high resistance ranges up to 1000 MΩ and high resistance as a dc voltmeter. The usual value of input resistance as a dc voltmeter is 10 MΩ, the same on all ranges.

DIGITAL MULTIMETER The digital multimeter (DMM) is the latest type. Instead of the analog meter movement where a pointer reads values on different scales, a digital readout is provided to three or four decimal places. An example is shown in Fig. 16-10, with an additional high-voltage probe.

The digital reading is often specified as 3½ digits. This means that the digits in three decimal places can be 0 to 9, but when the most significant digit to the left is in the fourth place, it can only be 0 or 1. For example, the meter can read 234 V but not 2340 V.

The DMM uses accurate voltage-comparison circuity with a precise reference. The high input resistance as a dc voltmeter is usually 10 MΩ, as with the VTVM.

For many people, the advantage of the DMM is that it eliminates the confusion of reading the different scales on an analog meter. A minor drawback is that the DMM is not convenient

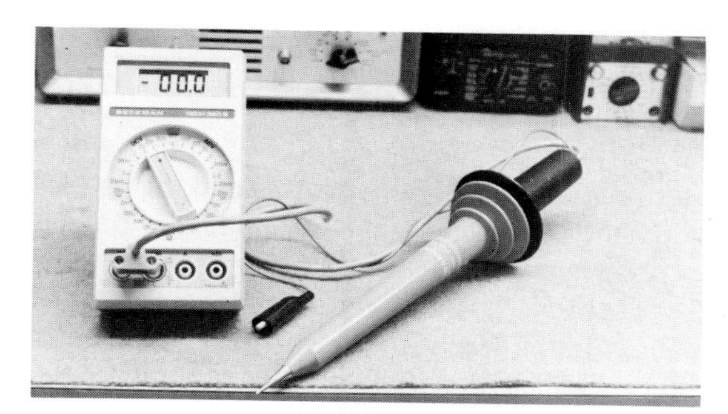

Fig. 16-10 Digital multimeter with high-voltage probe for measuring CRT anode voltage.

to use to make adjustments for a voltage null. The operator must keep track of the numbers displayed for such an adjustment.

HIGH-VOLTAGE MEASUREMENTS Often TV service requires checking of the anode voltage applied to the picture tube. The simple method of arcing the high-voltage connector establishes the presence of high voltage, but it can damage the semiconductor circuits. Also, you do not know how much the high voltage is, although an approximate rule is that 30 kV can make a spark 1 in. [25.4 mm] long. This method should be avoided in favor of direct measurement. High-voltage probes are available as an accessory for practically all multimeters (Fig. 16-10).

The high-voltage probe consists of an additional external multiplier resistor, housed in a large plastic case. The handle shape is designed to prevent arc-over along the surface. For a voltmeter with the standard 10-MΩ input resistance, the high-voltage accessory probe has an additional 990-MΩ series multiplier. So the total R is 1000 MΩ. The voltage division for the meter is 10 MΩ/1000 MΩ = $\frac{1}{100}$. At the probe 1 kV = 10 V at the meter. That is, a 100-V reading on the meter corresponds to 10 kV for the probe.

The instrument in Fig. 16-11 has a 50-μA meter movement built into the handle end of the probe. This type is used by itself. The full-scale reading is 40 kV, with a total resistance of 800 MΩ.

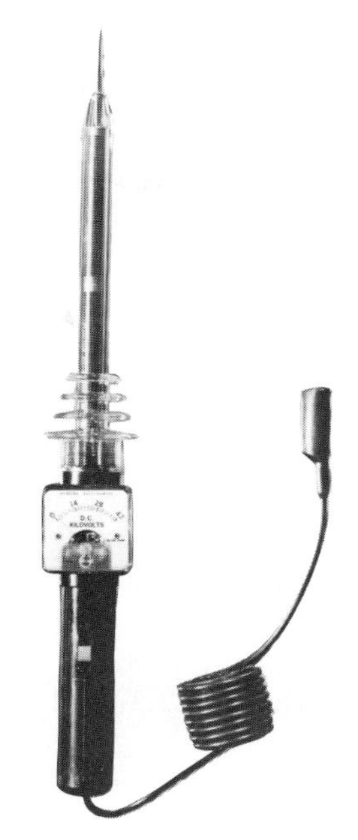

Fig. 16-11 High-voltage meter. (*Pomona Electronics*)

Test Point Questions 16-3

Answers at End of Chapter

a. Which has higher input resistance as a dc voltmeter, the VOM or the DMM?

b. Does meter loading increase or decrease the voltage reading?

c. Is the external multiplier for a high-voltage probe 990 MΩ or 990 Ω?

16-4 OSCILLOSCOPES

The signal output voltage from the video detector in a TV receiver is on the order of 0.5 V p-p or more. The bandwidth is approximately 4 MHz, which includes 3.58 MHz for chroma.

Therefore, a general-purpose oscilloscope is more than adequate for most TV servicing (Fig. 16-12). Typical specifications for the oscilloscope vertical amplifier are

10-MHz bandwidth for frequency response

20-mV/cm sensitivity for gain

The 10:1 low-capacitance probe (LCP) is used for all measurements. Such an oscilloscope permits inspection of voltage waveshapes in all parts of the receiver, including video, chroma, sync, and deflection, except for the RF and IF sections.

Note that 0.5 V p-p for probably the smallest video signal is equal to 500 mV. With a sensitivity of 20 mV/cm in the vertical amplifier and 10:1 voltage division by the probe, a 500-mV signal at the LCP produces a 2.5-cm trace height on the oscilloscope screen.

An oscilloscope with 50-MHz bandwidth could be used in the final IF amplifier, which has enough signal for a trace. However, even a low-capacitance probe would cause considerable detuning. Even more detuning would be produced by a detector probe. It is better to check the RF section with a "tuner subber," which is a substitute RF tuner. The IF section can be

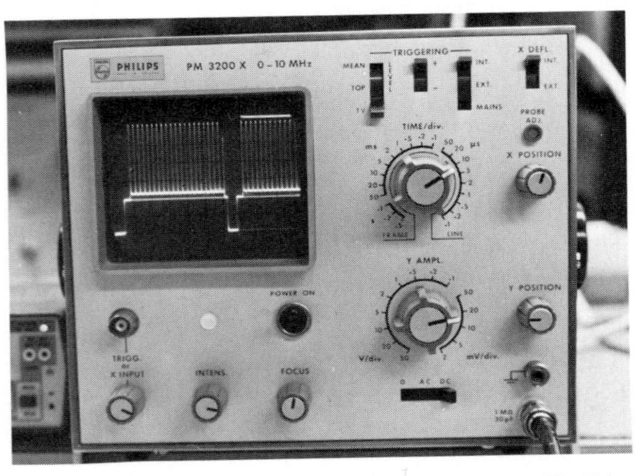

Fig. 16-12 Typical single-trace oscilloscope with 5-in. [127-mm] screen.

checked by signal injection and measuring the video detector output.

TV SWITCH Oscilloscopes for TV servicing usually provide a switch marked *V* and *H*, as part of the internal time-base selector, for convenience in observing waveshapes in a television receiver (see Fig. 16-12). The *V* and *H* indicate the television scanning frequencies. On the *V* position of internal sweep, the oscilloscope shows two cycles of signal for the vertical fields, with *V* sync and blanking pulses in the composite video signal. On the *H* position, the trace includes two cycles of signal for the horizontal scanning lines, with *H* sync and blanking in the composite video signal. In the oscilloscope, a TV type of sync separator circuit is used to establish definite triggering of the internal sweep generator at one-half the *V* and *H* rates.

DUAL-TRACE OSCILLOSCOPE With a dual-trace oscilloscope, two signals can be viewed at the same time. The oscilloscope has two vertical amplifier channels, usually labeled A and B for the two traces, but one horizontal time base. See Fig. 16-13. An electronic switch gates each channel on at the switching rate. This type should not be considered as a dual-beam oscilloscope, which actually has two separate electron guns in the CRT.

The dual-trace oscilloscope in Fig. 16-13 is being used to display a detected video signal in the upper trace and below it the delayed keying pulse used to turn on the burst amplifier in a color receiver. You can see that the peak of the keying pulse has been delayed by the correct amount to make it coincide with the burst signal. As a result, the burst can be separated properly in the TV receiver.

DELAYED SWEEP A delayed-sweep oscilloscope has two time bases for internal horizontal sweep (Fig. 16-14). The main time base is labeled A.

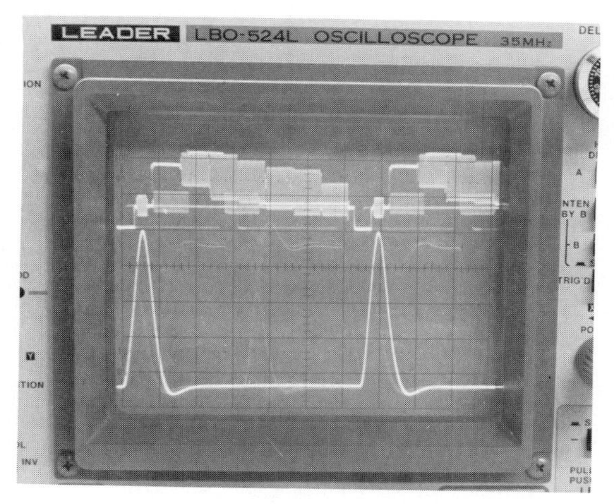

Fig. 16-13 Use of dual-trace oscilloscope. Here detected video signal at top in trace A is compared with burst keying pulse in trace B to see whether pulse is coincident with burst signal.

The B time base is switched on after an adjustable delay from the start of the A time base.

The B time base has a separate timing control so that its sweep interval can be made much shorter than for A. As a result, selected parts of the main display can be magnified for closer scrutiny.

In Fig. 16-14*a,* just the A time base is used. It is set to show a trace with a little more than one vertical field of video signal.

In Fig. 16-14*b,* the A-intensified-by-B button has been depressed. The trace continues to show the A time base, but the B time base appears highlighted. This effect is produced by an unblanking pulse equal to the duration of the B time base. Shortening the B time base narrows the highlighted part of the trace. Also, adjusting the DELAY TIME control moves the bright zone to the left or right. This control is a 10-turn potentiometer that adjusts the start of B time earlier or later with respect to the start of A time. In this example, the B-delay and time-base controls have been adjusted to highlight the leading edge of the vertical blanking pulse in the trace showing the composite video signal.

Finally, in Fig. 16-14*c,* the B trace button is depressed to show the B trace by itself. This trace shows the end of scanning field 1, with a half-line of video signal, followed by six equalizing pulses and the serrated vertical sync pulse. The delayed sweep is especially useful in servicing video cassette recorders when precise adjustment is required for video head switching with respect to the vertical sync pulse.

TUNER SUBBER It is practically impossible to use an oscilloscope to check the RF tuner, because of the high frequencies and low signal level. The opposite idea in troubleshooting is to use a substitute RF tuner (Fig. 16-15). This unit is a small, independent tuner for the VHF and UHF channels, with its own internal power supply and a gain control. The IF output signal is provided at an RCA type of phonograph jack, as in most tuners for receivers. Therefore, the IF cable of the receiver can be plugged into the tuner subber. If normal pictures are obtained only with the subber, then the IF section of the receiver may be assumed to be normal and the tuner section of the receiver must be defective.

Test Point Questions 16-4

Answers at End of Chapter

Answer True or False.

a. An oscilloscope with a 50-MHz bandwidth must be used for TV servicing.

b. The TV switch on an oscilloscope can be set for two cycles of video signal, at either the *V* or the *H* scanning rate.

c. A dual-trace oscilloscope has a CRT with two electron guns.

d. A delayed-sweep oscilloscope uses two internal time bases.

e. A tuner subber produces the IF output signal.

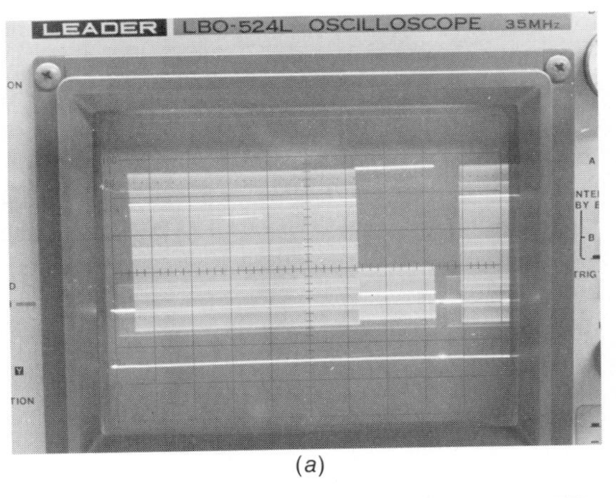

(*a*)

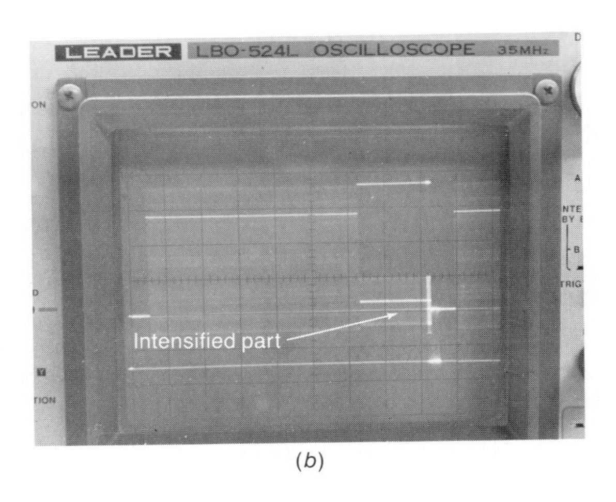

(*b*)

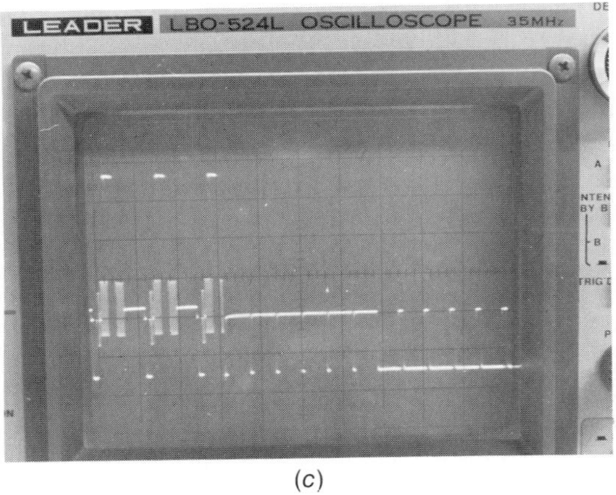

(*c*)

Fig. 16-14 Use of delayed sweep with dual-trace oscilloscope. (*a*) A trace alone. (*b*) A trace intensified by B trace. (*c*) B trace alone.

16-5
COLOR-BAR GENERATORS

The color bars are used for adjustments in the color circuits of TV receivers and video tape recorders. Most generators also supply a dot pattern and crosshatch pattern, in black and white. These patterns are used in the convergence adjustments for color picture tubes, as explained in Chap. 5. In addition, the equally spaced bars in the crosshatch pattern are convenient for checking linearity of the vertical and horizontal scanning.

NTSC COLOR-BAR GENERATOR The output of this signal generator conforms to EIA standard RS-189A adopted by the National Television Systems Committee. Some of the main characteristics are as follows:

1. There are color bars for the primary colors (red, green, and blue) with their complementary colors (yellow, cyan, and magenta).
2. The color bars have the standard amplitude of 75 IRE units.
3. There is a standard luminance signal of 100 IRE units.

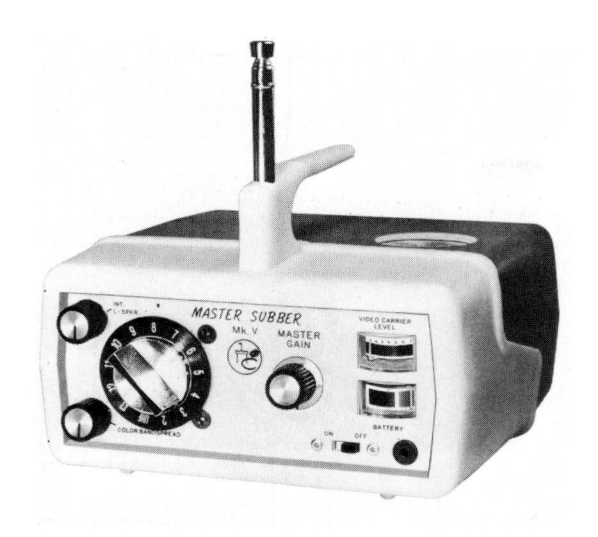

Fig. 16-15 Tuner subber. Width is 8 in. [203.2 mm].

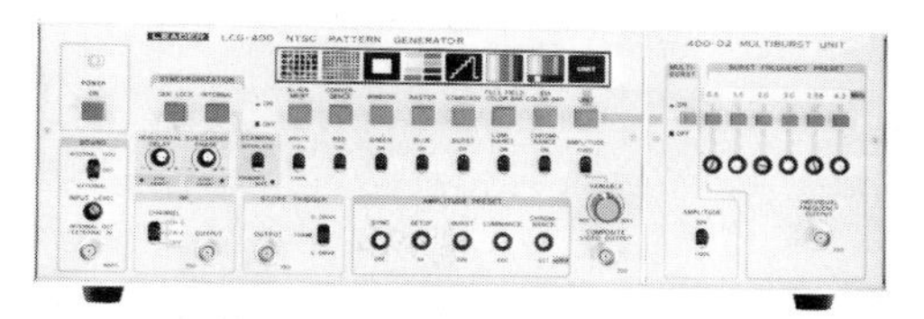

Fig. 16-16 Example of NTSC color-bar generator. Height is 4¾ in. [120.6 mm]. (*Leader Instruments Corp.*)

How this standard pattern looks on the screen and other features are described in Chap. 9, "Video Test Signals."

Standard NTSC color bars are required for proper adjustment of video cassette recorders, since the correct relation between chrominance and luminance signals must be established. The NTSC generator in Fig. 16-16 supplies additional test signals, including the window signal for luminance, the modulated stair-step signal for chroma with a black-and-white crosshatch pattern for convergence adjustments, and video sweep signals for testing video circuits.

PORTABLE COLOR-BAR GENERATOR For general-purpose servicing, a unit like the one in Fig. 16-17 can be used. This type is small and portable and costs much less than the NTSC generator. The output includes color bars, dot pattern, and crosshatch pattern. However, the color bars are in a rainbow pattern, from yellow through red and blue to cyan and green.

RAINBOW PRINCIPLE This method of producing color bars is an application of the rainbow effect that occurs when the color AFPC system in a TV receiver is out of sync. If the color oscillator frequency error is equal to the field rate, a complete rainbow of colors will appear from top to bottom of the screen, assuming a picture that is supposed to be a single solid hue. For larger frequency errors, the rainbow breaks into horizontal bands of color. When the error is equal to the horizontal scanning frequency, a complete rainbow of vertical color bars is displayed across the screen.

In a rainbow generator, the subcarrier oscillator operates at a frequency offset by the horizontal line-scanning rate. Specifically, this oscillator frequency is 3.579545 MHz, plus or minus

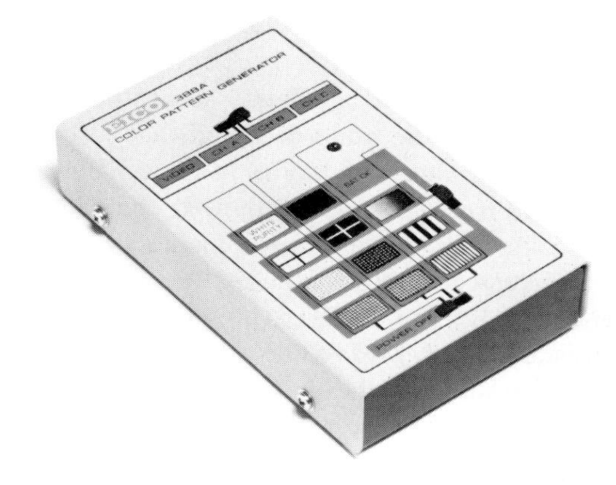

Fig. 16-17 Example of portable gated rainbow type of color-bar generator. Unit takes 9-V battery for power. Width is 3.6 in. [91.44 mm]. (Eico Electronic Instrument Company Inc.)

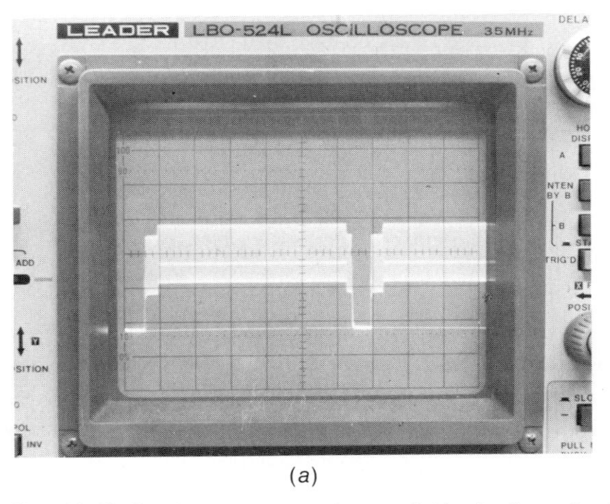

(a)

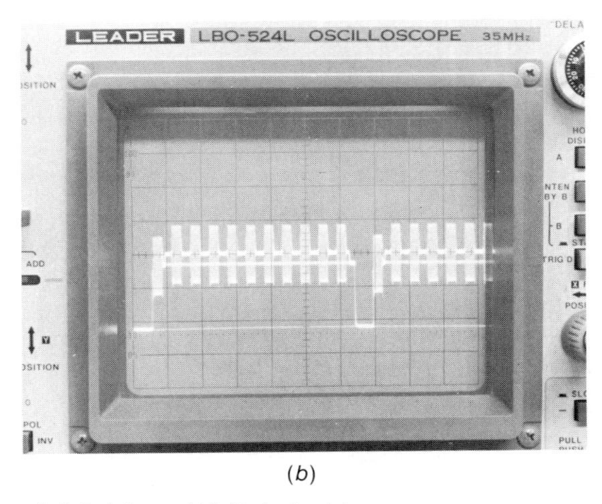

(b)

Fig. 16-18 Oscilloscope waveforms at *H* rate for color bars. (*a*) Rainbow. (*b*) Gated rainbow.

15,734 Hz, usually on the higher side. Note that 15,734 Hz is the *H* scanning rate for color television. The rainbow generator is also called an *offset-carrier generator.*

Figure 16-18*a* shows the oscilloscope waveform for the rainbow signal. Note that the amplitude is constant. There are no *Y* values of luminance signal, except for a small amount of setup. Some generators have more setup to produce a more pleasing display.

In a TV receiver, the burst separator gates out a sample of the rainbow signal that just follows *H* sync. This signal locks in the AFPC circuit of the receiver just as though the sample were color sync burst. The color oscillator in the receiver continues to run at the correct frequency of 3.579545 MHz, though, because of its crystal control. Meanwhile, the rainbow signal in the chroma circuits of the TV receiver goes through 360° of phase rotation in the time of a complete horizontal line. Therefore, the rainbow of color bars appears from left to right in the picture.

GATED RAINBOW A more useful display makes use of 12 equally spaced gated intervals. The output waveform is shown in Fig. 16-18*b*. The display of bars appears as shown in Fig. 16-19. From left to right are bars for yellow, orange, red, magenta, blue, cyan, and green hues. The colors can be seen in color plate X.

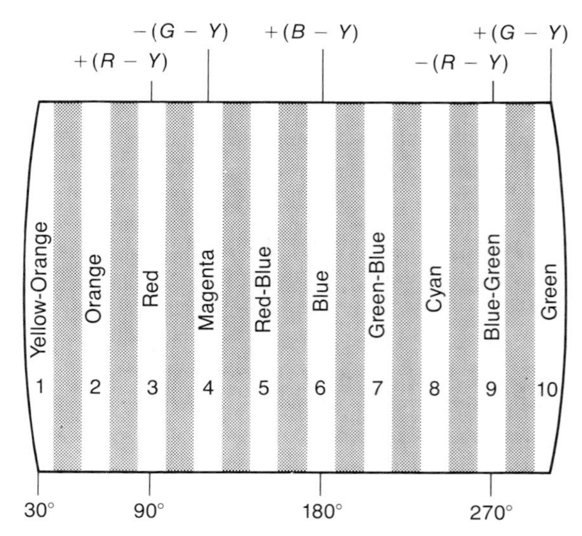

Fig. 16-19 Hues for bars of gated rainbow signal. Colors shown in color plate X.

The generator has gating pulses that cut off the signal output every 30° of the cycle. As a result, the generator output is divided into 360°/30° = 12 bars with different hues. Between each color bar is a black bar, which represents a low-level *Y* signal for luminance.

Of the 12 color bars, two are blanked out during horizontal blanking time, including *H* sync and color burst. So 10 color bars are visible. Sometimes fewer bars are seen when the TV receiver has too much horizontal overscan.

The 12 gated color signals provide a very useful pattern for testing. Since the 360° of hue phase is divided into 12 parts, the centers for each of the bars are exactly 30° apart. The bars are identified on the vector diagram of Fig. 16-20. Although the first bar is not visible, it is used as a color burst for the TV receiver. If we count clockwise in 30° steps, the third visible bar has the phase of the $+(R - Y)$ signal. Count three more bars to the sixth visible bar for the $+(B - Y)$ signal. The ninth bar is $-(R - Y)$. Also, $G - Y$ is close enough to the phase angle of the tenth bar. All the bars and their phase angles are listed in Table 16-1.

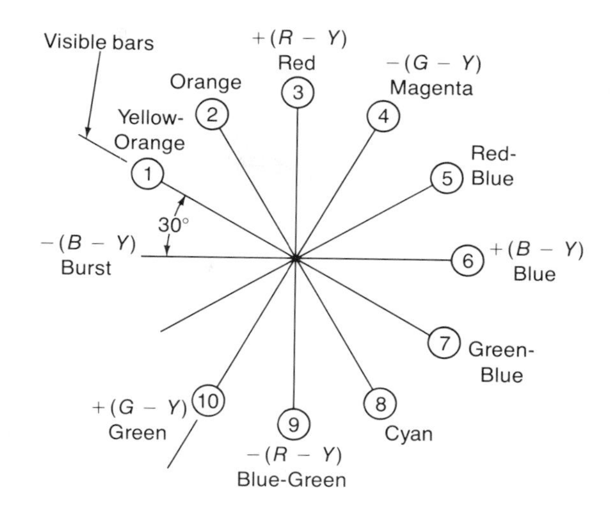

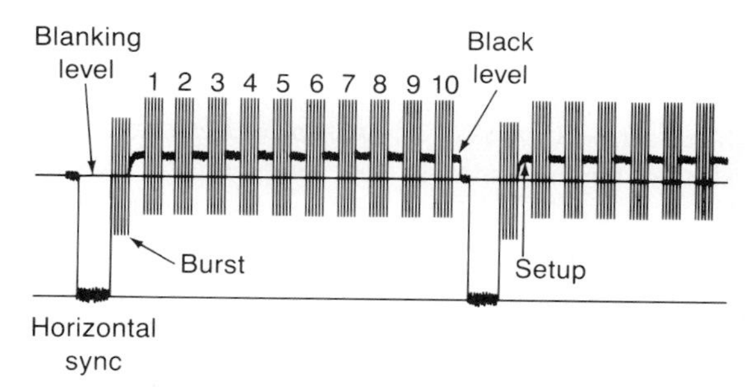

Fig. 16-20 Counting bars in the gated rainbow signal, 30° apart in phase. First bar at left is yellow-orange 30° clockwise from burst phase. The angles are listed in Table 16-1.

Test Point Questions 16-5

Answers at End of Chapter

Answer True or False.

a. The NTSC color-bar generator produces standard chroma and luminance values.

b. The color bars in a gated rainbow pattern differ in hue phase by 90°.

c. In Fig. 16-20, the third color bar is $R - Y$.

16-6 APPLICATIONS OF THE GATED RAINBOW SIGNAL

This signal can be used the following ways:

1. For signal tracing in the color circuits
2. As a visual check of proper hue, or tint
3. To check the range of the tint control
4. To check hues of the color demodulator output

In addition, the low-level luminance signal for the black bars produces voltage spikes that can be used to check the delay of luminance with respect to chrominance. The signal generator provides modulated RF output, on channel 3 or 4, to be connected to the antenna terminals of the TV receiver or video signal.

TINT-CONTROL RANGE The range can be judged by observing how may bars a particular

TABLE 16-1
COLOR BARS IN GATED RAINBOW PATTERN

ANGLE*	BAR	HUE	NOTES
0°	None	Yellow-green	Used as burst signal. Bar is blanked.
30°	1	Yellow-orange	First bar at left
60°	2	Orange	Phase of I
90°	3	Red	Phase of $R - Y$
120°	4	Magenta	Phase of $-(G - Y)$
150°	5	Red-blue	Phase of Q
180°	6	Blue	Phase of $B - Y$
210°	7	Green-blue	Complement of first bar
240°	8	Cyan	Phase of $-I$
270°	9	Blue-green	Phase of $-(R - Y)$
300°	10	Green	Phase of $G - Y$
330°	None	Yellow-green	Phase of $-Q$. Bar is blanked. H sync interval.

* Phase angles are clockwise from burst.

hue can be moved. For example, the fourth bar should be magenta. If that hue can be moved one bar to the left and one bar to the right, by rotating the tint control, then its range is ±30°. The required range is usually specified in the service notes.

CHECKING THE COLOR DEMODULATORS

These tests are useful for setting the tint or master phase adjustment and the phase shift for those demodulators not fed directly from the subcarrier oscillator. The method is illustrated by the three oscilloscope waveforms in Fig. 16-21.

In Fig. 16-21*a*, the waveform shows typical output from a $B - Y$ demodulator. Note that the sixth bar is maximum for the $B - Y$ phase. However, a more definite indication is that the third bar for $R - Y$ and ninth bar for $-(R - Y)$ are at zero amplitude. In this waveform the output is maximum for $B - Y$ phase and minimum for the quadrature hues. There is no maximum for the complementary hue of yellow-green because this bar is blanked out.

For $R - Y$ output in Fig. 16-21*b*, the $R - Y$ waveform has a positive peak at the third bar for $R - Y$ and a negative peak at the ninth bar for its complementary hue of $-(R - Y)$. The sixth bar for the $B - Y$ phase goes to zero, since this angle is in quadrature with the $R - Y$ axis.

For $G - Y$ output in Fig. 16-21*c*, the waveform has a positive peak at the tenth bar for $G - Y$ and a negative peak at the fourth bar for its complementary hue of magenta. There are two points at zero amplitude in this case, at the first and seventh bars for opposite quadrature hues.

Note the difference in level for the demodulator output signals in Fig. 16-21*a*, *b*, and *c*. The reason is that the gated rainbow generator produces all the signals at the same amplitude. However, the broadcast signal reduces $B - Y$ by a factor of 0.495 and $R - Y$ by 0.877. The gain values for the demodulated color signals are boosted at the receiver to restore their correct relative amplitudes. The $B - Y$ signal needs the most boost, $G - Y$ the least, and $R - Y$ is between. These differences in gain correspond to the different amplitudes for Fig. 16-21*a*, *b*, and *c*.

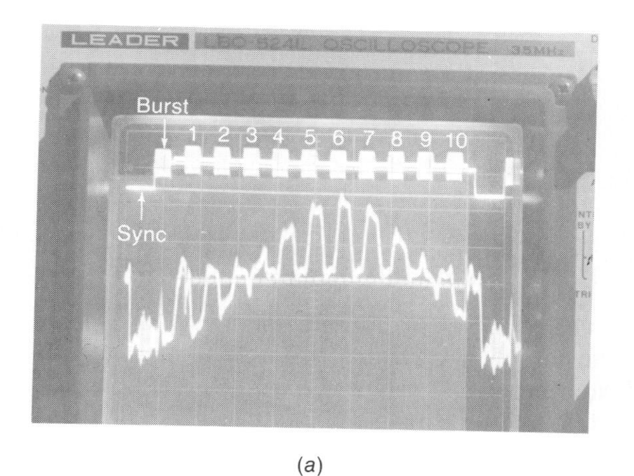

(a)

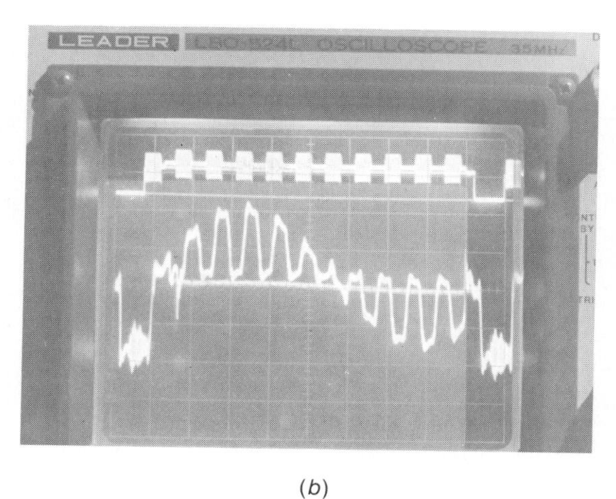

(b)

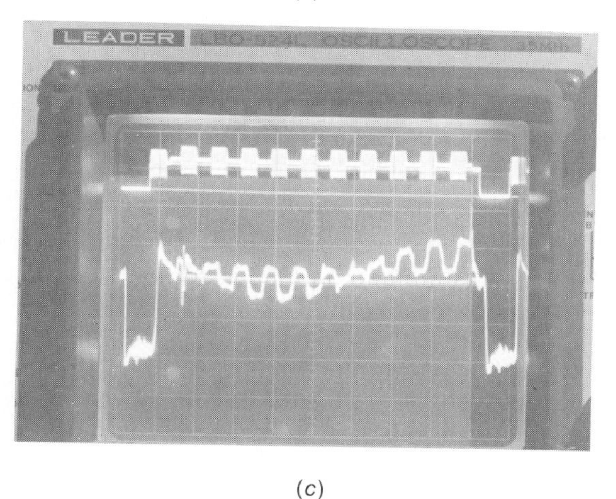

(c)

Fig. 16-21 Using the gated rainbow signal to check color demodulators. (*a*) $B - Y$ output. Note third and ninth bars at zero for quadrature hues. (*b*) The $R - Y$ output. Note sixth bar at zero. (*c*) The $G - Y$ output. Note first and seventh bars at zero.

For practical applications in the TV receiver, the relative gain values also are modified to avoid poor flesh tones which can occur when there is an error in burst phase owing to signal processing in network distribution. You can do a crude test of the correct relative amplitudes while looking at the gated rainbow display. Turn down the brightness control gradually. The green bars should disappear first, followed by red, leaving the blue bars.

Furthermore, the variation in relative gain between color channels accounts for the fact that color noise, or confetti, appears mainly as magenta. This hue combines blue and red, which have more gain than green.

VECTORSCOPE DISPLAY An oscilloscope can be set up as a vectorscope by using $X - Y$ operation, without the internal sweep. The gain must be identical in the Y direction for vertical deflection and X direction for horizontal scanning. The demodulated $B - Y$ signal from the receiver is applied to the horizontal deflection terminals of the oscilloscope and the $R - Y$ signal to the

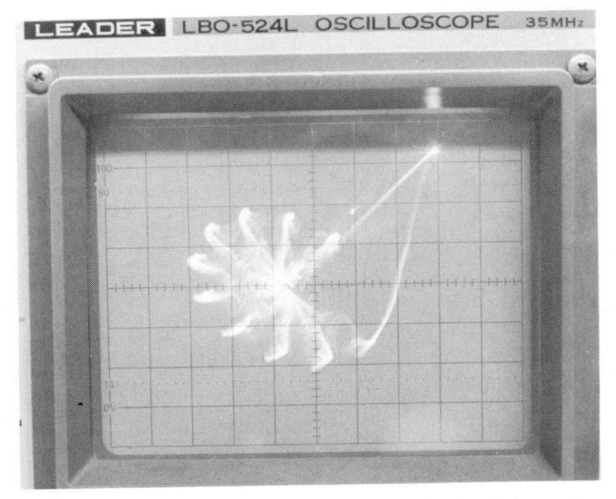

Fig. 16-22 Vectorscope display of gated rainbow signal, obtained with $B - Y$ signal for vertical axis of oscilloscope and $R - Y$ for horizontal axis.

vertical input. A typical display is shown in Fig. 16-22. The bars of the gated rainbow signal look like petals of a flower. In some cases, the service notes specify phase and gain values based on such a vectorscope display.

Keep in mind that negative color-difference signals appear at the cathodes of the picture tube. When these are used for the display, the direction is down on the screen of the oscilloscope for the $-(R - Y)$ signal applied to the vertical input terminals. Also, the $-(B - Y)$ signal is to the right on the display. If the generator being used also produces the luminance signal as white pedestals, this signal should be killed to avoid confusion with the color signals.

Test Point Questions 16-6

Answers at End of Chapter

a. How much is the range of the tint control when it can move a color one bar to the left and right?

b. Does Fig. 16-20*a, b,* or *c* show the output of the $R - Y$ demodulator?

c. Which color-difference signal has the same phase as the burst?

d. Which color bar has maximum output from a $B - Y$ demodulator?

16-7 TV RECEIVER SERVICING

The problems of no raster and no sound point to failure of a section that is common to both the raster and sound circuits. The first suspect is the power supply. However, keep in mind that the power supply is not a single unit in modern receivers. Often scanning-voltage supplies are used for different values of dc supply voltage. As shown before in Fig. 13-9, the main rectifier for the ac line supplies dc output to the horizontal deflection system only. Then the horizontal output stage supplies the pulse drive to several rectifiers. Therefore, a completely dead receiver also can be caused by failure in the horizontal output, driver, and oscillator stages.

Some basic observations can help to localize the problem. First, when a color receiver is switched on from a cold start, the automatic degaussing coils are activated for a fraction of a second. You can hear a transient mechanical noise caused by steel parts in the receiver that vibrate in the strong ac magnetic field produced by the degaussing coil. This sound tells you that the line cord, on-off switch, RF line filter, and the fuses or circuit breakers are all intact in the ac power input circuit. For a receiver with a lighted indicator for the channel number, check whether it goes on. If the vibration sound cannot be detected and the channel indicator light is not on, check the ac input circuit.

The next sound to notice is a slight rustling noise caused by high voltage coming up on the picture tube. This effect is caused by voltage stress on the picture tube and the insulating components. The sound is faint and may not be detected, but it is common in large-screen color receivers that use 25 to 30 kV for the anode voltage. As another effect of high voltage, you can feel the hair rise on your hand close to the screen. Either effect is a quick indicator of high voltage, even though you do not see a picture.

The presence of high voltage means that the main low-voltage power supply is operating for the horizontal deflection circuits that produce the flyback high voltage. Then the loss of raster and sound could be a problem that affects the audio signal and the auxiliary dc voltages for the picture tube. Check the scanning-voltage supplies.

KICK-START SYSTEM In many cases, the dc supply voltage for the horizontal oscillator-driver circuit is derived from a scanning rectifier in the horizontal output circuit. This is a closed-loop system, since the oscillator cannot function without the scanning voltage, which needs the oscillator for horizontal drive. However, the circuit uses a kick-start capacitor, marked C_1 in Fig. 16-23.

SUBSTITUTE POWER SUPPLY Kick-start systems can be complicated for servicing because of the feedback in the horizontal deflection circuit. In addition, many receivers use switching-mode regulators in the main power supply. The switching drive also comes from the horizontal deflection system. To avoid these closed-loop problems, it is often advantageous to check the horizontal oscillator and drive circuits by using an externally applied low-voltage source from a bench-type power supply. Figure 16-23 shows such a supply applied to the 18-V bus for the horizontal oscillator and driver stages. A bus is a line common to two or more connections. The receiver is operated "cold," without any power, except for the substituted supply voltage. This technique can be used with transistors and integrated circuits because there are no heaters to warm up, as in vacuum tubes. The power supply for this testing should be able to supply 12 to 30 V, up to 2 A, all dc ratings.

DC SUPPLY VOLTAGE IS TOO LOW The first symptom of low output from the main power supply is insufficient deflection, both vertically and horizontally. Black borders appear around the raster, as shown in Fig. 16-24, because of the small size of the scanning raster.

Receivers generally use a regulator in the main power supply to set the dc supply voltage at the value that will allow the picture to fill the screen

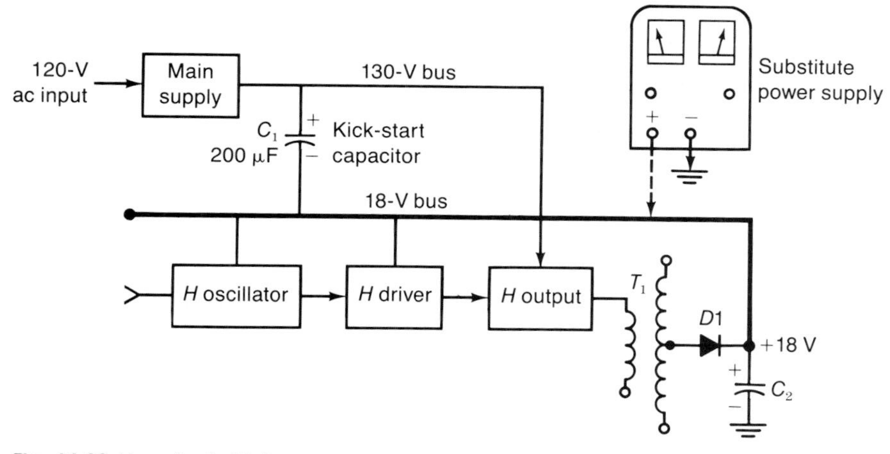

Fig. 16-23 Use of substitute power supply for troubleshooting kick-start systems.

Fig. 16-24 Small raster and picture caused by low value of dc supply voltage.

with a little overscan. However, a defective regulator or misadjustment can result in a small raster.

Test Point Questions 16-7

Answers at End of Chapter

Answer True or False.

a. The trouble in Fig. 16-24 could be caused by low output from the main power supply.
b. No horizontal output can kill the sound.
c. The kick-start capacitor in Fig. 16-23 is needed to operate the substitute bench supply shown.
d. A receiver with current in the ADG coils has ac power input.

16-8 POWER SUPPLY RIPPLE

Insufficient filtering in the dc output of the main power supply can cause interference in the picture. Typical effects are shown in Fig. 16-25.

HUM BARS When the video signal drive to the picture tube is modulated by ripple, horizontal

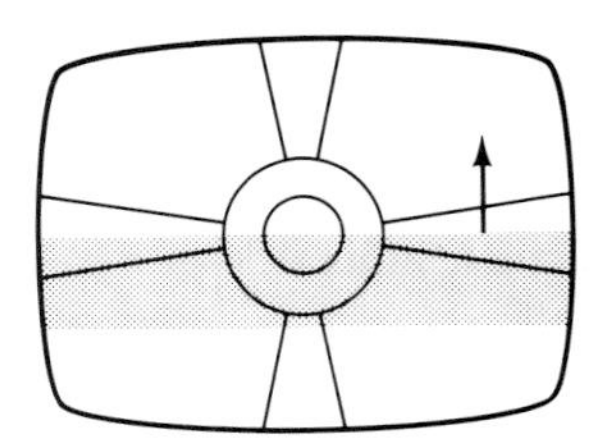

(*a*) 60-Hz ripple in video

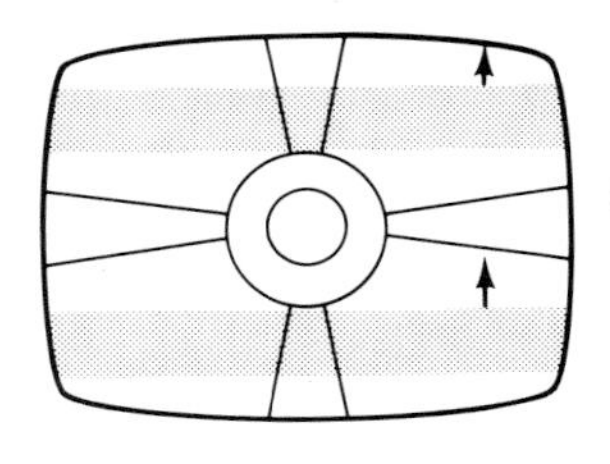

(*b*) 120-Hz ripple in video

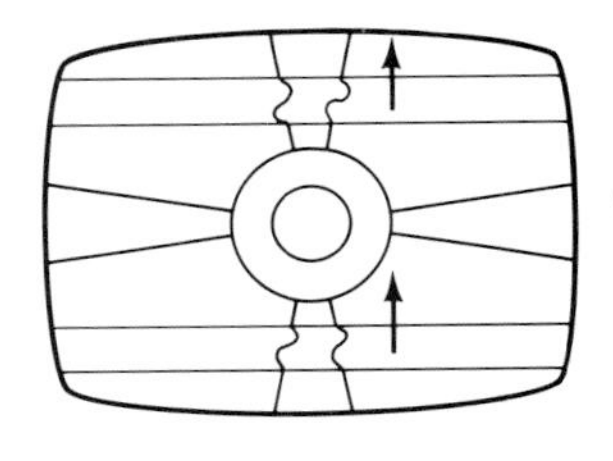

(*c*) 120-Hz ripple in sync

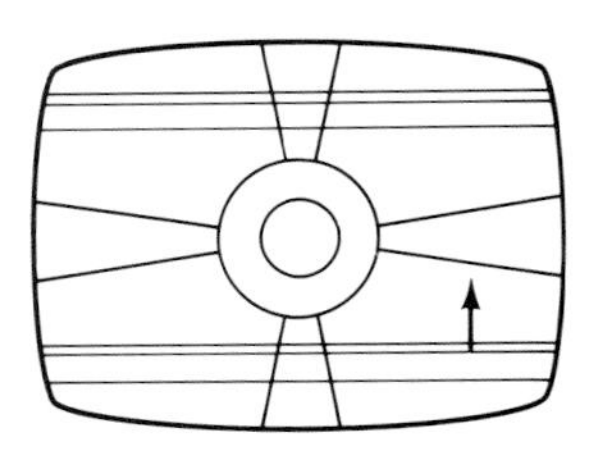

(*d*) 120-Hz radiated current transient from rectifier diodes

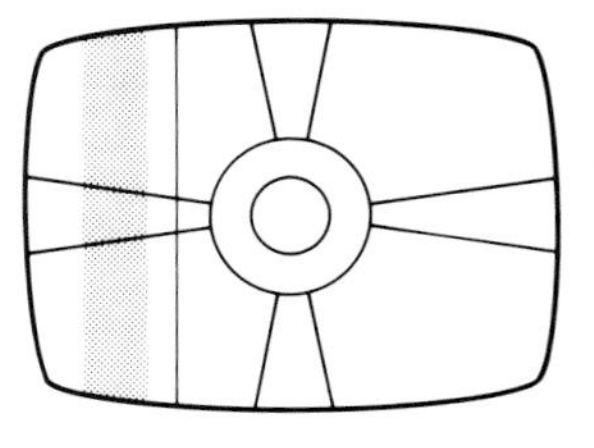

(*e*) 15,734-Hz ripple from switching-mode power supply

Fig. 16-25 Symptoms of interference in the picture from ac ripple in power supply. Arrows indicate motion of hum bars.

bars appear in the picture. For 60-Hz ripple from a half-wave rectifier, one bar is produced, as in Fig. 16-25*a*. Most receivers have full-wave rectifiers, though, which produce 120-Hz ripple. This interference produces two hum bars, as in Fig. 16-25*b*.

The horizontal hum bars vary in dark and light intensity as they drift slowly upward through the picture. The drift results from the fact that the power-line frequency is 60 Hz while the vertical scanning frequency is 59.94 Hz for color television.

HUM BEND When the horizontal sync or deflection is modulated by ripple, the picture has bends, or waves, that appear in horizontal bands across the screen, as shown in Fig. 16-25*c*. The bend also drifts slowly upward.

RADIATION OF TRANSIENTS FROM DIODE RECTIFIERS A problem common to silicon-diode power supplies is the radiation of very high order harmonics of the ripple frequency. The diodes are peak rectifiers. The rectifier conducts in a short burst just long enough to replenish the charge on the filter capacitors. The peak charging current is very high, to sustain the average drain of load current from the supply. Such pulses of current often produce faint but sharply defined horizontal lines that drift upward in the picture. See Fig. 16-25*d*. This interference often gets into the signal circuits by radiation from wiring in the power supply. Harmonic frequencies extend well into the VHF range. A clue that this is the problem is that the bars are stronger in the low-band VHF channels and may not appear at all in the higher channels.

A common cause of this problem is a missing or open bypass capacitor often found in parallel with each diode rectifier in the power supply. Each capacitor is typically 0.001 μF.

SWITCHING-MODE REGULATOR This type of power supply has an entirely different form of ripple interference, as shown in Fig. 16-25*e*. The ripple appears as dark vertical bands or faint vertical lines. They stay still because the switching rate is synchronous with the horizontal scanning frequency. The interfering signal often is picked up in the antenna or IF section by radiation from the power supply wiring.

Test Point Questions 16-8

Answers at End of Chapter

Answer True or False.

a. Two pairs of horizontal bars are produced by 120-Hz ripple in the video signal.

b. Hum in the sync can cause bend in the picture.

c. The ripple interference from a switching-mode regulator is usually 60 Hz, as shown in Fig. 16-25*e*.

16-9 HIGH-VOLTAGE TROUBLES

Failure of the high voltage is a common problem due to dielectric stress in the components and the possibility of arcing. Loss of high voltage is the first trouble to suspect when there is no brightness and no raster. Check for the presence of high voltage (HV) at the anode connector on the picture tube. Use a high-voltage probe, as shown in Fig. 16-11. Make sure that the ground lead of the meter is connected to the chassis first. Then slip the HV probe under the rubber or plastic cap on the anode connector to contact the metal spring clip.

HIGH-VOLTAGE LOADING Complete absence of high voltage usually points to a failure in the horizontal output section, including the HV rectifier. However, a relatively low value of about 2 kV also will fail to produce a raster. The lower voltage results from excessive load current on the HV supply. Remember that the load is the beam current in the picture tube. One possibility is a problem that makes the control grid $G1$ positive with respect to the cathode, which produces excessive beam current. Another possible cause is loss of vacuum in the picture tube. Ionized gas makes the picture tube act as a low-resistance load on the high-voltage supply.

To isolate this type of trouble, measure the high voltage without the picture tube, by disconnecting the anode clip lead:

1. Turn off the set.
2. Discharge the high-voltage connector with a screwdriver whose shaft has been grounded to chassis with a clip lead. Hold the screwdriver by its plastic handle.
3. Disconnect the anode connector by prying off the spring clip. Keep the anode lead and connector away from any metal part of the chassis.
4. Turn on the set, and measure the high voltage at the metal clip.

If the high voltage is normal now, then the horizontal output circuit and HV rectifier must be normal. The trouble is in the picture tube or the video drive circuits, causing excessive beam current as a load on the high-voltage supply.

CHECKING THE HV SUPPLY For the opposite case, the absence of high voltage with the supply unloaded means the trouble is in the HV rectifier circuit, including its ac input from the horizontal amplifier. Check for the presence of horizontal drive at the base or gate input terminal of the horizontal output stage. It can be a power transistor or silicon-controlled rectifier (SCR). If there is no drive, check the horizontal oscillator and driver stages.

If the horizontal output stage has drive at the input, check for flyback pulses in the output at the collector or anode terminal. Note that the flyback pulse here is in the order of kilovolts for large-screen color sets. The 10:1 probe of the oscilloscope is not enough to prevent excessive voltage at the input terminal. The HV probe can be used with the oscilloscope, but the calibration is meaningless. Also, the waveform will not look normal because the oscilloscope frequency compensation is not correct for the HV probe. Still, you can see whether there is output from the horizontal output stage.

The presence of flyback pulses at the output of the horizontal amplifier and the input to the HV rectifier, with no HV dc output, localizes the trouble to the rectifier block itself. In modern receivers, the HV supply uses silicon rectifiers, as either a single-diode unit or a combination of diodes in a voltage multiplier circuit. The multiplier is often a tripler circuit in one unit with the required capacitors, as shown in Fig. 16-26.

High-voltage rectifiers cannot be checked with an ohmmeter because they consist of several internal diodes in series. The internal battery of the ohmmeter cannot supply forward bias for the entire rectifier stack. So the most reliable method is to check the high-voltage rectifier by substitution of another unit.

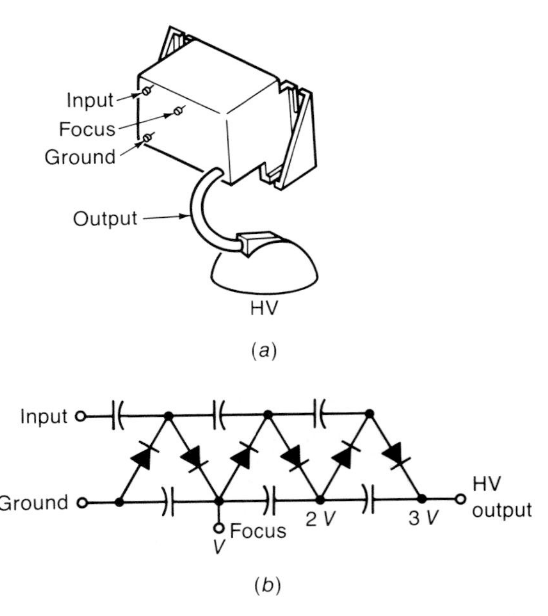

Fig. 16-26 Voltage tripler unit for high-voltage rectifier. Width is 3 in. [76.2 mm]. (*General Instruments*)

LOW ANODE VOLTAGE Besides less brightness, a drop in high voltage has two effects:

1. Poor focus.
2. The raster becomes bigger.

The increase in raster size occurs because the deflection system is working on an electron beam that has lost forward velocity with less accelerating voltage. We can consider the anode potential as providing a stiffening effect on the electron beam.

POOR HIGH-VOLTAGE REGULATION This problem shows up as a drop in anode voltage when the beam current increases. So as the brightness control is advanced, the picture grows in size while the focus becomes poorer. This effect is called *blooming*. The cause is often a faulty capacitor in the horizontal flyback circuit. Generally the horizontal output circuit is tuned to a harmonic of the horizontal scanning frequency for maximum efficiency. A change in the tuning components can affect the conduction angle of the high-voltage rectifier, causing a drop in the average output current.

CLUES TO HV TROUBLES Quite often, the problem can be localized if the viewer can describe the symptoms at the instant of failure. If the picture bloomed in size before the screen went black, the failure is probably in the rectifier block. The reason for temporary blooming is that the anode capacitance of the picture tube maintains some high voltage for a short time.

If the raster collapsed into a single vertical line for an instant just before the screen became blank, the failure is probably in the horizontal deflection and flyback circuits. In this case, the stored high voltage in the anode capacitance of the picture tube allows just enough time to see the real trouble of no *H* deflection before the screen goes black.

Test Point Questions 16-9

Answers at End of Chapter

a. If the anode potential drops a few kilovolts, will the raster be bigger or smaller?
b. Can a gassy picture tube make the anode voltage too high or too low?
c. Does blooming in the picture indicate poor HV regulation or excessive anode voltage?
d. Should the grounded clip lead be connected first or last in order to discharge the high voltage?
e. The picture shows a thin vertical line before the screen goes black. Is the trouble in the horizontal oscillator or the HV rectifier stack?

16-10 HIGH-VOLTAGE HOLD-DOWN CIRCUITS

To comply with regulations of the Department of Health, Education, and Welfare (HEW), television receivers operating with an anode voltage above 15 kV for the picture tube must be protected against circuit failures that act to raise the high voltage to values that might result in x-ray emission. An example is a short-circuited series-pass regulator in the main power supply. Such a failure can dramatically increase the dc supply voltage to the horizontal output stage, causing excessive high voltage. Certification of the equipment requires that checks of simulated key failures be made when the ac line is 130 V rms and all controls are set for maximum radiation.

To comply with the HEW rules, the high voltage must be killed or the picture made unintelligible during the failure. Automatic hold-down circuits are used for this purpose. The circuit must detect an abnormal rise in high voltage and then either reduce the voltage or spoil the picture so that the viewer will turn off the set. Common methods either kill the horizontal oscillator or increase its frequency considerably. This has two results: it kills both the picture and the high voltage or produces an out-of-sync condition that also limits the high voltage.

A basic hold-down circuit is illustrated in Fig. 16-27. The automatic hold-down is actually accomplished with low voltage, through one of the scanning rectifier power supplies in the horizontal output circuit. Note that $D2$ provides 18 V across C_4 for the 18-V bus. This positive voltage is applied to the cathode of the zener diode $D1$, in series with R_3 to the gate electrode of the SCR. Remember that a zener diode works with reverse voltage, which is positive at the cathode. Normally, $D1$ does not conduct. Then the SCR gate electrode is below the break-over voltage of the SCR. However, if the 18-V line rises in potential, because of more horizontal output, $D1$ can conduct to make the SCR gate positive. Then the SCR fires to conduct forward current. Anode voltage for the SCR is connected through R_1 from the 120-V supply. The conducting SCR is effectively a very low resistance that short-circuits the horizontal drive from the oscillator stage. After it is triggered, the SCR remains on to disable the horizontal deflection and high voltage. The only way to stop conduction in the SCR is to remove the anode voltage, by turning off the set.

A number of different systems are used for the automatic hold-down. Keep in mind, however, that the hold-down circuit itself can cause a loss of high voltage. For this reason, it may be necessary to disable the hold-down circuit when you troubleshoot the problem of no high voltage. For example, for the circuit in Fig. 16-27, remove the SCR.

All hold-down circuitry must be replaced and checked according to the manufacturer's specifications. Otherwise, the set is a hazard for emission of x-rays.

Test Point Questions 16-10

Answers at End of Chapter

Answer True or False for Fig. 16-27.

a. Transformer T_1 is the horizontal output transformer.

b. Normally the SCR is off.

c. Conduction in the SCR kills the high voltage.

16-11 VCR SERVICING

Test instruments for the video cassette recorder are similar to those used in TV servicing. The oscilloscope, bandwidth, and sensitivity requirements are the same. However, a dual-trace, delayed-sweep oscilloscope is especially useful for checking the head switching. One addition is a digital frequency counter. It should also count the period $T = 1/f$. This feature is useful for determining the exact free-running frequency of

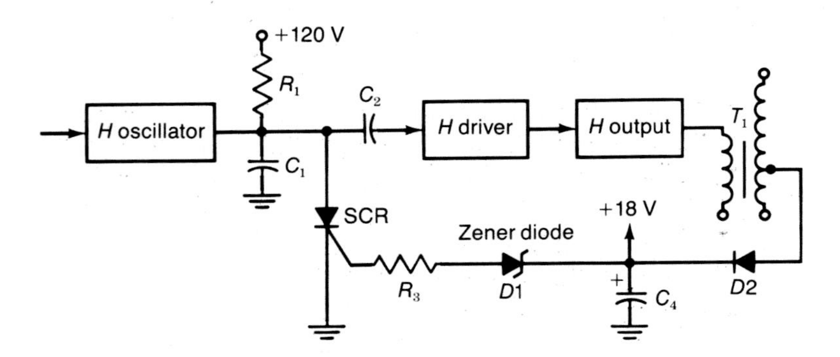

Fig. 16-27 Hold-down circuit kills horizontal drive if flyback high voltage rises above the limit.

the rotary scanner and capstan motors. (The operation of video cassette recorders is explained in Chap. 10.)

MECHANICAL JIGS AND FIXTURES The VCR is a precision machine. Therefore, a number of precise fixtures are provided by the manufacturer for special mechanical checks and adjustments. Figure 16-28 shows a typical setup. The fixtures provide references for the reel table height and the movable guidepost positions, such as the tape back-tension guide. The reel table height is critical because the reels must be lifted inside the cassette and clear the cassette floor. Also, the altitude at which the tape leaves the cassette affects the precision of the tape path.

ALIGNMENT TAPE Included in the fixture set is an alignment cassette. This cassette is the keystone of VCR service. It contains a number of video and audio recordings to permit correct adjustments for the following:

Video head switching (an important adjustment to allow interchange of tapes between machines)

Playback video level

Playback chroma

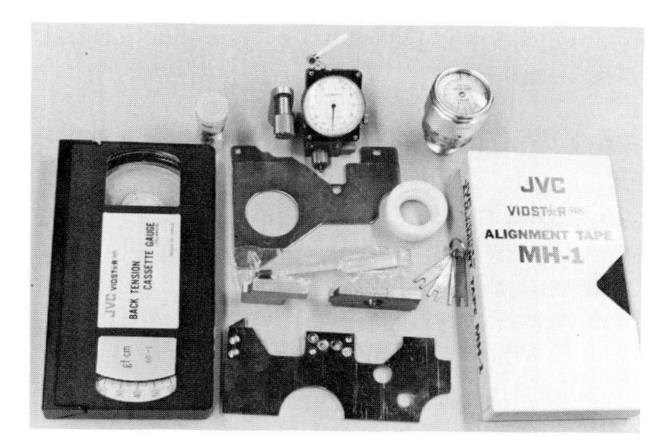

Fig. 16-28 Mechanical fixtures used in maintenance of VCR machines.

In addition, a recorded video sweep signal permits frequency-response adjustments for the playback preamplifier.

Of particular importance is adjustment of trimmer capacitors at the input to the preamplifier. These capacitors resonate with the inductance of the video head, at the high-frequency end of the band for the FM luminance signal. Any replacement of a video head requires alignment of the preamplifier, by using the video sweep signal. Also, the video head-switching adjustment is made by using a monoscope or the stair-step test signal.

The alignment cassettes should be stored in a cool, dry place. Use them sparingly, for their performance deteriorates slightly with each head pass.

It is a good idea to have at least one "work cassette," for general work, that was made on a machine known to be in proper adjustment. Otherwise, you might be using the expensive alignment cassette to work on a machine that wrinkles or damages the tape.

Keep in mind that alignment tapes are recorded on machines kept in the center of very precise mechanical and electrical specifications. It makes no sense at all to rely on the accuracy of an alignment tape that has been copied, since the faults of the machine making the copy will be transferred to the duplicate tape.

SYSTEM-CONTROL TROUBLES The system control makes the decisions that govern the tape threading and operating modes. A digital microprocessor is used. Computer techniques allow the viewer to choose between operating modes without first going to the STOP position, as was necessary in earlier machines.

The microprocessor is usually a 40-pin plug-in unit. Troubleshooting is mainly a question of checking the signal inputs and control outputs. The inputs to the system include the operator pushbuttons, the cassette-in switch that senses the presence of the cassette loaded into the machine, and the microswitches that sense completion of tape threading and unthreading cycles. In addition, sensors detect the end of the tape to trigger automatic stop and rewind cycles. These sensors use a magnetic-foil leader on the tape for Betamax machines or a clear, transparent leader on VHS tape. The clear leader is sensed by means of a light source and phototransistor at the supply and takeup sides of the cassette.

Other sensors detect conditions that can cause tape damage and trigger the automatic stop. An example is failure of the takeup reel to accumulate tape. This trouble can lead to a machine filled with loose tape, which is very discouraging. Some machines detect loose tape by microswitch sensors that indicate any slack in the tape path. Others use sensors that detect rotation of the takeup reel table.

Another source of tape damage is moisture condensation on the surface of the video scanner. Moisture increases the scanner-to-tape friction to the point that actually can cause the scanner to stall. Two systems are used to detect this condition. One method uses a moisture detector to trigger an automatic stop if condensation has occurred. In the second method, a head-switching signal generated by the rotating scanner is used to indicate that the scanner is spinning. Loss of this signal, a 30-Hz square wave, triggers an automatic stop. For both systems, check all these sensors when you are troubleshooting a machine that stays in the stop mode.

RECORD-PLAYBACK CHECKS The VCR has separate circuits for recording and playback. Therefore, a machine that produces abnormal playback symptoms with its own recording but plays back normally a prerecorded tape known to be good has trouble in its recording system. Also, a machine that plays back all tapes abnormally but whose recordings play normally on other machines has trouble in its playback system.

In general, the VCR plays back its own recording best. The reason is that any small errors in the tape path cancel in playback and recording. Interchange of tapes between machines requires an absolute minimum of error in the tape path. The model for adjustments must be the manufacturer's alignment tape and no other source. Any mechanical alignment should be avoided unless it has been determined that mechanical damage or tinkering is the cause of the problem.

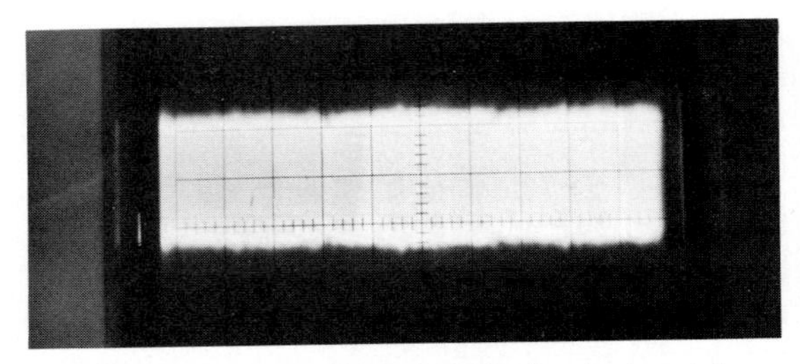

Fig. 16-29 Envelope of RF, FM playback signal for a VHS machine. Tracking is correct when signal is at peak amplitude and flat for each video head pass.

VCRs are aligned by using the alignment tape and monitoring the FM envelope produced by the preamplifiers. A typical oscilloscope waveform is shown in Fig. 16-29. Adjust for the signal that has maximum amplitude and is flat for each video head pass. Two critical factors in the adjustments are:

1. Position of the entrance-exit guide poles
2. Position of the audio and control-head stack along the tape path between the scanner and the capstan

COLOR TROUBLES The VCR does not encode and decode color. It simply heterodynes the color-signal frequencies from around 3.58 MHz down to around 629 kHz for VHS and 688 kHz for Betamax. The purpose is to move the color frequencies away from the frequencies used in recording the FM luminance signal. In playback, the color frequencies are heterodyned back up to their original values around 3.58 MHz. Troubleshooting is mainly a procedure of tracing the chroma signals through the processing circuits. For each heterodyne converter the two input signals required to produce the difference signal should be checked.

SERVOSYSTEM TROUBLES There are two servosystems. One regulates the speed and timing of the video-head scanner. The other regulates the speed and timing of the capstan motor.

Large errors in scanner speed cause the playback sync rate to change drastically. Then the playback picture breaks into diagonal segments. It looks like a TV picture with a large error in horizontal frequency. (See Fig. 13-10*a.*)

Smaller errors in scanner speed cause bands of noise, called *mistracking noise,* to roll up or down in the picture. The head-switching point also rolls up or down.

For the capstan servo, speed errors can be detected by the pitch of the audio signal as well as the effects in the picture. The visual effect is a rhythmic appearance of noise in the picture or bands of noise that roll up or down. The cause is that the video heads fail to follow their correct tracks. Either head can cross over the tracks made by the other video head.

A key place to check in troubleshooting servosystem problems is the timing comparator in each servosystem. The control circuit is almost always a sample-and-hold gate. In this circuit, a voltage ramp is sampled by a pulse signal. For example, in the scanner servosystem, the ramp is sampled by a feedback pulse generated in the scanner to indicate the start of the pass for reference video head. Both signals—the ramp and the sampling pulse—must be present at the sample-and-hold gate for the system to operate. For example, the oscilloscope waveform in Fig. 16-30 shows the sampling pulse located at the center of the ramp. This position shows that the timing is in the center of the control range. If both the ramp and the sample pulse are present but the servosystem does not lock in, the pulse will move past the ramp continuously. The problem must be after the sample-and-hold gate, in the circuit that controls the motor armature current. Or the motor itself may be defective.

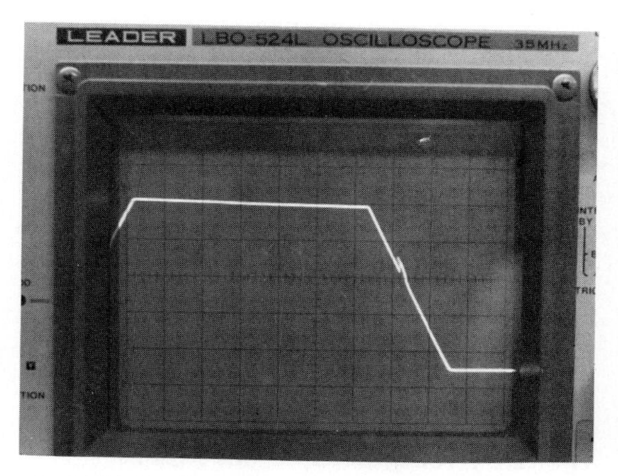

Fig. 16-30 Oscilloscope waveform photograph shows that sample-and-hold gate is a key point in determining any servosystem failure.

Test Point Questions 16-11

Answers at End of Chapter

Answer True or False.

a. An inexpensive way to obtain a good alignment tape is to copy the manufacturer's original.

b. The waveform in Fig. 16-30 is used to check the sample-and-hold gate.

c. A large error in scanner rotational speed makes the picture look as if it were out of horizontal sync.

d. Excessive moisture can trigger the automatic stop in a VCR.

16-12 SERVICING VIDEO CAMERAS

A properly illuminated test pattern and a video monitor are needed to service a video camera. A color TV receiver can be used as a color monitor in conjunction with the connections on a VCR. Connect the camera[1] output to the video

[1] The operation of video cameras is explained in Chap. 3.

input jack of the VCR, and use its RF output on channel 3 or 4 for the TV receiver. The VCR machine is set for playback. In addition, a wideband monochrome monitor is used. It should have an *underscanned* raster so that you can see the edges.

TEST-PATTERN ILLUMINATION The test pattern should be illuminated *uniformly* with studio-type lamps to provide at least 150 fc, or 1500 lux, of white light at a color temperature of 3200 K. Quartz iodide or halogen lamps provide a constant color temperature for the life of the bulb. They are recommended for this reason.

The lamps should be aimed at the test pattern in such a way that no direct reflection can occur to produce "hot spots" in the lighting. A simple monochrome camera is excellent for checking uniform illumination on a blank white or gray card substituted for the test pattern.

IMAGE SIZE Scanning size adjustments for the camera work opposite from the effects you would expect. For example, if the camera scan width is made larger, the picture on the monitor becomes narrower.

The purpose of scanning size adjustments in the camera is to cover the maximum area for the image on the faceplate of the pickup tube. One way to form an optical image of proper size on the target is to use a fixed test setup of specified dimensions, as shown in Fig. 16-31, with the test pattern at the correct distance from the camera. A fixed-focal-length lens is used in this setup. The scanning size is adjusted by using an underscanned monitor so that you can see when the test pattern just fills the raster.

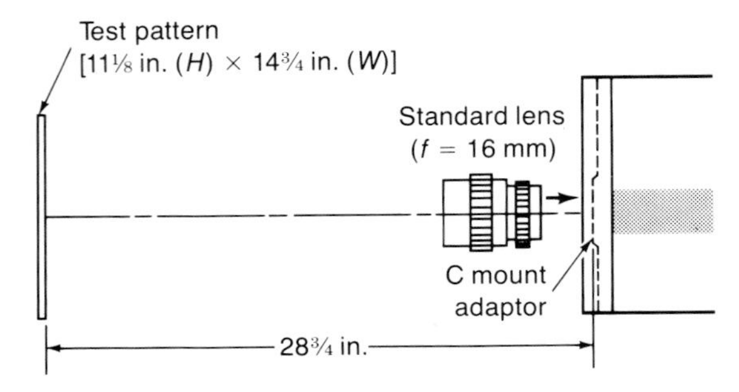

Fig. 16-31 Typical setup with dimensions of a camera test bed.

SINGLE-TUBE COLOR CAMERAS The scanning size and linearity are extremely critical in establishing the color signals. For this reason, the scanning size is not adjusted in the usual way, but is set to produce maximum signal output at the frequency determined by the pitch of the color-dissecting stripes. Each system is a little different, so follow the manufacturer's instructions.

TARGET VOLTAGE The target voltage is set at a specific dc value for the pickup tube. However, vidicons are often set for a specified amount of dark current. The dark current is evaluated in terms of the video signal output obtained with the lens capped.

BEAM CURRENT The grid-cathode bias in the pickup tube determines the beam current. The bias is set to just discharge the target for very bright subjects in the scene. The usual procedure is to increase illumination on the test pattern to a specific value and open the lens iris. Then the beam current is advanced to produce a specified p-p video signal output from the preamplifier. Insufficient beam current causes a low-contrast picture, in which the white areas lack detail. Too much beam current creates space-charge effects near the target, causing geometric distortion of the picture.

FOCUS Cameras have two focus adjustments. One is optical focus for the lens, and the other is the electrical focus for the electron beam in the camera tube. Both must be set in order to get good resolution.

In monochrome cameras, both focus adjustments are made by using a test pattern while observing the picture on a wideband black-and-white monitor. The same idea applies for three-tube color cameras.

However, for a single-tube color camera, the electrical focus has a drastic effect on the color operation. The focus is adjusted for the maximum output signal from the preamplifier at the multiplexer frequency caused by the stripe filter. A large spot size can make it impossible for the electron beam to pick out the fine mesh pattern in the color-stripe filter. Small errors in focus will result in no color, or only green, even though the picture looks reasonably sharp.

IMAGE BURN Care must be taken during camera service so that the test pattern is not burned into the target plate of the pickup tube. The image is steady with high illumination. It is good practice, therefore, to keep the lens cap in place at all times unless you are actually making the adjustments.

COLOR BALANCE A number of adjustments are made so that red, green, and blue are balanced. The balancing is done by pointing the camera at a stair-step reflectance chart, as shown in Fig. 16-32. The chart has reflectance values that vary from black to white with the same variations as light output from a picture tube. Note

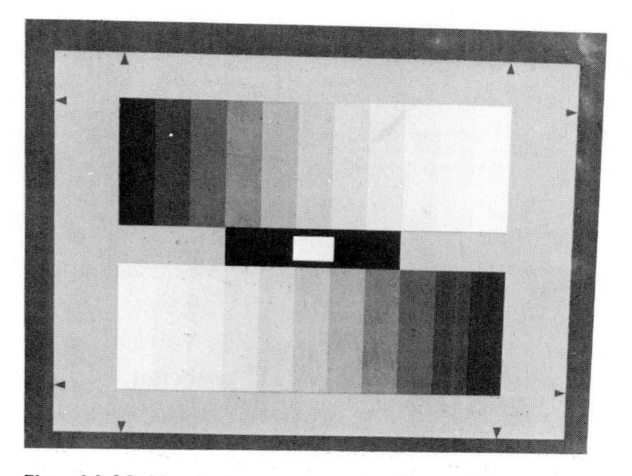

Fig. 16-32 Neutral gamma chart used for adjusting color balance.

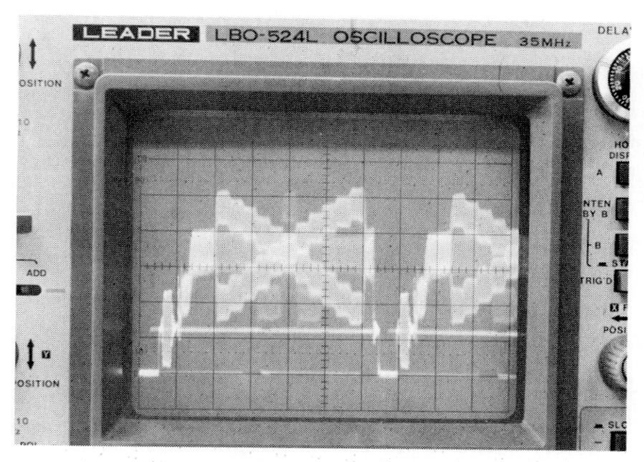

Fig. 16-33 Oscilloscope waveform shows color imbalance in the form of 3.58-MHz subcarrier signal on steps of modulated stair-step signal. At balance, color signal is nulled to zero.

that the chart has no color. All the shades are neutral gray, white, or black.

The balance adjustments are made by first setting up green for the proper amplitude and gamma correction. The red and blue are set to match green at all values from black to white.

In making the adjustments the indicator is the appearance of the 3.58-MHz subcarrier signal on the steps of the gray scale. When red, green, and blue are equal, the color-difference signals go to zero. Then the 3.58-MHz modulators are balanced, and they produce no subcarrier output. As a result, the subcarrier disappears from the steps of the stair-step pattern. This balancing must be matched at all values from black to peak white. The oscilloscope waveform in Fig. 16-33 shows an example of the balance not being perfect. Note the appearance of the 3.58-MHz subcarrier on the steps.

The nonlinear effect of gamma correction requires that intermediate shades of gray be balanced as well. Therefore, the red and blue gamma are adjusted to null out the subcarrier on the middle steps of the pattern.

SIGNAL TRACING An oscilloscope can be used to observe the signal at nearly all points in the camera, from the preamplifier to the video output jack. An exception is the high-gain preamplifier unit itself. Oscilloscope sensitivity is not high enough to allow checking of the signal level at the input to the preamplifier. In addition, often the preamplifier is sealed in a fully shielded compartment. To see whether the preamplifier is working, touch the target ring connector with a metal probe or screwdriver. A normal preamplifier will show a heavy herringbone interference pattern on the monitor, as stray RF signals are amplified by the high-gain preamplifier.

Many cameras now use a single direct-coupled IC chip for the preamplifier. Here, the test is relatively simple. Check for proper dc output voltage at the output. There is no problem inside the preamplifier that would not severely affect the dc output. As a result, an incorrect dc voltage reading at the output points to a defective preamplifier.

TERMINATIONS Keep in mind that the camera output must be terminated in 75 Ω for coaxial cable. The video voltage at the output jack without any terminating load will be approximately twice the standard output of 1 V p-p. Therefore, a 2-V signal at the camera output shows that the output cable is terminated in an open circuit.

Test Point Questions 16-12

Answers at End of Chapter

Answer True or False.

a. In a single-tube color camera, the problem of no color can be caused by poor electrical focus.

b. Balancing red, green, and blue for color cameras is done with a gated rainbow signal generator.

c. Insufficient beam current in a vidicon causes a low-contrast picture.

d. The standard output voltage from a color camera is 3 mV p-p.

16-13 INTERFERENCE PATTERNS

The way in which horizontal and vertical bars are produced on the screen of the picture tube can be illustrated experimentally by using an audio signal generator to supply the video signal. The variable-frequency generator has a range of 20 Hz to 200 kHz. The transmitted signal is not used. Instead, the output of the signal generator is coupled into the video amplifier, where the signal is amplified for the picture tube. As the generator signal varies the grid-cathode voltage of the picture tube, pairs of dark and light bars are formed on the raster. See Fig. 16-34.

Horizontal bars are produced when the frequency of the signal at the picture tube grid is less than 15,750 Hz. Above 15,750 Hz, the bars are vertical or diagonal. Since the sync for the deflection oscillators usually is taken from the video amplifier in the receiver, the generator signal also supplies synchronization. The bars can be locked when the generator frequency is an exact multiple of the scanning frequency. Just vary the signal generator frequency to obtain the desired number of bars, and adjust the hold control on the receiver to make the bars stay still.

HORIZONTAL BARS Suppose that a 60-Hz sine wave signal is varying the control-grid voltage in synchronism with the vertical scanning motion at the 60-Hz field frequency. During the positive half-cycle, the signal makes the grid more positive, increasing the beam current and screen illumination. During the negative half-cycle, the beam current and screen illumination are reduced. Since it takes $\frac{1}{120}$ s for a half-cycle of the 60-Hz signal, the scanning beam moves halfway down the screen during this time. Therefore, if the positive half-cycle of the sine wave signal coincides with the first half of the vertical scan, the top half of the picture will be brighter than the bottom half. Then the pattern on the screen is a pair of horizontal bars, one bright and the other dark.

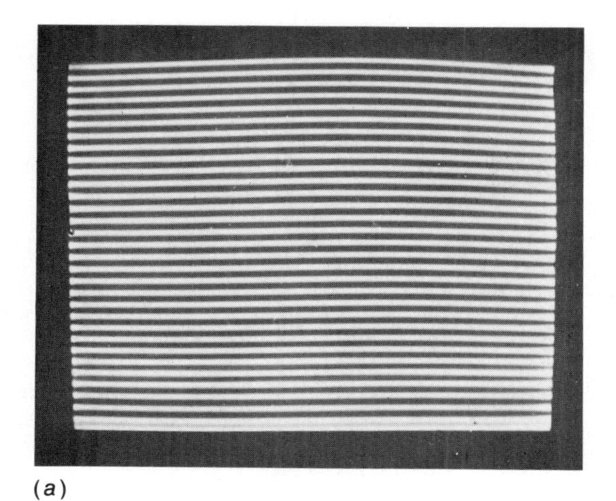

(a)

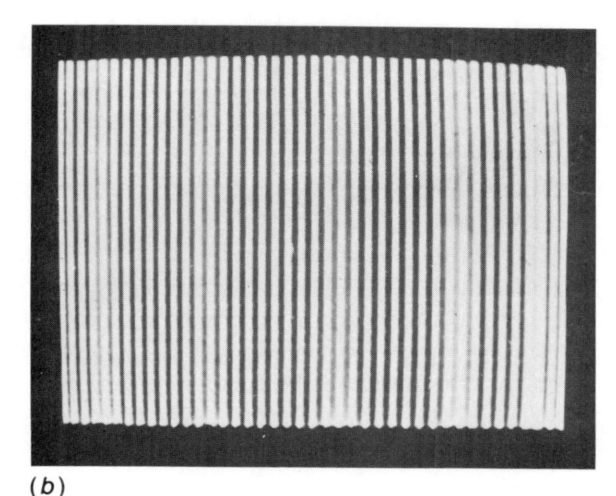

(b)

Fig. 16-34 Bar patterns produced by signal generator. (*a*) Horizontal bars at multiples of 60 Hz when frequency is below approximately 15,750 Hz. (*b*) Vertical bars for higher frequencies at multiples of 15,750 Hz.

When the signal generator output frequency is increased to multiples of 60 Hz, additional pairs of narrower horizontal bars will be formed on the screen, as shown in Fig. 16-34*a*. The number of pairs of bars is equal to the signal generator frequency divided by the vertical scanning frequency. However, also subtract any bars that may be produced during vertical retrace time if the signal frequency is high enough to produce more than about 20 pairs of bars. For example, a 240-Hz frequency results in 240/60 = 4 pairs of horizontal bars.

Vertical scanning linearity is indicated by the spacing between the parallel horizontal bars. If the vertical scanning motion is linear, the bars will be equally spaced. Otherwise, the bars will be spread out or crowded together.

VERTICAL BARS When the frequency of the modulating signal equals the horizontal line-scanning frequency, vertical bars are formed instead of horizontal bars. Consider the case of a 15,750-Hz sine wave signal that varies the grid voltage in phase with the horizontal scanning. During one horizontal line, the screen is made brighter for approximately one-half the picture width, as the positive half-cycle of the grid voltage increases the beam current. During the negative half-cycle, the screen becomes darker. The same effect occurs for succeeding horizontal lines, and the result is a pair of vertical bars on the screen, with one bar white and the other dark. If the frequency of the signal generator is increased to multiples of 15,750 Hz, additional pairs of narrower vertical bars will be produced on the screen, as shown in Fig. 16-34*b*. Their spacing indicates linearity of the horizontal scanning motion.

The number of pairs of vertical bars is equal to the frequency of the applied signal divided by the horizontal scanning frequency. For example, a 157.5-kHz frequency results in 10 pairs of vertical bars. However, not all the bars may be visible. Some are formed during the horizontal retrace time if the signal frequency is high enough to produce more than about 10 pairs of bars. These bars formed during the flyback are wider because of the fast retrace. They appear as variations of shading in the background, as can be seen in Fig. 16-34*b*. It is possible to determine the retrace time by counting the bars visible during the trace time and comparing this value with the total number that should be produced.

DIAGONAL BARS When the signal frequency is higher than, but not an exact multiple of, the horizontal line-scanning frequency, diagonal bars are seen. In this case, the light and dark parts of each line are displaced regularly in successive order at different positions with respect to the start of the trace, instead of lining up one under the other. Usually the diagonal bars do not stay still because the signal frequency is not an exact multiple of the horizontal line-scanning frequency and does not synchronize the deflection oscillator.

An interesting fact is that the bars can be made to disappear when the signal generator is adjusted carefully to certain frequencies—odd multiples of one-half the horizontal line-scanning frequency.

SOUND IN THE PICTURE There are three types of sound interference: horizontal bars from the audio signal, a fine-line pattern from the 4.5-MHz intercarrier sound signal, and a 920-kHz diagonal bar pattern as interference between the 4.5-MHz intercarrier sound and the 3.58-MHz color subcarrier. The 920-kHz beat is the most common form in which the sound signal interferes with the picture.

The 920-kHz beat can be seen in color plate XII. The value of 920 kHz is the frequency difference of 4.5 − 3.58 = 0.92 MHz. With an interfering signal at 920 kHz, the number of bars is 920.000/15.734, or approximately 60.

The audio sound bars are shown in Fig. 16-35. Slope detection can convert the modulation of the FM sound signal to audio voltage in the video detector output even though the diode is an AM detector. Then the audio combines with the video at the grid-cathode circuit of the picture tube. The result is horizontal bars, as seen in Fig. 16-35. The sound bars can be recognized because they vary with the audio

Fig. 16-35 Audio sound bars in the picture. Width and intensity of bars change with audio modulation in associated sound signal.

modulation and disappear when there is no voice or music.

The 4.5-MHz beat is shown in Fig. 16-36. The interference pattern has about 225 pairs of thin black-and-white lines with small wiggles like a herringbone weave. This effect is called a *wormy* picture. The number of pairs of lines is 4.5 MHz/15,750 Hz = 285 approximately. The fine lines are caused by the 4.5-MHz carrier signal, and the herringbone weave is a result of frequency variations in the FM sound signal. When there is no voice or music, the herringbone effect disap-

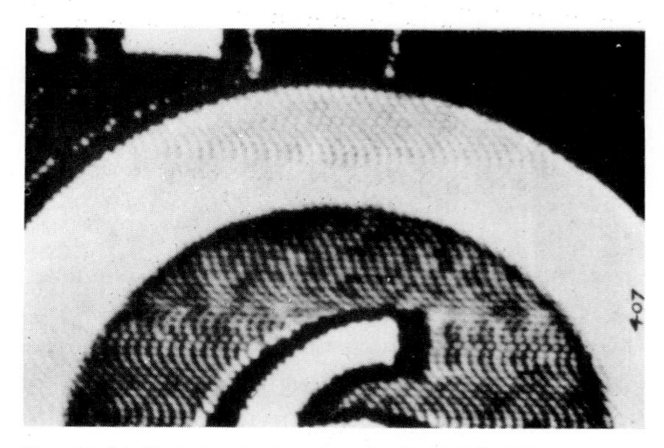

Fig. 16-36 Fine herringbone effect of 4.5-MHz beat in picture, with frequency modulation of sound signal.

pears but the thin lines remain, because they are produced by the sound carrier.

RF INTERFERENCE Frequencies that are not in the TV broadcast band can produce interference in the picture because of heterodyning effects that cause interfering beat frequencies. For example, the RF interference can beat with the local oscillator in the RF tuner to produce frequency differences that are in the IF passband of the receiver. Then the interfering signal beats with the picture carrier in the video detector to produce interference in the video signal. This causes interference in the picture. In addition, adjacent television broadcast channels can cause interference. Also, the interference can have frequencies in the IF band of 40 to 46 MHz.

All these examples are interfering signals external to the receiver. The receiver also can generate its own interference as harmonics of the detected video or sound signals and the horizontal scanning current, which are radiated back to the signal circuits. Typical examples of interference patterns are shown in Fig. 16-37. The uniform diagonal lines in Fig. 16-37*a* are caused by an unmodulated carrier wave (cw). They are of uniform thickness because there is no modulation. Usually the bars shift slowly from one diagonal position, through the vertical, and to the opposite diagonal as the interfering carrier wave drifts in frequency. This type of interference can be caused by local oscillator radiation from a nearby receiver or from any unmodulated cw. The number of bars and their thickness depend on the beat frequency produced by the cw interference. If the beat frequency resulting from the RF interference is less than 15,750 Hz, uniform horizontal bars will be produced, in a venetian-blind effect.

An interfering FM carrier wave produces interfering beats that vary in frequency. With a center frequency high enough to produce a fine-line interference pattern, the frequency modulation adds a herringbone weave to the vertical or diagonal bars. When the beat frequencies are too low for a diagonal line pattern, instead of horizontal bars the FM interference creates a watery effect through the entire picture. Then the picture looks as if it were covered with a silk gauze, as in Fig. 16-37*b*.

Diathermy machines and other medical or industrial equipment usually produce the RF interference pattern shown in Fig. 16-37*c*. There may be two dark bands across the screen instead of the one shown, and the bars will be darker if the interference is stronger. This RF interference pattern is produced because diathermy equip-

(*a*)

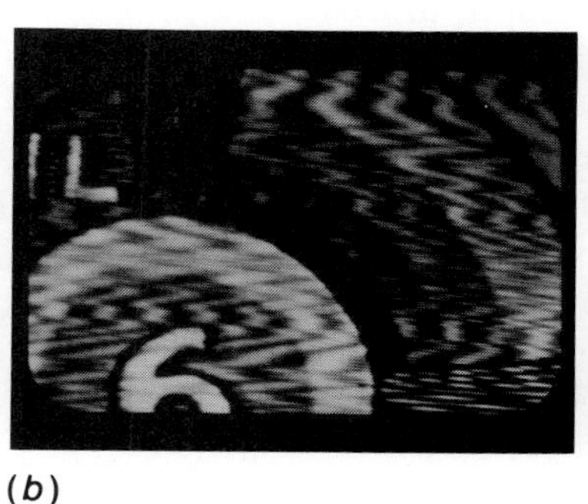

(*b*)

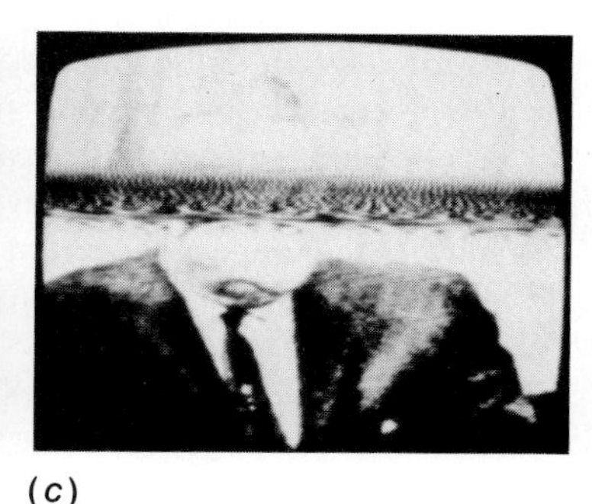

(*c*)

Fig. 16-37 Effects of RF interference. (*a*) Uniform diagonal bars caused by cw interference without any modulation. (*b*) Herringbone weave caused by frequency modulation. (*c*) Diathermy interference.

ment is effectively a transmitter. The weaving effect is caused by frequency variations. The single band shows that there is a strong 60-Hz component in the interference; with 120-Hz modulation, there would be two bands.

In addition to bar patterns in the picture, the light values are altered by the RF interference of sufficient amplitude. So a very strong interfering signal can produce a negative picture or black out the picture completely. The negative picture is a result of detection in an overloaded RF or IF amplifier, with the video signal modulating the picture carrier in reverse polarity.

Test Point Questions 16-13

Answers at End of Chapter

Which figures correspond to the following examples of interference?

a. Video signal at approximately 1800 Hz
b. Video signal at approximately 800 kHz
c. 4.5-MHz beat

16-14 SOURCES FOR SCHEMATIC DIAGRAMS

The manufacturer's service manual is the basic tool for all but the simple and obvious troubles. In the manual are schematic diagrams, instructions for the setup adjustments, including purity and convergence for the color picture tube, and a list of components and their part numbers. The manufacturer also supplies service bulletins and engineering change notices for specific models.

An independent service that provides schematic diagrams of all manufacturers is Howard W. Sams & Co., Inc. These packages of diagrams are sold through electronic parts distributors. In addition, books of schematic diagrams are available from independent publishers.

The following list gives addresses for service information from the manufacturer:

General Electric Co.
Television Division
College Boulevard
Portsmouth, Va. 23705

Heath Company
Benton Harbor, Mich. 49022

Hitachi Sales Corporation of America
401 W. Artesial Boulevard
Compton, Calif. 90220

JVC
41 Slater Drive
Elmwood Park, N.J. 07407

Magnavox
N.A.P. Consumer Electronics Corp.
Jefferson City, Tenn. 37760

Panasonic
Consumer Parts Division
P.O. Box 1457
Secaucus, N.J. 07094

J.C. Penney Co. Inc.
1301 Avenue of the Americas
New York, N.Y. 10019

Philco Television
NAPCEC
P.O. Box 555
Old Andrew Johnson Highway
Jefferson City, Tenn. 37760

Quasar Co.
9401 West Grand Avenue
Franklin Park, Ill. 60131

RCA Sales Corporation
600 North Sherman Drive
Indianapolis, Ind. 46201

Sampo Corporation of America
5550 Peach Tree Industrial Blvd.
Norcross, Ga. 30071

Sanyo Electric Inc.
1200 West Artesia Blvd.
Compton, Calif. 90220

Sharp Electronics
1909 East Cornell
Peoria, Ill. 61614

Sony National Parts Center
8281 N.W. 107th Terrace
Kansas City, Mo. 64153

Sylvania Television
NAPCEC
P.O. Box 555
Old Andrew Johnson Highway
Jefferson City, Tenn. 37760

Toshiba America Inc.
280 Park Avenue
New York, N.Y. 10017

Zenith Radio
11000 Seymour St.
Franklin Park, Ill. 60131

The following list gives independent sources for schematic diagrams:

Howard W. Sams & Co., Inc.
P.O. Box 7092
Indianapolis, Ind. 46206

Tab Books
Blue Ridge Summit, Pa. 17214

Tekfax
Harcourt, Brace, Jovanovich Inc.
1 East First Street
Duluth, Minn. 55802

Sams publishes the *Photofact Annual Index,* which contains listings on chassis and models of home entertainment equipment as well as service-related information. This publication should help locate specific diagrams.

SUMMARY

1. A hot chassis has a power supply that is not isolated from earth ground. An isolation transformer should be used when you troubleshoot the chassis.
2. The method in Fig. 16-8 is used to check for ac leakage from any exposed metal parts of the receiver to earth ground.
3. A high-voltage probe is used to measure the anode voltage on the picture tube.
4. A dual-trace oscilloscope has dual vertical amplifier channels to display two waveforms, one above the other (see Fig. 16-13).
5. A delayed-sweep oscilloscope has two horizontal time bases. Selected parts of the main display can be magnified for closer observation (Fig. 16-14).
6. A tuner subber is a separate RF unit that can be connected to the IF amplifier of the TV receiver.
7. The NTSC color-bar generator supplies the primary *R, G,* and *B* signals; their complementary colors; *I* and *Q* signals; and white level at standard IRE amplitudes, in addition to other test signals.
8. The gated rainbow signal generator produces color bars with hues every 30°, from yellow-green at the left to blue-green and green at the right. See color plate X. In addition, the generator supplies crosshatch and dot patterns for convergence adjustments on color picture tubes.

9. A vectorscope is an oscilloscope that can display hue phase angles, as shown in Fig. 16-22.
10. No output from the main power supply causes a dead receiver, without any raster, picture, or sound.
11. Weak dc output from the main power supply can cause a small picture, as shown in Fig. 16-24. A faulty or misadjusted regulator in the main power supply can produce this trouble.
12. The scanning supplies for low voltage depend on the horizontal output for their operation.
13. A kick-start capacitor is used to obtain dc voltage from the main power supply temporarily for the scanning rectifier that feeds the horizontal oscillator.
14. A substitute power supply can be used to localize troubles with scanning circuits. The supply is rated at 12 to 30 V dc and 2 A.
15. Excessive ac ripple in the dc output of the power supply can produce hum bars and bend in the picture, as shown in Fig. 16-25.
16. No high voltage for the CRT anode results in no brightness, raster, or picture. The trouble can be the HV rectifier or its ac input circuit from the horizontal amplifier or a gassy picture tube. Also a problem in the horizontal output can cause no sound because of the scanning rectifier supplies. If the trouble is a gassy picture tube, the high voltage will come back when the anode connector is removed.
17. The hold-down circuit is used to shut off high voltage or to make the picture unviewable when the anode voltage exceeds a specified limit. The purpose is to prevent emission of x-rays. The hold-down circuit itself can cause the trouble of no high voltage.
18. In VCR servicing, the manufacturer's alignment tape is used for making adjustments.
19. Sensors are used in the VCR to put the machine in the stop mode should troubles develop in takeup of the tape.
20. The VCR has separate circuits for recording and playback. To localize troubles, check each function separately.
21. In servicing video cameras, a test setup such as Fig. 16-31 is used, with an illuminated test pattern and an underscanned monitor. The raster size and scanning linearity are critical.
22. With single-tube color cameras, the beam focus determines the amount of color signal output.
23. Color balance in cameras is checked with a monochrome, neutral gamma chart, as shown in Fig. 16-32. Balance is indicated by a null in 3.58-MHz color signal. See Fig. 16-33.
24. Interfering video frequencies below approximately 15,750 Hz produce horizontal bars in the picture, in 60-Hz multiples. Frequencies above 15,750 Hz produce vertical bars in 15,750-Hz multiples. Diagonal bars result

from frequencies that are not exact multiples of the horizontal scanning frequency.

25. Interfering signals without modulation produce uniform bars. Amplitude modulation makes the bars vary in width and intensity. Frequency modulation adds a moiré effect or shimmering interference.

SELF-EXAMINATION

Answers at Back of Book

Match the letters in the column at the right with the numbers at the left.

1. Hot chassis
2. 0.75 V rms, maximum
3. Low-capacitance probe
4. High-voltage probe
5. IF output signal
6. Eight pairs of horizontal bars
7. Small raster
8. *H* oscillator far off frequency
9. Low ultor voltage
10. Hues every 30°
11. Alignment tape
12. Excessive tape friction
13. Servocontrol circuit
14. Color-under signal
15. Two pairs of horizontal bars
16. Underscanned monitor
17. No color in single-tube pickup
18. Focal length of lens
19. Image burn
20. Color balance

a. Gated rainbow
b. 990 MΩ
c. Camera scanning size
d. Poor beam focus
e. Optical focus
f. 120-Hz hum
g. VCR servicing
h. Automatic-stop trigger
i. AC leakage test
j. Electric shock
k. 629 kHz
l. Low V^+ supply
m. Sample-and-hold gate
n. Vidicon
o. Null in 3.58-MHz signal
p. 480 Hz
q. 1:10 voltage divider
r. Hold-down circuit
s. Big raster
t. Tuner subber

ESSAY QUESTIONS

1. Why is the ac leakage test important?
2. What are two possible ways to get an electric shock in working on a TV chassis?
3. What is meant by a "hot" chassis?
4. List two features each for the VOM, VTVM, and DMM.

5. Why is the low-capacitance probe for an oscilloscope called the 10:1 probe?
6. List the uses of five types of test equipment.
7. What is a vectorscope?
8. Name three differences between the NTSC color-bar generator and the gated rainbow generator.
9. Describe briefly three ways to use a dot-bar generator.
10. How is a tuner subber used?
11. How is a substitute low-voltage power supply used? Give typical ratings.
12. **(a)** How much is the *R* of a dc voltmeter on the 3-V range, with a sensitivity of 20,000 Ω/V? **(b)** Why is *R* the same for any reading in this range? **(c)** Why is *R* higher on the 10-V range?
13. Give the internal sweep frequencies for the *V* and *H* positions of an oscilloscope to show a trace with 2 cycles of signal.
14. Compare the following types of oscilloscopes: dual-trace, dual-beam, and delayed-sweep.
15. Describe how you could check the range of the tint control on a TV receiver by using the gated rainbow signal.
16. Why is color noise, or confetti, mainly magenta?
17. List two possible causes of a dead receiver, with no picture and no sound, but with ac input power.
18. Name two ways to check that the TV receiver has ac input power.
19. List three possible causes of no high voltage for the picture tube.
20. What is the effect of a gassy picture tube on the high voltage?
21. What is the purpose of the high-voltage hold-down circuit?
22. What is the function of a kick-start capacitor?
23. Name a possible cause of **(a)** too small a raster, **(b)** too big a raster.
24. What is meant by *blooming* in the picture?
25. List three results of excessive ac ripple in the dc power supply.
26. What is the purpose of an RF bypass capacitor across a silicon diode rectifier?
27. Why is it not possible to check high-voltage rectifiers with an ohmmeter?
28. What are two types of rectifier circuit used for the main power supply in a TV receiver?
29. What is the purpose of a voltage regulator?
30. List three functions of dc output voltages that use ac input from the horizontal deflection circuit.
31. Describe three ways that automatic stop can be triggered in a VCR.
32. List two uses of the manufacturer's alignment tape for a VCR.
33. Describe briefly how the color balance is adjusted for a single-tube color camera.
34. Compare the interference effects in the picture for **(a)** RF unmodulated carrier wave and audio signal, **(b)** AM and FM.
35. What are the causes of 4.5-MHz and 920-kHz beat interference patterns?

SPECIAL QUESTIONS

1. Compare two types of oscilloscopes. Which type would you use for TV and video servicing?
2. Give reasons why you would prefer using a VOM, VTVM, or DMM for servicing.
3. Name five types of test equipment for servicing and list their uses.

ANSWERS TO TEST POINT QUESTIONS

16-1 **a.** T **b.** F **c.** T

16-2 **a.** 0.5 mA **b.** 0.75 V

16-3 **a.** DMM **b.** Decrease **c.** 990 MΩ

16-4 **a.** F **b.** T **c.** F **d.** T **e.** T

16-5 **a.** T **b.** F **c.** T

16-6 **a.** ±30° **b.** Figure 16-20*b* **c.** $-(B - Y)$ **d.** Sixth **e.** Horizontal oscillator

16-7 **a.** T **b.** T **c.** F **d.** T

16-8 **a.** T **b.** T **c.** F

16-9 **a.** Bigger **b.** Low **c.** Poor HV regulation **d.** First

16-10 **a.** T **b.** T **c.** T

16-11 **a.** F **b.** T **c.** T **d.** T

16-12 **a.** T **b.** F **c.** T **d.** F

16-13 **a.** Figure 16-34*a* **b.** Figure 16-34*b* **c.** Figure 16-36

APPENDIX

TELEVISION BROADCAST CHANNEL FREQUENCIES

Channels 2 to 83 are listed in Table A-1. Channel 1 was broadcast at 44 to 50 MHz, but these frequencies have been assigned to land mobile radio services.

Channels 2 to 6 are the lowband VHF channels. Channels 7 to 13 are the highband VHF channels. Channels 14 to 83 are the UHF channels. UHF channels 70 to 83 may be reserved for special services.

TABLE A-1
TELEVISION BROADCAST CHANNELS

CHANNEL NUMBER	FREQUENCY BAND, MHz	PICTURE CARRIER FREQUENCY, MHz	SOUND CARRIER FREQUENCY, MHz
2	54–60	55.25	59.75
3	60–66	61.25	65.75
4	66–72	67.25	71.75
5	76–82	77.25	81.75
6	82–88	83.25	87.75
7	174–180	175.25	179.75
8	180–186	181.25	185.75
9	186–192	187.25	191.75
10	192–198	193.25	197.75
11	198–204	199.25	203.75
12	204–210	205.25	209.75
13	210–216	211.25	215.75
14	470–476	471.25	475.75
15	476–482	477.25	481.75
16	482–488	483.25	487.75
17	488–494	489.25	493.75
18	494–500	495.25	499.75
19	500–506	501.25	505.75
20	506–512	507.25	511.75
21	512–518	513.25	517.75
22	518–524	519.25	523.75
23	524–530	525.25	529.75
24	530–536	531.25	535.75
25	536–542	537.25	541.75
26	542–548	543.25	547.75
27	548–554	549.25	553.75
28	554–560	555.25	559.75
29	560–566	561.25	565.75
30	566–572	567.25	571.75
31	572–578	573.25	577.75
32	578–584	579.25	583.75
33	584–590	585.25	589.75
34	590–596	591.25	595.75
35	596–602	597.25	601.75
36	602–608	603.25	607.75
37	608–614	609.25	613.75
38	614–620	615.25	619.75
39	620–626	621.25	625.75
40	626–632	627.25	631.75
41	632–638	633.25	637.75
42	638–644	639.25	643.75
43	644–650	645.25	649.75
44	650–656	651.25	655.75
45	656–662	657.25	661.75
46	662–668	663.25	667.75
47	668–674	669.25	673.75
48	674–680	675.25	679.75
49	680–686	681.25	685.75
50	686–692	687.25	691.75
51	692–698	693.25	697.75
52	698–704	699.25	703.75
53	704–710	705.25	709.75
54	710–716	711.25	715.75
55	716–722	717.25	721.75
56	722–728	723.25	727.75
57	728–734	729.25	733.75
58	734–740	735.25	739.75
59	740–746	741.25	745.75
60	746–752	747.25	751.75
61	752–758	753.25	757.75
62	758–764	759.25	763.75
63	764–770	765.25	769.75
64	770–776	771.25	775.75
65	776–782	777.25	781.75
66	782–788	783.25	787.75
67	788–794	789.25	793.75
68	794–800	795.25	799.75
69	800–806	801.25	805.75
70	806–812	807.25	811.75
71	812–818	813.25	817.75
72	818–824	819.25	823.75
73	824–830	825.25	829.75
74	830–836	831.25	835.75
75	836–842	837.25	841.75
76	842–848	843.25	847.75
77	848–854	849.25	853.75
78	854–860	855.25	859.75
79	860–866	861.25	865.75
80	866–872	867.25	871.75
81	872–878	873.25	877.75
82	878–884	879.25	883.75
83	884–890	885.25	889.75

APPENDIX

B

CABLE TELEVISION CHANNELS

The cable TV channels in Tables B-1 and B-2 are in addition to the broadcast channels in App. A. The midband cable channel frequencies are between broadcast channels 6 and 7. Superband cable channel frequencies are above channel 13.

TABLE B-1
CABLE TV CHANNELS

LETTER DESIGNATION	NUMBER	VIDEO CARRIER, MHz
Midband channels		
A	14	121.25
B	15	127.25
C	16	133.25
D	17	139.25
E	18	145.25
F	19	151.25
G	20	157.25
H	21	163.25
I	22	169.25
Superband channels		
J	23	217.25
K	24	223.25
L	25	229.25
M	26	235.25
N	27	241.25
O	28	247.25
P	29	253.25
Q	30	259.25
R	31	265.25
S	32	271.25
T	33	277.25
U	34	283.25
V	35	289.25
W	36	295.25
X	37	301.25
Y	38	307.25
Z	39	313.25

NUMBER	VIDEO CARRIER, MHz
Superband channels without letters	
40	319.25
41	325.25
42	331.25
43	337.25
44	343.25
45	349.25
46	355.25
47	361.25
48	367.25
49	373.25
50	379.25
51	385.25
52	391.25
53	397.25
Additional midband assignments	
54	89.25
55	95.25
56	101.25
57	107.25
58	97.25
59	103.25
Nominal channel numbers for use with digital readout converters	
A-2 or 00	109.25
A-1 or 01	115.25

TABLE B-2
HARMONICALLY RELATED CARRIERS FOR CABLE TV CHANNELS

CHANNEL NUMBER	VIDEO CARRIER, MHz	CHANNEL NUMBER	VIDEO CARRIER, MHz
00	108.00	30	258.00
01	114.00	31	264.00
02	54.00	32	270.00
03	60.00	33	276.00
04	66.00	34	282.00
05	78.00	35	288.00
06	84.00	36	294.00
07	174.00	37	300.00
08	180.00	38	306.00
09	186.00	39	312.00
10	192.00	40	318.00
11	198.00	41	324.00
12	204.00	42	330.00
13	210.00	43	336.00
14	120.00	44	342.00
15	126.00	45	348.00
16	132.00	46	354.00
17	138.00	47	360.00
18	144.00	48	366.00
19	150.00	49	372.00
20	156.00	50	378.00
21	162.00	51	384.00
22	168.00	52	390.00
23	216.00	53	396.00
24	222.00	54	72
25	228.00	55	90
26	234.00	56	96
27	240.00	57	102
28	246.00	58	402
29	252.00	59	408

APPENDIX 

FCC FREQUENCY ALLOCATIONS

The frequencies in Table C-1 are assigned by the FCC. The range is from 30 kHz for very low radio frequencies all the way to 300,000 MHz for extremely high radio frequencies.

TABLE C-1
FCC FREQUENCY ALLOCATIONS FROM 30kHz to 300,000 MHz

BAND	ALLOCATION	REMARKS
30–535 kHz	Includes maritime communications and navigation	500 kHz is international distress frequency
535–1605 kHz	Standard radio broadcast band	AM broadcasting
1605 kHz–30 MHz	Includes amateur radio and international short-wave broadcast	Amateur bands 3.5–4.0 MHz and 28–29.7 MHz
30–50 MHz	Government and nongovernment, fixed and mobile	Includes police, fire, forestry, highway, and railroad services
50–54 MHz	Amateur radio	6-m band
54–72 MHz	Television broadcast channels 2 to 4	Also fixed and mobile services
72–76 MHz	Government and nongovernment services	Aeronautical marker beacon on 75 MHz
76–88 MHz	Television broadcast channels 5 and 6	Also fixed and mobile services
88–108 MHz	FM broadcast	Also available for facsimile broadcast; 88–92-MHz educational FM broadcast
108–122 MHz	Aeronautical navigation	Localizers, radio range, and air traffic control
122–174 MHz	Government and nongovernment, fixed and mobile, amateur	144–148-MHz amateur band
174–216 MHz	Television broadcast channels 7 to 13	Also fixed and mobile services
216–470 MHz	Amateur, government and nongovernment, fixed and mobile, aeronautical navigation	Radio altimeter, glide path, and meteorological equipment; civil aviation 225–400 MHz
470–890 MHz	Television broadcasting	UHF television broadcast channels 14 to 83; translator stations in channels 70 to 83
890–3000 MHz	Aeronautical radio navigation, amateur, studio-transmitter relay, government and nongovernment, fixed and mobile	Radar bands 1300–1600 MHz; educational television 2500–2690 MHz; microwave ovens at 2450 MHz
3000–30,000 MHz	Government and nongovernment fixed and mobile, amateur, radio navigation	Superhigh frequencies (SHF); radio relay; Intelsat satellites
30,000–300,000 MHz	Experimental, government, amateur	Extremely high frequencies (EHF)

RADIO-FREQUENCY BANDS

The main groups of radio frequencies and their wavelengths are as follows:

VLF = Very low frequencies, 3 to 30 kHz; wavelengths 100 to 10 km
LF = Low frequencies, 30 to 300 kHz; wavelengths 10 to 1 km
MF = Medium frequencies, 0.3 to 3 MHz; wavelengths 1000 to 100 m
HF = High frequencies, 3 to 30 MHz; wavelengths 100 to 10 m
VHF = Very high frequencies, 30 to 300 MHz; wavelengths 10 to 1 m
UHF = Ultrahigh frequencies, 300 to 3000 MHz; wavelengths 1000 to 100 mm
SHF = Superhigh frequencies, 3 to 30 GHz; wavelengths 100 to 10 mm
EHF = Extra-high frequencies, 30 to 300 GHz; wavelengths 10 to 1 mm

Note that wavelengths are shorter for higher frequencies. Also 1 GHz = 1×10^9 Hz = 1000 MHz.

Microwaves have wavelengths of 1 m down to 1 mm (300 GHz). The spectrum of light rays starts at frequencies of 300 GHz and up, with infrared radiation having wavelengths from 1 mm to 10 μm.

RADIO SERVICES AND TELEVISION INTERFERENCE

Principal services that can cause interference in television receivers are in the following list. The interference is generally at a harmonic frequency or image frequency. All frequencies are in megahertz.

AMATEUR RADIO These bands include 1.8 to 2, 3.5 to 4, 7 to 7.3, 14 to 14.25, 21 to 21.45, 28 to 29.7, 50 to 54, 144 to 148, 220 to 225, 420 to 450.

INDUSTRIAL, SCIENTIFIC, AND MEDICAL This band is 13.36 to 14, with diathermy equipment at 13.56. The old frequencies were 27.12 and 40.66 to 40.70.

CITIZEN'S RADIO This band includes channels 1 to 40 in the band of 26.965 to 27.405 MHz for class D service.

FM BROADCAST This band is 88 to 108, with 100 channels spaced 0.2 MHz apart.

PUBLIC SAFETY (POLICE, FIRE, ETC.) These frequencies are around 33, 37, 39, 42, 44, 154, 156, and 158.

APPENDIX D

TELEVISION SYSTEMS AROUND THE WORLD

Many countries use television standards that are not the same as those in the United States. These systems are listed in Table D-1, along with our own FCC standards. The field rate of 50 Hz for vertical scanning is used where this is the ac power-line frequency, instead of 60 Hz as in this country. Note that the combination of 625 lines per frame and 25 frames per second, as used in Western Europe, results in the line-scanning frequency of 15,625 Hz, which is very close to the 15,750 Hz in our standards. The scanning frequencies for color television are not listed, but they are very close to the monochrome standards, for compatibility. In all cases, odd-line interlacing is used with two fields per frame, the aspect ratio is 4:3, and AM is used for the picture carrier with multiplexing of the color subcarrier.

TABLE D-1
PRINCIPAL TELEVISION SYSTEMS

	NORTH AND SOUTH AMERICA;* INCLUDES U.S., CANADA, MEXICO, AND JAPAN	WESTERN EUROPE; INCLUDES GERMANY, ITALY, AND SPAIN	ENGLAND†	FRANCE‡	U.S.S.R.
Lines per frame	525	625	625	625	625
Frames per second	30	25	25	25	25
Field frequency, Hz	60	50	50	50	50
Line frequency, Hz	15,750	15,625	15,625	15,625	15,625
Video bandwidth, MHz	4.2	5 or 6	5.5	6	6
Channel width, MHz	6	7 or 8	8	8	8
Video modulation	Negative	Negative	Negative	Positive	Negative
Sound signal	FM	FM	FM	AM	FM
Color system	NTSC	PAL	PAL	SECAM	SECAM
Color subcarrier, MHz	3.58	4.43	4.43	4.43	4.43

* Exceptions are Argentina and Brazil, which use PAL.
† England also uses 405-line system in 5-MHz channel.
‡ France also uses 819-line system in 14-MHz channel.
Note: NTSC is National Television Systems Committee; PAL is phase alternation by line; and SECAM is sequential chrominance and memory.

APPENDIX

E WORLDWIDE TYPE DESIGNATIONS FOR PICTURE TUBES

A new system starting in 1982 has been developed jointly by the Electronic Industries Association (EIA) of the United States, the EIA of Japan, and Pro Electron of Europe in order to promote international standardization. Each type designation has numbers and letters in five or six groups of symbols, as illustrated in Fig. E-1 for the picture tube A48DHM36X09, for example.

The first symbol is either A for a picture tube or M for a monitor tube. This example is for a picture tube. The second symbol gives the screen diagonal in centimeters. This example is 48 cm, which is approximately 19 in. Next is a three-letter symbol, such as DHM, that defines a general family of tubes.

The fourth symbol is a two-digit number for color tubes or a one-digit number for monochrome tubes, which distinguishes small variations of types within a general family.

The fifth symbol gives the phosphor designation. The letter X here corresponds to P22 for color picture tubes. However, color monitor tubes can have any other single letter, excluding I, O, or W. For monochrome pictures, the phosphor symbol is WW, corresponding to P4. Monochrome monitor tubes also can use WW or some other two-letter combination, excluding I and O.

The sixth symbol is a number from 01 to 99 but is assigned only for tubes having integral-neck components, such as the deflection yoke.

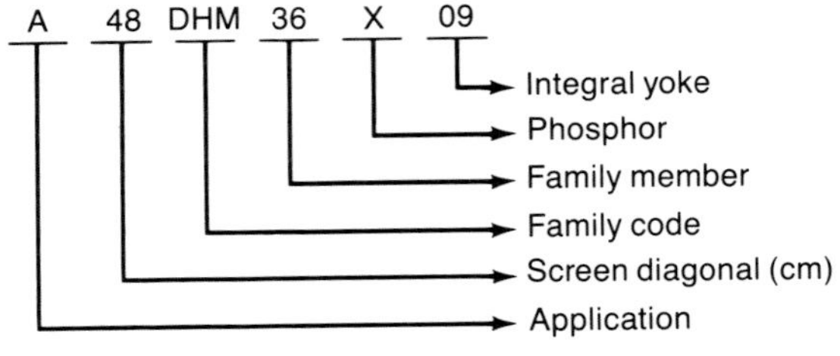

Fig. E-1

ANSWERS TO SELF-EXAMINATIONS

CHAPTER 1

1. (k)
2. (f)
3. (p)
4. (b)
5. (a)
6. (g)
7. (l)
8. (m)
9. (n)
10. (q)
11. (j)
12. (o)
13. (r)
14. (e)
15. (i)
16. (d)
17. (h)
18. (c)

CHAPTER 2

1. 30
2. 525
3. 2
4. 262½
5. 15,750
6. 15,750
7. 60
8. Contrast
9. Camera
10. Picture
11. 6
12. AM
13. FM
14. 60 to 66
15. 4.5
16. Sync
17. Blanking
18. Zero
19. 3.58
20. Chrominance

CHAPTER 3

1. (b)
2. (d)
3. (a)
4. (b)
5. (c)
6. (c)
7. (b)
8. (c)
9. (d)
10. (d)
11. (a)
12. (a)

CHAPTER 4

1. T
2. F
3. T
4. T
5. T
6. F
7. T
8. T
9. F
10. T
11. T
12. T
13. F
14. F
15. F

CHAPTER 5

1. F
2. T
3. F
4. T
5. F
6. T
7. T
8. T
9. T
10. T
11. F
12. T

CHAPTER 6

1. (b)
2. (a)
3. (d)
4. (a)
5. (b)
6. (c)
7. (d)
8. (a)
9. (b)
10. (d)

CHAPTER 7

1. T
2. T
3. F
4. T
5. F
6. F
7. F
8. T
9. T
10. T
11. T
12. T
13. F
14. T
15. T
16. T
17. T
18. F

CHAPTER 8

1. (c)
2. (a)
3. (d)
4. (a)
5. (d)
6. (a)
7. (d)
8. (b)
9. (b)
10. (c)
11. (c)
12. (a)

CHAPTER 9

1. T
2. F
3. T
4. T
5. T
6. T
7. F
8. F
9. T
10. T
11. F
12. T
13. T
14. T
15. T
16. F
17. T
18. T
19. T
20. T
21. F
22. T
23. T
24. T

CHAPTER 10

1. (c)
2. (d)
3. (a)
4. (b)
5. (b)
6. (b)
7. (b)
8. (a)
9. (c)
10. (d)
11. (d)
12. (b)
13. (b)
14. (d)
15. (a)

CHAPTER 11

1. (b)
2. (b)
3. (d)
4. (a)
5. (c)
6. (d)
7. (a)
8. (c)
9. (c)
10. (b)

CHAPTER 12

Part A

1. (d)
2. (c)
3. (b)
4. (a)
5. (i)
6. (e)
7. (f)
8. (g)
9. (h)
10. (j)

Part B

1. (b)
2. (d)
3. (e)
4. (c)
5. (a)

Part C

1. (b)
2. (e)
3. (d)
4. (h)
5. (a)
6. (c)
7. (f)
8. (g)

CHAPTER 13

Part A

1. T
2. T
3. F
4. T
5. T
6. T
7. T
8. F
9. T
10. T

Part B

1. *V* sync
2. Oscillator
3. Horizontal AFC
4. *H* output
5. *H* hold
6. Height
7. Damper
8. Sawtooth
9. *H* deflection
10. *V* linearity

CHAPTER 14

1. (b)
2. (b)
3. (c)
4. (b)
5. (c)
6. (d)
7. (c)
8. (c)
9. (b)
10. (d)
11. (a)
12. (b)
13. (c)
14. (c)
15. (b)

CHAPTER 15

1. (c)
2. (b)
3. (a)
4. (b)
5. (a)
6. (b)
7. (c)
8. (c)
9. (a)
10. (d)
11. (a)
12. (b)
13. (b)
14. (a)

CHAPTER 16

1. (j)
2. (i)
3. (q)
4. (b)
5. (t)
6. (p)
7. (l)
8. (r)
9. (s)
10. (a)
11. (g)
12. (h)
13. (m)
14. (k)
15. (f)
16. (c)
17. (d)
18. (e)
19. (n)
20. (o)

ANSWERS TO ODD-NUMBERED PROBLEMS

CHAPTER 2

1. 120,000
3. 0.25 μs
5. **(a)** 31.75 μs
(b) 64 μs

CHAPTER 3

1. 25,000 fc
3. 52.6 mm (or 5.26 cm)
5. 4 μA

CHAPTER 5

1. **(a)** 0.8 mA
(b) 1.2 mA
3. 20.8 MΩ

CHAPTER 6

1. 8 and 16
3. **(a)** 63.5 μs
(b) 1⁄60 s
5. **(a)** 60 Hz
(b) 15,750 Hz
(c) 18.8 kHz

CHAPTER 7

1. 2.82 MHz
3. **(a)** 1000 μs
(b) 960 μs
(c) 5.2 kHz
5. **(a)** 63.5 μs
(b) 64 μs

CHAPTER 8

1. 0.11, 0.30, 0.59, 0.89, and 1.0
3. **(a)** $C = 0.5$
(b) Hue is magenta
5. 0.2 in [5.08 mm]

CHAPTER 9

1. **(a)** 2.5 MHz
(b) 4 MHz
3. **(a)** 0.125 μs
(b) 0.25 μs
(c) 15.6 μs
(d) 2.5 μs
5. 25 percent

CHAPTER 10

1. 9.529×10^{-9} m
3. 30.72 kHz
5. 40 MHz
7. 1129 and 129 kHz

CHAPTER 11

1. **(a)** 55.0, 55.5, and 55.25 MHz
(b) 80.25 and 77.25 MHz
(c) 470.75, 471.75, and 471.25 MHz
(d) 475.25 and 471.25 MHz
3. **(a)** 12.5 percent
(b) 100 percent
(c) 75 percent
(d) 67.5 percent
(e) 40 percent
5. **(a)** 3.58 MHz
(b) 920 kHz
7. 55.24 MHz
9. **(a)** 20 percent
(b) 40 percent
(c) 100 percent
11. 1.26×10^{-10} μW

CHAPTER 12

1. **(a)** 129 MHz
(b) 221 MHz
(c) 257 MHz
(d) 517 MHz
3. **(a)** 10,000
(b) 80
5. **(a)** 84 V
(b) 70 V

CHAPTER 13

1. 100 μs
3. 48 W
5. 32 μs
7. 990 Ω

CHAPTER 14

1. 6.4
3. **(a)** 4.5 MHz
(b) 3.58 MHz
(c) 0.92 MHz
5. 3.38 and 3.78 MHz

CHAPTER 15

1. 151 Ω
3. 1.5
5. −40 dB
7. **(a)** 0 dBmV
(b) 6 dBmV
(c) 9.5 dBmV

INDEX

G

H

O

P

Q

T

U

W

X

Y

Z